Middle School 2-1
학교시험 완벽대비

1학기 전과정

적중 100 plus

영어 기출문제집

중 **2**

능률 | 김성곤

Best Collection

구성과 특징

교과서의 주요 학습 내용을 중심으로 학습 영역별 특성에 맞춰 단계별로 다양한 학습 기회를 제공하여
단원별 학습능력 평가는 물론 중간 및 기말고사 시험 등에 완벽하게 대비할 수 있도록 내용을 구성

Words & Expressions

Step1   Key Words 단원별 핵심 단어 설명 및 풀이
Key Expression 단원별 핵심 숙어 및 관용어 설명
Word Power 반대 또는 비슷한 뜻 단어 배우기
English Dictionary 영어로 배우는 영어 단어

Step2   실력평가 단원별 수시평가 대비 주관식, 객관식 문제풀이

Step3   서술형 대비 학업성취도 및 수행능력평가 대비 서술형 문제풀이

Conversation

Step1   핵심 의사소통 소통에 필요한 주요 표현 방법 요약
핵심 Check 기본적인 표현 방법 및 활용능력 확인

Step2   대화문 익히기 교과서 대화문 심층 분석 및 확인

Step3   교과서 확인학습 빈칸 채우기를 통한 문장 완성 능력 확인

Step4   기본평가 시험대비 기초 학습 능력 평가

Step5   실력평가 단원별 수시평가 대비 주관식, 객관식 문제풀이

Step6   서술형 대비 학업성취도 및 수행능력평가 대비 서술형 문제풀이

Grammar

Step1   주요 문법 단원별 주요 문법 사항과 예문을 알기 쉽게 설명
핵심 Check 기본 문법사항에 대한 이해 여부 확인

Step2   기본평가 시험대비 기초 학습 능력 평가

Step3   실력평가 단원별 수시평가 대비 주관식, 객관식 문제풀이

Step4   서술형 대비 학업성취도 및 수행능력평가 대비 서술형 문제풀이

Reading

Step1   구문 분석 단원별로 제시된 문장에 대한 구문별 분석과 내용 설명
확인문제 문장에 대한 기본적인 이해와 인지능력 확인

Step2   확인학습A 빈칸 채우기를 통한 문장 완성 능력 확인

Step3   확인학습B 제시된 우리말을 영어로 완성하여 작문 능력 키우기

Step4   실력평가 단원별 수시평가 대비 주관식, 객관식 문제풀이

Step5   서술형 대비 학업성취도 및 수행능력평가 대비 서술형 문제풀이
교과서 구석구석 교과서에 나오는 기타 문장까지 완벽 학습

Composition

|영역별 핵심문제|

단어 및 어휘, 대화문, 문법, 독해 등 각 영역별 기출문제의 출제 유형을 분석하여 실전에 대비하고 연습할 수 있도록 문제를 배열

|단원별 예상문제|

기출문제를 분석한 후 새로운 시험 출제 경향을 더하여 새롭게 출제될 수 있는 문제를 포함하여 시험에 완벽하게 대비할 수 있도록 준비

|서술형 실전 및 창의사고력 문제|

학교 시험에서 점차 늘어나는 서술형 시험에 집중 대비하고 고득점을 취득하는데 만전을 기하기 위한 학습 코너

|단원별 모의고사|

영역별, 단계별 학습을 모두 마친 후 실전 연습을 위한 모의고사

교과서 파헤치기

- **단어Test1~3** 영어 단어 우리말 쓰기, 우리말을 영어 단어로 쓰기, 영영풀이에 해당하는 단어와 우리말 쓰기
- **대화문Test1~2** 대화문 빈칸 완성 및 전체 대화문 쓰기
- **본문Test1~5** 빈칸 완성, 우리말 쓰기, 문장 배열연습, 영어 작문하기 복습 등 단계별 반복 학습을 통해 교과서 지문에 대한 완벽한 습득
- **구석구석지문Test1~2** 지문 빈칸 완성 및 전문 영어로 쓰기

Express Yourself

의사소통 기능

- 관심사 묻고 답하기
  A: What are you interested in?
  B: I'm interested in baseball.

- 허락 요청하고 답하기
  A: May I take a picture here?
  B: Yes, you may. / No, you may not.

언어 형식

- 동명사
  Taking selfies is part of daily life for many teens.

- 감각동사
  My pictures **look good** when I use filters.

Words & Expressions

Key Words

- **appropriate** [əpróupriət] 형 적절한
- **awesome** [ɔ́:səm] 형 멋진, 굉장한
- **baseball** [béisbɔ̀:l] 명 야구
- **borrow** [bárou] 동 빌리다 (↔ lend)
- **bother** [báðər] 동 괴롭히다
- **break** [breik] 동 (법률·약속 등을) 어기다
- **bring** [briŋ] 동 가져오다, 데려오다
- **carefully** [kέərfəl] 부 신중하게, 조심스럽게
- **carrier** [kǽriər] 명 캐리어, 운반[이동] 장치
- **choose** [tʃu:z] 동 고르다
- **clothes** [klouz] 명 옷
- **comment** [kάment] 명 의견, 논평
- **copy** [kάpi] 동 복사하다
- **dictionary** [díkʃənèri] 명 사전
- **display** [displéi] 동 (작품을) 전시하다, 보여주다
- **environment** [inváiərənmənt] 명 환경
- **etiquette** [étikit] 명 에티켓, 예절
- **exciting** [iksáitiŋ] 형 신나는, 흥미진진한
- **fact** [fækt] 명 사실
- **filter** [fíltər] 명 필터, 여과기
- **finally** [fáinəli] 부 마지막으로, 마침내
- **healthy** [hélθi] 형 건강에 좋은, 건강한
- **hurt** [hə:rt] 동 다치다, 해치다
- **impossible** [impάsəbl] 형 불가능한 (↔ possible)
- **incorrect** [ìnkərékt] 형 틀린, 정확하지 않은 (↔ correct)
- **interesting** [íntərəstiŋ] 형 흥미로운, 재미있는
- **leave** [li:v] 동 남기다
- **nervous** [nə́:rvəs] 형 긴장되는, 불안해 하는
- **outdoors** [áutdɔrz] 부 야외에서, 옥외에서
- **part** [pɑrt] 명 부분
- **perfect** [pə́:rfikt] 형 완벽한
- **personal** [pə́rsənl] 형 개인의, 사적인
- **photography** [fətάgrəfi] 명 사진술
- **post** [poust] 동 올리다, 게시하다
- **poster** [póustər] 명 포스터
- **prepare** [pripέər] 동 준비하다
- **probably** [prάbəbli] 부 아마도
- **public** [pʌ́blik] 형 공공의
- **recipe** [résəpi] 명 조리법
- **report** [ripɔ́:rt] 명 보고서
- **restroom** [réstru:m] 명 화장실
- **result** [rizʌ́lt] 명 결과 (↔ cause)
- **rude** [ru:d] 형 무례한
- **selfie** [sélfi:] 명 셀피
- **share** [ʃɛər] 동 공유하다
- **silly** [síli] 형 바보 같은, 어리석은
- **solve** [sɑlv] 동 해결하다
- **sometimes** [sʌ́mtàimz] 부 가끔
- **subject** [sʌ́bdʒikt] 명 과목
- **surprisingly** [sərpráiziŋli] 부 놀랍게도
- **survey** [sərvéi] 명 조사
- **teens** [ti:nz] 명 십대
- **topic** [tάpik] 명 주제
- **understand** [ʌndərstǽnd] 동 이해하다

Key Expressions

- **agree with** ~에 동의하다
- **around the world** 세계 곳곳에, 세계적으로
- **be interested in** ~에 관심[흥미]이 있다
- **break the law** 법을 어기다
- **check out** 확인하다
- **find out** 발견하다, 찾아보다
- **first of all** 무엇보다도
- **from A to B** A에서 B로
- **have fun** 즐거운 시간을 보내다
- **in front of** ~ 앞에
- **just like** 꼭 ~와 같이
- **keep in mind** 명심하다
- **look at** ~을 보다
- **sound + 형용사** ~하게 들리다
- **spend 시간 -ing** ~하는 데 시간을 보내다
- **take a picture[photo] (of)** (~의) 사진을 찍다

Word Power

※ 서로 반대되는 뜻을 가진 단어

□ **appropriate**(적절한) ↔ **inappropriate**(부적절한)
□ **carefully**(신중하게) ↔ **carelessly**(부주의하게)
□ **exciting**(신나는) ↔ **boring**(지루한)
□ **finally**(마지막으로) ↔ **firstly**(첫 번째로)
□ **impossible**(불가능한) ↔ **possible**(가능한)

□ **incorrect**(틀린) ↔ **correct**(맞는)
□ **outdoors**(야외에서) ↔ **indoors**(실내에서)
□ **perfect**(완벽한) ↔ **imperfect**(불완전한)
□ **public**(공공의) ↔ **private**(사적인)
□ **rude**(무례한) ↔ **polite**(공손한)

※ 서로 비슷한 뜻을 가진 단어

□ **bother**(괴롭히다) : **annoy**(귀찮게 하다)
□ **comment**(의견) : **remark**(견해)
□ **display**(전시하다) : **exhibit**(전시하다)
□ **fact**(사실) : **truth**(진실)

□ **finally**(마지막으로) : **lastly**(마지막으로)
□ **hurt**(해치다) : **injure**(다치게 하다)
□ **nervous**(불안해 하는) : **anxious**(불안해 하는)
□ **result**(결과) : **consequence**(결과)

English Dictionary

□ **appropriate** 적절한
→ correct or suitable for a particular time, situation, or purpose
특정한 시간, 장소 또는 목적에 맞거나 적합한

□ **bring** 가져오다, 데려오다
→ to take something or someone with you to the place where you are now, or to the place you are talking about
어떤 사람이나 사물을 지금 당신이 있는 장소나 말하는 장소로 데려오거나 가져오다

□ **comment** 의견, 논평
→ an opinion that you express about someone or something
어떤 사람이나 사물에 대해 표현하는 의견

□ **etiquette** 에티켓, 예절
→ the formal rules for polite behavior in society or in a particular group
사회나 특정한 그룹 안에서 공손한 행동에 대한 공식적 규칙

□ **fact** 사실
→ a piece of information that is known to be true
진실이라고 알려진 정보

□ **healthy** 건강에 좋은
→ good for your body
몸에 좋은

□ **post** 올리다
→ to put a message or computer document on the Internet so that other people can see it
다른 사람들이 볼 수 있도록 인터넷에 메시지나 컴퓨터 서류를 올리다

□ **prepare** 준비하다
→ to make plans or arrangements for something that will happen in the future
미래에 발생할 무언가를 위해 계획하거나 준비를 하다

□ **public** 공공의
→ available for anyone to use
누구든지 사용 가능한

□ **recipe** 조리법
→ a set of instructions for cooking a particular type of food
특정한 종류의 음식을 요리하기 위한 일련의 지시 사항

□ **result** 결과
→ something that happens or exists because of something that happened before
이전에 발생한 어떤 것 때문에 발생하거나 존재하는 어떤 것

□ **rude** 무례한
→ speaking or behaving in a way that is not polite and is likely to offend or annoy people
공손하지 않거나, 사람들의 기분을 상하게 하거나, 짜증나게 하기 쉬운 방식의 말과 행동을 하는

□ **share** 공유하다
→ to have or use something with other people
다른 사람과 함께 무언가를 갖거나 사용하다

□ **solve** 해결하다
→ to find or provide a way of dealing with a problem
어떤 문제를 처리하는 방식을 발견하거나 제공하다

서답형

01 다음 짝지어진 단어의 관계가 같도록 빈칸에 알맞은 말을 쓰시오.

> perfect : imperfect – possible : _____

[02~03] 다음 빈칸에 들어갈 말로 적절한 것은?

02
> They're _____ the law by employing such young children.

① displaying ② leaving
③ catching ④ bringing
⑤ breaking

03
> The loud noise made sleep _____.

① impossible ② appropriate
③ healthy ④ incorrect
⑤ careful

04 다음 빈칸에 공통으로 들어갈 말로 알맞은 것은?

> • Do you _____ to go swimming?
> • He acts just _____ a child.

① alike ② similar
③ like ④ play
⑤ as

중요

05 다음 밑줄 친 부분과 의미가 가장 가까운 것을 고르시오.

> The information you gave us was <u>not true</u>.

① proper ② incorrect
③ accurate ④ complete
⑤ correct

중요

06 다음 중 밑줄 친 부분의 뜻풀이가 바르지 <u>않은</u> 것은?

① It would not be <u>appropriate</u> for me to discuss that now. (적절한)
② Would it <u>bother</u> you if I put on some music? (괴롭히다)
③ Can I <u>borrow</u> your pen for a minute? (빌려주다)
④ I've got some very <u>exciting</u> news for you. (재미있는, 흥미로운)
⑤ Style and colour are a matter of <u>personal</u> taste. (개인의)

[07~08] 다음 영영풀이에 해당하는 단어를 고르시오.

중요

07
> to put a message or computer document on the Internet so that other people can see it

① prepare ② post
③ download ④ publish
⑤ report

08
> good for your body

① health ② healthy
③ exercise ④ wealthy
⑤ worthy

서답형

09 다음 빈칸에 들어갈 알맞은 단어를 〈보기〉에서 찾아 쓰시오. (형태 변화 가능)

> ┤ 보기 ├
> hurt   understand   display   share

(1) All the exam results will be _____ on the notice board.
(2) Was anyone _____ in the accident?
(3) Tom and Bill _____ the same room.
(4) She doesn't _____ English.

01 다음 짝지어진 두 단어의 관계가 같도록 빈칸에 알맞은 말을 쓰시오. (주어진 철자가 있는 경우, 주어진 철자로 시작할 것)

(1) big : small = polite : r_____

(2) stupid : smart = private : _____

(3) reason : cause = consequence : _____

02 다음 빈칸에 공통으로 들어갈 말을 쓰시오.

• We'll have to check him _____ before we employ him.

• Did you find _____ whether there are any seats left?

---

03 다음 빈칸에 들어갈 말을 〈보기〉에서 찾아 쓰시오.

보기

> carefully   impossible
> perfect   interesting

(1) That's a(n) _____ question.

(2) You need to think very _____ about which course you want to take.

(3) You're very lucky to have _____ teeth.

(4) He was faced with a seemingly _____ task.

04 다음 주어진 우리말에 맞게 빈칸을 채우시오. (철자가 주어진 것도 있음)

(1) Paul은 발표를 해야 할 때마다 항상 긴장한다.
➡ Paul _____ gets n_____ whenever he has to give a presentation.

(2) 그것은 아마도 내가 지금까지 본 영화 중 가장 최고의 영화이다.
➡ It's _____ the _____ movie I have ever seen.

05 다음 우리말에 맞게 주어진 단어를 바르게 배열하시오.

(1) 몇몇의 친구를 파티에 데려와도 괜찮나요?
(to, if, it, some, bring, the, OK, is, party, I, friends, ?)
➡ _____

(2) 이 문서를 복사하고 보내주시겠어요?
(it, send, this, out, copy, and, could, letter, you, ?)
➡ _____

(3) 그들의 마지막 콘서트는 정말로 멋졌어.
(last, awesome, really, their, was, concert)
➡ _____

06 다음 영영풀이에 해당하는 말을 주어진 철자로 시작하여 쓰고, 알맞은 것을 골라 문장을 완성하시오. (형태 변화 가능)

• c_____ : an opinion that you express about someone or something

• e_____ : the formal rules for polite behaviour in society or in a particular group

• r_____ : something that happens or exists because of something that happened before

---

(1) He died as a _____ of his injures.

(2) You will be able to learn all about court _____ .

(3) He made helpful _____ on my work.

Conversation

1 관심사 묻고 답하기

> A What are you interested in? 너는 무엇에 관심이 있니?
>
> B I'm interested in baseball. 나는 야구에 관심이 있어.

- 'What are you interested in?'은 '너는 무엇에 관심이 있니?'라는 의미로 상대방의 관심을 물을 때 쓰는 표현이다.
- 'I'm interested in ~.'은 '나는 ~에 관심이 있다.'의 의미로 관심을 나타내는 표현이며 in 뒤에는 명사나 동명사가 올 수 있다.
- 'Are you interested in ~?'은 '너는 ~에 관심이 있니?'의 의미로 상대방의 관심을 물어볼 때 사용하는 표현이다. 관심 여부에 대해 'Yes, I am.' 또는 'No, I'm not.'으로 대답할 수 있다.

관심 묻기

- What are you interested in? 너는 무엇에 관심이 있니?
- Which ~ are you interested in? 너는 어느 ~에 관심이 있니?

관심사 대답하기

- I'm interested in ~.
- I have an interest in ~. 나는 ~에 관심이 있다.

관심을 표현하기

- I like ~. 나는 ~을 좋아한다.
- I love ~. 나는 ~을 아주 좋아한다.
- I enjoy ~. 나는 ~을 즐긴다.
- I'm into ~. 나는 ~에 빠져 있다.

핵심 Check

1. 다음 우리말과 일치하도록 빈칸에 알맞은 말을 쓰시오.

   A: _____ are you _____ in? (너는 무엇에 관심이 있니?)

   B: _____ really _____ in magic. (나는 정말 마술에 관심이 있어.)

2. 다음 주어진 단어를 이용하여 대화를 완성하시오.

   (1) A: _____? (animals, interested, are, in, you)

   B: No, I'm not. _____. (in, I'm, plants, interested)

   (2) A: _____?

   (are, in, what, subject, you, interested)

   B: I'm interested in economics.

② 허락 요청하고 답하기

> **A** May I take a picture here? 여기서 사진을 찍어도 되나요?
> **B** Yes, you may. / No, you may not. 네, 됩니다. / 아니요, 안 됩니다.

■ 'May I+동사원형 ~?'을 사용하여 상대방에게 허락의 여부를 물을 수 있다.

허락을 요청하는 표현

• May I 동사원형 ~?	• Can I+동사원형 ~?	• Is it OK if I ~?
• I'm wondering if I ~.	• Would it be all right if I ~?	• Do you mind if I ~?

■ 'Do you mind if ~?'로 시작하는 의문문에서 mind는 '싫어하다, 꺼리다'라는 뜻이므로 Of course not. 이나 Not at all.이 '전혀 꺼리지 않는다.'는 의미로 허락의 의미를 나타낸다.

허락을 구하는 질문에 대한 대답 (mind가 쓰이지 않은 경우)

1. 허락하기
   - Yes, you may[can].
   - Sure.
   - Of course.
   - Certainly.
   - Why not?
   - No problem.
   - Sure. Go ahead.
   - Okay.

2. 거절하기
   - No, you may[can] not.
   - I'm sorry, but you can't.
   - I'm afraid you can't.
   - Not right now.
   - I'm afraid not.
   - No way!

■ 허락을 요청하는 말에 거절하는 경우에는, 보통 간단히 이유를 덧붙인다.

핵심 Check

3. 다음 우리말과 일치하도록 빈칸에 알맞은 말을 쓰시오.

(1) **A:** _____ _____ okay _____ I _____ your pen? (네 펜을 빌려도 될까?)

   B: Of course. (물론이지.)

(2) **A:** May _____ turn _____ the TV? (내가 TV를 켜도 될까?)

   B: I'm _____ not. I'm doing my homework. (유감이지만 안 돼. 나는 숙제를 하는 중이야.)

4. 다음 주어진 단어를 이용하여 대화를 완성하시오.

   A: _____ _____ _____ _____ _____ _____ _____ _____.

   (umbrella, share, I, I'm, your, if, can, wondering)

   B: Sure.

A. Listen & Talk 1 A

G: ❶Look at these club posters. ❷What are you interested in?

B: ❸I'm interested in cooking. ❹What about you?

G: I'm interested in ❺photography.

G: 동아리 포스터들을 봐. 너는 어떤 것에 관심이 있니?
B: 나는 요리에 관심이 있어. 너는 어때?
G: 나는 사진에 관심이 있어.

❶ look at: ~을 보다
❷ 'What are you interested in?'은 '너는 무엇에 관심이 있니?'라는 의미로 상대방의 관심을 물을 때 쓰는 표현이다.
❸ I'm interested in ~.은 '나는 ~에 관심이 있다.'의 의미로 관심을 나타내는 표현이며 in 뒤에는 명사나 동명사가 올 수 있다.
❹ 'What about you?'는 상대방의 의견을 묻기 위한 표현으로, 'How about you?'로 바꾸어 쓸 수 있다.
❺ photography: 사진

Check(√) True or False

(1) They are looking at club posters.　　T ☐ F ☐

(2) They are all interested in cooking.　　T ☐ F ☐

B. Listen & Talk 1 B

B: What ❶are you going to do this weekend?

G: I'm going to go to a baseball game with my brother.

B: ❷Are you interested in baseball?

G: ❸Not really. I'm going to the baseball game ❹because my brother likes baseball.

B: You're so ❺nice! Then what are you interested in?

G: I'm more interested in soccer. I ❻want to go to a soccer game ❼ someday.

B: 이번 주말에 뭐 할 거야?
G: 나는 동생하고 야구 보러 갈 거야.
B: 너는 야구에 관심 있니?
G: 사실은 좋아하지 않아. 나는 내 동생이 좋아해서 야구 보러 가는 거야.
B: 너 정말 착하다! 그럼 너는 어떤 것에 관심이 있니?
G: 나는 축구에 더 관심 있어. 언젠가 축구 경기를 보러 가고 싶어.

❶ be going to 동사원형: ~할 예정이다　this weekend: 이번 주말에
❷ 'Are you interested in ~?'은 '너는 ~에 관심이 있니?'의 의미로 상대방의 관심을 물어볼 때 사용하는 표현이다.
❸ Not really: 사실은 그렇지 않아.
❹ because는 이유를 나타내는 접속사로 because 다음에는 주어와 동사가 오며, '~이기 때문에'의 의미를 지닌다.
❺ nice: 친절한(= kind)
❻ want to 동사원형: ~하기를 원하다
❼ someday: (미래의) 언젠가

Check(√) True or False

(3) The girl's brother likes baseball.　　T ☐ F ☐

(4) The girl is interested in soccer.　　T ☐ F ☐

Listen & Talk 1 C

G: ❶What are you looking at?

B: I'm looking at TV program listings. ❷What show should I watch?

G: Well, ❸what are you interested in?

B: I'm interested in music.

G: Then ❹how about watching the *Friday Pop Music Show*?

B: I'm actually not ❺a big fan of pop music. I like to listen to rap music.

G: Then ❻why don't you watch *Hit the Beat*?

B: Good idea.

❶ look at: ~을 보다 What are you looking at?: 뭐 보고 있니?

❷ What+명사: what이 의문형용사로 쓰인 것이다. should: ~해야 한다

❸ what are you interested in?: 너는 무엇에 관심이 있니?

❹ 'how about (동)명사 ~?'는 권유하는 말로, 'what about (동)명사 ~?'로 바꾸어 말할 수 있다.

❺ big fan: 열렬한 팬

❻ Why don't you ~?는 상대방에게 권유할 때 쓰이는 표현으로 '~하는 게 어때?'라는 의미이다.

Listen & Talk 2 A

B: ❶May I bring my dog on the bus?

W: ❷Yes, you may. But you ❸should put your dog in the carrier.

❶ May I 동사원형 ~?은 허락을 요청하는 표현으로 Can I 동사원형 ~?으로 바꾸어 쓸 수 있다. bring: 데려오다

❷ May I 동사원형 ~?으로 질문했으므로, Yes, you may.나 No, you may not.으로 대답할 수 있다.

❸ should는 '~해야 한다'라는 의미의 조동사로 뒤에 동사원형을 쓴다.

Listen & Talk 2 B

G: Hi. ❶Can I go in now?

M: Sure. Let me see your ticket, please.

G: Here it is. May I ❷record the music in the concert hall?

M: ❸No, you may not.

G: Okay. May I ❹take pictures of the band?

M: No, you may not. You can ❺only take pictures in front of the concert hall. Please enjoy the concert.

G: Oh, okay. Thank you.

❶ May I go in now?와 같은 의미이다.

❷ record: 녹음하다, 녹화하다

❸ May I 동사원형 ~?의 허락을 요청하는 말에 대한 거절의 대답으로 No, you may not.이 사용되었다. 다른 표현으로 I'm afraid not.을 쓸 수 있다.

❹ take pictures of ~: ~의 사진을 찍다

❺ only: 오직, 오로지 in front of: ~ 앞에

Listen & Talk 2 C

B: Excuse me.

M: Hello. ❶What can I do for you?

B: May I ❷borrow this new science book?

M: No, you may not. Students can't take new books home.

B: Then ❸may I copy some pages from the book? I need ❹them for my science report.

M: Yes, you may. But please don't ❺share them online.

B: Okay, I ❻won't. Thank you!

❶ What can I do for you?: 무엇을 도와드릴까요? (= How can I help you?)

❷ borrow: 빌리다

❸ May I 동사원형 ~?: ~해도 될까요? copy: 복사하다 some: 조금, 약간, 일부

❹ them은 앞 문장의 some pages (from the book)를 의미한다.

❺ share: 공유하다

❻ won't = will not

Let's communicate 1

A: What are you interested in?

B: ❶I'm interested in music.

A: ❷Why don't you go to a concert hall this weekend?

B: ❸Sounds good. May I record the music there?

A: Yes, you may. / No, you may not.

❶ be interested in: ~에 관심이 있다

❷ Why don't you ~?: ~하는 게 어때? (= How about (동)명사 ~? = What about (동)명사 ~?)

❸ sound + 형용사: ~하게 들리다

● 다음 우리말과 일치하도록 빈칸에 알맞은 말을 쓰시오.

Listen & Talk 1 A

G: Look at these club _____. _____ are you interested in?

B: I'm interested _____ _____. What about you?

G: I'm interested _____ _____.

Listen & Talk 1 B

B: _____ are you _____ _____ _____ this weekend?

G: _____ _____ to go to a baseball game _____ my brother.

B: _____ you interested _____ baseball?

G: Not really. I'm going to the baseball game _____ my brother likes baseball.

B: You're so nice! Then _____ _____ _____ interested in?

G: I'm _____ _____ in soccer. I want to _____ _____ a soccer game _____.

Listen & Talk 1 C

G: What are you looking at?

B: I'm looking at TV program listings. _____ _____ should I watch?

G: Well, _____?

B: _____ _____ _____ music.

G: Then how _____ _____ the *Friday Pop Music Show*?

B: I'm actually not _____ _____ _____ pop music. I like to listen to rap music.

G: Then why _____ _____ watch *Hit the Beat*?

B: Good idea.

Listen & Talk 1 D

A: _____ are you interested _____?

B: _____ interested in games and social media. What about you?

A: I'm _____ _____ music and _____ _____.

B: _____ are _____ interested in social media.

Listen & Talk 2 A

B: May I _____ my dog on the bus?

W: _____, _____ _____. But you should put your dog _____ _____ _____.

해석

G: 동아리 포스터들을 봐. 너는 어떤 것에 관심이 있니?
B: 나는 요리에 관심이 있어. 너는 어때?
G: 나는 사진에 관심이 있어.

B: 이번 주말에 뭐 할 거야?
G: 나는 동생하고 야구 보러 갈 거야.
B: 너는 야구에 관심 있니?
G: 사실은 좋아하지 않아. 나는 내 동생이 좋아해서 야구 보러 가는 거야.
B: 너 정말 착하다! 그럼 너는 어떤 것에 관심 있니?
G: 나는 축구에 더 관심 있어. 언젠가 축구 경기를 보러 가고 싶어.

G: 뭐 보고 있니?
B: TV 프로그램 편성표 보고 있어. 어떤 걸 봐야 할까?
G: 음, 너 어떤 분야에 관심이 있니?
B: 나는 음악에 관심이 있어.
G: 그러면 "Friday Pop Music Show"를 보는 게 어때?
B: 사실 팝 음악을 많이 좋아하지는 않아. 나는 랩 음악 듣는 걸 좋아해.
G: 그러면 "Hit the Beat"을 보는 건 어때?
B: 좋은 생각이야.

A: 너는 무엇에 관심이 있니?
B: 나는 게임과 소셜 미디어에 관심이 있어. 너는 어때?
A: 나는 음악과 소셜 미디어에 관심이 있어.
B: 우리는 둘 다 소셜 미디어에 관심이 있구나.

B: 버스에 제 개를 데리고 타도 되나요?
W: 네, 됩니다. 하지만 당신은 개를 캐리어에 넣어야 해요.

Listen & Talk 2 B

G: Hi. Can I _____ in now?

M: Sure. _____ me _____ your ticket, please.

G: Here it is. May I _____ the music in the concert hall?

M: No, you _____ _____.

G: Okay. May I _____ pictures of the band?

M: _____, _____ _____ _____. You can only take pictures _____ _____ _____ the concert hall. Please enjoy the concert.

G: Oh, okay. Thank you.

Listen & Talk 2 C

B: Excuse me.

W: Hello. What _____ _____ do for you?

B: May I _____ this new science book?

W: No, you _____ _____. Students can't _____ new books home.

B: Then may I _____ some pages from the book? I need them for my science report.

W: Yes, you _____. But please don't _____ them online.

B: Okay, I _____. Thank you!

Let's communicate 1

A: _____ _____ you interested in?

B: _____ _____ in music.

A: _____ don't you go to a concert hall this weekend?

B: Sounds good. _____ _____ record the music there?

A: Yes, you may. / No, you may not.

Do It Yourself A

M: Hey, Yumi. What are you _____?

G: Hello, Mr. King. I'm preparing for tomorrow's _____. It is about one of my _____.

M: That sounds fun! What _____ _____ _____ in?

G: _____ _____ photography. I will talk about it tomorrow.

M: Oh, _____ _____ photography, too.

G: Really? Then may I _____ you _____ _____ _____ for my presentation?

M: Sure.

G: 안녕하세요. 지금 안에 들어가도 되나요?

M: 그럼요. 티켓을 보여 주시겠어요?

G: 여기 있어요. 콘서트홀 안에서 노래를 녹음해도 되나요?

M: 아니요, 안 됩니다.

G: 알겠습니다. 밴드 사진은 찍어도 되나요?

M: 아니요, 안 됩니다. 콘서트홀 앞에서만 사진을 찍을 수 있어요. 즐거운 관람되세요.

G: 아, 알겠습니다. 감사합니다.

B: 실례합니다.

W: 안녕하세요. 무엇을 도와드릴까요?

B: 이 새로 출시된 과학책 빌려도 될까요?

W: 아뇨, 불가능합니다. 학생들은 새로 출시된 책을 집으로 가져갈 수 없어요.

B: 그러면 책에서 몇 장 정도 복사해도 될까요? 과학 보고서 쓰는 데 필요해서요.

W: 네, 그러세요. 하지만 그걸 인터넷상에 공유하지는 마세요.

B: 네, 안 그럴게요. 감사합니다!

A: 너는 무엇에 관심이 있니?

B: 나는 음악에 관심이 있어.

A: 이번 주말에 콘서트홀에 가는 건 어때?

B: 그거 좋겠다. 거기서 음악을 녹음해도 될까?

A: 그래, 돼. / 아니, 안 돼.

M: 유미야, 뭐 하고 있니?

G: 안녕하세요, King씨. 저는 내일 발표를 준비하고 있어요. 제 관심사 중 하나에 대한 거예요.

M: 그거 재미있겠다! 너는 어떤 것에 관심이 있니?

G: 저는 사진에 관심이 있어요. 저는 그것에 대해 내일 이야기할 거예요.

M: 오, 나도 역시 사진에 관심이 있어.

G: 정말요? 그렇다면 제 발표에 대해 몇 가지 조언을 부탁해도 될까요?

M: 물론이지.

01 다음 주어진 문장과 의미하는 바가 <u>다른</u> 하나를 고르시오.

> May I take pictures here?

① I'm wondering if I can take pictures here.
② Can I take pictures here?
③ Is it okay if I take pictures here?
④ Could you take pictures here?
⑤ Do you mind if I take pictures here?

02 다음 대화의 빈칸에 들어갈 말로 적절하지 <u>않은</u> 것은?

> A: May I borrow this new science book?
> B: _____ Students can't take new books home.

① I'm afraid not.　　　② I'm sorry, but you can't.
③ Why not?　　　④ No, you may not.
⑤ I'm afraid you can't.

03 다음 주어진 문장 뒤에 나올 대화의 순서로 가장 적절한 것은?

> What are you interested in?
> (A) Sounds good. May I bring my pet there?
> (B) I'm interested in soccer.
> (C) Why don't you go to a soccer filed this weekend?
> (D) Yes, you may.

① (B) - (A) - (C) - (D)　　　② (B) - (A) - (D) - (C)
③ (B) - (C) - (A) - (D)　　　④ (C) - (A) - (B) - (D)
⑤ (C) - (B) - (A) - (D)

[01~03] 다음 대화를 읽고, 물음에 답하시오.

G: What are you looking at?
B: I'm looking at TV program listings. What show should I watch? (①)
G: Well, what are you interested in?
B: I'm interested in ___(A)___. (②)
G: Then how about watching the *Friday Pop Music Show*? (③)
B: (④) I like to listen to rap music.
G: (⑤) Then why don't you watch *Hit the Beat*?
B: Good idea.

01 위 대화의 ①~⑤ 중 주어진 문장이 들어갈 알맞은 곳은?

| I'm actually not a big fan of pop music. |

① ② ③ ④ ⑤

02 위 대화의 빈칸 (A)에 들어갈 말로 적절한 것은?

① science ② art
③ fashion ④ movies
⑤ music

03 위 대화의 내용과 일치하지 않는 것은?

① They are talking about what show the boy will watch.
② The boy is looking at TV program listings.
③ The *Friday Pop Music Show* is related to rap music.
④ The boy likes rap music.
⑤ The boy can listen to rap music from *Hit the Beat*.

[04~07] 다음 대화를 읽고, 물음에 답하시오.

B: Excuse me.
M: Hello. ①What can I do for you?
B: ②May I borrow this new science book?
M: ___(A)___ ③Students can't take new books home.
B: ④Then may I copy some pages from the book? I need ⓐthem for my science report.
M: Yes, you may. But please don't share ⓐthem online.
B: ⑤Okay, I will. Thank you!

04 Where are they now?

① library ② theater
③ hospital ④ classroom
⑤ concert hall

05 위 대화의 빈칸 (A)에 들어갈 말로 적절한 것은?

① Yes, you may.
② No, you may not.
③ Yes, you can.
④ No problem.
⑤ Why not?

서답형
06 위 대화의 밑줄 친 ⓐthem이 공통으로 가리키는 것을 본문에서 찾아 쓰시오. (6 단어)

➡ _____

서답형
07 위 대화의 ①~⑤ 중 어색한 곳을 고르고 바르게 고치시오.

_____ ➡ _____

[08~09] 다음 대화를 읽고, 물음에 답하시오.

> A: ①What are you interested in?
> B: ②I'm interested in animals.
> A: ③Why don't you go to an art museum this weekend?
> B: ④Sounds good. 거기서 새들에게 먹이를 줘도 되나요?
> A: ⑤No, you may not.

08 위 대화의 ①~⑤ 중 흐름상 어색한 문장을 고르시오.

①   ②   ③   ④   ⑤

서답형

09 위 대화의 밑줄 친 우리말을 영작하시오. (6단어)

➡ _____

10 다음 짝지어진 대화가 어색한 것은?

① A: Is it okay if I take photos of the paintings there?
   B: Sure, go ahead.

② A: Excuse me. May I sit here?
   B: Of course. It's already taken.

③ A: Would it be alright if I leave early?
   B: No problem.

④ A: Can I bring my pet to your house?
   B: Certainly.

⑤ A: May I borrow your pen now?
   B: I'm afraid not. This is the only one that I have.

[11~13] 다음 대화를 읽고, 물음에 답하시오.

> M: Hey, Yumi. What are you doing?
> G: Hello, Mr. King. (①) ⓐIt is about one of my interest. (②)
> M: ⓑThat sounds fun! What are you interested in?
> G: ⓒI'm interested in photography. (③) ⓓI will talk about it tomorrow.
> M: Oh, I'm interested in photography, too.
> G: Really? (④) ⓔThen may I ask you for some advice for my presentation?
> M: Sure. (⑤)

11 위 대화의 ①~⑤ 중 주어진 문장이 들어갈 알맞은 곳은?

> I'm preparing for tomorrow's presentation.

①   ②   ③   ④   ⑤

서답형

12 위 대화의 ⓐ~ⓔ 중 어색한 곳을 고르고 바르게 고치시오.

_____ ➡ _____

서답형

13 위 대화의 내용과 일치하도록 빈칸을 완성하시오.

> Both Yumi and Mr. King _____
> _____ in _____. Yumi _____
> give a _____ about photography
> _____. Yumi asks Mr. King _____
> _____ for _____ _____.

[01~03] 다음 대화를 읽고, 물음에 답하시오.

B: _____(A)_____ are you going to do this weekend?

G: ①I'm going to go to a baseball game with my brother.

B: (in, you, are, baseball, interested, ?)

G: ②Not really. ③I'm going to the baseball game because my brother likes baseball.

B: ④You're so nice! Then _____(B)_____ are you interested in?

G: ⑤I'm less interested in soccer. I want to go to a soccer game someday.

01 위 대화의 (A)와 (B)에 알맞은 의문사를 쓰시오.

(A) _____ (B) _____

02 위 대화의 괄호 안에 주어진 단어를 알맞게 배열하시오.

➡ _____

03 위 대화의 ①~⑤ 중 어색한 곳을 고르고 바르게 고치시오.

_____ ➡ _____

[04~05] 다음 대화를 읽고, 물음에 답하시오.

B: May I bring my dog on the bus?

W: _____(A)_____ But you should put your dog in the carrier.

04 다음 영영풀이에 해당하는 단어를 대화에서 찾아 쓰시오.

to take something or someone with you to the place where you are now, or to the place you are talking about

➡ _____

05 위 대화의 흐름상 빈칸 (A)에 들어갈 말을 쓰시오. (3 단어)

➡ _____

06 다음 대화의 순서를 바르게 배열하시오.

(A) Then how about watching the *Friday Pop Music Show*?

(B) I'm interested in music.

(C) I'm actually not a big fan of pop music. I like to listen to rap music.

(D) What are you interested in?

➡ _____

07 다음 대화의 ①~⑤ 중 어색한 곳을 모두 고르고 바르게 고치시오.

M: Hey, Yumi. ①What are you doing?

G: Hello, Mr. King. ②I'm preparing for tomorrow's presentation. It is about one of my interests.

M: That sounds fun! ③What are you interested in?

G: I'm interested in photography. ④I talk about it tomorrow.

M: Oh, I'm interested in photography, too.

G: Really? ⑤Then may I ask you for some advise for my presentation?

M: Sure.

➡ _____

Grammar

① 동명사

> • **Taking** a walk in the evening is her habit. 저녁에 산책하는 것은 그녀의 습관이다.
> • **Seeing** is **believing**. 보는 것이 믿는 것이다. (백문이 불여일견)

- 동명사는 '동사원형+-ing'의 형태로 '~하는 것, ~하기'라는 의미로 문장에서 주어, 보어, 목적어 역할을 한다.
- 동명사가 주어로 쓰이는 경우, 동사는 단수 동사를 쓴다.
- 동명사는 주어를 보충하는 말인 주격보어로 사용될 수 있다.
- 명사 역할을 하지만 동사의 성격을 가지므로 뒤에 보어나 목적어를 가질 수 있다.
- 동명사는 타동사의 목적어로 쓰이며, 전치사의 목적어로도 쓰인다. 부정사는 전치사의 목적어로 쓰일 수 없음에 주의한다.
- avoid, consider, deny, enjoy, finish, give up, keep, mind, recommend, stop, suggest 등은 동명사를 목적어로 갖는 동사이다. like, love, begin, start 등은 동명사와 부정사를 둘 다 목적어로 가질 수 있다.
  - **Becoming** a scientist is difficult. [주어] 과학자가 되는 것은 어렵다.
  - My hobby is **singing**. [주격 보어] 나의 취미는 노래하는 것이다.
  - I like **dancing**. = I like to dance. [목적어] 나는 춤추는 것을 좋아한다.

동명사 vs. 현재분사

- 동명사와 현재분사의 형태는 동일하지만 쓰임은 서로 다르다.
- 동명사는 뒤에 보어나 목적어를 가지면서 명사의 역할을 하지만, 현재분사는 be동사와 함께 진행형을 만들거나 명사를 수식하는 형용사 역할을 한다.
  - I stopped **playing** computer games. [동명사] 나는 컴퓨터 게임을 하는 것을 멈추었다.
  - The boy **playing** computer games is Tom. [현재분사] 컴퓨터 게임을 하는 소년은 Tom이다.

핵심 Check

1. 다음 괄호 안에서 알맞은 것을 고르시오.
   (1) (Taking / Take) selfies is part of daily life for many teens.
   (2) I finished (reading / to read) the book.

2. 다음 문장에서 <u>틀린</u> 부분을 찾아 바르게 고쳐 쓰시오.
   Make silly faces is really fun!

   _____ ➡ _____

② 감각동사

> • Monica **felt** happy as her husband was with her. Monica는 남편이 함께 있어서 행복했다.
> • Jake **looked** worried when he heard the news. Jake는 그 소식을 듣고 걱정스러워 보였다.

■ 감각동사란 냄새 맡고, 맛보고, 느끼는 등의 감각을 표현하는 동사를 말한다. 감각동사 다음에 형용사를 쓰면 주어의 상태가 '~하게 보이다, 들리다, 냄새가 나다, 맛이 나다, 느껴지다' 등의 의미가 된다.

  • look ~하게 보이다, smell ~한 냄새가 나다, sound ~하게 들리다, taste ~한 맛이 나다, feel ~하게 느끼다

■ 감각동사는 형용사를 보어로 취한다. 우리말 해석으로는 부사일 것 같지만 영어 표현에서는 부사를 쓰지 않으므로 주의해야 한다.

  • Robert **looks** happy. (○) Robert는 행복해 보인다.
   Robert looks happily. (×)

  • The roses **smell** good. 장미들이 좋은 냄새가 난다.

  • The food **tastes** great. 그 음식은 좋은 맛이 난다.

■ 감각동사 뒤에 보어로 명사나 대명사가 올 때는 명사 앞에 like를 쓴다.

  • It **felt like** a rock. 그것은 바위같이 느껴졌다.

핵심 Check

3. 다음 괄호 안에서 알맞은 것을 고르시오.

  (1) I feel (nervous / nervously).

  (2) Kim looked (sad / sadly).

  (3) The music sounds (interesting / interestingly).

4. 다음 문장에서 **틀린** 부분을 찾아 바르게 고쳐 쓰시오.

  But sometimes my selfies don't look me.

  _____ ➡ _____

Grammar 시험대비 기본평가

01 다음 문장에서 어법상 <u>어색한</u> 부분을 바르게 고쳐 쓰시오.

(1) Walk is good for your health.

_____ ➡ _____

(2) Playing sports are interesting.

_____ ➡ _____

(3) These cookies taste sweetly.

_____ ➡ _____

(4) It looked a star.

_____ ➡ _____

02 다음 빈칸에 알맞은 것은?

_____ in a few years is very difficult.

① English master   ② Master English
③ Mastering English   ④ Mastered English
⑤ English to master

03 다음 중 어법상 <u>어색한</u> 문장은?

① Joel doesn't like eating pizza.
② Riding a bike is not difficult.
③ She finished writing the report.
④ Playing online games are boring.
⑤ Do you need to hand in your homework today?

04 다음 빈칸에 알맞은 것은?

The scarf felt _____.

① beautifully   ② rough   ③ hardly
④ softly   ⑤ smoothly

01 다음 중 밑줄 친 부분의 성격이 <u>다른</u> 것은?

① When I was young, <u>riding</u> a bike in the park was fun.
② Belma finished <u>cleaning</u> her room.
③ My hobby is <u>listening</u> to music.
④ Her daughter was <u>sleeping</u>.
⑤ Jenny is good at <u>dancing</u>.

02 중요 다음 중 어법상 올바른 문장은?

① The music played by the band didn't sound sweetly.
② The soup that my mom cooked for me smelled deliciously.
③ Jane looked beautifully today.
④ The pizza tasted sweetly.
⑤ Mike felt hungry.

03 서답형 다음 괄호 안에서 알맞은 것을 고르시오.

(1) She sounded (excited / excitedly).
(2) Cinderella felt (like a princess / a princess).
(3) (Grow / Growing) beautiful flowers is her hobby.
(4) Daniel is fond of (exercise / exercising) *Teakwondo*.

04 다음 빈칸에 알맞은 것은?

> Terry _____ very shy last night.

① heard   ② looked
③ saw   ④ found
⑤ thought

05 다음 중 어법상 <u>어색한</u> 문장은?

① Donald's hobby is practice drawing.
② I enjoy taking selfies.
③ She likes to listen to music.
④ Brook finished reading the book.
⑤ Jogging in the morning is good for your health.

06 중요 다음 빈칸에 들어갈 알맞은 말을 <u>모두</u> 고르시오.

> They _____ swimming in the river last summer.

① decided   ② wanted
③ enjoyed   ④ practiced
⑤ agreed

07 서답형 다음 우리말과 의미가 같도록 괄호 안의 어구를 이용하여 영작하시오.

(1) TV로 올림픽 경기를 보지 않을래?
   (the Olympic Games, how, watch, on TV)
   ➡ _____

(2) 그녀의 노래는 아름답게 들린다. (sound)
   ➡ _____

08 다음 빈칸에 알맞지 <u>않은</u> 것은?

> The boy looked _____.

① very lonely　　② carefully
③ tired　　④ strong
⑤ like a hero

09 다음 그림을 보고 주어진 어휘를 이용하여 빈칸에 한 단어씩 채워 문장을 완성하시오.

> _____ _____ is really fun. (play)

10 다음 중 어법상 올바른 문장은?

① Kenneth agreed practicing to play the piano every day.
② Gloria loves singing when she has free time.
③ Erica couldn't finish to do the dishes.
④ Do you mind to come here?
⑤ Harry gave up to go to the concert on account of a bad cold.

11 다음 두 문장의 빈칸에 알맞은 말이 바르게 짝지어진 것은?

> • Grace felt _____.
> • This bread smells _____.

① sick – nice　　② sickly – nicely
③ sick – nicely　　④ sickly – nice
⑤ sickness – nicely

12 다음 문장의 빈칸에 알맞은 말을 쓰시오.

> The music sounds _____ an electric piano.

13 다음 문장의 빈칸에 알맞은 것은?

> Will you stop _____ so much noise? I am studying for the final exam.

① make　　② made
③ to make　　④ making
⑤ to making

14 다음 중 어법상 <u>잘못된</u> 것은?

① The cookies she gave to me tasted delicious.
② Her dress smelled like a rose.
③ Tony felt greatly when he won the race.
④ The girl wearing the glasses looked friendly.
⑤ Thomas looked tired after the hard work.

15 다음 빈칸에 괄호 안에 주어진 어휘를 변형하거나 다른 어휘를 추가하여 쓰시오.

(1) Why did you give up _____ the guitar? (play)
(2) _____ a lot makes me happy. (smile)
(3) Have you finished _____ your report? (write)
(4) I'm interested in _____ to Switzerland. (go)

16 다음 밑줄 친 부분 중 어법상 틀린 것은?

① June felt very <u>ill</u> after he finished the work.

② The crowd sounded <u>excited</u> with the goal in the second half.

③ The soup smells <u>like a fish</u>.

④ Both Victoria and her sister look <u>lovely</u>.

⑤ The vegetables Davis bought tasted <u>freshly</u>.

17 다음 〈보기〉의 밑줄 친 부분과 쓰임이 같은 것은?

> ┌ 보기 ┐
> He recommended <u>going</u> to a doctor instead of using home treatments.

① <u>Being</u> a good friend is important.

② My greatest pleasure is <u>watching</u> my son play center forward for his team.

③ At that time, she was <u>doing</u> her math homework.

④ They enjoyed <u>singing</u> to the guitar last night.

⑤ Kim is afraid of <u>speaking</u> in front of people.

18 다음 빈칸에 알맞은 말이 순서대로 짝지어진 것은?

> • Strawberry juice _____ cold.
> • His voice _____ upset.

① feels – sounds
② sounds – feels
③ tastes – smells
④ smells – tastes
⑤ looks – tastes

19 다음 주어진 단어를 알맞게 변형하여 빈칸을 완성하시오.

(1) Teresa practices _____ the violin every day. (play)

(2) _____ healthy food is very important. (have)

(3) My last wish is _____ her again. (see)

(4) Children are fond of _____ as high as possible. (swing)

20 다음 문장 중 어법상 옳지 않은 것은?

① The spaghetti my mom made for me last night tasted great.

② The mountain covered with trash looked terrible.

③ The cake was very cold and hard, so it felt a rock.

④ Dancing is my hobby.

⑤ My dad likes cooking dinner for us on holidays.

21 다음 문장에서 틀린 부분을 찾아 바르게 고쳐 다시 쓰시오.

(1) Solving math problems are interesting.

➡ _____

(2) Lisa is good at solve difficult math problems.

➡ _____

(3) Strawberry candy tastes sweetly.

➡ _____

(4) You look a totally new person in that suit.

➡ _____

01 다음 빈칸에 괄호 안에 주어진 어휘의 알맞은 형태를 쓰시오. (필요한 경우 단어를 추가할 것.)

(1) What does the woman suggest _____ next time? (do)

(2) _____ a good friend is important. (have)

(3) I'm fond of _____ books. (read)

(4) Thank you for _____ me to your party. (invite)

02 다음 〈보기〉와 같이 두 문장을 한 문장으로 만들 때 빈칸을 알맞게 채우시오.

┌─── 보기 ───────────────────┐
I enjoy in-line skating. It's my hobby.
➡ In-line skating is my hobby.
└────────────────────────────┘

(1) Isaac likes playing sports. It is fun.
➡ _____ sports is _____ for Isaac.

(2) Kelly wants to be a doctor. But it is difficult.
➡ _____ a doctor is _____ for Kelly.

(3) My pet dog likes sleeping. It makes him happy.
➡ _____ makes my pet dog _____.

(4) Abe does not eat fast food. It makes him healthy.
➡ _____ _____ fast food makes Abe _____.

(5) Buzz works hard every day. It makes him tired.
➡ _____ hard every day makes Buzz _____.

03 다음 빈칸을 괄호 안의 단어를 이용하여 적절하게 채우시오. (필요하면 어형을 바꾸시오.)

(1) Cindy cooked many Korean foods for us last night. (taste, delicious)
➡ They _____ _____.

(2) Vivian cleaned her house all day long yesterday. (feel, tire)
➡ She _____ _____.

(3) Laura got wonderful gifts on her birthday. (look, happy)
➡ She _____ _____.

(4) Tom bought some roses and gave them to Molly. (smell, nice)
➡ They _____ _____.

(5) Mike broke the window. (sound, upset)
➡ His mom _____ _____.

04 다음 그림을 보고 주어진 어휘를 이용하여 빈칸에 한 단어씩 채워 문장을 완성하시오.

┌────────────────────────────┐
The *samgyupsal* we had yesterday _____ _____.
└────────────────────────────┘

05 자신의 경우에 맞게 다음 질문에 답하시오.

(1) What are you interested in?
➡ _____

(2) What do you usually enjoy doing when you have free time?
➡ _____

06 다음 그림을 보고 주어진 어휘를 이용하여 빈칸에 한 단어씩 채워 문장을 완성하시오.

She loves _____ healthy food. She looks _____ for her recipes. (cook, famous)

07 다음 우리말과 같도록 주어진 표현을 활용하여 문장을 완성하시오.

Sarah는 좋은 의사처럼 보였다.
➡ Sarah _____ _____ _____ _____ doctor. (look, good)

08 우리말에 맞게 주어진 어휘를 활용하여 문장을 완성하시오.

(1) 수영을 배우는 것은 그렇게 어렵지 않다. (learn)
➡ _____ to swim is not so difficult.

(2) 바다에서 수영하는 것은 쉽지 않다. (swim)
➡ _____ in the sea _____ _____ _____.

(3) 지석이는 바둑을 잘 둔다. (play)
➡ Jiseok is good at _____ baduk.

(4) Clark는 휴일에 식구들을 위해 요리하는 것을 좋아한다. (cook)
➡ Clark likes _____ for his family on holidays.

(5) Mary의 취미는 동물을 돌보는 것이다. (take)
➡ Mary's hobby is _____ _____ _____ animals.

09 다음 문장에서 어색한 곳을 찾아 바르게 고쳐 전체 문장을 다시 쓰시오.

(1) Grandmother's story sounded really interestingly.
➡ _____

(2) Judy didn't like the food. She said the food tasted very bitterly.
➡ _____

(3) The meat we had at the restaurant didn't taste beef.
➡ _____
_____

(4) Watch action movies are exciting.
➡ _____

(5) Keep early hours are good for the health.
➡ _____

10 다음 괄호 안의 단어의 어형을 어법에 맞게 바꿔 빈칸에 한 단어씩 써 넣으시오.

(1) After the conversation, she sounded _____. (nerve)

(2) The flowers look _____. (beauty)

(3) I like _____ to music. _____ to music is a lot of fun. (listen)

(4) I have to avoid _____ junk food. _____ junk food is not good. (eat)

11 다음 우리말을 영작하시오. (3 단어)

요리하는 것은 재미있어 보인다.

➡ _____

Reading

교과서

All About Selfies!

#Selfie Facts

Are you interested in selfies? You probably like to post selfies on
be interested in: ~에 관심[흥미]이 있다   = posting
social media, but how much do you know about selfies? Here are some
            얼마나 많이   동사 주어
interesting facts.

1. Robert Cornelius took the world's first selfie in 1839.
                    take the selfie: 셀피를 찍다
2. *Selfie* became a new word in the dictionary in 2013.
        전치사 in은 공간이나 장소를 나타내는 '…에서'의 의미와 특정 연대를 나타내는 '…에'의 의미가 있다.
3. Buzz Aldrin took the first space selfie in 1966.
                            우주 셀피

#*Selfie* Survey

Taking selfies is part of daily life for many teens, but do teens really
동명사구 Taking selfies가 주어로 쓰였는데, 이때 동명사구는 3인칭 단수로 취급한다.
enjoy it? To find out, we did a survey. We asked three questions to 300
        부사적 용법(목적)
students from ages 14 to 16. Let's look at the results. Surprisingly, 90
        from A to B: A부터 B까지   ~을 보다
percent of the girls take selfies, but only 15 percent of the boys take
percents (X)   단지
selfies. Also, 93 percent of these students said that they use filters.
            percents (X) 지시형용사   접속사
The survey also showed that the students take selfies at school the
                        접속사
most. Check out some of the students' comments.
    확인해 보라   s로 끝나는 복수명사는 소유격을 만들 때 어포스트로피만 붙인다.

interest 관심, 흥미
post 게시하다
social media 소셜 미디어
survey (설문) 조사
result 결과
filter 필터, 여과기
outdoors 옥외[야외]에서
comment 논평, 의견

확인문제

● 다음 문장이 본문의 내용과 일치하면 T, 일치하지 <u>않으면</u> F를 쓰시오.

1 People are interested in selfies and know about selfies very much. ☐

2 In 1839, Robert Cornelius took a selfie for the first time in the world. ☐

3 Before 2013, it wasn't possible to look up the word *selfie* in the dictionary. ☐

4 In 1966, Buzz Aldrin took the world's first selfie. ☐

5 The students take selfies at home the most. ☐

Lewis, 14, England   Selfies are awesome. Making silly faces is really fun!

경탄할 만한, 기막히게 좋은   동명사구 Making silly faces가 주어로 쓰였는데, 이때 동명사구는 3인칭 단수로 취급한다.

Minwoo, 16, Korea   I enjoy taking selfies, but some students spend too much time doing it.

taking은 동사 enjoy의 목적어로 쓰인 동명사이다.
spend+시간+ ~ing: ~하는 데 시간을 쓰다

Kate, 15, Denmark   My pictures look good when I use filters. But sometimes my selfies don't look like me.

look(…하게 보이다), sound(…하게 들리다), feel(…하게 느끼다) 등의 감각동사 뒤에는 형용사가 온다.
빈도부사 sometimes는 문장 맨 앞에 써도 된다   look like+명사: ~처럼 보이다

#Selfie Etiquette

You should follow etiquette for selfies. Ask yourself these questions before you take, post, or look at selfies.

셀피 예절   간접목적어   직접목적어
접속사

1. Where am I?

Choose appropriate places to take selfies. Don't take selfies in hospitals or public restrooms. It may bother other people.

부정명령문은 명령문 앞에 Don't를 쓴다.
= to take selfies in hospitals or public restrooms

2. Who can see this?

Keep in mind that anyone can see your selfies. Choose carefully when you post them.

명심하라
your selfies

3. What kinds of comments should I leave?

Leave nice comments on other people's selfies. Don't be rude.

부정명령문은 명령문 앞에 Don't를 쓴다.

That sounds easy, doesn't it? Follow these tips and have fun with your selfies!

look(…하게 보이다), sound(…하게 들리다), feel(…하게 느끼다) 등의 감각동사 뒤에는 형용사가 온다.   즐거운 시간을 보내다

awesome 경탄할 만한, 기막히게 좋은, 굉장한

silly 우스꽝스러운, 어리석은, 유치한

etiquette (사회·특정 직종 구성원 사이의) 예의, 예절

appropriate 적절한, 알맞은

public 공공의, 대중의

restroom 화장실

bother 신경 쓰이게 하다, 귀찮게 하다

leave 남기다, 떠나다

rude 무례한, 버릇없는

확인문제

● 다음 문장이 본문의 내용과 일치하면 T, 일치하지 않으면 F를 쓰시오.

1 Sometimes Kate's selfies don't look like her. ☐

2 You should choose suitable places to take selfies. ☐

3 You should carefully choose when to post selfies. ☐

4 Don't be rude when you leave comments on other people's selfies. ☐

● 우리말을 참고하여 빈칸에 알맞은 말을 쓰시오.

1 All _____ Selfies!

2 #Selfie _____

3 _____ you _____ _____ selfies?

4 You probably like _____ _____ _____ on social media, but _____ _____ do you know about selfies?

5 _____ _____ some interesting facts.

6 Robert Cornelius _____ _____ _____ _____ _____ in 1839.

7 *Selfie* _____ _____ _____ _____ in the dictionary in 2013.

8 Buzz Aldrin _____ _____ _____ _____ in 1966.

9 #Selfie _____

10 _____ _____ is part _____ _____ _____ for many teens, but do teens really enjoy it?

11 _____ _____ _____, we did a survey.

12 We asked three questions to 300 students _____ _____ _____ _____ _____ .

13 _____ _____ _____ the results.

14 Surprisingly, _____ _____ _____ _____ take selfies, but only 15 percent of the boys _____ _____ .

15 _____, 93 percent of these students said that _____ _____ _____ .

16 The survey also showed that the students _____ _____ _____ _____ the most.

17 Check out _____ _____ _____ _____ _____ .

18 Lewis, 14, England   Selfies are _____ .

1 셀피에 대한 모든 것!

2 셀피와 관련된 사실들

3 당신은 셀피에 관심이 있는가?

4 당신은 아마 소셜 미디어에 셀피를 게시하기를 좋아할지도 모르지만, 셀피에 대해 얼마나 많이 알고 있는가?

5 여기 몇 가지 재미있는 사실들이 있다.

6 로버트 코닐리어스가 1839년에 전 세계 최초의 셀피를 찍었다.

7 selfie는 2013년에 사전에 신조어로 등재되었다.

8 버즈 올드린이 1966년에 최초의 우주 셀피를 찍었다.

9 셀피 설문 조사

10 셀피 찍기는 많은 십대들에게 일상생활의 한 부분인데, 십대들은 정말로 그것을 즐기고 있는가?

11 알아보기 위해 우리는 설문 조사를 했다.

12 우리는 14세에서 16세 사이의 학생 300명에게 세 가지를 질문했다.

13 그 결과를 보자.

14 놀랍게도, 소녀들의 90퍼센트가 셀피를 찍지만, 소년들의 15퍼센트만이 셀피를 찍는다.

15 또한 이 학생들의 93퍼센트는 필터를 사용한다고 대답했다.

16 설문은 또한 학생들이 학교에서 가장 많이 셀피를 찍는다는 것을 보여 주었다.

17 학생들의 의견 몇 가지를 확인해 보라.

18 루이스, 14세, 영국: 셀피는 굉장하다.

19 _____ _____ _____ is really fun!

20 Minwoo, 16, Korea I enjoy _____ _____, but some students spend too much time _____ _____.

21 Kate, 15, Denmark My pictures _____ _____ when I use filters.

22 But sometimes my selfies _____ _____ _____ _____.

23 #Selfie _____

24 You should _____ _____ _____ selfies.

25 _____ _____ these questions _____ you take, post, or look at selfies.

26 1. Where _____ _____?

27 Choose _____ _____ to take selfies.

28 _____ _____ _____ in hospitals or public restrooms.

29 It may _____ other people.

30 2. Who can _____ _____?

31 _____ _____ _____ that anyone can see your selfies.

32 _____ _____ when you post them.

33 3. _____ _____ _____ comments should I _____?

34 _____ nice _____ _____ other people's selfies.

35 Don't _____ _____. That _____ _____, _____ _____?

36 Follow these tips and _____ _____ _____ your selfies.

---

19 우스꽝스러운 표정을 짓는 것은 정말로 재미있다!

20 민우, 16세, 한국: 나는 셀피 찍는 것을 즐기지만 몇몇 학생들은 그것을 하는 데 너무 많은 시간을 쓴다.

21 케이트, 15세, 덴마크: 내 사진은 필터를 사용할 때 멋져 보인다.

22 하지만 가끔 나의 셀피가 나처럼 보이지 않는다.

23 셀피 예절

24 당신은 셀피 예절을 따라야 한다.

25 셀피를 찍고, 게시하거나 보기 전에 스스로 이 질문들을 물어보라.

26 1. 내가 어디에 있는가?

27 셀피를 찍기에 적합한 장소를 선택하라.

28 병원이나 공중화장실에서 셀피를 찍지 마라.

29 그것은 다른 사람들을 신경 쓰이게 할 수 있다.

30 2. 누가 이것을 볼 수 있는가?

31 누구나 당신의 셀피를 볼 수 있다는 것을 명심하라.

32 그것들을 게시할 때 신중하게 골라라.

33 3. 어떤 코멘트를 남겨야 하는가?

34 다른 사람들의 셀피에 상냥한 코멘트를 남겨라.

35 무례하게 굴지 마라. 쉬운 것처럼 들린다, 그렇지 않은가?

36 이러한 조언들을 따라서 당신의 셀피와 즐거운 시간을 보내라!

● 우리말을 참고하여 본문을 영작하시오.

1 셀피에 대한 모든 것!

➡ _____

2 셀피와 관련된 사실들

➡ _____

3 당신은 셀피에 관심이 있는가?

➡ _____

4 당신은 아마 소셜 미디어에 셀피를 게시하기를 좋아할지도 모르지만, 셀피에 대해 얼마나 많이 알고 있는가?

➡ _____

5 여기 몇 가지 재미있는 사실들이 있다.

➡ _____

6 로버트 코닐리어스가 1839년에 전 세계 최초의 셀피를 찍었다.

➡ _____

7 selfie는 2013년에 사전에 신조어로 등재되었다.

➡ _____

8 버즈 올드린이 1966년에 최초의 우주 셀피를 찍었다.

➡ _____

9 셀피 설문 조사

➡ _____

10 셀피 찍기는 많은 십대들에게 일상생활의 한 부분인데, 십대들은 정말로 그것을 즐기고 있는가?

➡ _____

11 알아보기 위해 우리는 설문 조사를 했다.

➡ _____

12 우리는 14세에서 16세 사이의 학생 300명에게 세 가지를 질문했다.

➡ _____

13 그 결과를 보자.

➡ _____

14 놀랍게도, 소녀들의 90퍼센트가 셀피를 찍지만, 소년들의 15퍼센트만이 셀피를 찍는다.

➡ _____

15 또한 이 학생들의 93퍼센트는 필터를 사용한다고 대답했다.

➡ _____

16 설문은 또한 학생들이 학교에서 가장 많이 셀피를 찍는다는 것을 보여 주었다.

➡ _____

17 학생들의 의견 몇 가지를 확인해 보라.

➡ _____

18 루이스, 14세, 영국: 셀피는 굉장하다.

➡ _____

19 우스꽝스러운 표정을 짓는 것은 정말로 재미있다!

➡ _____

20 민우, 16세, 한국: 나는 셀피 찍는 것을 즐기지만 몇몇 학생들은 그것을 하는 데 너무 많은 시간을 쓴다.

➡ _____

21 케이트, 15세, 덴마크: 내 사진은 필터를 사용할 때 멋져 보인다.

➡ _____

22 하지만 가끔 나의 셀피가 나처럼 보이지 않는다.

➡ _____

23 셀피 예절

➡ _____

24 당신은 셀피 예절을 따라야 한다.

➡ _____

25 셀피를 찍고, 게시하거나 보기 전에 스스로 이 질문들을 물어보라.

➡ _____

26 내가 어디에 있는가?

➡ _____

27 셀피를 찍기에 적합한 장소를 선택하라.

➡ _____

28 병원이나 공중화장실에서 셀피를 찍지 마라.

➡ _____

29 그것은 다른 사람들을 신경 쓰이게 할 수 있다.

➡ _____

30 누가 이것을 볼 수 있는가?

➡ _____

31 누구나 당신의 셀피를 볼 수 있다는 것을 명심하라.

➡ _____

32 그것들을 게시할 때 신중하게 골라라.

➡ _____

33 어떤 코멘트를 남겨야 하는가?

➡ _____

34 다른 사람들의 셀피에 상냥한 코멘트를 남겨라.

➡ _____

35 무례하게 굴지 마라. 쉬운 것처럼 들린다, 그렇지 않은가?

➡ _____

36 이러한 조언들을 따라서 당신의 셀피와 즐거운 시간을 보내라.

➡ _____

[01~03] 다음 글을 읽고, 물음에 답하시오.

Are you (A)[interested / interesting] in selfies? You probably like to post selfies on social media, but how much do you know about selfies? Here (B)[is / are] some (C)[interested / interesting] facts.
1. Robert Cornelius took the world's first selfie in 1839.
2. *Selfie* became a new word in the dictionary in 2013.
3. Buzz Aldrin took the first space selfie in 1966.

서답형

01 괄호 (A)~(C)에서 어법상 알맞은 낱말을 골라 쓰시오.

(A)_____ (B)_____ (C)_____

02 위 글의 제목으로 알맞은 것을 고르시오.

① Are You Interested in Selfies?
② Selfie Survey
③ Who Took the World's First Selfie?
④ Selfie Facts
⑤ Selfie Etiquette

03 위 글의 내용과 일치하지 <u>않는</u> 것은?

① 위 글은 셀피에 관한 몇 가지 재미있는 사실들을 소개하고 있다.
② 사람들은 소셜 미디어에 셀피를 게시하려고 셀피를 찍는다.
③ 세계 최초로 셀피를 찍은 사람은 Robert Cornelius이다.
④ selfie가 사전에 신조어로 등재된 것은 2013년이다.
⑤ 우주에서 처음 셀피를 찍은 사람은 Buzz Aldrin이다.

[04~06] 다음 글을 읽고, 물음에 답하시오.

#Selfie Survey

ⓐTaking selfies is part of daily life for many teens, but do teens really enjoy it? To find out, we did a survey. ⓑWe asked three questions to 300 students from ages 14 to 16. Let's look at the results.

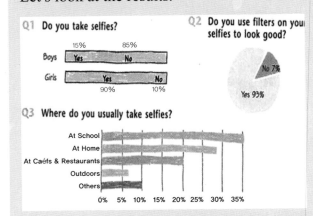

Surprisingly, 90 percent of the girls take selfies, but only 15 percent of the boys take selfies. Also, 93 percent of these students said that they use filters. The survey also showed that the students take selfies at school the most. Check out some of the students' comments.

중요

04 위 글의 밑줄 친 ⓐTaking과 문법적 쓰임이 같은 것을 고르시오.

① I was <u>listening</u> to music.
② They were <u>working</u> over there.
③ My hobby is <u>playing</u> baseball.
④ He was <u>dancing</u> on the floor.
⑤ She was <u>eating</u> dinner.

서답형

05 위 글의 밑줄 친 ⓑ를 우리말로 옮기시오.

➡ _____

_____

06 위 도표의 내용과 일치하지 <u>않는</u> 것은?

① 소년들의 85%가 셀피를 찍지 않는다.

② 소녀들의 10%가 셀피를 찍지 않는다.

③ 7%의 학생들은 필터를 사용하지 않는다.

④ 학생들이 두 번째로 셀피를 많이 찍는 장소는 카페나 식당이다.

⑤ 카페나 식당보다 학교에서 셀피를 찍는 학생들이 15% 더 많다.

[07~09] 다음 글을 읽고, 물음에 답하시오.

#Selfie Etiquette

You should follow etiquette for selfies. Ask yourself ⓐ<u>these questions</u> before you take, post, or look at selfies.

1. Where am I?

Choose appropriate places ⓑ<u>to take</u> selfies. Don't take selfies in hospitals or public restrooms. It may bother other people.

2. Who can see this?

Keep in mind that anyone can see your selfies. Choose carefully when you post them.

3. What kinds of comments should I leave?

Leave nice comments on other people's selfies. Don't be rude.

서답형

07 위 글의 밑줄 친 ⓐ가 가리키는 것을 본문에서 찾아 쓰시오.

(1) _____

(2) _____

(3) _____

08 위 글의 밑줄 친 ⓑ<u>to take</u>와 to부정사의 용법이 같은 것을 고르시오.

① I am glad to meet you again.

② He must be smart to solve it.

③ Give me a chair to sit on.

④ It is not easy to learn English.

⑤ She grew up to be a scientist.

서답형

09 다음 문장에서 위 글의 내용과 <u>다른</u> 부분을 찾아서 고치시오.

Before you take, post, or look at selfies, you should keep in mind that no one can see your selfies.

➡ _____ ➡ _____

[10~12] 다음 글을 읽고, 물음에 답하시오.

#Selfie Facts

Are you interested in selfies? You ⓐ<u>probably</u> like to post selfies on social media, but ⓑ셀피에 대해 얼마나 많이 알고 있니? Here are some interesting facts.

1. Robert Cornelius took the world's first selfie in 1830.

2. *Selfie* became a new word in the dictionary in 2013.

3. Buzz Aldrin took the first space selfie in 1966.

10 위 글의 밑줄 친 ⓐ<u>probably</u>와 바꿔 쓸 수 있는 말을 모두 고르시오.

① perhaps   ② actually

③ exactly   ④ maybe

⑤ completely

11 위 글의 밑줄 친 ⓑ의 우리말에 맞게 한 단어를 보충하여, 주어진 어휘를 알맞게 배열하시오.

> selfies / know / much / you / about / do

➡ _____

12 다음 질문에 대한 알맞은 대답을 완성하시오.

> Q: Who took the first space selfie?
> A: It was _____.

[13~16] 다음 글을 읽고, 물음에 답하시오.

#Selfie Survey

Taking selfies is part of daily life for many teens, but do teens really enjoy it? ⓐTo find out, we did a survey. We asked three questions to 300 students from ages 14 to 16. Let's look at the results.

Surprisingly, 90 percent of the girls take selfies, but only 15 percent of the boys take selfies. Also, 93 percent of these students said that they use filters. The survey also showed that the students take selfies at school the most. Check out some of the students' comments.

Lewis, 14, England   Selfies are ___ⓑ___. Making silly faces is really fun!

Minwoo, 16, Korea   I enjoy taking selfies, but some students spend too much time doing it.

Kate, 15, Denmark   My pictures look good when I use filters. But sometimes my selfies don't look like me.

13 위 도표를 보고 대답할 수 <u>없는</u> 질문은?

① What percent of the girls said that they take selfies?

② How many students use filters to look good?

③ What percent of the students take selfies at school?

④ Why do students like to take selfies at school?

⑤ Where do students take selfies more, at home or at cafés & restaurants?

14 위 글의 밑줄 친 ⓐTo find와 to부정사의 용법이 <u>다른</u> 것을 고르시오.

① I use my computer <u>to do</u> the work.

② I have much work <u>to do</u> today.

③ He stopped <u>to listen</u> to music.

④ This book is easy <u>to read</u>.

⑤ He must be foolish <u>to do</u> such things.

15 위 글의 빈칸 ⓑ에 들어갈 알맞은 말을 고르시오.

① terrible   ② awkward

③ boring   ④ disappointing

⑤ awesome

16 다음 질문에 대한 알맞은 대답을 주어진 단어로 시작하여 쓰시오. (3단어)

> Q: Why does Kate say that sometimes her selfies don't look like her?
> A: Because _____.

[17~19] 다음 글을 읽고, 물음에 답하시오.

#Selfie Etiquette
　You should follow etiquette for selfies. Ask yourself these questions before you take, post, or look at selfies.
1. (A)[Where is here? / Where am I?]
　Choose ⓐappropriate places to take selfies. Don't take selfies in hospitals or public restrooms. It may bother other people.
2. Who can see it?
　Keep in mind that anyone can see your selfies. Choose carefully when you post (B)[it / them].
3. What kinds of comments should I leave?
　Leave nice comments ⓑ____ other people's selfies. Don't be rude.
　That sounds (C)[easy / easily], doesn't it? Follow these tips and have fun ⓒ____ your selfies.

서답형

17 위 글의 괄호 (A)~(C)에서 어법상 알맞은 것을 골라 쓰시오.

　(A)_____　(B)_____　(C)_____

18 위 글의 밑줄 친 ⓐappropriate와 바꿔 쓸 수 있는 말을 모두 고르시오.

① popular　　　② proper
③ common　　　④ favorite
⑤ suitable

중요

19 위 글의 빈칸 ⓑ와 ⓒ에 들어갈 전치사가 바르게 짝지어진 것은?

① on – for　　　② in – with
③ in – from　　　④ for – to
⑤ on – with

[20~22] 다음 대화를 읽고, 물음에 답하시오.

Boy: Bonny, did you see the results of the selfie survey?
Bonny: No, I didn't. Are ⓐthey interesting?
Boy: Yes. (①) Not many boys take selfies. (②) Also, a lot of teens use filters on their selfies. (③) Where do students take selfies most often? (④)
Bonny: I don't know. (⑤) Maybe at a restaurant?
Boy: No. It's at school!
Bonny: Oh, you're right. My classmates also take selfies in the classroom.

서답형

20 위 대화의 밑줄 친 ⓐthey가 가리키는 것을 본문에서 찾아 쓰시오.

➡ _____

21 위 대화의 흐름으로 보아, 주어진 문장이 들어가기에 가장 적절한 곳은?

| Can you guess? |

①　　　②　　　③　　　④　　　⑤

22 위 대화의 내용과 일치하지 않는 것은?

① Bonny는 셀피 설문조사의 결과를 보지 못했다.
② 소년은 설문조사의 결과가 흥미롭다고 생각한다.
③ Bonny는 학생들이 셀피를 가장 많이 찍는 장소를 알고 있다.
④ 소년은 학생들이 셀피를 가장 많이 찍는 장소가 학교라고 말했다.
⑤ Bonny의 학급 친구들도 교실에서 셀피를 찍는다.

[01~03] 다음 글을 읽고, 물음에 답하시오.

#Selfie Facts

ⓐ Are you interested in selfies? You probably like to post selfies on social media, but how much do you know about selfies? ⓑ 여기에 몇 가지 재미있는 사실들이 있다.

1. Robert Cornelius took the world's first selfie in 1839.
2. *Selfie* became a new word in the dictionary in 2013.
3. Buzz Aldrin took the first space selfie in 1966.

01 위 글의 밑줄 친 ⓐ를 다음과 같이 바꿔 쓸 때 빈칸에 알맞은 말을 쓰시오.

> Do you have an _____ in selfies?

02 위 글의 밑줄 친 ⓑ의 우리말에 맞게 주어진 어휘를 이용하여 5단어로 영작하시오.

> some

➡ _____

03 다음 문장에서 위 글의 내용과 다른 부분을 찾아서 고치시오.

> It was possible to look up *selfie* in the dictionary before 2013.

➡ _____ _____

[04~06] 다음 글을 읽고, 물음에 답하시오.

#Selfie Etiquette

You should follow etiquette for selfies. Ask yourself these questions before you take, post, or look at selfies.

1. Where am I?
   ⓐ 셀피를 찍기에 적절한 장소를 선택해라. Don't take selfies in hospitals or public restrooms. It may bother other people.
2. Who can see this?
   Keep in mind that anyone can see your selfies. Choose carefully when you post them.
3. What kinds of comments should I leave?
   Leave nice _____ ⓑ _____ on other people's selfies. Don't be rude.

04 위 글의 밑줄 친 ⓐ의 우리말에 맞게 주어진 어휘를 이용하여 6단어로 영작하시오.

> appropriate

➡ _____

05 다음 질문에 대한 알맞은 대답을 주어진 단어로 시작하여 쓰시오. (5 단어)

> Q: Why shouldn't we take selfies in hospitals or public restrooms?
> A: Because _____ .

06 위 글의 빈칸 ⓑ에 들어갈 알맞은 말을 본문에서 찾아 쓰시오.

➡ _____

[07~09] 다음 글을 읽고, 물음에 답하시오.

#Selfie Facts

Are you ___ⓐ___ in selfies? You probably like to ___ⓑ___ selfies on social media, but how much do you know about selfies? Here are some interesting facts.

1. Robert Cornelius took the world's first selfie in 1839.
2. *Selfie* became a new word in the dictionary in 2013.
3. Buzz Aldrin took the first space selfie in 1966.

07 본문의 한 단어를 변형하여 위 글의 빈칸 ⓐ에 들어갈 알맞은 말을 쓰시오.

➡ _____

08 다음 주어진 영영풀이를 참고하여 빈칸 ⓑ에 철자 p로 시작하는 단어를 쓰시오.

> to publish something such as a message or picture on a website or using social media

➡ _____

09 다음 질문에 대한 알맞은 대답을 주어진 단어로 시작하여 쓰시오. (2 단어)

> Q: When did Robert Cornelius take the world's first selfie?
>
> A: It was _____ .

[10~12] 다음 글을 읽고, 물음에 답하시오.

#Selfie Survey

Taking selfies is part of daily life for many teens, but do teens really enjoy ⓐit? To find out, we did a survey. We asked three questions to 300 students from ages 14 to 16. Let's look at the results.

Surprisingly, 90 percent of the girls take selfies, but only 15 percent of the boys take selfies. Also, 93 percent of these students said that they use filters. The survey also showed that the students take selfies ___ⓑ___ the most. Check out some of the students' comments.

10 위 글의 밑줄 친 ⓐit이 가리키는 것을 본문에서 찾아 쓰시오.

➡ _____

11 다음 질문에 대한 알맞은 대답을 빈칸에 쓰시오.

> Q: How many students take selfies at cafés & restaurants?
>
> A: _____ students take selfies at cafés & restaurants.

12 위 글의 빈칸 ⓑ에 들어갈 알맞은 말을 쓰시오.

➡ _____

Project Link

Our group is interested in dance. We made a dance. We recorded a dance
be interested in: ~에 관심[흥미]이 있다   make의 과거형   record: 녹음하다, 녹화하다

video and posted it online. You can see it at www.yutu.com.
recorded와 posted가 병렬구조   = a dance video

구문해설 • post: 올리다, 게시하다

우리 그룹은 춤에 관심이 있다. 우리는 춤을 만들었다. 우리는 춤 비디오를 녹화하고 그것을 온라인에 올렸다. 너는 그것을 www.yutu.com.에서 볼 수 있다.

Think and Write

Be a Great Internet User!

When we use the internet, we should follow some rules. Then we can enjoy
~할 때   follow the rule: 규칙을 따르다   그러면

the internet more. First of all, we should follow language rules because people
= Above all   ~해야만 한다   because + 주어 + 동사

may not understand us. Also, we should post only true information. People
~이 아닐지도 모른다   = In addition

may believe our incorrect information. Finally, we should not leave rude
~일지도 모른다(추측)   마지막으로

comments. We can hurt others' feelings. Keep these rules in mind. Then you
s로 끝난 말의 소유격: others's(X)   지시형용사, this(X)

will be a great internet user!
~이 될 것이다

구문해설 • follow the rule: 규칙을 따르다 • first of all: 우선, 다른 무엇보다 먼저

• post: 게시하다 • incorrect: 부정확한 • rude: 무례한 • keep in mind: 명심하다

멋진 인터넷 사용자가 되어라! 우리가 인터넷을 사용할 때, 우리는 몇 가지 규칙을 따라야 한다. 그러면 우리는 인터넷을 더 즐길 수 있다. 무엇보다, 사람들이 우리를 이해하지 못할 수도 있기 때문에 우리는 언어 규칙들을 따라야 한다. 또한, 우리는 오직 사실인 정보만을 게시해야 한다. 사람들은 우리의 부정확한 정보를 믿을지도 모른다. 마지막으로, 무례한 코멘트를 남기지 말아야 한다. 우리는 다른 사람들의 감정을 다치게 할 수 있다. 이런 규칙들을 명심해라. 그러면 너는 멋진 인터넷 사용자가 될 것이다!

Culture Link

A student from the United States is interested in the environment. He created

a cartoon superhero, *GoGreenMan*, and posted it online. He also helps the
명사+콤마(,)+명사: 동격

environment just like his character, *GoGreenMan*.
~와 꼭 같이   동격

구문해설 • environment: 환경 • character: 캐릭터, 등장인물

미국 출신의 한 학생은 환경에 관심이 있다. 그는 GoGreenMan이라는 만화의 수퍼 영웅을 만들어 인터넷에 게시했다. 그는 또한 그의 캐릭터 GoGreenMan과 꼭 같이 환경을 돕는다.

영역별 핵심문제

01 다음 제시된 단어를 사용하여 자연스러운 문장을 만들 수 없는 것은? (형태 변화 가능)

┌─ 보기 ┐
leave display understand prepare
└─────┘

① Various styles of suits are _____ in the shop windows.
② _____ the sauce while the pasta is cooking.
③ Danny, don't _____ Ellen while she's reading.
④ She _____ a message on his phone.
⑤ I'm sorry, I don't _____. Can you explain that again?

02 다음 우리말에 맞게 빈칸을 완성하시오.

(1) 나는 가끔 늦게까지 일을 해야 한다.
➡ I _____ have _____ work late.
(2) 바보 같은 질문을 그만해.
➡ Stop asking _____ questions.
(3) 이 근처에 공중전화가 있나요?
➡ Is _____ a _____ telephone near here?
(4) 오늘밤은 야외에서 밥을 먹기에 충분히 따뜻한 날씨이다.
➡ It's _____ enough to eat _____ tonight.

03 다음 빈칸에 들어갈 알맞은 말을 〈보기〉에서 골라 쓰시오. (형태 변화 가능)

┌─ 보기 ┐
do   have   sound   spend
└─────┘

(1) His ideas _____ interesting.
(2) Stacey _____ all her free time painting.
(3) We _____ a survey of parents in the village last year.
(4) The children were _____ so much fun.

04 다음 짝지어진 낱말의 관계가 나머지 넷과 다른 것은?

① display – exhibit
② exciting – boring
③ fact – truth
④ hurt – injure
⑤ nervous – anxious

05 다음 빈칸에 알맞은 말이 순서대로 바르게 나열된 것은?

┌─────────────────────────────┐
│ • _____ beginning to end, the movie's plot is awesome.
│ • He could not keep _____ mind what she was saying.
│ • The average child spends three to four hours _____ front of the TV.
└─────────────────────────────┘

① From – in – from
② From – at – in
③ From – in – in
④ For – at – in
⑤ For – in – from

06 다음 짝지어진 대화가 <u>어색한</u> 것은?

① A: May I use your cup?
   B: I'm afraid not. It's broken.
② A: What sport are you interested in?
   B: I like to play volleyball.
③ A: Is it okay if I clean the blackboard?
   B: I'm sorry, but some students are still taking notes.
④ A: Can I borrow your notebook?
   B: Of course. I'm sorry.
⑤ A: I'm afraid you can't take pictures in the concert hall.
   B: I'm sorry. I didn't know that.

[07~10] 다음 대화를 읽고, 물음에 답하시오.

B: What are you _____(A)_____ (go) to do this weekend?
G: I'm ___(B)___ (go) to go to a baseball game with my brother.
B: ①Are you interesting in baseball?
G: ②Not really. I'm going to the baseball game ___(C)___ my brother likes baseball.
B: ③You're so nice! ④Then what are you interested in?
G: I'm more interested in soccer. ⑤I want to go to a soccer game someday.

07 위 대화의 주어진 go를 이용해 빈칸 (A)와 (B)에 공통으로 들어갈 말을 쓰시오.

➡ _____

08 위 대화의 빈칸 (C)에 들어갈 알맞은 말을 고르시오.

① because   ② when
③ therefore   ④ though
⑤ while

09 위 대화의 밑줄 친 ①~⑤ 중에서 <u>어색한</u> 것을 고르고 바르게 고치시오.

_____ ➡ _____

10 위 대화를 읽고 답할 수 <u>없는</u> 질문은?

① What will the girl do this weekend?
② What does the girl's brother like?
③ Does the girl like baseball?
④ What is the boy interested in?
⑤ Where does the girl want to go someday?

[11~12] 다음 대화를 읽고, 물음에 답하시오.

A: (A)너는 무엇에 관심이 있니?
B: I'm interested in games and social media. What about you?
A: I'm interested in music and social media.
B: (B)(both, in, are, media, we, social, interested)

11 위 대화의 (A)의 밑줄 친 우리말과 일치하도록 영작하시오.

➡ _____

12 위 대화의 (B)의 괄호 안에 있는 단어를 바르게 배열하시오.

➡ _____

13 다음 괄호 안의 말을 이용하여 빈칸에 알맞게 쓰시오.

(1) Thanks for _____ me. (invite)
(2) _____ soccer is exciting. (play)

14 다음 중 어법상 올바른 것은?

① Emma cooked some Indian food and it tasted greatly.

② The girls who greet us at the gate look friendly.

③ The flowers Joyce gave to me smelled sweetly.

④ Belma sounded seriously after she heard the news.

⑤ Her dress which was made of pure silk felt smoothly.

15 다음 밑줄 친 부분의 쓰임이 다른 하나는?

① Writing a story is exciting.

② Angie loves watching movies.

③ There are some birds singing in the tree.

④ His dream job is becoming a kindergarten teacher.

⑤ She is really excited about going to Hawaii.

16 다음 우리말을 영어로 바르게 옮긴 것은?

> 당신의 연설을 들은 후로 저는 새로 태어난 사람 같습니다.

① I felt a new man after I listened to your speech.

② I felt a new man like after I listened to your speech.

③ I felt a new man after I like listened to your speech.

④ I felt a new man after I listened to your speech like.

⑤ I felt like a new man after I listened to your speech.

17 다음 우리말과 같은 뜻이 되도록 주어진 어구를 활용하여 문장을 완성하시오.

(1) 영화를 보는 것은 하나의 모험이다. (watch, a movie, adventure) (6 단어)

➡ _____

(2) 이 책을 읽는 것은 친구와 커피 한 잔 하는 것 같았다. (like, have, a coffee) (11 단어)

➡ _____

_____

(3) 제 사생활에 대해선 그만 얘기하고 싶어요. (stop, talk, personal life) (9 단어)

➡ _____

(4) 원은 각이 없기 때문에 부드럽게 느껴진다. (circles, have no angles) (8 단어)

➡ _____

(5) 내 컴퓨터에서 이상한 소리가 나요. (sound) (4 단어)

➡ _____

18 다음 문장에서 어법상 잘못된 부분을 찾아 바르게 고쳐 쓰시오.

(1) All the food smells greatly.

_____ ➡ _____

(2) It neither smells nor tastes fish.

_____ ➡ _____

19 다음 중 어법상 어색한 것은?

① Amy is interested in climbing mountains.

② The strawberry cake looks delicious.

③ Jogging in the morning can keep your heart strong.

④ Stop to read that book, and go out and play.

⑤ The music the band is playing sounds good.

20 다음 문장에서 어법상 잘못된 부분을 찾아 바르게 고쳐 쓰시오.

(1) Mike denied to spend time with the bad people at that time.

————————— ➡ —————————

(2) Break bad habits are not easy to do in a short period.

————————— ➡ —————————

Reading

[21~23] 다음 글을 읽고, 물음에 답하시오.

#Selfie Facts

Are you interested ⓐ selfies? You probably like ⓑto post selfies ⓒ social media, but how (A)[many / much] do you know about selfies? Here are some (B)[boring / interesting] facts.
1. Robert Cornelius took the world's first selfie in 1839.
2. *Selfie* became a (C)[new / famous] word in the dictionary in 2013.
3. Buzz Aldrin took the first space selfie in 1966.

21 위 글의 빈칸 ⓐ와 ⓒ에 들어갈 전치사를 빈칸에 쓰시오.

ⓐ——————— ⓒ———————

22 위 글의 밑줄 친 ⓑto post와 to부정사의 용법이 같은 것을 고르시오.

① He has no friends to play with.
② He began to read the book.
③ This cell phone is easy to use.
④ I want something to write with.
⑤ I should be happy to go with you.

23 위 글의 괄호 (A)~(C)에서 문맥상 알맞은 낱말을 골라 쓰시오.

(A)——————— (B)——————— (C)———————

[24~26] 다음 글을 읽고, 물음에 답하시오.

#Selfie Survey

(A)Taking selfies is part of daily life for many teens, but do teens really enjoy it? To find out, we did a survey. We asked three questions to 300 students from ages 14 to 16. Let's look at the results.

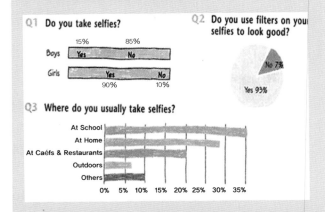

Surprisingly, ⓐ percent of the girls take selfies, but only ⓑ percent of the boys take selfies. Also, ⓒ percent of these students said that they use filters. The survey also showed that the students take selfies at school the most. Check out some of the students' comments.

Lewis, 14, England Selfies are awesome. Making silly faces is really fun!

Minwoo, 16, Korea I enjoy taking selfies, but some students spend too much time doing it.

Kate, 15, Denmark My pictures look good when I use filters. But sometimes my selfies don't look like me.

24 위 글의 밑줄 친 (A)Taking과 바꿔 쓸 수 있는 말을 쓰시오.

➡ ———————————————

25 위 글의 빈칸 ⓐ~ⓒ에 들어갈 알맞은 숫자를 쓰시오.

ⓐ＿＿＿＿＿ ⓑ＿＿＿＿＿ ⓒ＿＿＿＿＿

26 위 글의 내용과 일치하지 <u>않는</u> 것은?

① Lewis comments that selfies are amazing.
② Minwoo enjoys taking selfies.
③ Minwoo spends too much time taking selfies.
④ Kate's pictures look good when she uses filters.
⑤ Sometimes Kate's selfies don't look like her.

[27~28] 다음 글을 읽고, 물음에 답하시오.

You should follow etiquette for selfies. Ask yourself these questions before you take, post, or look at selfies.
1. Where am I?
   Choose appropriate places to take selfies. Don't take selfies in hospitals or public restrooms. It may bother other people.
2. Who can see this?
   Keep in mind that anyone can see your selfies. Choose carefully when you post them.
3. What kinds of comments should I leave?
   Leave nice comments on other people's selfies. Don't be rude.

27 위 글의 제목으로 알맞은 것을 고르시오.

① How to Ask Yourself Questions
② Selfie Etiquette
③ Selfie Facts
④ Have Fun with Your Selfies
⑤ Selfie Survey

28 위 글을 읽고 대답할 수 <u>없는</u> 질문은?

① What is the etiquette for selfies?
② When should you ask yourself the questions about etiquette for selfies?
③ Who can see your selfies?
④ Where should you post your selfies?
⑤ What kinds of comments should you leave on other people's selfies?

[29~30] 다음 글을 읽고, 물음에 답하시오.

Selfie ＿①＿
• Robert Cornelius took the world's first selfie.
• ⓐ*Selfie* became a new word in the dictionary in 2013.
• Buzz Aldrin took the first space selfie.
Selfie ＿②＿
• Do you take selfies?
• ⓑDo you use filters on your selfies looking good?
• ⓒWhere usually do you take selfies?
Selfie ＿③＿
• ⓓChoose appropriate places to take selfies.
• Choose your selfies carefully when you post them.
• ⓔLeave nice comments on other people's selfies.

29 위 글의 빈칸 ①~③에 들어갈 알맞은 말을 쓰시오.

ⓐ＿＿＿＿＿ ⓑ＿＿＿＿＿ ⓒ＿＿＿＿＿

30 위 글의 밑줄 친 ⓐ~ⓔ 중 어법상 틀린 개수를 고르시오.

① 1개 ② 2개 ③ 3개 ④ 4개 ⑤ 5개

출제율 95%

01 다음 〈보기〉와 같은 관계가 되도록 빈칸에 알맞은 말을 쓰시오.

┌─── 보기 ────┐
outdoors – indoors
└────────────┘

(1) carelessly – _____

(2) correct – _____

출제율 85%

02 다음 제시된 의미에 맞는 단어를 주어진 철자로 시작하여 빈칸에 쓰고, 알맞은 것을 골라 문장을 완성하시오.

- a_____ : correct or suitable for a particular time, situation, or purpose
- p_____ : available for anyone to use
- r_____ : speaking or behaving in a way that is not polite and is likely to offend or annoy people

(1) _____ libraries are good for finding information.

(2) I didn't mean to be _____, but I had to leave early.

(3) I don't think jeans can be _____ for the party.

[03~04] 다음 밑줄 친 단어와 바꿔 쓸 수 있는 단어를 고르시오.

출제율 90%

03

The exam was <u>unexpectedly</u> easy.

① usually   ② luckily
③ surprisingly ④ interestingly
⑤ strangely

출제율 100%

04

Charlie thinks that money will <u>deal with</u> all his problems.

① improve   ② solve   ③ decide
④ share   ⑤ spend

출제율 90%

05 다음 중 의도하는 바가 나머지와 <u>다른</u> 하나는?

① May I eat snacks in the theater?
② Can I eat snacks in the theater?
③ Is it okay if I eat snacks in the theater?
④ Are you sure that I can eat snacks in the theater?
⑤ Do you mind my eating snacks in the theater?

출제율 90%

06 다음 주어진 문장의 뒤에 나올 대화의 순서를 알맞게 쓰시오.

What are you doing?
(A) That sounds fun! What are you interested in?
(B) Oh, I'm interested in photography, too.
(C) I'm interested in photography. I will talk about it tomorrow.
(D) Really? Then may I ask you for some advice for my presentation?
(E) I'm preparing for tomorrow's presentation. It is about one of my interests.

➡ _____

[07~10] 다음 대화를 읽고, 물음에 답하시오.

> G: Hi. (A)Can I go in now?
> M: Sure. (①)
> G: Here it is. (②) May I record the music in the concert hall?
> M: No, you may not. (③)
> G: Okay. May I take pictures of the band? (④)
> M: _____(B)_____ You can only take pictures in front of the concert hall. Please enjoy the concert. (⑤)
> G: Oh, okay. Thank you.

07 위 대화의 ①~⑤ 중 주어진 문장이 들어갈 알맞은 곳은?

> Let me see your ticket, please.

① ② ③ ④ ⑤

08 주어진 〈보기〉에서 (A)와 바꾸어 쓸 수 있는 것의 개수를 고르시오.

> ┌ 보기 ┐
> May   Will   Should
> Is it okay if   Would it be all right if

① 1개   ② 2개   ③ 3개   ④ 4개   ⑤ 5개

09 위 대화의 흐름상 빈칸 (B)에 들어갈 수 있는 말을 주어진 단어를 이용하여 쓰시오.

➡ _____ (may)

10 위 대화를 읽고 답할 수 <u>없는</u> 질문은?

① Where are they?
② What kind of music does the band play?
③ Is it possible to take pictures of the band?
④ Where can the girl take pictures?
⑤ Can the girl record the music in the concert hall?

[11~12] 다음 대화를 읽고, 물음에 답하시오.

> B: Excuse me.
> M: Hello. (①) What can I do for you?
> B: May I borrow this new science book? (②)
> M: No, you may not. (③)
> B: Then may I copy some pages from the book? (④) I need them for my science report.
> M: Yes, you may. (⑤) But please don't share them online.
> B: Okay, I won't. Thank you!

11 위 대화의 ①~⑤ 중 주어진 문장이 들어갈 알맞은 곳은?

> Students can't take new books home.

① ② ③ ④ ⑤

12 위 대화의 내용과 일치하지 <u>않는</u> 것을 <u>모두</u> 고르시오.

① 남자아이는 과학 보고서를 위해 책을 빌리는 것을 원했다.
② 남자아이는 과학 보고서에 필요한 새 책을 복사할 수 있다.
③ 남자아이는 복사한 것을 온라인에 공유해서는 안 된다.
④ 학생들은 책을 집에 가져갈 수 없다는 것이 원칙이다.
⑤ 남자아이는 과학에 관한 프레젠테이션이 내일 있다.

출제율 95%

13 다음 우리말과 같도록 빈칸에 알맞은 말을 쓰시오.

> Kate는 웃을 때 사랑스럽게 보인다.
> ➡ Kate _____ _____ when she smiles.

출제율 95%

14 다음 중 어법상 자연스러운 문장은?

① He gave up to become a lawyer and decided to be a teacher.
② Breaking this wall looks almost impossible!
③ Practice to make eye contact with yourself in the mirror.
④ Eat strawberries is great!
⑤ Do you mind to park my car here?

출제율 90%

15 다음 문장에서 어법상 잘못된 부분을 찾아 바르게 고쳐 쓰시오.

(1) Read a story is exciting.

_____ ➡ _____

(2) They are just watching each other without say a word.

_____ ➡ _____

(3) I like chocolate cake because it tastes sweetly.

_____ ➡ _____

(4) You always sound a broken record.

_____ ➡ _____

[16~18] 다음 글을 읽고, 물음에 답하시오.

#Selfie Facts
　Are you interested in selfies? You probably like to post selfies on social media, but how much do you know about selfies? Here are ⓐ some interesting facts.
1. Robert Cornelius ___ⓑ___ the world's first selfie in 1839.
2. *Selfie* became a new word in the dictionary in 2013.
3. Buzz Aldrin ___ⓒ___ the first space selfie in 1966.

출제율 95%

16 위 글의 밑줄 친 ⓐ가 가리키는 것을 우리말로 쓰시오.

(1) _____
(2) _____
(3) _____

출제율 100%

17 위 글의 빈칸 ⓑ와 ⓒ에 공통으로 들어갈 알맞은 말을 고르시오.

① had　　　　② took
③ kept　　　　④ gave
⑤ did

출제율 90%

18 다음 문장에서 위 글의 내용과 다른 부분을 찾아서 고치시오.

> There were many space selfies before 1966.

➡ _____

[19~21] 다음 글을 읽고, 물음에 답하시오.

#Selfie Etiquette

You should follow etiquette for selfies. Ask yourself these questions before you take, post, or look at selfies.

1. Where am I?

Choose appropriate places to take selfies. Don't take selfies in hospitals or public restrooms. It may bother other people.

2. Who can see this?

Keep in mind that anyone can see your selfies. Choose carefully when you post them.

3. What kinds of comments should I leave?

Leave nice comments on other people's selfies. Don't be rude.

ⓐThat sounds easy, isn't that? Follow these tips and have fun with your selfies.

출제율 95%

19 위 글의 내용을 다음과 같이 정리하고자 한다. 빈칸 (A)와 (B)에 들어갈 알맞은 단어를 본문에서 찾아 쓰시오.

> When you take selfies, there is (A) to follow. You should take, post, or look at selfies after asking yourself three (B) such as 'Where am I?', 'Who can see this?' and 'What kinds of comments should I leave?'

(A) _____ (B) _____

출제율 90%

20 다음 중 셀피 예절에 속하지 <u>않는</u> 것을 고르시오.

① 병원이나 공중 화장실에서는 셀피를 찍지 마라.
② 누구나 당신의 셀피를 볼 수 없도록 해야 한다는 것을 명심해라.
③ 셀피를 게시할 때는 신중하게 골라라.
④ 다른 사람들의 셀피에 상냥한 코멘트를 남겨라.
⑤ 무례하게 굴지 마라.

출제율 95%

21 위 글의 밑줄 친 ⓐ에서 어법상 틀린 부분을 찾아 고치시오.

_____ ➡ _____

[22~23] 다음 글을 읽고, 물음에 답하시오.

> What do you think about posting selfies? Which do you agree with?
>
> ☐ It is awesome and fun!
> ☑ It has some bad points.
>
> Why? Some students use filters on their selfies too much. And they post the same selfies again and again. I think it's a ⓐwaste of time!

출제율 85%

22 위 글에서 셀피를 온라인상에 게시하는 행위에 대해 부정적으로 생각하는 이유 두 가지를 우리말로 쓰시오.

(1) _____
(2) _____
_____

출제율 100%

23 위 글의 밑줄 친 ⓐwaste와 같은 의미로 쓰인 것을 고르시오.

① Don't <u>waste</u> your energy on them.
② We should recycle industrial <u>waste</u>.
③ I don't want to <u>waste</u> this opportunity.
④ It's a <u>waste</u> of money to buy it.
⑤ <u>Waste</u> water is pumped into the river.

[01~03] 다음 대화를 읽고, 물음에 답하시오.

> M: Hey, Yumi. What are you doing?
> G: Hello, Mr. King. I'm preparing ___ⓐ___ tomorrow's presentation. It is about one ___ⓑ___ my interests.
> M: That sounds fun! What are you interested ___ⓒ___?
> G: I'm interested in photography. I will talk ___ⓓ___ it tomorrow.
> M: Oh, I'm interested __(A)__, too.
> G: Really? Then 제 발표에 대해 몇 가지 조언을 부탁해도 될까요?(may, some, advice)
> M: Sure.

01 위 대화의 빈칸 ⓐ~ⓓ에 들어갈 전치사를 〈보기〉에서 찾아 쓰시오.

> ┤ 보기 ├
>
> about   of   in   for

ⓐ_____ ⓑ_____ ⓒ_____ ⓓ_____

02 위 대화의 빈칸 (A)에 들어갈 알맞은 어구를 본문에서 찾아 쓰시오.

➡ _____

03 위 대화의 밑줄 친 우리말을 주어진 단어를 이용해 영어로 옮기시오.

➡ _____

04 다음 문장에서 어법상 잘못된 부분을 찾아 바르게 고쳐 쓰시오.

(1) Watch sports is fun.

_____ ➡ _____

(2) Keep to do it until the sugar stops completely melting.

_____ ➡ _____

(3) Her wish was become a friend of animals.

_____ ➡ _____

(4) On arrive in Tokyo, I called him.

_____ ➡ _____

(5) My pictures look nicely when I use filters.

_____ ➡ _____

(6) Some say the coffee beans smell sweet chocolate.

➡ _____

05 다음 우리말을 주어진 어구를 이용하여 영작하시오.

(1) 영어를 배우는 것은 재미있다. (interesting) (4 단어)

➡ _____

(2) 학생들은 컴퓨터 게임을 하는 데 너무 많은 시간을 보낸다. (spend, do computer games) (8 단어)

➡ _____

(3) 그녀는 그 소식을 듣고 얼굴이 창백해졌다. (turn, pale, at) (7 단어)

➡ _____

(4) 그 과일은 딸기 같은 맛이 나지 않았다. (fruit, strawberries) (6 단어)

➡ _____

(5) 그것들은 아주 부드럽고 따뜻하게 느껴졌다. (they, so, soft, warm) (6 단어)

➡ _____

06 다음 주어진 대화의 내용과 일치하도록 빈칸을 알맞게 채워 대화를 요약하는 문장을 완성하시오.

> **Ella:** Your computer game is very loud. I can't study at all. I have a test tomorrow.
> **Eric:** Sorry. I will turn off my computer.

➡ Eric will stop _____.

[07~08] 다음 글을 읽고, 물음에 답하시오.

> Lewis, 14, England Selfies are awesome. Making silly faces is really fun!
> Minwoo, 16, Korea I enjoy taking selfies, but some students spend too much time ⓐdoing it.
> Kate, 15, Denmark ⓑ내 사진들은 필터를 사용할 때 좋아 보인다. But sometimes my selfies don't look like me.

07 위 글의 밑줄 친 ⓐdoing it이 가리키는 것을 본문에서 찾아 쓰시오.

➡ _____

08 위 글의 밑줄 친 ⓑ의 우리말에 맞게 한 단어를 보충하여, 주어진 어휘를 알맞게 배열하시오.

> look / I / pictures / filters / use / my / when

➡ _____

[09~11] 다음 글을 읽고, 물음에 답하시오.

> #Selfie Etiquette
>   You should follow etiquette for selfies. Ask yourself these questions before you take, post, or look at selfies.
> 1. Where am I?
>   Choose (A)[appropriate / unsuitable] places to take selfies. Don't take selfies in hospitals or public restrooms. ⓐIt may (B)[bother / encourage] other people.
> 2. Who can see this?
>   Keep in mind that anyone can see your selfies. Choose carefully when you post them.
> 3. What kinds of comments should I leave?
>   Leave nice comments on other people's selfies. Don't be (C)[polite / rude].
>   That sounds easy, doesn't it? Follow these tips and ⓑhave fun with your selfies.

09 위 글의 괄호 (A)~(C)에서 문맥상 알맞은 낱말을 골라 쓰시오.

(A)_____ (B)_____ (C)_____

10 위 글의 밑줄 친 ⓐIt이 가리키는 것을 본문의 단어를 이용하여 쓰시오. (필요한 경우 형태를 바꾸시오.)

➡ _____

_____

11 위 글의 밑줄 친 ⓑhave fun과 바꿔 쓸 수 있는 말을 쓰시오.

➡ _____

창의사고력 서술형 문제

01 다음 그림을 참고하여 관심사를 묻고, 갈 장소를 권유하는 대화를 완성하시오.

사진촬영금지

A: _____
B: I'm interested in historical works of art.
A: _____
B: Sounds good. _____ there?
A: _____

02 다음 A와 B에 주어진 어휘를 한 번씩만 사용하여 〈보기〉와 같은 형식의 문장을 완성하시오.

> 보기
>
> That sounds interesting.

A: feel, look, sound, smell, taste
B: nervous, happy, good, terrible, sweet

(1) _____
(2) _____
(3) _____
(4) _____
(5) _____

03 인터넷 사용 규칙과 그 규칙을 만든 이유를 바탕으로 건강한 인터넷을 만들도록 권유하는 글을 쓰시오.

Rules	Reasons
We should follow language rules.	Because people may not understand us.
We should post true information.	Because people may believe our incorrect information.
We shouldn't leave rude comments.	Because we can hurt others' feelings.

When we use the internet, we should follow some rules. Then we can enjoy the internet more. First of all, we should follow (A)_____ because people may not understand us. Also, we should post only true information. People may believe our (B)_____ information. (C)_____, we should not leave rude comments. We can hurt others' feelings. Keep these rules (D)_____. Then you will be a great internet user!

단원별 모의고사

01 다음 밑줄 친 단어와 바꿔 쓸 수 <u>없는</u> 단어를 고르시오.

> This school is <u>awesome</u> and I like my classmates, too.

① amazing   ② terrific
③ fantastic   ④ terrible
⑤ great

02 다음 짝지어진 두 단어의 관계가 <u>다른</u> 하나를 고르시오.

① rude – polite   ② finally – lastly
③ bother – annoy   ④ comment – remark
⑤ advice – tip

03 다음 우리말과 일치하도록 빈칸을 채우시오. (주어진 철자가 있을 경우 주어진 철자로 시작할 것)

(1) 궁중 예절에 관한 모든 것을 배울 수 있을 것이다.
➡ You _____ be _____ to learn all about court e_____.

(2) 그것은 흥미로운 질문이다.
➡ That's _____ _____ _____.

(3) 나는 새 옷 쇼핑하는 것을 즐긴다.
➡ I _____ _____ for new _____.

(4) 우리가 새 카펫을 고르는 데 많은 시간이 걸렸다.
➡ It took us a _____ of time to _____ a new carpet.

04 〈보기〉의 어휘를 사용하여 문장을 완성하시오. (형태 변화 가능)

┌─ 보기 ┤
agree   spend   sound   look
└────────────────

(1) The twins _____ at each other and smiled.
(2) That _____ wonderful.
(3) I'm afraid I don't _____ with that.
(4) I think you _____ too much time playing computer games.

05 다음 대화의 괄호 (A)~(C)에서 알맞은 것을 골라 쓰시오.

> A: What are you interested in?
> B: I'm interested in (A)[animals / movies / music / books].
> A: (B)[Which / Why / How / What] don't you go to a theater this weekend?
> B: Sounds good. May I (C)[take photos of the paintings / eat snacks / feed the birds / record the music] there?
> A: No, you may not.

(A)_____ (B)_____ (C)_____

[06~08] 다음 대화를 읽고, 물음에 답하시오.

> B: Excuse me.
> M: Hello. ①<u>What can I do for you?</u>
> B: May I ___(A)___ this new science book?
> M: No, you may not. ②<u>Students can take new books home.</u>
> B: Then may I ___(B)___ some pages from the book? ③<u>I need them for my science report.</u>
> M: Yes, you may. ④<u>But please don't share them online.</u>
> B: ⑤<u>Okay, I won't.</u> Thank you!

06 위의 대화는 도서관에서 이루어지는 것이다. (A)와 (B)에 들어갈 단어를 〈보기〉에서 골라 쓰시오.

보기
advise spend borrow solve hurt copy

(A)_____ (B)_____

07 주어진 영영풀이에 해당하는 단어를 대화에서 찾아 쓰시오.

to have or use something with other people

➡ _____

08 위 대화의 밑줄 친 ①~⑤ 중 흐름상 어색한 것을 고르시오.

①   ②   ③   ④   ⑤

[09~10] 다음 대화를 읽고, 물음에 답하시오.

A: What are you interested in?
B: _____(A)_____ What about you?
A: _____(B)_____
B: 우리는 둘 다 소셜 미디어에 관심이 있어.

09 A와 B의 관심을 나타낸 그림을 보고 빈칸 (A)와 (B)에 알맞은 말을 쓰시오.

A   B

음악   소셜 미디어   게임

(A) _____
(B) _____

10 위 대화의 밑줄 친 우리말을 영작하시오.

➡ _____

[11~12] 다음 대화를 읽고, 물음에 답하시오.

G: Hi. Can I go in now?
M: Sure. Let me see your ticket, please.
G: Here it is. May I record the music ___(A)___ the concert hall?
M: No, you may not.
G: Okay. 밴드의 사진을 찍어도 될까요? (pictures, of, I, the band, may, take ?)
M: No, you may not. You can only take pictures ___(B)___ front of the concert hall. Please enjoy the concert.
G: Oh, okay. Thank you.

11 위 대화의 밑줄 친 우리말에 맞게 주어진 어구를 바르게 배열하시오.

➡ _____

12 위 대화의 빈칸 (A)와 (B)에 공통으로 들어갈 전치사를 쓰시오.

➡ _____

13 다음 중 어법상 어색한 것은?

① Did you enjoy playing soccer with your friends after school?
② Cooking is a useful hobby.
③ I'm proud of win the prize.
④ May I have dinner after I finish reading this book?
⑤ Harold didn't like to clean his room.

14 다음 빈칸에 공통으로 들어갈 수 <u>없는</u> 것은?

- Angelina _____ lonely.
- It _____ soft.

① is   ② seems   ③ feels
④ wants   ⑤ looks

15 다음 〈보기〉의 밑줄 친 말과 용법이 <u>다른</u> 하나는?

┌── 보기 ──┐
Harry enjoyed <u>playing</u> soccer with his friends after school.

① Some students practiced <u>playing</u> soccer.
② <u>Speaking</u> a foreign language is difficult.
③ Marianne is good at <u>singing</u>.
④ His dream is <u>traveling</u> around the world.
⑤ She saw her daughter <u>swimming</u> in the pool.

16 다음 그림을 참고하여 빈칸에 알맞은 말을 쓰시오.

This hotel room smells _____

_____ _____.

17 다음 문장에서 어법상 어색한 부분을 찾아 바르게 고쳐 다시 쓰시오.

(1) My pictures look beautifully when I use filters.

➡ _____

(2) Stop play games and be sincere.

➡ _____

[18~19] 다음 글을 읽고, 물음에 답하시오.

#Selfie Facts

Are you interested in selfies? You probably like ⓐto post selfies on social media, but how much do you know about selfies? Here are some interesting facts.

18 위 글의 밑줄 친 ⓐto post와 바꿔 쓸 수 있는 단어를 쓰시오.

➡ _____

19 위 글의 뒤에 올 내용으로 가장 알맞은 것을 고르시오.

① 소셜 미디어의 발전
② 셀피에 관한 몇 가지 재미있는 사실들
③ 셀피에 대한 사람들의 반응
④ 셀피에 많은 시간을 보내는 사람들
⑤ 소셜 미디어에 셀피를 게시하는 법

[20~22] 다음 글을 읽고, 물음에 답하시오.

#Selfie Survey

Taking selfies is part of daily life for many teens, but do teens really enjoy it? To find out, we did a survey. We asked three questions to 300 students from ages 14 to 16. Let's look at the results.

Q1 Do you take selfies?

	15%	85%
Boys	Yes	No
Girls	Yes	No
	90%	10%

Q2 Do you use filters on your selfies to look good?

No 7%
Yes 93%

Q3 Where do you usually take selfies?

At School
At Home
At Caéfs & Restaurants
Outdoors
Others

0% 5% 10% 15% 20% 25% 30% 35%

Surprisingly, 90 percent of the girls take selfies, but only 15 percent of the boys take selfies. Also, 93 percent of these students said that they use filters. The survey also showed that the students take selfies at school the most. Check out some of the students' ___ⓐ___.

Lewis, 14, England　Selfies are (A)[awful / awesome]. Making silly faces is really fun!

Minwoo, 16, Korea　I enjoy taking selfies, but some students spend too much time doing it.

Kate, 15, Denmark　My pictures look (B)[good / well] when I use filters. But sometimes my selfies don't look (C)[at / like] me.

20 위 글의 빈칸 ⓐ에 들어갈 알맞은 말을 고르시오.

① reports　　　　② comments
③ articles　　　　④ essays
⑤ summaries

21 위 글의 괄호 (A)~(C)에서 문맥상 알맞은 낱말을 골라 쓰시오.

(A)_____　(B)_____　(C)_____

22 위 도표의 내용과 일치하지 않는 것은?

① 85 percent of the boys don't take selfies.
② 10 percent of the girls don't take selfies.
③ 7 percent of the girls don't use filters on their selfies.
④ More than one third of the students take selfies at school.
⑤ There are much more students who take selfies at home than those who do so outdoors.

[23~25] 다음 글을 읽고, 물음에 답하시오.

#Selfie Etiquette

You should follow etiquette for selfies. ⓐAsk yourself these questions after you take, post, or look at selfies.

1. Where am I?
   Choose appropriate places to take selfies. Don't take selfies in hospitals or public restrooms. It may bother other people.
2. Who can see it?
   ⓑKeep in mind that anyone can see your selfies. Choose carefully when you post them.
3. What kinds of comments should I leave?
   Leave nice comments on other people's selfies. Don't be rude.

That sounds easy, doesn't it? Follow these ⓒtips and have fun with your selfies.

23 위 글의 밑줄 친 ⓐ에서 문맥상 낱말의 쓰임이 적절하지 않은 것을 찾아 알맞게 고치시오.

_____ ➡ _____

24 위 글의 밑줄 친 ⓑ를 다음과 같이 바꿔 쓸 때 빈칸에 알맞은 말을 쓰시오.

> Be sure to _____ that anyone can see your selfies.

25 위 글의 밑줄 친 ⓒtips와 다른 의미로 쓰인 것을 고르시오.

① Give me some tips for buying a computer.
② He gave the waiters generous tips.
③ Can you tell me useful tips on how to save money?
④ You should take my tips for a race.
⑤ I want to get good tips on the trip.

Lesson 2

Eat Right, Be Happy!

🎙 의사소통 기능

- 충고하기
  You'd better eat breakfast every day.

- 추천 요청하고 답하기
  A: What do you recommend?
  B: I recommend the pizza.

🎙 언어 형식

- 주격 관계대명사
  What do students **who** live in other countries eat for lunch?

  A plantain is a fruit **which** looks like a banana.

- 빈도 부사
  We **usually** eat a salad as an appetizer.

Words & Expressions

Key Words

- **add** [æd] 통 더하다
- **also** [ɔ́:lsou] 분 또한
- **always** [ɔ́:lweiz] 분 항상
- **appetizer** [ǽpitàizer] 명 식전 음식
- **as** [æz] 전 ~로서
- **balanced** [bǽlənst] 형 균형이 잡힌
- **bean** [bi:n] 명 콩
- **breakfast** [brékfəst] 명 아침 식사
- **British** [brítiʃ] 형 영국의
- **carrot** [kǽrət] 명 당근
- **celebrate** [séləbrèit] 통 축하하다, 기념하다
- **choice** [tʃɔis] 명 선택, 종류
- **common** [kámən] 형 흔한
- **contest** [kántest] 명 대회, 콘테스트
- **culture** [kʌltʃər] 명 문화
- **curry** [kə́:ri] 명 카레
- **delicious** [dilíʃəs] 형 맛있는
- **drop** [drap] 통 떨어뜨리다
- **Eastern** [í:stərn] 형 동양의
- **else** [els] 형 그 밖의, 다른
- **enough** [inʌf] 형 충분한
- **especially** [ispéʃəli] 분 특히
- **exercise** [éksərsàiz] 통 운동하다
- **fresh** [freʃ] 형 신선한
- **fried** [fraid] 형 튀겨진
- **fry** [frai] 통 튀기다
- **grocery** [gróusəri] 명 식료품
- **have** [həv] 통 먹다
- **health** [helθ] 명 건강
- **healthy** [hélθi] 형 건강에 좋은
- **include** [inklú:d] 통 포함하다
- **Indian** [índiən] 형 인도의
- **instead** [instéd] 분 대신에
- **less** [les] (양·정도가) 더 적은
- **local** [lóukəl] 형 현지의, 지역의
- **main dish** 주요리
- **meat** [mi:t] 명 고기, 육류
- **mixed** [mikst] 형 섞인, 복합된
- **more** [mɔ:r] 형 더 큰, 더 많은
- **noodle** [nú:dl] 명 국수
- **often** [ɔ́:fən] 분 종종, 자주
- **onion** [ʌ́njən] 명 양파
- **order** [ɔ́:rdər] 통 주문하다
- **other** [ʌ́ðər] 형 다른
- **paella** [paielə] 명 파엘라(쌀, 닭고기, 생선, 채소를 넣은 스페인 요리)
- **part** [pa:rt] 명 부분
- **pho** [fou] 명 포(베트남 쌀국수)
- **plantain** [plǽntən] 명 열대의 파초속(屬)의 일종; 그 과실(**cooking banana**)
- **recommend** [rékəménd] 통 추천하다
- **rule** [ru:l] 명 규칙
- **serve** [sə:rv] 통 음식물을 제공하다[권하다]
- **side dish** 반찬
- **slowly** [slóuli] 분 천천히
- **sometimes** [sʌ́mtàimz] 분 가끔, 때때로
- **Spanish** [spǽniʃ] 형 스페인의
- **special** [spéʃəl] 형 특별한
- **suggestion** [səgdʒéstʃən] 명 제안
- **sweet** [swi:t] 형 달콤한, 단
- **sweets** [swi:ts] 명 단 음식, 단것
- **tired** [taiərd] 형 피곤한
- **traditional** [trədíʃənl] 형 전통적인
- **turkey** [tə́:rki] 명 칠면조
- **usually** [jú:ʒuəli] 분 보통, 대개
- **vegetable** [védʒətəbl] 명 야채
- **Vietnamese** [viètnə:mí:z] 형 베트남의
- **Western** [wéstərn] 형 서양의

Key Expressions

- **a lot of** 많은
- **at least** 적어도, 최소한
- **at the end of** ~의 끝에
- **be ready to** 동사원형 ~할 준비가 되다
- **both A and B** A와 B 둘 다
- **check out** 확인하다, 조사하다
- **come from** ~에서 나오다, ~ 출신이다
- **come with** ~와 함께 나오다, ~이 딸려 있다
- **feel like** ~ ~하게 느끼다
- **for a long time** 오랫동안
- **get a cold** 감기에 걸리다
- **get a discount** 할인받다
- **had better** 동사원형 ~하는 것이 좋다[낫다]
- **have ~ in common** 공통으로 ~을 가지다
- **heat ~ up** ~을 덥히다
- **How about** (동)명사~? ~은 어때?
- **put A in B** : A를 B에 넣다
- **stay at** ~에 머무르다
- **such as** ~와 같은
- **take care of** ~을 돌보다
- **taste** 형용사 ~한 맛이 나다
- **thank (you) for** ~에 대해 감사하다
- **these days** 요즘, 최근
- **throw away** 버리다
- **try** + 음식 음식을 먹어 보다, 맛을 보다
- **win an award** 상을 받다

Words Power

※ 서로 반대되는 뜻을 가진 단어

- **add**(더하다) ↔ **subtract**(빼다)
- **different**(다른) ↔ **same**(같은)
- **fresh**(신선한) ↔ **rotten**(상한, 부패한)
- **less**((양·정도가) 더 적은) ↔ **more**(더 큰, 더 많은)

- **common**(흔한) ↔ **rare**(희귀한, 드문)
- **part**(부분) ↔ **whole**(전체)
- **include**(포함하다) ↔ **exclude**(배제하다)
- **Eastern**(동양의) ↔ **Western**(서양의)

※ 서로 비슷한 뜻을 가진 단어

- **celebrate**(축하하다, 기념하다) : **congratulate**(축하하다)
- **delicious**(맛있는) : **tasty**(맛있는)

- **exercise**(운동하다) : **work out**(운동하다)
- **enough**(충분한) : **sufficient**(충분한)

※ 요리와 관련된 동사

- **add**(더하다)
- **bake**(굽다)
- **boil**(끓이다)
- **chop**(자르다)
- **cut**(자르다)
- **fry**(튀기다)
- **mix**(섞다)

English Dictionary

- **appetizer** 식전 음식
  → a small dish that you eat before a meal
  식사 전에 먹는 적은 요리
- **breakfast** 아침 식사
  → the meal you have in the morning 아침에 먹는 식사
- **common** 흔한
  → happening often and to many people or in many places 자주 그리고 많은 사람이나 장소에서 발생하는
- **contest** 대회, 콘테스트
  → a competition or a situation in which two or more people or groups are competing with each other 대회나 둘 또는 그 이상의 사람이나 그룹이 서로 경쟁하는 상황
- **fried** 튀겨진
  → having been cooked in hot oil 뜨거운 기름 안에서 요리되는
- **grocery** 식료품
  → food and other goods that are sold by a grocer or a supermarket
  식료품 잡화상이나 슈퍼마켓에 의해서 팔려지는 음식이나 다른 상품들
- **local** 현지의, 지역의
  → relating to the particular area you live in, or the area you are talking about 당신이 살고 있는 특정한 지역과 관련 있는 아니면 당신이 얘기하고 있는 장소
- **mixed** 섞인, 복합된
  → consisting of several different types of things or people 몇몇의 다른 종류의 사물이나 사람으로 구성되어 있는
- **noodle** 국수
  → a long thin piece of food made from a mixture of flour, water, and eggs, usually cooked in soup or boiling water
  밀가루, 물, 달걀의 혼합물로 만들어진 보통 국이나 끓는 물에서 요리되는 길고 얇은 음식의 조각

- **order** 주문하다
  → to ask for food or a drink in a restaurant, bar etc.
  식당이나 술집에서 음식이나 음료를 요청하다
- **recommend** 추천하다
  → to advise someone to do something, especially because you have special knowledge of a situation or subject 특히 당신이 그 상황이나 주제에 대한 특별한 지식을 갖고 있기 때문에 누군가에게 무엇을 하라고 조언하다
- **serve** 음식물을 제공하다
  → to give someone food or drink, especially as part of a meal or in a restaurant, bar etc. 식당이나 술집 등에서 특히 식사의 일부분으로 누군가에게 음식이나 음료를 주다
- **suggestion** 제안
  → an idea, plan, or possibility that someone mentions, or the act of mentioning it 누군가가 언급한 생각, 계획, 가능성이나 그것을 언급하는 행동
- **sweets** 단 음식, 단것
  → a small piece of sweet food made of sugar or chocolate 설탕이나 초콜릿으로 만들어진 작은 조각의 단 음식
- **tired** 피곤한
  → feeling that you want to sleep or rest
  자거나 쉬기를 원하는 감정
- **usually** 보통, 대개
  → used to talk about what happens on most occasions or in most situations
  어떤 일이 대부분의 경우나 상황에서 벌어지는 것을 언급할 때 쓰이는
- **vegetable** 야채
  → a plant that is eaten raw or cooked, such as a cabbage, a carrot, or peas 예를 들어 양배추, 당근 또는 완두콩 같은 날것으로 먹거나 요리해 먹는 식물
- **Western** 서양의
  → in or from the west of a country or area
  어떤 나라 지역의 서쪽에서 또는 서쪽으로부터

서답형

[01~02] 다음 〈보기〉와 같은 관계가 되도록 주어진 빈칸에 알맞은 말을 쓰시오. (주어진 철자로 시작할 것)

01
┌ 보기 ┐
Korea - Korean

(1) tradition – _____
(2) Vietnam – _____

02
┌ 보기 ┐
suggest - suggestion

(1) choose – _____
(2) arrive – _____

서답형

03 다음 우리말에 맞게 주어진 단어를 이용해 빈칸을 완성하시오.

학교는 건강에 좋은 음식만을 제공하려고 애쓴다.
➡ The school tries to offer only _____ food. (health)

중요

04 다음 중 밑줄 친 부분의 뜻풀이가 바르지 <u>않은</u> 것은?

① I help the students to <u>fry</u> onions. (튀기다)
② I <u>recommend</u> this book to anyone with an interest in animation. (추천하다)
③ I chose this coat because the <u>other</u> ones were all too expensive. (다른)
④ Women <u>usually</u> live longer than men. (종종, 자주)
⑤ We had bacon and eggs for <u>breakfast</u>. (아침 식사)

[05~06] 다음 빈칸에 들어갈 말로 적절한 것을 고르시오.

05
Vitamin A is found in liver and green _____.

① vegetables ② meat
③ flower ④ carrot
⑤ meal

중요

06
I will be in a speech _____ tomorrow.

① contest ② concert
③ content ④ compete
⑤ prize

07 다음 밑줄 친 부분과 의미가 가장 가까운 것을 고르시오.

<u>Trying</u> new foods is an exciting experience.

① Touching ② Turning
③ Tasting ④ Smelling
⑤ Chewing

서답형

08 다음 빈칸에 들어갈 알맞은 단어를 〈보기〉에서 찾아 쓰시오. (형태 변화 가능)

┌ 보기 ┐
slowly   more   often

(1) You'll have to be _____ careful next time.
(2) How _____ do you see your parents?
(3) She spoke _____, choosing her words carefully.

[01~02] 다음 빈칸에 공통으로 들어갈 말을 쓰시오.

01
> • Bad dreams are fairly _____ among children.
> • All successful people have one thing in _____.

02
> • When I _____ a cold, I often blow my nose.
> • Children and seniors can _____ a discount of 3 dollars.

03 다음 주어진 우리말에 맞게 빈칸을 채우시오. (철자가 주어진 것도 있음)

(1) It's Dad's birthday and we're _____ out for a meal to c_____. (오늘은 아빠의 생일이야, 그래서 우리는 축하하기 위해 외식할 거야.)

(2) Have I given you _____ _____? (내가 너에게 충분한 돈을 주었니?)

(3) _____ _____ and _____ provide fiber and vitamins. (신선한 과일과 채소는 섬유질과 비타민을 제공한다.)

04 다음 짝지어진 두 단어의 관계가 같도록 빈칸에 알맞은 말을 쓰시오.

(1) high : low = rare : _____

(2) awesome : wonderful = sufficient : _____

05 다음 영영풀이에 해당하는 단어를 골라 빈칸에 쓰시오.

> ┤ 보기 ├
> sweets   celebrate   contest   cookies

(1) a competition or a situation in which two or more people or groups are competing with each other

➡ _____

(2) a small piece of sweet food made of sugar or chocolate

➡ _____

06 다음 문장의 빈칸에 알맞은 것을 〈보기〉에서 찾아 쓰시오.

> ┤ 보기 ├
> side dish   grocery   onion   suggestion

(1) Can I order the potatoes as a _____ _____?
(2) Are you all happy with his _____?
(3) Chop the _____ finely.
(4) He started to work at a _____ store.

07 다음 우리말에 맞게 주어진 어구를 바르게 배열하시오.

(1) 너는 내가 케이크를 자르기를 원하니?
(me, the cake, do, to, cut, want, you ?)

➡ _____

(2) 나는 항상 파리에 가기를 원해 왔다.
(wanted, Paris, I've, to, always, to, go)

➡ _____

Conversation

1 충고하기

> You'd better eat breakfast every day. 너는 매일 아침밥을 먹는 게 좋아.

- 'had better + 동사원형'은 '~하는 게 좋겠다'라는 의미로 상대방에게 충고나 조언을 하는 표현이다.

- 충고하는 말에 대답할 경우, 상대방의 충고에 대해 고마움을 표현하거나 자신의 생각을 덧붙여 대답할 수 있다.

충고하기

- You'd better + 동사원형. ~하는 게 좋겠다.
- (I think) you should + 동사원형 ~.
- Maybe you should + 동사원형 ~.
- Why don't you ~?

- 'I think you should + 동사원형~.'에서 think 다음에 접속사 that이 생략되어 있다. should는 도덕적 의무를 이야기할 때 사용하는 조동사로 must, have to에 비해 일상 회화 표현에서 자주 사용한다.

충고의 말에 답하기

- That's a good idea. 좋은 생각이다.
- I guess I should. 그래야 할 것 같아.
- OK, I will. Thanks. 그렇게 할게. 고마워

핵심 Check

1. 다음 우리말과 일치하도록 빈칸에 알맞은 말을 쓰시오.

   A: _____ _____ stop watching TV _____ going to bed. (너는 잠자리에 들기 전에 TV를 그만 보는 게 좋겠다.)

   B: Okay, _____ try. Thanks. (좋아. 노력할게. 고마워.)

2. 다음 대화의 순서를 바르게 배열하시오.

   (A) Fast food is not good. You'd better eat healthy food.

   (B) How often do you eat fast food?

   (C) Okay, I will.

   (D) Three times a week.

   ➡ _____

② 추천 요청하고 답하기

> **A** What do you recommend? 무엇을 추천하시겠어요?
> **B** I recommend the pizza. 저는 피자를 추천합니다.

■ recommend(추천하다)를 사용하여 추천을 요청하고 대답할 수 있다. What do you recommend?는 '무엇을 추천하시겠어요?'라는 의미로 추천을 요청하는 표현이다.

추천 요청하기

- What do you recommend?
- What would you recommend?
- What 명사 do you recommend?
- Which 명사 do you recommend?
- Do you have any recommendations?
- Can[Could] you recommend ~?

추천 요청에 답하기

- I [strongly] recommend ~.
- I'd like to recommend ~.
- I suggest ~.
- I advise ~.
- ~ is recommended.

recommend

- 주어 recommend 명사 ~.
  ex) I recommend a sandwich for lunch. (나는 점심식사로 샌드위치를 추천한다.)
- 주어 recommend (that) 주어 동사 ~.
  ex) I recommend (that) you should consult your doctor. (나는 네가 의사와 상담하기를 권고한다.)
  = It is recommended (that) you should consult your doctor.

핵심 Check

3. 다음 우리말과 일치하도록 빈칸에 알맞은 말을 쓰시오.

A: Can _____ _____ any good Chinese restaurants near here? (이 근처에 좋은 중국 음식점 있으면 추천해 주시겠어요?)

B: _____ is one next to the bank. (은행 옆에 하나 있어요.)

4. 다음 우리말과 일치하도록 빈칸에 알맞은 말을 쓰시오.

A: _____ (어떤 운동을 추천하시겠어요?)

B: _____ hiking. (나는 하이킹을 강력히 추천합니다.)

5. 다음 주어진 단어를 이용하여 대화를 완성하시오.

A: _____ (recommend, you, book, do, what)

B: _____ (this, like, book, I'd, to, recommend)

A. Listen and Talk 1 A

G: I think ❶I eat too many ❷sweets ❸these days.

B: ❹That's not good for your health. ❺You'd better eat fruit instead.

G: 나 요즘 단 걸 너무 많이 먹는 것 같아.

B: 그건 건강에 좋지 않아. 대신에 과일을 먹는 게 좋아.

❶ think와 I 사이에는 접속사 that이 생략되어 있다.
❷ sweets: 단 음식, 단것
❸ these days: 요즘, 최근
❹ That은 앞 문장의 내용인 eating too many sweets를 가리킨다. be good for: ~에 좋다 health: 건강
❺ You'd better ~. = You had better ~. : ~하는 게 좋겠다. had better 다음에는 동사원형이 나와야 한다. instead: 대신에

Check(√) True or False

(1) The girl likes to eat fruit.   T ☐ F ☐

(2) The girl will eat sweets a lot.   T ☐ F ☐

B. Listen and Talk 1 B

G: You ❶look very tired today. Didn't you sleep well?

B: Yes, I did. But I ❷often feel tired these days, ❸especially in the morning.

G: Do you usually eat breakfast?

B: No, I don't.

G: You'd better eat breakfast. Breakfast ❹gives you energy.

B: I didn't know that. Do you have ❺any other suggestions?

G: Well, you ❻should also exercise every day. That will help you.

B: Okay. I will.

G: 너 오늘 매우 피곤해 보인다. 잠을 잘 못 잤니?

B: 아니, 잘 잤어. 그런데, 나 요즘 자주, 특히 아침에 쉽게 피곤해져.

G: 너 아침밥을 주로 먹니?

B: 아니, 먹지 않아.

G: 아침밥을 먹는 게 좋아. 아침밥은 너한테 힘을 주거든.

B: 나 그건 몰랐어. 또 다른 제안 해 줄 것 있니?

G: 음, 너는 또한 매일 운동해야 해. 그게 도움이 될 거야.

B: 알겠어. 그럴게.

❶ look + 형용사: ~하게 보이다 tired: 피곤한
❷ 빈도부사는 일반동사의 앞에, be동사와 조동사의 뒤에 위치한다. often: 종종, 자주
❸ especially: 특히 in the morning: 아침에
❹ give는 4형식 동사로 간접목적어(~에게), 직접목적어(~을, 를)를 취한다. give you energy: 너에게 에너지를 주다
❺ any other: 어떤 다른 suggestion: 제안
❻ should + 동사원형: ~해야 한다

Check(√) True or False

(3) The boy slept well but didn't eat breakfast.   T ☐ F ☐

(4) The girl knows that breakfast is important.   T ☐ F ☐

Listen and Talk 1 C

G: Justin, our school cooking ❶contest is tomorrow. ❷What are you going to make?

B: I'm going to make sandwiches.

G: What do you want to put in ❸them?

B: Chicken, cheese, and eggs.

G: You'd better ❹put vegetables in your sandwiches. How about onions and carrots?

B: No, I'm not going to ❺add them. I don't like ❻those vegetables.

G: That's not a good idea. Mr. Kim said we should make ❼healthy food for the contest.

B: You're right. I should go ❽grocery shopping and buy onions and carrots.

❶ contest: 대회, 콘테스트(= competition)
❷ be going to 동사원형: ～할 것이다
❸ them은 sandwiches를 지칭한다.
❹ put A in B: A를 B에 넣다
❺ add: 더하다, them은 onions and carrots를 가리킨다.
❻ vegetables가 복수형이므로 that이 아니라 those를 사용해야 한다.
❼ healthy: 건강에 좋은
❽ grocery: 식료품

Listen and Talk 2 A

G: ❶It's my first time here. ❷What do you recommend?

M: I recommend ❸the pizza and salad.

❶ It's my first time here: 저 여기 처음 왔어요.
❷ What do you recommend?: 무엇을 추천해 주시겠어요? recommend: 추천하다
❸ pizza: 피자 salad: 샐러드

Listen and Talk 2 B

B: Good morning, Jiwoo. ❶What are you doing right now?

G: I'm ❷searching for a restaurant for my class party.

B: Wow! When is the party?

G: It's next Friday. We ❸want to go to Bella's

Restaurant, but ❹it is too expensive.

B: ❺Why don't you check out Chang's Restaurant? I ❻went there once. The food and prices were good.

G: Sounds great. What do you recommend there?

B: I recommend the noodle soup.

G: ❼I think we should go there. Thank you.

❶ are doing은 현재진행형(be동사의 현재형+동사ing)으로 '～하고 있다'라는 뜻이다. What are you doing?: 너는 무엇을 하고 있니?
❷ search for: ～를 찾다
❸ want+to부정사: ～하기를 원하다 go to 장소: ～에 가다
❹ it = Bella's Restaurant
❺ Why don't you ～?: ～하는 게 어때? check out: 확인하다, 조사하다
❻ once: 한 번
❼ I think 다음에 that이 생략되어 있다. 'I think (that) 주어 should 동사원형 ～.'는 '나는 ～해야 한다고 생각한다'라는 뜻이다.

Listen and Talk 2 C

W: Hello. ❶Are you ready to order?

B: It's my first time here. What do you recommend?

W: I recommend the chicken sandwich. ❷It is the most popular item at our restaurant.

B: Well, I don't like chicken very much. ❸ Could you recommend something else?

W: How about the turkey sandwich?

B: Oh, I love turkey. I'll have that.

W: ❹Why don't you order a drink with the sandwich? You ❺can get a 500-won discount.

B: That's great. Then I'll have an orange juice, too.

❶ be ready to 동사원형: ～할 준비가 되다
❷ It은 the chicken sandwich를 가리킨다. the most popular는 popular의 최상급 형태로 '가장 인기 있는'이라는 뜻이다.
❸ Could you recommend something else? = What else do you recommend?: 다른 거 추천해 주시겠어요? -thing으로 끝나는 부정대명사(something, anything, nothing 등)는 보통의 다른 명사들과 달리 형용사가 뒤에서 수식한다.
❹ Why don't you ～?: ～하는 게 어때? (= How about (동)명사 ～?= What about (동)명사 ～?)
❺ get a discount: 할인받다

● 다음 우리말과 일치하도록 빈칸에 알맞은 말을 쓰시오.

Listen & Talk 1 A

G: _____ _____ _____ _____ too many _____ _____

_____.

B: That's not _____ _____ your _____. _____ _____ eat

fruit _____.

해석
G: 나 요즘 단 걸 너무 많이 먹는 것 같아.
B: 그건 건강에 좋지 않아. 대신에 과일을 먹는 게 좋아.

Listen & Talk 1 B

G: You _____ very tired today. Didn't you sleep well?

B: Yes, I did. But I _____ _____ _____ these days, especially

in the morning.

G: Do you _____ _____ breakfast?

B: No, I don't.

G: _____ _____ _____ breakfast. Breakfast _____ _____

_____.

B: I didn't know that. Do you have _____ _____ _____?

G: Well, you _____ _____ _____ every day. That will help

you.

B: Okay. I will.

G: 너 오늘 매우 피곤해 보인다. 잠을 잘 못 잤니?
B: 아니, 잘 잤어. 그런데, 나 요즘 자주, 특히 아침에 쉽게 피곤해져.
G: 너 아침밥을 주로 먹니?
B: 아니, 먹지 않아.
G: 아침밥을 먹는 게 좋아. 아침밥은 너한테 힘을 주거든.
B: 나 그건 몰랐어. 또 다른 제안해 줄 것 있니?
G: 음, 너는 또한 매일 운동해야 해. 그게 도움이 될 거야.
B: 알겠어. 그럴게.

Listen & Talk 1 C

G: Justin, our school cooking _____ is tomorrow. What are you

_____ _____ make?

B: I'm going to make sandwiches.

G: _____ do you want to _____ _____ _____?

B: Chicken, cheese, and eggs.

G: _____ _____ put vegetables _____ your sandwiches. How

_____ onions and carrots?

B: No, _____ _____ _____ _____ add them. I don't like

those vegetables.

G: That's not a good idea. Mr. Kim said _____ _____ make

_____ food for the contest.

B: You're right. _____ _____ go grocery shopping and buy onions

and carrots.

G: Justin, 우리 학교 요리 대회가 내일이야. 뭐 만들 거니?
B: 샌드위치 만들 거야.
G: 뭐 넣을 거니?
B: 치킨이랑 치즈랑 계란.
G: 너 샌드위치에 채소 넣는 게 좋을 거야. 양파랑 당근은 어때?
B: 싫어. 안 넣을 거야. 나 그 채소들 싫어해.
G: 그건 좋은 생각이 아니야. 김 선생님은 요리 대회에서 건강에 좋은 음식을 만들어야 한다고 했어.
B: 네 말이 맞아. 나 식료품 쇼핑 가서 양파와 당근을 사야겠다.

Listen and Talk 2 A

G: _____ my _____ _____ here. _____ do you _____?

M: _____ _____ the pizza and salad.

Listen and Talk 2 B

B: Good morning, Jiwoo. _____ _____ _____ _____ right now?

G: I'm _____ _____ a restaurant for my class party.

B: Wow! _____ is the party?

G: It's next Friday. We want to go to Bella's Restaurant, but it is _____ _____.

B: Why _____ _____ _____ out Chang's Restaurant? I _____ there once. The food and prices were good.

G: _____ great. _____ _____ you _____ there?

B: I _____ _____ _____ _____.

G: I _____ _____ _____ go there. Thank you.

Listen and Talk 2 C

W: Hello. _____ _____ _____ to order?

B: It's my first time here. _____ _____ _____ _____?

W: I _____ the chicken _____. It is _____ _____ item at our restaurant.

B: Well, I don't like chicken very much. Could you _____ _____?

W: How _____ the turkey sandwich?

B: Oh, I love turkey. I'll have that.

W: Why _____ _____ order a drink _____ the sandwich? You can _____ a 500-won _____.

B: That's great. Then I'll have an orange juice, too.

Do It Yourself A

G: _____ for lunch today?

B: We have four choices. Which _____ do you want?

G: Well, I want some noodles. _____ _____ _____ _____?

B: I recommend the _____ noodles.

G: That _____ _____. I will have that. What about you?

B: I don't know. I'm not hungry.

G: But for your _____, you'd _____ have some food. Why _____ _____ _____ some tomato soup?

B: All right. I _____.

G: 저 여기 처음 왔어요. 추천해 주시겠어요?

M: 저는 피자와 샐러드를 추천해요.

B: 안녕, Jiwoo. 너 지금 뭐 하고 있니?

G: 학급 파티 때 갈 식당을 찾고 있어.

B: 와! 파티가 언제야?

G: 다음 주 금요일이야. 우리는 Bella 식당에 가고 싶은데, 너무 비싸.

B: Chang 식당을 찾아보는 건 어때? 나 거기 한번 간 적 있어. 음식이랑 가격 다 괜찮았어.

G: 좋을 것 같아. 거기서 어떤 것을 추천하니?

B: 나는 국수를 추천해.

G: 내 생각에 우리 거기 가야겠다. 고마워.

W: 안녕하세요. 주문하시겠어요?

B: 저 여기 처음 왔어요. 추천해주시겠어요?

W: 치킨 샌드위치 추천합니다. 그게 우리 식당에서 가장 인기 있는 메뉴에요.

B: 음, 제가 치킨을 별로 안 좋아해요. 다른 거 추천해주시겠어요?

W: 칠면조 샌드위치는 어떠세요?

B: 아, 저 칠면조 좋아해요. 그걸로 주세요.

W: 음료랑 샌드위치를 같이 주문하는 게 어떠세요? 500원 할인받을 수 있어요.

B: 좋네요. 그럼 오렌지 주스도 주세요.

G: 오늘 점심은 어떤 거야?

B: 우리에겐 네 개의 선택들이 있어. 너는 어떤 것을 원하니?

G: 글쎄, 나는 면을 원해. 너는 어떤 것을 추천하니?

B: 나는 볶음면을 추천해.

G: 그거 맛있겠다. 나는 그걸 먹을래. 너는 어때?

B: 나는 잘 모르겠어. 배가 고프지 않아.

G: 하지만, 너의 건강을 위해서는 음식을 좀 먹는 게 좋아. 토마토 수프를 먹어 보는 게 어떻겠니?

B: 그래. 그렇게 할게.

01 다음 주어진 문장과 바꾸어 쓸 수 있는 것은?

> You'd better eat breakfast every day.

① What do you think about eating breakfast every day?
② Do you want to eat breakfast every day?
③ Do you eat breakfast every day?
④ Why do you eat breakfast every day?
⑤ Why don't you eat breakfast every day?

[02~03] 다음 대화의 빈칸에 알맞은 것을 고르시오.

02
> G: I think I eat too many sweets these days.
> B: That's not good for your health. ＿＿＿＿＿＿＿＿

① You'd better eat more.
② You'd better eat fruit instead.
③ You'd better gain more weight.
④ You'd better go to school by bus.
⑤ You'd better read books.

03
> G: It's my first time here. What do you recommend?
> M: ＿＿＿＿＿＿＿＿＿＿＿＿＿＿

① You'd better go there one more time.
② I'll make the pizza and salad.
③ She made us a delicious salad.
④ I recommend the pizza and salad.
⑤ Why don't we have the pizza and salad?

04 다음 주어진 문장의 뒤에 나올 대화의 순서를 알맞게 쓰시오.

> I have a cold.

> (A) I recommend green tea.
> (B) What do you recommend?
> (C) You'd better drink some tea.

➡ ＿＿＿＿＿＿＿＿＿＿＿＿＿＿＿

[01~04] 다음 대화를 읽고, 물음에 답하시오.

G: You look very (A)_____ today. Didn't you sleep well?

B: Yes, I did. (①) (B)_____ I often feel tired these days, especially in the morning. (②)

G: Do you usually eat breakfast?

B: No, I don't. (③)

G: (④) Breakfast gives you energy.

B: I didn't know that. Do you have any other suggestions? (⑤)

G: Well, you should also exercise every day. (C)That will help you.

B: Okay. I will.

01 위 대화의 ①~⑤ 중 주어진 문장이 들어갈 알맞은 곳은?

You'd better eat breakfast.

①　　　②　　　③　　　④　　　⑤

02 빈칸 (A)에 들어갈 말로 적절한 것은?

① happy　　② tired　　③ angry

④ interested　　⑤ excited

03 빈칸 (B)에 들어갈 말로 적절한 것은?

① So　　② Because　　③ And

④ Since　　⑤ But

04 밑줄 친 (C)That이 가리키는 것을 본문에서 찾아 쓰시오.

➡ _____

[05~08] 다음 대화를 읽고, 물음에 답하시오.

G: Justin, our school cooking contest is tomorrow. (A)_____

B: I'm going to make ⓐsandwiches.

G: What do you want to put (B)_____ ⓑthem?

B: Chicken, cheese, and eggs.

G: You'd better put vegetables (C)_____ ⓒthem. How about ⓓonions and carrots?

B: No, I'm not going to add ⓔthem. I don't like those vegetables.

G: That's not a good idea. Mr. Kim said we should make healthy food for the contest.

B: You're right. I should go grocery shopping and buy onions and carrots.

05 빈칸 (A)에 들어갈 말로 적절한 것은?

① What are you doing?

② Where are you going to go?

③ What are you going to make?

④ Did you make sandwiches?

⑤ How are you going to make sandwiches?

06 빈칸 (B)와 (C)에 공통으로 들어갈 말로 적절한 것은?

① in　　② for　　③ to

④ with　　⑤ by

07 밑줄 친 ⓐ~ⓔ가 가리키는 것이 같은 것끼리 짝지어진 것을 고르시오.

① ⓐ, ⓑ, ⓒ　　② ⓐ, ⓑ, ⓔ

③ ⓐ, ⓒ, ⓔ　　④ ⓑ, ⓒ, ⓓ

⑤ ⓑ, ⓓ, ⓔ

서답형

08 다음 영영풀이에 해당하는 단어를 대화에서 찾아 쓰시오.

> a plant that is eaten raw or cooked, such as a cabbage, a carrot, or peas

➡ _____

09 다음 짝지어진 대화가 어색한 것은?

① A: You'd better go to bed early.
   B: OK, I will. Thanks.
② A: I think you should exercise every day.
   B: That's a good idea.
③ A: What kind of pet do you recommend?
   B: The dog is recommended.
④ A: Why don't you go home early and rest?
   B: You'll be okay.
⑤ A: I recommend the pizza and salad.
   B: Thanks for your recommendations.

서답형

10 괄호 안의 단어를 순서대로 배열하여 충고하는 말을 완성하시오.

> A: I want to be taller.
> B: Then _____ _____ _____
> _____ _____. (milk, had, you, drink, better)
> A: Thank you for your advice.

[11~14] 다음 대화를 읽고, 물음에 답하시오.

> B: Good morning, Jiwoo. What are you doing (A)right now?
> G: ①I'm searching for a restaurant for my class party.
> B: Wow! When is the party?
> G: ②It's next Friday. We want to go to Bella's Restaurant, ③but it is too expensive.

> B: (B)Why don't you check out Chang's Restaurant? ④I've never been there. The food and prices were good.
> G: Sounds great. What do you recommend there?
> B: ⑤I recommend the noodle soup.
> G: I think we should go there. Thank you.

11 위 대화의 ①~⑤중 흐름상 어색한 문장을 고르시오.

①   ②   ③   ④   ⑤

12 밑줄 친 (A)right과 같은 의미로 쓰인 문장을 고르시오.

① The clock in my room never told the right time.
② People have the right to determine their own future.
③ The bookstore is actually right next to my company.
④ People should always try to do the right thing and help others.
⑤ Walk straight ahead and you'll see the post office on your right.

중요

13 밑줄 친 (B)의 의도로 알맞은 것은?

① 확신   ② 변명   ③ 충고
④ 사과   ⑤ 소망

14 위 대화를 읽고 알 수 없는 내용은?

① What kind of food does the boy recommend?
② What is Jiwoo doing right now?
③ What kind of party will be held next Friday?
④ Where is Chang's Restaurant?
⑤ What does Jiwoo think about the boy's recommendations?

[01~02] 다음 주어진 문장의 뒤에 나올 대화의 순서를 알맞게 쓰시오.

01

> What's for lunch today?

> (A) I recommend the fried noodles.
> (B) Well, I want some noodles. What do you recommend?
> (C) We have four choices. Which one do you want?
> (D) That sounds delicious. I will have that.

➡ _____

02 중요

> What are you going to make?

> (A) Chicken, cheese, and eggs.
> (B) I'm going to make sandwiches.
> (C) What do you want to put in them?

➡ _____

[03~05] 다음 대화를 읽고, 물음에 답하시오.

G: ①You look very tired today. Didn't you sleep well?
B: Yes, I did. ②But I often feel tired these days, especially in the morning.
G: Do you usually eat breakfast?
B: ③Yes, I do.
G: You'd better eat breakfast. ④Breakfast gives you energy.
B: ⑤I didn't know that. Do you have any other (A)suggest?
G: Well, (B)너는 또한 매일 운동해야 해. That will help you.
B: Okay. I will.

03 중요 위 대화의 ①~⑤ 중 흐름상 어색한 곳을 바르게 고치시오.

➡ _____

04 밑줄 친 (A)suggest를 알맞은 형태로 쓰시오.

➡ _____

05 밑줄 친 (B)의 우리말을 영작하시오.

➡ _____

[06~08] 다음 대화를 읽고, 물음에 답하시오.

B: Good morning, Jiwoo. (A)_____ are you doing right now?
G: I'm searching ⓐ_____ a restaurant ⓑ_____ my class party.
B: Wow! (B)_____ is the party?
G: It's next Friday. We want to go to Bella's Restaurant, but ⓒit is too expensive.
B: (C)_____ don't you check out Chang's Restaurant? I went ⓓthere once. The food and prices were good.

06 중요 빈칸 (A)~(C)에 알맞은 의문사를 쓰시오.

➡ (A)_____ (B)_____ (C)_____

07 빈칸 ⓐ와 ⓑ에 공통으로 들어갈 단어를 쓰시오.

➡ _____

08 밑줄 친 ⓒ와 ⓓ가 가리키는 것을 대화에서 찾아 쓰시오.

➡ _____

Grammar

① 주격 관계대명사

- He wanted to talk to friends **who** were far away. 그는 멀리 있는 친구들과 이야기하고 싶어 하였다.
- I have a dog **which** has a long tail. 나는 긴 꼬리를 가진 개를 갖고 있다.

■ 관계대명사는 접속사와 대명사의 역할을 한다. 관계대명사절은 명사를 수식해 주는 절로 관계대명사절이 꾸며 주는 말을 선행사라고 하고 관계대명사는 앞의 선행사와 같은 대상을 가리킨다. 관계대명사절이 되기 전의 문장에서 주어로 쓰였으면 주격 관계대명사로, 소유격으로 쓰였으면 소유격 관계대명사로, 목적격으로 쓰였으면 목적격 관계대명사가 된다. 주격 관계대명사는 관계대명사절에서 주어 역할을 하므로 그 다음에는 동사가 온다.

- This is the book. It(=The book) has many pictures.
  = This is the book **which**[**that**] has many pictures. (주격)
- This is the book. He bought it(=the book).
  = This is the book **which**[**that**] he bought. (목적격)
- This is the book. Its(=The book's) cover is white.
  = This is the book **whose** cover is white. (소유격)

■ 관계대명사는 선행사에 따라 다음과 같이 사용되며, 목적격 관계대명사는 생략할 수 있다.

	주격	소유격	목적격
사람	who/that	whose	whom[who]/that
동물, 사물	which/that	whose/of which	which/that

- I saw a man **who**[**that**] was wearing a black shirt. 나는 검은 셔츠를 입고 있는 남자를 보았다.

■ 관계대명사 that은 who, whom과 which 대신 사용할 수 있으며 소유격은 없다. 또한 선행사가 '사람+동물[사물]'인 경우에는 반드시 that을 써야 한다.

- There were a boy and his dog **that** lived in a small house. 작은 집에 사는 소년과 그의 개가 있었다.

핵심 Check

1. 다음 우리말에 맞게 빈칸에 알맞은 말을 쓰시오.

(1) 노래하고 있는 저 소년을 봐라.
  ➡ Look at that boy _____ is singing.

(2) 나는 Hemingway에 의해 쓰여진 책을 읽었다.
  ➡ I read the book _____ was written by Hemingway.

② 빈도부사

> • He is **always** busy. 그는 항상 바쁘다.
> • He **never** gets up early. 그는 절대로 일찍 일어나지 않는다.

■ 빈도부사

빈도부사는 빈번함의 정도나 횟수를 나타내는 부사로, 주로 일반동사 앞에, be동사나 조동사 뒤에 위치한다.

■ 빈도부사의 종류

always (항상, 언제나) 〉 usually (대개, 보통) 〉 often[frequently] (종종, 자주) 〉 sometimes (때때로, 가끔) 〉 rarely[seldom, hardly] (드물게, 거의 ~ 않는) 〉 never (결코 ~ 않는)

• Mike is **always** late for school. (Mike는 항상 학교에 늦는다.)

• I **often** play soccer with my friends after school. (나는 방과 후에 종종 친구들과 축구한다.)

• She **sometimes** watches movies on TV. (그녀는 때때로 TV에서 영화를 본다.)

• He **never** does the dishes after dinner. (그는 저녁 식사 후에 절대로 설거지를 하지 않는다.)

■ 빈도부사가 조동사 앞에 오는 경우

조동사 used to, have to, ought to의 경우, 보통 빈도부사가 그 앞에 위치한다.

• We **always** have to be careful of others. (우리는 언제나 다른 사람들을 신경 써야 해.)

핵심 Check

2. 다음 우리말에 맞게 빈칸에 알맞은 말을 쓰시오.

(1) 그는 항상 일간 신문을 읽는다.

➡ He _____ reads a daily newspaper.

(2) 그 여자는 종종 운동을 한다.

➡ The woman _____ does exercise.

(3) 버스가 시간을 전혀 안 지켜요.

➡ The bus is _____ on time.

01 다음 빈칸에 들어갈 알맞은 것은?

> He was looking for the person _____ came to meet him.

① who   ② whose   ③ whom
④ which   ⑤ what

02 다음 문장에서 어법상 <u>어색한</u> 부분을 바르게 고쳐 쓰시오.

(1) She bought a book who looked very heavy.

_____ ➡ _____

(2) Richard is the man which helped me yesterday.

_____ ➡ _____

(3) Mary helps sometimes her mom.

_____ ➡ _____

4) I always will miss you.

_____ ➡ _____

03 다음 빈칸에 들어갈 말로 알맞은 것은?

> He doesn't like computer games. So he _____ plays computer
> games.

① always   ② usually   ③ often
④ sometimes   ⑤ seldom

04 다음 우리말에 맞게 괄호 안에 주어진 어구를 빈칸에 바르게 배열하시오. (필요하면 어형을 바꿀 것)

(1) 나는 꿈이 있는 사람이다. (a man, a dream, has, who)

➡ I am _____.

(2) 저는 종종 산책을 합니다. (go, walk, often, a, for)

➡ I _____.

01 다음 빈칸에 들어갈 알맞은 것은?

> Nara is wearing a hat _____ is too big for her.

① who
② whose
③ whom
④ which
⑤ where

 02 다음 밑줄 친 부분 중 어법상 바르지 <u>않은</u> 것은?

① Main dishes <u>often include</u> meat or fish.
② I <u>always</u> drink a glass of milk in the morning.
③ People <u>usually can</u> see auroras in the polar areas.
④ Bella is <u>sometimes</u> late for school.
⑤ I <u>never mix</u> business with pleasure.

03 다음 빈칸에 들어갈 수 있는 말이 <u>다른</u> 하나는?

① There was a king _____ name was Alexander.
② What do students _____ live in other countries eat for lunch?
③ He read the book _____ his dad bought for him.
④ Nancy heard the news _____ made her happy.
⑤ Did you meet the girl _____ wanted to talk with you?

서답형
04 다음 문장에서 never가 들어갈 곳은?

> • One ① is ② too ③ old ④ to ⑤ learn.

서답형
05 다음 괄호 안에서 알맞은 말을 고르시오.

(1) Andy (rarely goes / goes rarely) to a night club.
(2) Success (is often / often is) reached through the little thing.
(3) Mr. Kim is a doctor (who / which) lives in Seoul.
(4) There was a box (who / which) was full of books.
(5) The white dog (who / that) is playing with Jane is very cute.

 06 다음 중 어법상 옳은 문장은?

① A plantain is a fruit who looks like a banana.
② This is the girl which showed me the way.
③ A dog who has a long tail runs after a boy.
④ The man was the thief which stole her purse.
⑤ Is this the computer which you bought last Saturday?

서답형
07 다음 우리말에 맞게 주어진 단어를 넣어 문장을 다시 쓰시오.

> 나의 엄마는 항상 아침에 일찍 일어나신다.
> ➡ My mom gets up early in the morning. (always)

➡ _____

08 다음 두 문장을 한 문장으로 바르게 바꾸면?

> • The woman has long hair.
> • The woman is drinking water.

① The woman has that long hair is drinking water.
② The woman who she has long hair is drinking water.
③ The woman whom has long hair is drinking water.
④ The woman who has long hair is drinking water.
⑤ The woman which has long hair is drinking water.

서답형
09 다음 주어진 단어를 이용하여 적절한 질문을 쓰시오.

> **A:** _____ ?
>   (often)
> **B:** I sometimes help him after school.

서답형
10 다음 우리말에 맞게 괄호 안의 말을 넣어 문장을 다시 쓰시오.

(1) 네가 서두르면, 너는 항상 학교에 제시간에 갈 수 있다.
   • If you hurry up, you can go to school on time. (always)
   ➡ _____

(2) 부모는 그들의 자식을 위해 자주 큰 희생을 한다.
   • Parents make great sacrifices for their children. (often)
   ➡ _____

(3) 이곳은 거의 그 문제에 대해 토론할 장소가 아니다.
   • This is the place to talk about the problem. (hardly)
   ➡ _____

 중요
11 다음 밑줄 친 that의 용법이 나머지 넷과 다른 것은?

① Jiho is a boy that is always kind to others.
② Winter is the season that comes after autumn.
③ People used to believe that the earth was a flat surface.
④ The book that Mary gave me has many interesting stories.
⑤ I have a friend that lives in New York.

서답형
12 다음 문장에서 생략할 수 있는 것을 찾아 쓰시오.

(1) Seaweed is a food that we often eat.
(2) Look at the boy who is talking with a girl.
➡ (1) _____ (2) _____

서답형
13 다음 괄호 안에 주어진 단어들을 바르게 배열하여 문장을 완성하시오.

(1) (the nest, Americans, fly, usually) at age 18.
   ➡ _____

(2) (hard, it, always, so, to, is) say goodbye to friends.
   ➡ _____

(3) (will, do, anything, I, never) like this in future.
   ➡ _____

서답형

14 다음 두 문장을 주어진 관계대명사를 이용하여 한 문장으로 연결하시오.

(1) • A baguette is a type of bread.
   • The bread is popular in France. (which)
   ➡ _____

(2) • I met the woman.
   • She came from England. (who)
   ➡ _____

(3) • I have a dog.
   • It has brown hair. (that)
   ➡ _____

(4) • There is a house.
   • Its windows are broken. (whose)
   ➡ _____

(5) • I like the book.
   • Mom bought it for me. (that)
   ➡ _____

15 다음 중 어법상 올바른 문장은?

① John eats sometimes junk food.
② Samantha is always kind to me.
③ My mom used to rarely take a walk after dinner.
④ When do usually you get up?
⑤ I never will trust him again.

16 다음 빈칸에 들어갈 알맞은 것은?

| This is a Vietnamese restaurant _____. |

① which it looks very nice
② that I like it very much
③ who sells rice noodle soup
④ that it sells rice noodle soup
⑤ that sells rice noodle soup

17 다음 빈칸에 들어갈 말로 알맞은 것은?

| I like reading books a lot. So I _____ try to read books. |

① always   ② seldom   ③ rarely
④ sometimes   ⑤ never

18 다음 빈칸에 들어갈 말을 순서대로 바르게 연결한 것은?

• People _____ live in Singapore come from many different cultures.
• I want to visit Paris _____ has many nice museums.

① which – that   ② which – which
③ who – that   ④ who – who
⑤ that – who

19 다음 빈칸에 들어갈 수 없는 것은?

| He _____ avoids making decisions. |

① sometimes   ② often
③ always   ④ frequent
⑤ seldom

서답형

20 다음 문장에서 어법상 어색한 것을 바르게 고쳐 다시 쓰시오.

(1) Are you the person which dropped this?
   ➡ _____

(2) We have to break the bad habits who can cause serious problems.
   ➡ _____

(3) She uses always my phone without asking.
   ➡ _____

01 두 문장을 관계대명사를 이용하여 한 문장으로 썼을 때, 빈칸에 해당하는 문장을 쓰시오.

(1) • _____
   • She is wearing glasses.
   → The girl who is wearing glasses is eating rice noodle soup.

(2) • This is the smart phone.
   • _____
   → This is the smart phone which is made in Korea.

(3) • _____
   • It is really cool.
   → Emily bought a new computer that is really cool.

(4) • Degas liked to paint the ladies.
   • _____
   → Degas liked to paint the ladies that were dancing.

02 The following table shows how often each student studied math last week. Look carefully and answer the questions in a full sentence using a frequency adverb.

Name	Amy	Ann	Don	Elle
Times	0	2~3	5~6	8

(1) How often did Amy study math last week?
(2) How often did Don study math last week?
(3) How often did Ann study math last week?

➡ (1) _____
   (2) _____
   (3) _____

03 우리말과 일치하도록 괄호 안의 어구를 순서대로 배열하시오.

(1) 빨간 치마를 입고 있는 소녀가 내 딸이다. (a, my daughter, the girl, skirt, wearing, red, is, is, who)
   ➡ _____

(2) Jenny는 바이올린을 잘 켜는 남동생이 있다. (Jenny, brother, violin, has, plays, a, well, who, the)
   ➡ _____

(3) Cheetah는 빨리 달릴 수 있는 동물이다. (animal, cheetah, can, is, run, that, fast, a, an)
   ➡ _____

(4) Bill은 일요일에 항상 늦게 일어난다. (Bill, Sundays, gets, late, always, on, up)
   ➡ _____

(5) Cindy는 월말에는 종종 바쁘다. (Cindy, busy, the month, often, the end, is, at, of)
   ➡ _____

04 다음 빈칸에 알맞은 말을 쓰시오.

(1) The girl is my sister. She is reading a book.
   = The girl _____ a book is my sister.
   = The girl _____ _____ _____ a book is my sister.

(2) The dog is very cute. It is sleeping beside the sofa.
   = The dog _____ beside the sofa is very cute.
   = The dog _____ _____ _____ beside the sofa is very cute.

05 다음은 Bella의 일상생활에 관한 표이다. 표의 내용에 맞게 〈보기〉와 같이 빈도부사를 사용하여 빈칸을 채워, Bella의 일상생활을 묘사하는 문장을 3개 쓰시오.

what	always	usually	often	never
watch TV			✓	
be late				✓
send text messages	✓			
use the Internet		✓		

┌─ 보기 ┐
Bella often watches TV.

➡ Bella _____ for school.

➡ Bella _____ .

➡ Bella _____ .

06 다음 두 문장을 한 문장으로 바꿔 쓸 때, 빈칸을 어법에 맞게 채우시오.

David is my friend. I spent my vacation with him.

(1) David is my friend _____ I spent my vacation with.

(2) David is my friend _____ I spent my vacation with.

(3) David is my friend _____ _____ I spent my vacation.

(4) David is my friend _____ _____ _____ _____ _____ .

07 다음 우리말에 맞게 괄호 안의 어휘를 바르게 배열하시오. (필요할 경우 단어를 바꿀 것.)

너를 보려고 거의 기다릴 수 없어. (어서 보고 싶어.)
(I, you, wait, can, see, hard, to)

➡ _____

08 Put the following words in order adding a relative pronoun to complete the sentence. (Do not use that.)

doctors, sons, has, became, two

➡ Dan _____ .

09 다음 문장을 주어진 빈도부사를 이용하여 다시 쓰시오.

(1) On a hot day, sunlight is enough to melt chocolate. (usually)

➡ _____

(2) He wears very clean clothes. (always)

➡ _____

(3) I can find a parking space downtown. (never)

➡ _____

10 다음 그림을 참고하여 빈칸에 알맞은 말을 쓰시오.

In China, noodles mean long life. On their birthday, they eat noodles _____

_____ .

11 다음 문장을 어법에 맞게 고쳐 쓰시오.

(1) It is a TV show who is always popular.

➡ _____

(2) The painting shows a couple which are dancing.

➡ _____

(3) I took the train that it had a restaurant.

➡ _____

(4) I never am late for school.

➡ _____

Reading

School Lunches Around the World

Hello, this is food reporter Minjun from Korea.
사람을 소개할 때 사용

For many students, lunch is the best part of the school day.
good의 최상급

In Korea, we often eat rice and soup for lunch.
빈도부사 often은 일반동사와 쓰일 경우 일반동사 앞에 위치한다.

We also have side dishes, such as *Bulgogi* or *Gimchi*.
반찬 = like: ~와 같은 (예를 들어)

Sometimes our school serves special dishes, such as pizza, *Bibimbap*,
빈도부사 sometimes는 문장 맨 앞에 써도 된다. = like

or pasta. What do students who live in other countries eat for lunch?
who는 선행사 students를 수식하는 주격 관계대명사이다.

Let's hear from our food reporters!

reporter 기자, 리포터
side dish 반찬, 곁들임 요리
serve (음식을) 내다, 제공하다

📎 **확인문제**

● 다음 문장이 본문의 내용과 일치하면 T, 일치하지 않으면 F를 쓰시오.

1. Minjun is a reporter for a daily newspaper. ☐
2. For many students, lunch is the best part of the school day. ☐
3. In Korea, students often eat rice and soup for breakfast. ☐
4. Sometimes Minjun's school serves special dishes. ☐

Belle, France

Our school serves healthy and balanced meals.
(음식을) 내다, 제공하다

We usually eat a salad as an appetizer. Main dishes often include meat
as는 '…으로'라는 의미로 사용된 전치사이다.

or fish. We also eat fresh fruit at the end of the lunch.
~의 끝에

Oh, I can never forget about baguettes! They're great with cheese.
= baguettes

Our school also has a special rule.

We must stay at the lunch table for at least 30 minutes.
적어도

balanced 균형 잡힌
appetizer 식전 음식
rule 규칙, 규정

📎 **확인문제**

● 다음 문장이 본문의 내용과 일치하면 T, 일치하지 않으면 F를 쓰시오.

1. Belle's school serves healthy and balanced meals. ☐
2. Students usually eat a salad as a main dish at Belle's school. ☐
3. Baguettes are great with cheese. ☐
4. Students must stay at the lunch table for an hour in France. ☐

Bruno, Brazil

<u>Usually</u>, we have beans and rice for lunch.
빈도부사 usually는 문장 맨 앞에 써도 된다.

Meat and vegetables are <u>common</u> in our side dishes.
흔한

My favorite lunch comes with plantains. A plantain is a fruit <u>which</u>
which는 선행사 a fruit을 수식하는 주격 관계대명사이다.

<u>looks like</u> a banana. We <u>usually</u> fry plantains. Our school lunches are
look like+명사:~처럼 보이다. 빈도부사 usually는 일반동사가 있으면 보통 일반동사 앞에 위치한다.

fresh <u>because</u> the vegetables and fruit come from local farms.
because + 주어 + 동사

common 흔한, 공통의
local (특정한) 지방의, 현지의

📎 확인문제

● 다음 문장이 본문의 내용과 일치하면 T, 일치하지 <u>않으면</u> F를 쓰시오.

1 Usually, Bruno's school serves beans and rice for lunch. ☐

2 Meat and vegetables are common in Bruno's main dishes. ☐

3 A plantain is a fruit which looks like a banana. ☐

4 Bruno's school lunches include fruit from other countries. ☐

Nicole, Singapore

People <u>who</u> live in Singapore come from many different cultures, so
who는 선행사 People을 수식하는 주격 관계대명사이다.

we have <u>both</u> Eastern <u>and</u> Western dishes at lunch.
both A and B: A와 B 둘 다

Students can choose from many dishes, <u>such as</u> curry, noodle soup, or
= like: ~와 같은 (예를 들어)

pasta, each day. My school <u>won an award</u> for healthy school food last
상을 받았다

year. Our lunches are <u>always</u> healthy, and they taste <u>good</u>, too!
빈도부사 always는 be동사와 쓰였으므로 be동사 뒤에 위치한다.   감각동사 taste 뒤에 형용사 good이 보어로 쓰였다.

Which school lunch do you want <u>to try</u>?
명사적 용법(목적어)

Does it <u>have</u> anything <u>in common</u> with your school lunch?
└~을 공통으로 지니다.┘

Please <u>leave</u> your comments at www.chopchoplunch.com.
~을 남기다

both A and B A와 B 둘 다
Eastern 동양의, 동쪽에 위치한
Western 서양의, 서쪽에 위치한
award 상, 수상
have ~ in common ~을 공통적으로 지니다

📎 확인문제

● 다음 문장이 본문의 내용과 일치하면 T, 일치하지 <u>않으면</u> F를 쓰시오.

1 In Singapore, people come from many different cultures. ☐

2 Nicole has only Eastern dishes at lunch. ☐

3 Nicole's school won an award for healthy food this year. ☐

4 Nicole's school lunches are always healthy. ☐

5 Nicole's school lunches don't taste good. ☐

6 You may leave your comments at www.chopchoplunch.com. ☐

● 우리말을 참고하여 빈칸에 알맞은 말을 쓰시오.

1 School Lunches _____ _____ _____

2 Hello, _____ _____ food reporter Minjun _____ Korea.

3 For many students, lunch is _____ _____ _____ of the school day.

4 In Korea, we _____ eat rice and soup _____ _____.

5 We also _____ _____ _____, such as *Bulgogi* or *Gimchi*.

6 Sometimes our school _____ _____ _____, such as pizza, *Bibimbap*, or pasta.

7 What do students _____ _____ _____ _____ countries eat for lunch?

8 Let's _____ _____ our food reporters!

9 Belle, _____

10 Our school serves _____ _____ _____ meals.

11 We _____ eat a salad _____ _____ _____.

12 Main dishes _____ _____ meat or fish.

13 We also eat fresh fruit _____ _____ _____ _____ _____ _____.

14 Oh, I _____ _____ _____ about baguettes!

15 They're great _____ _____.

16 Our school also _____ _____ _____ _____.

17 We must stay at the lunch table _____ _____ _____ 30 _____.

1	세계 각국의 학교 급식
2	안녕하세요, 저는 한국에서 온 음식 취재 기자 민준입니다.
3	많은 학생들에게 점심시간은 학교 일과 중 가장 좋은 부분입니다.
4	한국에서는 점심으로 자주 밥과 국을 먹습니다.
5	우리는 불고기나 김치 같은 반찬도 먹습니다.
6	때때로 우리 학교는 피자, 비빔밥 또는 파스타 같은 특식을 제공합니다.
7	다른 나라에서 사는 학생들은 점심으로 무엇을 먹을까요?
8	우리 음식 취재 기자들에게서 들어보겠습니다!
9	벨, 프랑스
10	우리 학교는 건강하고 균형 잡힌 식사를 제공합니다.
11	우리는 보통 식전 음식으로 샐러드를 먹습니다.
12	주요리는 보통 고기나 생선을 포함합니다.
13	우리는 점심의 끝에 신선한 과일도 먹습니다.
14	오, 절대 바게트를 빠뜨릴 수는 없죠!
15	바게트는 치즈와 잘 어울립니다.
16	우리 학교에는 또한 특별한 규칙이 있습니다.
17	우리는 적어도 30분간 점심 식탁에 반드시 머물러야 합니다.

18 Bruno, _____

19 Usually, we have _____ _____ _____ for lunch.

20 Meat and vegetables are _____ _____ our side dishes.

21 My favorite lunch _____ _____ _____.

22 A plantain is a fruit _____ _____ _____ a banana.

23 We _____ _____ plantains.

24 Our school lunches are fresh because the vegetables and fruit _____ _____ _____ _____.

25 Nicole, _____

26 People _____ live in Singapore come _____ _____ _____ _____, so we have _____ _____ _____ _____ _____ at lunch.

27 Students can _____ _____ many dishes, _____ _____ curry, noodle soup, or pasta, each day.

28 My school _____ _____ _____ _____ healthy school food last year.

29 Our lunches are always _____, and they _____ _____, too!

30 _____ _____ _____ do you want to try?

31 Does it _____ anything _____ _____ _____ your school lunch?

32 Please _____ your comments _____ www.chopchoplunch.com.

---

18 브루노, 브라질

19 보통, 우리는 점심으로 콩과 밥을 먹습니다.

20 우리의 곁들임 음식에는 고기와 채소가 흔히 나옵니다.

21 내가 가장 좋아하는 점심에는 플랜테인이 나옵니다.

22 플랜테인은 바나나처럼 생긴 과일입니다.

23 우리는 보통 플랜테인을 튀깁니다.

24 채소와 과일이 현지 농장에서 오기 때문에 우리 학교 급식은 신선합니다.

25 니콜, 싱가포르

26 싱가포르에 사는 사람들은 매우 다양한 문화권에서 오기 때문에, 우리는 점심에 동양식과 서양식을 모두 먹습니다.

27 학생들은 매일 카레, 국수 또는 파스타와 같이 많은 요리 중에서 선택할 수 있습니다.

28 우리 학교는 작년에 건강한 학교 음식 상을 받았습니다.

29 우리의 점심은 항상 건강에 좋고, 맛 또한 좋습니다!

30 여러분은 어떤 학교 급식을 먹어 보고 싶나요?

31 그것이 여러분의 학교 급식과 공통되는 것이 있습니까?

32 여러분의 의견을 www.chopchoplunch.com에 남겨 주세요.

● 우리말을 참고하여 본문을 영작하시오.

1 ▶ 세계 각국의 학교 급식
➡ _____

2 ▶ 안녕하세요, 저는 한국에서 온 음식 취재 기자 민준입니다.
➡ _____

3 ▶ 많은 학생들에게 점심시간은 학교 일과 중 가장 좋은 부분입니다.
➡ _____

4 ▶ 한국에서는 점심으로 자주 밥과 국을 먹습니다.
➡ _____

5 ▶ 우리는 불고기나 김치 같은 반찬도 먹습니다.
➡ _____

6 ▶ 때때로 우리 학교는 피자, 비빔밥 또는 파스타 같은 특식을 제공합니다.
➡ _____

7 ▶ 다른 나라에서 사는 학생들은 점심으로 무엇을 먹을까요?
➡ _____

8 ▶ 우리 음식 취재 기자들에게서 들어보겠습니다!
➡ _____

9 ▶ 벨, 프랑스
➡ _____

10 ▶ 우리 학교는 건강하고 균형 잡힌 식사를 제공합니다.
➡ _____

11 ▶ 우리는 보통 식전 음식으로 샐러드를 먹습니다.
➡ _____

12 ▶ 주요리는 보통 고기나 생선을 포함합니다.
➡ _____

13 ▶ 우리는 점심의 끝에 신선한 과일도 먹습니다.
➡ _____

14 ▶ 오, 절대 바게트를 빠뜨릴 수는 없죠!
➡ _____

15 ▶ 바게트는 치즈와 잘 어울립니다.
➡ _____

16 ▶ 우리 학교에는 또한 특별한 규칙이 있습니다.
➡ _____

17 ▶ 우리는 적어도 30분간 점심 식탁에 반드시 머물러야 합니다.
➡ _____

18 브루노, 브라질

➡ _____

19 보통, 우리는 점심으로 콩과 밥을 먹습니다.

➡ _____

20 우리의 곁들임 음식에는 고기와 채소가 흔히 나옵니다.

➡ _____

21 내가 가장 좋아하는 점심에는 플랜테인이 나옵니다.

➡ _____

22 플랜테인은 바나나처럼 생긴 과일입니다.

➡ _____

23 우리는 보통 플랜테인을 튀깁니다.

➡ _____

24 채소와 과일이 현지 농장에서 오기 때문에 우리 학교 급식은 신선합니다.

➡ _____

25 니콜, 싱가포르

➡ _____

26 싱가포르에 사는 사람들은 매우 다양한 문화권에서 오기 때문에, 우리는 점심에 동양식과 서양식을 모두 먹습니다.

➡ _____

27 학생들은 매일 카레, 국수 또는 파스타와 같이 많은 요리 중에서 선택할 수 있습니다.

➡ _____

28 우리 학교는 작년에 건강한 학교 음식 상을 받았습니다.

➡ _____

29 우리의 점심은 항상 건강에 좋고, 맛 또한 좋습니다!

➡ _____

30 여러분은 어떤 학교 급식을 먹어 보고 싶나요?

➡ _____

31 그것이 여러분의 학교 급식과 공통되는 것이 있습니까?

➡ _____

32 여러분의 의견을 www.chopchoplunch.com에 남겨 주세요.

➡ _____

[01~03] 다음 글을 읽고, 물음에 답하시오.

Hello, this is food reporter Minjun from Korea. For many students, lunch is the best part of the school day. In Korea, we often eat rice and soup for lunch. We also have side dishes, such as *Bulgogi* or *Gimchi*. Sometimes our school serves special dishes, such as pizza, *Bibimbap*, or pasta. What do students ___@___ live in other countries eat for lunch? Let's hear from our food reporters!

01 위 글의 빈칸 @에 들어갈 알맞은 말을 모두 고르시오.

① which
② who
③ whom
④ that
⑤ what

02 위 글의 제목으로 알맞은 것을 고르시오.

① Food Reporters Around the World
② School Lunch in Korea
③ The Best Part of the Day
④ Famous Side Dishes of Korea
⑤ Wow! Pizza, Today's Special Dish

03 위 글의 내용과 일치하지 <u>않는</u> 것은?

① 민준이는 한국에서 온 음식 취재 기자이다.
② 많은 학생들에게 점심시간은 학교 일과 중 가장 좋은 부분이다.
③ 한국에서는 점심으로 자주 밥과 국을 먹는다.
④ 한국에서는 급식에 불고기나 김치 같은 반찬도 먹는다.
⑤ 민준이네 학교는 피자와 파스타 같은 특식을 항상 제공해 준다.

[04~06] 다음 글을 읽고, 물음에 답하시오.

Bruno, Brazil
Usually, we have beans and rice for lunch. Meat and vegetables are common in our side dishes. My favorite lunch comes ___@___ plantains. A plantain is a fruit which looks ⓑlike a banana. We usually fry plantains. Our school lunches are fresh because the vegetables and fruit come ___ⓒ___ local farms.

04 위 글의 빈칸 @와 ⓒ에 들어갈 전치사가 바르게 짝지어진 것은?

① with – from
② in – for
③ on – from
④ for – at
⑤ with – for

05 위 글의 밑줄 친 ⓑlike와 같은 의미로 쓰인 것을 고르시오.

① Does she <u>like</u> her new house?
② Which dress do you <u>like</u> best?
③ How did you <u>like</u> the movie?
④ I hope you <u>like</u> it, too!
⑤ You sound <u>like</u> a professor.

서답형
06 다음 질문에 대한 알맞은 대답을 영어로 쓰시오. (6 단어)

Q: What do the students usually have for lunch at Bruno's school?
A: _____

[07~08] 다음 글을 읽고, 물음에 답하시오.

Belle, France
Our school serves healthy and balanced meals. We usually eat a salad as an appetizer.

(①) Main dishes often include meat or fish. (②) We also eat fresh fruit at the end of the lunch. (③) Oh, I can never forget about baguettes! (④) Our school also has ⓐa special rule. (⑤) We must stay at the lunch table for at least 30 minutes.

07 위 글의 흐름으로 보아, 주어진 문장이 들어가기에 가장 적절한 곳은?

> They're great with cheese.

① ② ③ ④ ⑤

서답형
08 위 글의 밑줄 친 ⓐ가 가리키는 내용을 우리말로 쓰시오.

➡ _____

[09~11] 다음 글을 읽고, 물음에 답하시오.

Nicole, Singapore
People who live in Singapore come from many different ___ⓐ___, so we have both Eastern and Western dishes at lunch. Students can choose from many dishes, ⓑ such as curry, noodle soup, or pasta, each day. My school won an award for healthy school food last year. Our lunches are always healthy, and they taste good, too!

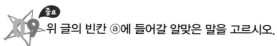

09 위 글의 빈칸 ⓐ에 들어갈 알맞은 말을 고르시오.

① opinions   ② purposes
③ concerns   ④ cultures
⑤ beliefs

서답형
10 니콜의 학교 급식의 특징 두 가지를 우리말로 쓰시오.

➡ 1. _____
  2. _____

서답형
11 위 글의 밑줄 친 ⓑ와 바꿔 쓸 수 있는 한 단어를 쓰시오.

➡ _____

12 주어진 글 다음에 이어질 글의 순서로 가장 적절한 것은?

> Hello, this is food reporter Minjun from Korea.

(A) We also have side dishes, such as *Bulgogi* or *Gimchi*. Sometimes our school serves special dishes, such as pizza, *Bibimbap*, or pasta.

(B) What do students who live in other countries eat for lunch? Let's hear from our food reporters!

(C) For many students, lunch is the best part of the school day. In Korea, we often eat rice and soup for lunch.

① (A) – (C) – (B)   ② (B) – (A) – (C)
③ (B) – (C) – (A)   ④ (C) – (A) – (B)
⑤ (C) – (B) – (A)

[13~14] 다음 글을 읽고, 물음에 답하시오.

Hello, this is food reporter Minjun from Korea. For many students, lunch is the best part of the school day. In Korea, we often eat rice and soup for lunch. We also have side ⓐdishes, such as *Bulgogi* or *Gimchi*.

Sometimes our school serves special dishes, such as pizza, *Bibimbap*, or pasta. What do students who live in other countries eat for lunch? Let's hear from our food reporters!

13 위 글의 밑줄 친 ⓐdishes와 같은 의미로 쓰인 것을 고르시오.

① I'll do the <u>dishes</u>.

② Can you <u>dish</u> out the potatoes?

③ How do I eat these <u>dishes</u>?

④ He broke the <u>dishes</u> by mistake.

⑤ The dirty <u>dishes</u> were still in the sink.

14 한국의 급식 반찬에 해당하는 것을 <u>모두</u> 고르시오.

① *Bulgogi*　　　② *Bibimbap*

③ soup　　　④ *Gimchi*

⑤ pasta

[15~16] 다음 글을 읽고, 물음에 답하시오.

Belle, France

　Our school serves healthy and (A) [balancing / balanced] meals. We usually eat a salad as an appetizer. Main dishes often (B) [include / exclude] meat or fish. We also eat fresh fruit at the end of the lunch. Oh, I can never forget about baguettes! ⓐThey're great with cheese. Our school also has a special rule. We must stay at the lunch table for (C)[at last / at least] 30 minutes.

서답형
15 위 글의 괄호 (A)~(C)에서 문맥이나 어법상 알맞은 낱말을 골라 쓰시오.

➡ (A)_____ (B)_____ (C)_____

서답형
16 위 글의 밑줄 친 ⓐThey가 가리키는 것을 본문에서 찾아 쓰시오.

➡ _____

[17~19] 다음 글을 읽고, 물음에 답하시오.

Bruno, Brazil

　Usually, we have beans and rice for lunch. Meat and vegetables are common in our side dishes. My favorite lunch comes with plantains. A plantain is a fruit ⓐwhich looks like a banana. We usually fry plantains. Our school lunches are fresh because the vegetables and fruit come from local farms.

17 위 글의 밑줄 친 ⓐwhich와 문법적 쓰임이 <u>다른</u> 것을 고르시오.

① This is the book <u>which</u> I like most.

② I don't know <u>which</u> car goes faster.

③ Look at the bird <u>which</u> is in the cage.

④ Give me the pen <u>which</u> you have.

⑤ This is the backpack <u>which</u> I chose.

서답형
18 다음 빈칸 (A)와 (B)에 알맞은 단어를 넣어 Bruno의 학교 급식을 정리하시오.

• main dishes: (A)_____
• common side dishes: (B)_____

서답형
19 다음 빈칸 (A)와 (B)에 알맞은 단어를 넣어 플랜테인에 대한 소개를 완성하시오.

A plantain is a fruit which looks like (A)_____ _____. People usually (B)_____ plantains in Brazil.

[20~23] 다음 글을 읽고, 물음에 답하시오.

　Which school lunch do you want ⓐto try? Does ⓑit have anything ⓒ공통적으로 ⓓ_____ your school lunch? Please leave your comments ⓔ_____ www.chopchoplunch.com.

20 위 글의 밑줄 친 @to try와 to부정사의 용법이 다른 것을 모두 고르시오.

① He decided to try it.
② Show me something easier to try.
③ It is good to try this new coffee.
④ Her plan was to try the project.
⑤ He went there to try surfing.

서답형
21 위 글의 밑줄 친 ⓑ가 가리키는 것을 우리말로 쓰시오.

➡ _____

서답형
22 위 글의 밑줄 친 ⓒ의 우리말을 두 단어로 쓰시오.

➡ _____

중요
23 위 글의 빈칸 @와 ⓔ에 들어갈 전치사가 바르게 짝지어진 것은?

① with – from   ② at – by
③ for – to   ④ with – at
⑤ for – at

[24~26] 다음 글을 읽고, 물음에 답하시오.

　This is a Vietnamese restaurant ＿＿@＿＿ sells rice noodle soup. The man ＿＿ⓑ＿＿ works at the restaurant is serving food. The woman who has long hair is drinking water. ⓒ안경을 끼고 있는 소녀는 쌀국수를 먹고 있다. ⓓAll of them look so happily!

서답형
24 위 글의 빈칸 @와 ⓑ에 공통으로 알맞은 말을 쓰시오.

➡ _____

서답형
25 위 글의 밑줄 친 ⓒ의 우리말에 맞게 be동사를 보충하여, 주어진 어구를 알맞게 배열하시오.

glasses / eating / who / rice noodle soup / is wearing / the girl

➡ _____
　 _____

서답형
26 위 글의 밑줄 친 ⓓ에서 어법상 틀린 부분을 찾아 고치시오.

➡ _____

[27~28] 다음 대화를 읽고, 물음에 답하시오.

A: Which country's school lunch do you want to try?
B: I want to try a school lunch from France. I love baguettes and cheese. Also, they must stay at the lunch table for at least 30 minutes. That's an interesting rule.
C: I'm interested in trying a school lunch from Singapore. @Choosing both Eastern and Western dishes for lunch sounds fun. How about you?
A: I think Korean school lunches are the best. I love *Gimchi* so much!

서답형
27 위 대화를 읽고 A, B, C가 어느 나라 학교 급식을 먹고 싶어 하는지와 그 이유를 각각 우리말로 쓰시오.

➡ A: _____
　 B: _____
　 　 _____
　 C: _____
　 　 _____

28 위 대화의 밑줄 친 @Choosing과 문법적 쓰임이 같은 것을 고르시오.

① I know the girl singing a song.
② He enjoys reading books.
③ I saw him entering the room.
④ They are learning English now.
⑤ Take good care of the crying baby.

[01~03] 다음 글을 읽고, 물음에 답하시오.

Hello, this is food reporter Minjun from Korea. For many students, lunch is the best part of the school day. In Korea, we often eat rice and soup for lunch. We also have side dishes, ⓐ _Bulgogi_ or _Gimchi_. Sometimes our school serves special dishes, ⓑ pizza, _Bibimbap_, or pasta. ⓒWhat do students who lives in other countries eat for lunch? Let's hear from our food reporters!

01 다음 질문에 대한 알맞은 대답을 빈칸에 쓰시오.

> Q: In Korea, what do students often eat for lunch?
> A: They often eat _____ _____ _____ for lunch.

02 위 글의 빈칸 ⓐ와 ⓑ에 공통으로 들어갈 알맞은 말을 쓰시오.

➡ _____

03 위 글의 밑줄 친 ⓒ에서 어법상 틀린 부분을 찾아 고치시오.

_____ ➡ _____

[04~06] 다음 글을 읽고, 물음에 답하시오.

Belle, France
Our school serves healthy and balanced meals. We usually eat a salad as an appetizer. Main dishes often include meat or fish. ⓐWe also eat fresh fruit at the end of the lunch. Oh, I can never forget about baguettes! They're great with cheese. Our school also has a special rule. ⓑWe must stay at the lunch table during at least 30 minutes.

04 위 글의 밑줄 친 ⓐ를 다음과 같이 바꿔 쓰려고 한다. 주어진 영영 풀이를 참고하여 아래 빈칸에 철자 d로 시작하는 단어를 쓰시오.

> something sweet, such as fruit or a pudding, which you eat at the end of a meal

➡ We also eat fresh fruit as a _____ at the end of the lunch.

05 위 글의 밑줄 친 ⓑ에서 어법상 어색한 부분을 찾아 고치시오.

_____ ➡ _____

06 다음 질문에 대한 알맞은 대답을 주어진 어구로 시작하여 쓰시오. (11 단어)

> Q: What is the special rule of Belle's school?
> A: The students _____
> _____.

[07~09] 다음 글을 읽고, 물음에 답하시오.

Bruno, Brazil
Usually, we have beans and rice for lunch. Meat and vegetables are common in our side dishes. My favorite lunch comes with plantains. A plantain is a fruit which looks (A)[at / like] a banana. We usually (B)[fly / fry] plantains. Our school lunches are fresh because the vegetables and fruit come from (C)[global / local] farms.

07 위 글의 괄호 (A)~(C)에서 문맥상 알맞은 낱말을 골라 쓰시오.

➡ (A)_____ (B)_____ (C)_____

08 본문의 내용과 일치하도록 다음 빈칸 (A)와 (B)에 알맞은 단어를 쓰시오.

> At Bruno's school, (A)_____ and (B)_____ are common in their side dishes.

09 다음 문장에서 위 글의 내용과 다른 부분을 찾아서 고치시오.

> Bruno's favorite lunch comes with fried potatoes.

_____ ➡ _____

[10~12] 다음 글을 읽고, 물음에 답하시오.

> Nicole, Singapore
>
> People who live in Singapore come from many different cultures, so we have both Eastern and Western dishes at lunch. Students can choose from many dishes, such as curry, noodle soup, or pasta, each day. My school ⓐwon an award for healthy school food last year. Our lunches are always healthy, and they taste good, too!

10 다음 질문에 대한 알맞은 대답을 주어진 단어로 시작하여 쓰시오. (10 단어)

> Q: Why do the students have both Eastern and Western dishes at lunch at Nicole's school?
> A: Because _____
> _____.

11 본문의 내용과 일치하도록 다음 빈칸에 공통으로 들어갈 알맞은 단어를 쓰시오.

> Nicole's school lunches are _____ for the health, and they also taste _____!

➡ _____

12 위 글의 밑줄 친 ⓐ를 다음과 같이 바꿔 쓸 때 빈칸에 알맞은 말을 쓰시오.

> won a _____

[13~15] 다음 글을 읽고, 물음에 답하시오.

> ____ⓐ____ of My Favorite Restaurant
>
> My favorite restaurant is Antonio's Restaurant. It is a Spanish restaurant. It is near my home. Mixed paella is the most popular dish at this restaurant. ⓑAll of the food is really fresh and delicious, and the prices are high. I recommend this restaurant!
>
> My Rating ★★★★☆

13 위 글의 빈칸 ⓐ에 철자 R로 시작하는 알맞은 말을 쓰시오.

➡ _____

14 위 글의 밑줄 친 ⓑ에서 흐름상 어색한 부분을 찾아 고치시오.

_____ ➡ _____

15 본문의 내용과 일치하도록 다음 빈칸 (A)와 (B)에 알맞은 단어를 쓰시오.

> The writer recommends Antonio's Restaurant because of its really (A)_____ and (B)_____ food.

구석구석

Project Link

Let's Make *Gimchi* Fried Rice!
Let's 동사원형: ~하자   fried: 튀긴

1. Cut the *Gimchi*, onions and carrots.
   cut: 자르다   3개 이상 나열할 때 A. B. and C 형식으로 쓴다.

2. Put the oil in a pan, and heat it up.
   put A in B: A를 B에 넣다   heat ~ up: ~을 덥히다

3. Add the *Gimchi*, and fry it for one minute.
   for + 수사가 붙은 기간: ~ 동안

4. Add and fry the rice and vegetables.

5. Fry an egg, and add it on top.
   = an egg   맨 위에

구문해설 • fry: 튀기다 • carrot: 당근 • add: 첨가하다

김치 볶음밥을 만들자!
1. 김치, 양파 그리고 당근을 자르세요.
2. 후라이팬에 오일을 넣고, 가열하세요.
3. 김치를 넣고, 잠시 동안 볶아주세요.
4. 밥과 야채를 넣고 볶으세요.
5. 계란을 부치고 맨 위에 놓으세요.

Think and Write

Review of My Favorite Restaurant

My favorite restaurant is Antonio's Restaurant.

It is a Spanish restaurant. It is near my home.
=Antonio's Restaurant   = Antonio's Restaurant
Mixed paella is the most popular dish at this restaurant.
popular의 최상급

All of the food is really fresh and delicious, and the prices are low. I
price가 비싸거나 싼 것을 표현할 때는 보통 high나 low를 사용한다.

recommend this restaurant!

My Rating ★★★★☆

구문해설 • favorite: 매우 좋아하는 • Spanish: 스페인의 • paella: 파엘라(쌀, 닭고기, 생선, 채소를 넣은 스페인 요리) • recommend: 추천하다

내가 가장 좋아하는 음식점 방문 후기
내가 가장 좋아하는 음식점은 Antonio's Restaurant이야. 그곳은 스페인 음식점이야. 그곳은 나의 집에서 가까워. 이 음식점에서 가장 인기 있는 음식은 혼합 파엘라야. 모든 음식이 정말 신선하고 맛있으며 가격도 싸. 나는 이 음식점을 추천해.
        나의 평가 ★★★★☆

Culture Link

In China, people eat noodles on their birthday. Chinese people don't want to
on+특정한 날
break the noodles to live a long life.
부사적 용법(목적)
Doro wat is a chicken curry from Ethiopia. There are a lot of vegetables in it.
=many
People eat this dish for New Year's dinner.
요리
Bánh xu xê is a traditional Vietnamese cake. People eat this cake at weddings.
tradition+al (형용사 어미)
Eating the cake means the husbands and wife will have a happy life together.

In the United States, people eat turkey to celebrate Thanksgiving. They give
부사적 용법(목적)
thanks for the food and their health.

구문해설 • a lot of: 많은(= many) • dish: 음식, 요리 • traditional: 전통적인 • celebrate: 축하하다
• give thanks for: ~에 대해 감사하다

중국에서 사람들은 그들의 생일에 국수를 먹는다. 중국 사람들은 장수하려고 국수를 자르려 하지 않는다.
Doro wat은 에티오피아의 치킨 카레 요리이다. 그 안에 많은 야채가 들어 있다. 사람들은 이 요리를 새해 만찬으로 먹는다.
Bánh xu xê는 전통적인 베트남 케이크이다. 사람들은 이 케이크를 결혼식에서 먹는다. 이 케이크를 먹는 것은 남편과 아내가 함께 행복한 삶을 살 것을 의미한다.
미국에서 사람들은 추수감사절을 기념하기 위해 칠면조 요리를 먹는다. 그들은 음식과 그들의 건강에 대해 감사한다.

영역별 핵심문제

Words & Expressions

01 다음 밑줄 친 부분의 우리말 뜻으로 알맞지 <u>않은</u> 것은?

① If you wash your hair too <u>often</u>, it can get too dry. (종종, 자주)

② Eating <u>sweets</u> is bad for your teeth. (달콤한)

③ Smoking can seriously damage your <u>health</u>. (건강)

④ Art books are expensive to produce, <u>especially</u>, if they contain color illustrations. (특히)

⑤ <u>Cut</u> the orange in half. (자르다)

02 다음 빈칸에 알맞은 단어를 고르시오.

> *Gimchi* is one of the _____ Korean foods.

① fast　　② modern　　③ free
④ traditional　　⑤ fried

03 다음 제시된 단어를 사용하여 자연스러운 문장을 만들 수 <u>없는</u> 것은?

> ┌ 보기 ┐
> contest　appetizer　choice　culture

① You have a _____ – you can stay here on your own or you can come with us.

② In our _____, it is rude to ask someone how much they earn.

③ Sara had to leave her job due to ill _____.

④ The finals of the _____ were held in the United States.

⑤ Crackers are also excellent as a(n) _____.

04 다음 대화의 밑줄 친 have와 같은 의미로 쓰인 문장을 고르시오.

> A: I'm not hungry.
> B: But for your health, you'd better <u>have</u> some food.

① He <u>had</u> to go to Germany.

② You <u>have</u> beautiful eyes.

③ We <u>had</u> our money stolen.

④ Will you <u>have</u> some more cake?

⑤ Do you <u>have</u> any brothers and sisters?

05 다음 빈칸에 공통으로 들어갈 단어를 고르시오.

> • All of them _____ from wealthy, upper class families.
> • You should install the software that _____ with the drive.

① came　　② went　　③ lived
④ checked　　⑤ got

Conversation

[06~07] 우리말과 일치하도록 빈칸에 알맞은 말을 쓰시오.

06
> A: I want to be taller.
> B: Then _____. (우유를 마시는 게 좋아.)
> A: Thank you _____. (너의 충고 고마워.)

07
> G: _____. (저 여기 처음 왔어요.) What do you recommend?
> M: _____ and salad. (저는 피자와 샐러드를 추천해요.)

08 다음 대화의 ①~⑤ 중 어색한 곳을 모두 바르게 고치시오.

> A: ①I eat too much snacks.
> B: ②You'd better eating ③more healthy food.
> A: ④What do you recommend?
> B: ⑤I recommend chicken salad.

➡ _____ ➡ _____

_____ ➡ _____

[09~12] 다음 대화를 읽고, 물음에 답하시오.

> G: You look very tired today. Didn't you sleep well?
> B: Yes, I did. (①) But I often feel tired these days, especially in the morning.
> G: (A)Do you eat breakfast? (②)
> B: No, I don't.
> G: You'd better (B)_____ (eat) breakfast. Breakfast (C)_____ (give) you energy. (③)
> B: I didn't know that. (④)
> G: Well, you (D)_____ also exercise every day. That will help you. (⑤)
> B: Okay. I will.

09 위 대화의 ①~⑤ 중 주어진 문장이 들어갈 알맞은 곳은?

> Do you have any other suggestions?

① ② ③ ④ ⑤

10 밑줄 친 (A)에 '보통, 대개'의 의미를 지닌 부사를 넣어 질문을 만드시오.

➡ _____

11 주어진 단어를 이용해 빈칸 (B)와 (C)를 완성하시오.

➡ (B) _____ (C) _____

12 위 대화의 빈칸 (D)에 알맞은 말을 고르시오.

① might   ② will   ③ should
④ could   ⑤ have

[13~15] 다음 대화를 읽고, 물음에 답하시오.

> W: Hello. Are you ready (A)_____ order?
> B: ①It's my first time here. ②What do you recommend?
> W: ③I recommend the chicken sandwich. ④It is the more popular item at our restaurant.
> B: Well, I don't like chicken very much. ⑤Could you recommend something else?
> W: How (B)_____ the turkey sandwich?
> B: Oh, I love turkey. I'll have that.
> W: Why don't you order a drink (C)_____ the sandwich? You can get a 500-won discount.
> B: That's great. Then I'll have an orange juice, too.

13 위 대화의 ①~⑤ 중 어법상 어색한 것을 고르시오.

① ② ③ ④ ⑤

14 빈칸 (A)~(C)에 알맞은 것을 〈보기〉에서 골라 쓰시오.

> ┌─ 보기 ─┐
> for   about   in   with   to

➡ (A)_____ (B)_____ (C)_____

15 위 대화의 내용과 일치하지 <u>않는</u> 것은?

① The boy visits the restaurant for the first time.
② When the boy orders a drink with the sandwich, the price will be discounted.
③ The woman works for the restaurant.
④ The turkey sandwich is the most popular at the restaurant.
⑤ The boy doesn't like chicken.

Grammar

16 다음 주어진 문장의 밑줄 친 부분과 같은 역할을 하는 것을 두 개 고르시오.

> Eddie is a boy <u>who</u> often goes to the movies.

① Ken loves the lady <u>who</u> he worked with.
② The woman <u>who</u> is talking on the phone is my mother.
③ The girl <u>who</u> I met yesterday is my sister.
④ <u>Who</u> are you going to travel Europe with?
⑤ A scientist is someone <u>who</u> studies science.

17 다음 밑줄 친 부분의 쓰임이 <u>어색한</u> 것은?

① I <u>often</u> play computer games at home.
② His room is <u>always</u> in order.
③ Esther <u>never</u> will fail to earn popularity.
④ We <u>usually</u> eat a salad as an appetizer.
⑤ Kyle <u>sometimes</u> takes a walk to the park.

18 다음 밑줄 친 부분이 어법상 <u>어색한</u> 것은?

① It's a special phone <u>which</u> works well in the water.
② Monica lives in a house <u>which</u> has a beautiful garden.
③ Cathy is worried about the baby <u>that</u> is sick in bed.
④ *Taekwondo* is a very exciting exercise <u>who</u> started in Korea.
⑤ Where is the book <u>that</u> I gave you yesterday?

19 다음 중 어법상 올바른 것은?

① He seldom changed the opinion he had formed.
② I play sometimes sports.
③ We fry usually plantains.
④ I will do that again never.
⑤ I have a few free afternoons often a week.

20 다음 그림을 참고하고 괄호 안에 주어진 어휘를 이용하여 빈칸에 알맞은 말을 쓰시오.

Chang's Restaurant   Jin's Restaurant   Bella's Restaurant

(1) Jiwoo will go to Chang's Restaurant
_____. (noodles)
(2) Jiwoo will go to Jin's Restaurant
_____. (sushi)
(3) Jiwoo will go to Bella's Restaurant
_____. (pizza)

21 다음 괄호 안에서 어법상 올바른 것을 고르시오.

(1) Our lunches (are always / always are) healthy, and they taste good, too.
(2) I (knew rarely / rarely knew) that Mike liked Ann.
(3) We (should always / always should) do something to solve problems.

22 다음 중 어법상 옳은 것은?

① She will miss always him.
② My mom watches usually TV after dinner.
③ I wake often up late on weekends.
④ You take never care of your brother.
⑤ I sometimes hang out with my friends after work.

23 주어진 어구를 이용하여 다음 우리말을 영작하시오. (관계대명사 that 사용 금지)

(1) 나는 버스에 휴대폰을 놓고 내린 소녀를 찾고 있는 중이다. (her cell phone, on the bus, look for, leave)

➡ _____

(2) 코끼리는 코가 긴 동물이다. (an animal, a long nose, have)

➡ _____

(3) 많은 책이 있는 그 상자는 아주 무겁다. (many, very, the box, have)

➡ _____

(4) 아빠는 항상 매우 조심해서 운전하신다. (Dad, carefully, drive his car)

➡ _____

(5) 너는 아기를 혼자 두어서는 절대로 안 된다. (never, alone, a baby, leave, should)

➡ _____

Reading

[24~26] 다음 글을 읽고, 물음에 답하시오.

Hello, this is food reporter Minjun ⓐ Korea. (①) ⓑ many students, lunch is the best part of the school day. (②) In Korea, we often eat rice and soup ⓑ lunch. (③) We also have side dishes, such as *Bulgogi* or *Gimchi*. (④) Sometimes our school serves special dishes, such as pizza, *Bibimbap*, or pasta. (⑤) Let's hear ⓐ our food reporters!

24 위 글의 흐름으로 보아, 주어진 문장이 들어가기에 가장 적절한 곳은?

> What do students who live in other countries eat for lunch?

① ② ③ ④ ⑤

25 위 글의 빈칸 ⓐ와 ⓑ에 각각 공통으로 들어갈 전치사가 바르게 짝지어진 것은? (대·소문자 무시)

① from – to　　② in – by
③ in – from　　④ from – for
⑤ on – for

26 위 글을 읽고 대답할 수 없는 질문은?

① Where is Minjun from?
② Why is lunch the best part of the school day for many students?
③ What do students often eat as main dishes for lunch in Korea?
④ What side dishes do students have in Korea?
⑤ What does Minjun's school serve as special dishes?

[27~28] 다음 글을 읽고, 물음에 답하시오.

Belle, France

Our school serves healthy and balanced meals. We usually eat a salad ⓐas an appetizer. Main dishes often include meat or fish. We also eat fresh fruit at the end of the lunch. Oh, I can never forget about baguettes! They're great with cheese. Our school also has a special rule. We must stay at the lunch table for at least 30 minutes.

27 위 글의 밑줄 친 ⓐas와 같은 의미로 쓰인 것을 고르시오.

① Do as you like.
② This box will serve as a table.
③ As she was tired, she soon fell asleep.
④ He runs as fast as you.
⑤ As I entered the room, he was crying.

28 벨의 학교 급식에서 볼 수 <u>없는</u> 음식을 고르시오.

① a salad　　　② meat or fish
③ fresh fruit　　④ curry
⑤ baguettes

29 주어진 글 다음에 이어질 글의 순서로 가장 적절한 것은?

> Usually, we have beans and rice for lunch.

(A) A plantain is a fruit which looks like a banana. We usually fry plantains.
(B) Meat and vegetables are common in our side dishes. My favorite lunch comes with plantains.
(C) Our school lunches are fresh because the vegetables and fruit come from local farms.

① (A) – (C) – (B)　　② (B) – (A) – (C)
③ (B) – (C) – (A)　　④ (C) – (A) – (B)
⑤ (C) – (B) – (A)

[30~31] 다음 글을 읽고, 물음에 답하시오.

> Bruno, Brazil
> Usually, we have beans and rice for lunch. Meat and vegetables are common in our side dishes. My favorite lunch comes with plantains. A plantain is a fruit ___ⓐ___ looks like a banana. We usually fry plantains. Our school lunches are fresh because the vegetables and fruit come from local farms.

30 위 글의 내용과 일치하지 <u>않는</u> 것은?

① 브루노는 보통 점심으로 콩과 밥을 먹는다.
② 브루노가 좋아하는 점심에는 플랜테인이 나온다.
③ 플랜테인은 기름에 튀긴 바나나이다.
④ 브루노의 학교 급식 재료인 채소와 과일은 현지 농장에서 온다.
⑤ 브루노의 학교 급식은 신선하다.

31 위 글의 빈칸 ⓐ에 알맞은 말을 <u>모두</u> 고르시오.

① that　　　② who
③ what　　　④ which
⑤ whom

[32~33] 다음 글을 읽고, 물음에 답하시오.

> Nicole, Singapore
> People ⓐ<u>that</u> live in Singapore come from many different cultures, so we have ⓑ<u>both</u> Eastern and Western dishes at lunch. Students can choose from many dishes, such as curry, noodle soup, or pasta, ⓒ<u>each days</u>. My school ⓓ<u>won</u> an award for healthy school food last year. Our lunches are always healthy, and Ⓐ<u>they</u> taste good, ⓔ<u>either</u>!

32 위 글의 밑줄 친 ⓐ~ⓔ 중 어법상 <u>틀린</u> 개수를 고르시오.

① 1개　② 2개　③ 3개　④ 4개　⑤ 5개

33 위 글의 밑줄 친 Ⓐthey가 가리키는 것을 본문에서 찾아 쓰시오.

➡ ＿＿＿＿＿＿＿＿＿＿＿＿

[01~02] 다음 대화를 읽고, 물음에 답하시오.

> G: I think I eat too many sweets these days.
> B: That's good for your health. 대신에 과일을 먹는 게 좋아.

✏️ 출제율 90%
01 위 대화에서 흐름상 어색한 부분을 찾아 고치시오.

_____ ➡ _____

✏️ 출제율 85%
02 위 대화의 밑줄 친 우리말을 영작하시오.

➡ _____

[03~04] 다음 빈칸에 공통으로 알맞은 단어를 쓰시오.

✏️ 출제율 100%
03
> • Get _____ earlier, and you will become healthy.
> • Most toasters take a few minutes to heat the bread _____.

➡ _____

✏️ 출제율 90%
04
> • He'll stay in bed for _____ least half a month.
> • This happens _____ the end of summer.

➡ _____

[05~06] 다음 빈칸에 가장 알맞은 단어를 고르시오.

✏️ 출제율 90%
05
> A: I'm going to the Spanish restaurant. What do you recommend there?
> B: I recommend the _____. It is delicious.

① sushi ② *bulgogi* ③ curry
④ paella ⑤ fish and chips

✏️ 출제율 90%
06
> A: My new home is too far from school.
> B: You'd better take public _____.
> A: What do you recommend?
> B: I recommend the bus.

① accommodation ② traffic
③ transform ④ transportation
⑤ equipment

✏️ 출제율 100%
07 다음 〈보기〉와 같은 관계가 되도록 주어진 빈칸에 알맞은 말을 쓰시오. (주어진 철자로 시작할 것)

> ┤ 보기 ├
> Eastern — Western

(1) rotten – f_____ (2) same – d_____
(3) rare – c_____ (4) exclude – i_____

✏️ 출제율 90%
08 대화 내용의 흐름상 어색한 부분을 고르시오.

> A: ①My mom's birthday is coming, but ②I have enough money.
> B: ③You'd better make a gift yourself.
> A: ④What do you recommend?
> B: ⑤I recommend chocolate.

① ② ③ ④ ⑤

✏️ 출제율 95%
09 다음 대화의 빈칸에 알맞은 것은?

> A: I usually have a pain in my stomach after lunch.
> B: _____

① Then you should make lunch.
② I've been eating for an hour.
③ Then you'd better eat slowly.
④ Thanks for your advice.
⑤ I should go grocery shopping.

[10~12] 다음 대화를 읽고, 물음에 답하시오.

G: Justin, our school cooking contest is tomorrow. ⓐ<u>What are you going to make?</u>

B: ⓑ<u>I'm going to make sandwiches.</u>

G: What do you want to (A)_____?

B: Chicken, cheese, and eggs. (①)

G: ⓒ<u>You'd better put vegetables in your sandwiches.</u> How about onions and carrots? (②)

B: No, I'm not going to add them. ⓓ<u>I like those vegetables.</u> (③)

G: ⓔ<u>That's not a good idea.</u> Mr. Kim said we should make healthy food for the contest. (④)

B: You're right. (⑤)

출제율 85%

10 위 대화의 ①~⑤ 중 주어진 문장이 들어갈 알맞은 곳은?

> I should go grocery shopping and buy onions and carrots.

①　　　②　　　③　　　④　　　⑤

출제율 95%

11 위 대화의 빈칸 (A)에 들어갈 말로 적절한 것은?

① put them in
② put it in
③ put in them
④ put in it
⑤ put it in them

출제율 90%

12 위 대화의 ⓐ~ⓔ 중 흐름상 어색한 것을 고르시오.

① ⓐ　② ⓑ　③ ⓒ　④ ⓓ　⑤ ⓔ

출제율 90%

13 다음 빈칸에 들어갈 알맞은 말을 모두 고르시오.

> Joel is a person _____ sometimes listens to classical music.

① who
② whose
③ whom
④ that
⑤ which

출제율 95%

14 다음 중 어법상 옳은 문장은?

① Terry eats never anything after 7 p.m.
② She drinks usually a cup of coffee after breakfast.
③ Does your mom go often for a walk?
④ I always am nice to him.
⑤ I sometimes play baduk with Jack.

출제율 90%

15 괄호 안에 주어진 어구를 사용해 다음을 영작하시오. (that 사용 금지)

(1) 나는 주머니가 많은 조끼를 사고 싶다. (a vest, pocket, want, have, 10 단어)

➡ _____

(2) 나는 버스에서 음악을 듣고 있던 Eva를 만났다. (on the bus, 11 단어)

➡ _____

(3) 그녀는 100 단어를 말할 수 있는 앵무새를 가지고 있다. (a parrot, words, have, speak, 9 단어)

➡ _____

(4) 수학 문제는 내게 항상 어렵다. (math problems, for me, difficult, 7 단어)

➡ _____

16 주어진 어휘를 알맞은 곳에 넣어 문장을 다시 쓰시오.

(1) Dad goes to work by bike. (usually)

➡ _____

(2) Dorothy is busy every day. (always)

➡ _____

(3) I can forget about baguettes. (never)

➡ _____

[17~19] 다음 글을 읽고, 물음에 답하시오.

Hello, (A)[it / this] is food reporter Minjun from Korea. For many students, lunch is the best part of the school day. In Korea, we often eat rice and soup for lunch. We also have side dishes, such as *Bulgogi* or *Gimchi*. Sometimes our school serves special dishes, such as pizza, *Bibimbap*, or pasta. (B)[What / How] do students ⓐwho live in other countries (C)[eat / to eat] for lunch? Let's hear from our food reporters!

출제율 90%

17 위 글의 괄호 (A)~(C)에서 어법상 알맞은 낱말을 골라 쓰시오.

➡ (A)_____ (B)_____ (C)_____

출제율 100%

18 위 글의 밑줄 친 ⓐwho와 문법적 쓰임이 같은 것을 고르시오.

① I wonder who wrote that letter.
② Who ever told you that?
③ The man who called you is my dad.
④ Nobody knew who he was.
⑤ Who is the captain?

출제율 95%

19 본문의 내용과 일치하도록 다음 빈칸 (A)와 (B)에 알맞은 단어를 쓰시오.

Minjun introduces the school (A)_____ of Korea, (B)_____ _____ main dishes, side dishes, and special dishes.

출제율 90%

20 주어진 글 다음에 이어질 글의 순서로 가장 적절한 것은?

Our school serves healthy and balanced meals.

(A) They're great with cheese. Our school also has a special rule. We must stay at the lunch table for at least 30 minutes.
(B) We also eat fresh fruit at the end of the lunch. Oh, I can never forget about baguettes!
(C) We usually eat a salad as an appetizer. Main dishes often include meat or fish.

① (A) – (C) – (B)   ② (B) – (A) – (C)
③ (B) – (C) – (A)   ④ (C) – (A) – (B)
⑤ (C) – (B) – (A)

[21~22] 다음 글을 읽고, 물음에 답하시오.

Belle, France
Our school serves healthy and balanced meals. We usually eat a salad as an ___ⓐ___. Main dishes often include meat or fish. We also eat fresh fruit at the end of the lunch. Oh, I can never forget about baguettes! They're great ___ⓑ___ cheese. Our school also has a special rule. We must stay at the lunch table ___ⓒ___ at least 30 minutes.

출제율 95%

21 주어진 영영풀이를 참고하여 빈칸 ⓐ에 철자 a로 시작하는 단어를 쓰시오.

the first course of a meal which includes a small amount of food

➡ _____

22 위 글의 빈칸 ⓑ와 ⓒ에 들어갈 전치사가 바르게 짝지어진 것은?

① for – from ② with – by
③ with – for ④ to – for
⑤ on – in

[23~24] 다음 글을 읽고, 물음에 답하시오.

> Bruno, Brazil
> Usually, we have beans and rice for lunch. Meat and vegetables are common in our side dishes. My favorite lunch comes with plantains. A plantain is a fruit which looks like a banana. We usually fry plantains. Our school lunches are fresh because the vegetables and fruit come from local farms.

23 위 글을 읽고 알 수 <u>없는</u> 것을 고르시오.

① What do the students have for lunch at Bruno's school?
② What is common in their side dishes at Bruno's school?
③ What does Bruno's favorite lunch come with?
④ What is a plantain?
⑤ Why do they usually fry plantains?

24 다음 질문에 대한 알맞은 대답을 주어진 단어로 시작하여 쓰시오. (8 단어)

> Q: Why are Bruno's school lunches fresh?
> A: Because _____
> _____ .

[25~27] 다음 글을 읽고, 물음에 답하시오.

> Nicole, Singapore
> ⓐPeople which live in Singapore come from many different cultures, so we have both ___ⓑ___ and ___ⓒ___ dishes at lunch. Students can choose from many dishes, such as curry, noodle soup, or pasta, each day. My school won an award for healthy school food last year. Our lunches are always healthy, and they taste good, too!

25 위 글의 밑줄 친 ⓐ에서 어법상 <u>틀린</u> 부분을 찾아 고치시오.

_____ ➡ _____

26 위 글의 빈칸 ⓑ와 ⓒ에 East와 West를 각각 알맞은 형태로 쓰시오.

➡ ⓑ_____, ⓒ_____

27 위 글의 내용과 일치하지 <u>않는</u> 것은?

① 싱가포르에 사는 사람들은 매우 다양한 문화권에서 왔다.
② 니콜의 학교는 점심에 동양식과 서양식을 모두 먹는다.
③ 학생들은 매일 카레, 국수, 또는 파스타와 같은 많은 요리 중에 선택할 수 있다.
④ 니콜의 학교는 올해 건강한 학교 급식상을 받았다.
⑤ 니콜의 학교 급식은 항상 건강에 좋고 맛 또한 좋다.

서술형 실전문제

[01~03] 다음 대화를 읽고, 물음에 답하시오.

G: You look very tired today. Didn't you sleep well?

B: ①No, I didn't. But I often feel tired these days, especially in the morning.

G: ②Do you usually eat breakfast?

B: No, I don't.

G: ③You'd better eat breakfast. Breakfast gives you energy.

B: I didn't know that. ④Do you have any other suggestions?

G: Well, you should also exercise every day. ⑤That will help you.

B: Okay. I will.

01 위 대화의 밑줄 친 ①~⑤ 중 흐름상 어색한 부분을 골라 바르게 고치시오.

_____ ➡ _____

02 주어진 영영풀이에 해당하는 단어를 위 대화에서 찾아 쓰시오.

> the meal you have in the morning

➡ _____

03 위 대화의 내용에 맞게 빈칸을 채우시오.

> The boy _____ _____ _____ these days, especially in the morning. The girl thinks _____ _____ _____ eat breakfast and _____ _____ _____.

04 다음 두 문장을 관계대명사를 이용하여 한 문장으로 연결하시오.

(1) • I think Minhee is a girl.
 • She is always kind.

➡ _____
_____

(2) • Teresa is singing on the stage.
 • She has a beautiful voice.

➡ _____
_____

(3) • Cloe lives in a house.
 • It has a nice swimming pool.

➡ _____
_____

(4) • I like the dog.
 • It belongs to Kelly.

➡ _____

(5) • There were a man and his horse.
 • They were crossing the river.

➡ _____
_____

05 다음 문장에서 잘못된 부분을 바르게 고쳐 문장을 다시 쓰시오

(1) The man which works at this restaurant is serving food.

➡ _____
_____

(2) These are the poems who was written by Robert Frost.

➡ _____
_____

(3) The girl is very pretty whom wears a white dress.

➡ _____
_____

Hello, this is food reporter Minjun from Korea. For many students, lunch is the best part of the school day. In Korea, we often eat rice and soup for lunch. ⓐ우리는 또한 불고기나 김치 같은 반찬도 먹습니다. Sometimes our school serves special dishes, such as pizza, *Bibimbap*, or pasta. ⓑWhat do students who live in another countries eat for lunch? Let's hear from our food reporters!

06 다음 질문에 대한 알맞은 대답을 쓰시오. (1 단어)

Q: For many students, what is the best part of the school day?

A: _____ .

07 위 글의 밑줄 친 ⓐ의 우리말에 맞게 한 단어를 보충하여, 주어진 어구를 알맞게 배열하시오.

Gimchi / side dishes / or / such as / *Bulgogi* / have / we

➡ _____

_____

08 위 글의 밑줄 친 ⓑ에서 어법상 틀린 부분을 찾아 고치시오.

_____ ➡ _____

Belle, France
Our school serves healthy and balanced meals. We usually eat a salad as an appetizer. Main dishes often include meat or fish. We also eat fresh fruit at the end of the lunch. Oh, I can never forget about baguettes! They're great with cheese. Our school also has a special rule. We must stay at the lunch table for at least 30 minutes.

09 본문의 내용과 일치하도록 다음 빈칸 (A)와 (B)에 알맞은 단어를 쓰시오.

The (A)_____ _____ at Belle's school is that students must stay at the lunch table (B)_____ _____

_____ _____ _____ .

10 다음 빈칸 (A)∼(C)에 알맞은 단어를 넣어 벨의 학교 급식을 정리하시오.

• appetizer: (A)_____
• main dishes: (B)_____
• dessert: (C)_____

11 다음 빈칸에 알맞은 단어를 넣어 바게트를 맛있게 먹는 방법을 완성하시오.

Baguettes taste great _____ _____ .

창의사고력 서술형 문제

01 다음 대화의 빈칸에 주어진 단어를 이용하여 알맞은 충고의 말을 쓰시오.

> A: I had a fight with my best friend. What should I do?
> B: _____ (had)
> A: Do you have any other suggestions?
> B: _____ (should, think)

02 관계대명사를 이용하여 자신이 갖고 있는 것을 설명하는 문장을 쓰시오.

> (1) I have _____ .
> (2) I have _____ .
> (3) I have _____ .
> (4) I have _____ .

03 다음 정보를 바탕으로 음식점 방문 후기를 작성하시오.

1. What is the name of the restaurant?	Antonio's Restaurant
2. What kind of restaurant is it?	a Spanish restaurant
3. Where is it?	near my home
4. What is the most popular dish there?	mixed paella
5. How is the food?	fresh and delicious
6. How are the prices?	low

> **Review of My Favorite Restaurant**
> My favorite restaurant is Antonio's Restaurant. It is a (A)_____ restaurant. It is near my home.
> (B)_____ _____ is the most popular dish at this restaurant. All of the food is really (C)
> _____ and _____, and the prices are (D)_____. I recommend this restaurant!
>
> My Rating ★ ★ ★ ★ ☆

단원별 모의고사

[01~02] 다음 빈칸에 공통으로 알맞은 단어를 쓰시오.

01

- He lived _____ Busan seven years ago.
- They put some coins _____ the piggy bank.

➡ _____

02

- He continued working _____ a long time.
- That's not good _____ your health.
- Thanks _____ your advice.

➡ _____

03 다음 제시된 의미에 맞는 단어를 주어진 철자로 시작하여 빈칸에 쓰고, 알맞은 것을 골라 문장을 완성하시오.

- l_____ : relating to the particular area you live in, or the area you are talking about
- r_____ : to advise someone to do something, especially because you have special knowledge of a situation or subject
- m_____ : consisting of several different types of things or people

(1) Wine _____ with vinegar was good.
(2) We visited the _____ markets and saw beautiful earrings.
(3) What do you _____ for the woman?

04 〈보기〉의 어휘를 사용하여 문장을 완성하시오. (형태 변화 가능)

┌─── 보기 ───┐
take   such   check   these   taste
└──────────┘

(1) Let's _____ out the new restaurant down the street.
(2) Foods _____ as fish, mushrooms, and milk have vitamin D.
(3) Don't worry about me. I can _____ care of myself.
(4) The milk I drank for lunch _____ sweet.

05 다음 대화에서 어법상 어색한 부분을 모두 찾아 고치시오. (3개)

A: I get often colds these days.
B: Then you'd better drink a lot water and washed your hands often.
A: Thank you for your advice.

➡ (1) _____
   (2) _____
   (3) _____

06 다음 밑줄 친 문장과 같은 의미가 되도록 주어진 단어를 이용해 영작하시오.

A: I'm going to the British restaurant. <u>What do you recommend there?</u>
B: I recommend the fish and chips. It is delicious.

➡ (1) _____ (which)
   (2) _____
   (recommendations)

[07~09] 다음 대화를 읽고, 물음에 답하시오.

> B: Good morning, Jiwoo. (A)_____
> G: ①I'm searching for a restaurant for my class party.
> B: Wow! (B)_____
> G: ②It's next Friday. ③We want to go to Bella's Restaurant, ④but it is too expensive.
> B: (C)_____ I went there once. ⑤The food and prices was good.
> G: Sounds great. (D)_____
> B: I recommend the noodle soup.
> G: (E)(we, I. go, think, there, should). Thank you.

07 (A)~(D)에 들어갈 말을 〈보기〉에서 골라 쓰시오.

┤ 보기 ├

- Why don't you check out Chang's Restaurant?
- Do you have any other recommendations?
- What do you recommend there?
- When is the party?
- What do you want to do?
- What are you doing right now?

➡ (A) _____
　 (B) _____
　 (C) _____
　 (D) _____

08 위의 대화의 ①~⑤ 중 어법상 어색한 것을 고르시오.

① 　　② 　　③ 　　④ 　　⑤

09 괄호 (E) 안에 주어진 단어들을 바르게 배열하여 문장을 완성하시오.

➡ _____

[10~14] 다음 대화를 읽고, 물음에 답하시오.

> W: Hello. Are you ready to order?
> B: It's my first time here. (①) What do you recommend?
> W: (②) It is the most popular item at our restaurant.
> B: Well, I don't like chicken very much. (③) (A)(else, something, could, recommend, you)?
> W: (④) How about the turkey sandwich?
> B: Oh, I love turkey. I'll have that.
> W: (⑤) Why don't you order a drink with the sandwich? You can (B)_____ a 500-won discount.
> B: That's great. Then I'll have an orange juice, too.

10 위 대화의 ①~⑤ 중 주어진 문장이 들어갈 알맞은 곳은?

I recommend the chicken sandwich.

① 　　② 　　③ 　　④ 　　⑤

11 Where are they now?

① hospital　　② school　　③ home
④ bakery　　⑤ restaurant

12 주어진 영영풀이에 해당하는 단어를 대화에서 찾아 쓰시오.

to ask for food or a drink in a restaurant, bar, etc.

➡ _____

13 위 대화의 괄호 (A) 안에 주어진 단어들을 바르게 배열하여 문장을 완성하시오.

➡ _____

14 위 대화의 빈칸 (B)에 알맞은 단어를 고르시오.

① do   ② take   ③ give
④ get   ⑤ allow

15 다음 밑줄 친 that과 바꿔 쓸 수 있는 것은?

> I want to visit the Netherlands that is famous for its windmill.

① what   ② who
③ whose   ④ whom
⑤ which

16 다음 중 밑줄 친 부분이 어색한 것은?

① She has a cat that has blue eyes.
② A computer is a thing which is usually on our teacher's desk.
③ One never is too old to learn.
④ I often use the Internet.
⑤ Buzz Aldrin was the astronaut who took the first space selfie.

17 다음 중 밑줄 친 that의 쓰임이 다른 것을 고르시오.(2개)

① That the earth is round is common knowledge today.
② Here is a fish that I caught this morning.
③ It's possible that he has not received the letter.
④ He is the greatest novelist that has ever lived.
⑤ She warned me that I should be more careful.

18 괄호 안의 어휘를 이용하여 우리말에 맞게 알맞은 빈도부사를 써서 영어로 옮기시오.

(1) 엄마는 아침에 대개 7시에 일어나신다. (mom, get up)
(2) Abigail은 항상 친절하고 자주 미소 짓는다. (smile, frequently, kind)
(3) Richard는 드물게 그 강으로 수영하러 갔었다. (seldom, go swimming)

➡ (1) _____
　 (2) _____
　 (3) _____

19 다음 문장에서 어법상 어색한 것을 찾아 고치시오.

(1) Pasta is a dish who is never popular for lunch.
(2) Look at the boy which he is dancing on the street.
(3) He helps never me.

➡ _____
　 _____
　 _____

[20~22] 다음 글을 읽고, 물음에 답하시오.

Hello, this is food reporter Minjun from Korea. For many students, lunch is the best part of the school day. ①In Korea, we often eat rice and soup for lunch. ②We also have side dishes, such as *Bulgogi* or *Gimchi*. ③ There are many delicious side dishes in the world. ④Sometimes our school ⓐ special dishes, such as pizza, *Bibimbap*, or pasta. ⑤ What do students who live in other countries eat for lunch? Let's hear from our food reporters!

20 위 글의 ①~⑤ 중에서 전체 흐름과 관계 <u>없는</u> 문장은?

    ①   ②   ③   ④   ⑤

21 위 글의 빈칸 ⓐ에 들어갈 알맞은 말을 고르시오.

  ① keeps   ② holds   ③ builds
  ④ serves   ⑤ carries

22 위 글의 뒤에 나올 내용으로 가장 알맞은 것을 고르시오.

  ① 민준이네 학교의 특별한 점심
  ② 점심에 대한 다른 나라 음식 취재 기자들의 보고
  ③ 점심시간에 가능한 여가활동에 대한 다른 나라 리포터들의 소개
  ④ 건강에 좋은 점심을 만드는 방법 소개
  ⑤ 동양과 서양의 점심 문화의 차이점 소개

[23~25] 다음 글을 읽고, 물음에 답하시오.

> Bruno, Brazil
> Usually, we have beans and rice for lunch. (①) Meat and vegetables are common in our side dishes. (②) A plantain is a fruit which looks like a banana. (③) We usually fry plantains. (④) ⓐOur school lunches are fresh because of the vegetables and fruit come from local farms. (⑤)

23 위 글의 흐름으로 보아, 주어진 문장이 들어가기에 가장 적절한 곳은?

> My favorite lunch comes with plantains.

    ①   ②   ③   ④   ⑤

24 위 글의 밑줄 친 ⓐ에서 어법상 <u>틀린</u> 부분을 찾아 고치시오.

  _____ ➡ _____

25 다음 빈칸에 알맞은 단어를 넣어 plantain의 요리법에 대한 소개를 완성하시오.

> People in Brazil usually _____ plantains.

[26~27] 다음 글을 읽고, 물음에 답하시오.

> Nicole, Singapore
> People who live in Singapore come from many different cultures, so we have ⓐboth Eastern and Western dishes at lunch. Students can choose ⓑ many dishes, such as curry, noodle soup, or pasta, each day. My school won an award ⓒ healthy school food last year. Our lunches are always healthy, and they taste good, too!

26 위 글의 밑줄 친 ⓐ에 해당하는 음식을 본문에서 찾아 쓰시오.

  ➡ _____

27 위 글의 빈칸 ⓑ와 ⓒ에 들어갈 전치사가 바르게 짝지어진 것은?

  ① from – for   ② in – by
  ③ for – from   ④ from – to
  ⑤ on – for

Lesson 3

Understand the World

 의사소통 기능

- 경험 묻고 답하기
  A: Have you ever been to Brazil?
  B: Yes, I have. / No, I haven't.
- 의미 묻고 답하기
  A: What does that mean in Korea?
  B: It means good luck.

언어 형식

- 현재완료
  For a long time, Koreans **have thought** that fish are good guards.
- so ... that 구문
  It's **so** old **that** I can't really tell, but is it a fish?

  I'm enjoying this trip **so** much **that** I want to stay longer.

교과서 Words & Expressions

Key Words

- **arrive** [əráiv] 동 도착하다
- **bat** [bæt] 명 박쥐
- **beach** [biːtʃ] 명 해변, 바닷가
- **bow** [bau] 동 (인사를 위해) 머리를 숙이다, 절하다
- **calendar** [kǽləndər] 명 달력
- **Chinese** [tʃainíːz] 형 중국의 명 중국어
- **clothes** [klouz] 명 옷, 의복
- **colored** [kʌ́lərd] 형 채색된, 색깔이 있는
- **crow** [krou] 동 (닭이) 울다 명 까마귀
- **darkness** [dɑ́ːrknis] 명 어둠, 암흑
- **evil** [íːvəl] 형 사악한, 악마의
- **experience** [ikspíəriəns] 명 경험 동 경험하다
- **face** [feis] 동 ~을 향하다
- **festival** [féstəvəl] 명 축제
- **full moon** 보름달
- **gift shop** 선물 가게
- **good luck** 행운
- **greet** [griːt] 동 맞이하다, 환영하다
- **guard** [ɡɑːrd] 명 보초, 경비병
- **guest** [ɡest] 명 손님
- **half moon** 반달
- **Indian** [índiən] 형 인도의, 인도 사람의
- **international** [ìntərnǽʃənəl] 형 국제적인, 세계적인
- **last** [læst] 동 계속되다, 지속되다
- **last year** 작년에
- **lock** [lak] 명 자물쇠 동 잠그다
- **luck** [lʌk] 명 운

- **musical** [mjúːzikəl] 명 뮤지컬
- **mean** [miːn] 동 의미하다
- **palm** [paːm] 명 손바닥, 야자나무
- **pay** [pei] 동 지불하다
- **peace** [piːs] 명 평화, 화해
- **pillow** [pílou] 명 베개
- **powder** [páudər] 명 가루, 분말
- **protect** [prətékt] 동 보호하다
- **remind** [rimáind] 동 생각나게 하다, 상기시키다
- **represent** [rèprizént] 동 나타내다, 상징하다
- **rooster** [rúːstər] 명 수탉
- **rude** [ruːd] 형 무례한
- **scary** [skɛ́əri] 형 무서운, 두려운, 겁나는
- **separation** [sèpəréiʃən] 명 분리, 이별
- **shake** [artwərk] 동 흔들다, 흔들리다
- **sister school** 자매 학교
- **spirit** [spírit] 명 영혼, 정신
- **symbol** [símbəl] 명 상징(물), 기호
- **tell** [tel] 동 말하다, (정확히) 알다
- **toward** [tɔːrd] 전 ~쪽으로
- **traditional** [trədíʃənl] 형 전통의, 전통적인
- **try** [trai] 동 한번 해 보다
- **umbrella** [ʌmbrélə] 명 우산
- **valuable** [vǽljuəbl] 형 값비싼, 귀중한, 가치 있는
- **victory** [víktəri] 명 승리, 성공
- **Vietnamese** [viètnəmíːz] 형 베트남의 명 베트남어

Key Expressions

- **be afraid of** ~을 두려워하다
- **be full of** ~으로 가득 차다
- **blow one's nose** 코를 풀다
- **go away** 사라지다, 떠나가다
- **have been to** 장소 ~에 가 본 적이 있다
- **listen to** ~을 듣다

- **point at** ~을 가리키다
- **remind A of B** A에게 B를 생각나게 하다
- **so** 형용사/부사 **that** 주어 동사 너무 ~해서 …하다
- **take off** (옷 등을) 벗다
- **talk about** ~에 대해 이야기하다
- **watch over** ~을 주시하다, 지키다

Word Power

※ 서로 비슷한 뜻을 가진 단어

□ **evil**(사악한, 악의) – **wicked**(못된, 사악한)

□ **greet**(맞이하다, 환영하다) – **welcome**(환영하다)

□ **international**(국제적인, 세계적인) – **global**(세계적인)

□ **last**(계속되다, 지속되다) – **continue**(계속하다, 지속하다)

□ **remind**(생각나게 하다, 상기시키다) – **recall**(기억해 내다, 상기하다)

□ **represent**(나타내다, 상징하다) – **symbolize**(상징하다)

□ **go away** – **disappear**: 사라지다, 떠나가다

□ **rude**(무례한) – **impolite** (버릇없는, 무례한)

□ **separation**(분리, 이별) – **division** (분할)

□ **spirit**(영혼, 정신) – **soul**(정신, 마음)

□ **symbol**(상징(물), 기호) – **sign**(기호, 부호)

□ **traditional**(전통의, 전통적인) – **conventional**(전통적인)

□ **try**(한번 해 보다) – **attempt**(시도하다)

□ **victory**(승리, 성공) – **success**(성공, 성과)

□ **afraid**(두려워하는) – **frightened**(두려워하는)

□ **watch over** – **guard**: ~을 주시하다, 지키다

English Dictionary

□ **bow** (인사를 위해) 머리를 숙이다, 절하다
→ to lower your head or bend your body 머리를 낮추거나 몸을 구부리다

□ **crow** (닭이) 울다
→ to make the loud sound that a rooster makes 수탉이 내는 큰 소리를 만들다

□ **darkness** 어둠, 암흑
→ no light 빛이 없음

□ **evil** 사악한, 악마의
→ morally bad or wicked 도덕적으로 나쁘거나 사악한

□ **face** ~을 향하다
→ to have the front part toward something 앞 부분을 어떤 것 쪽으로 향하게 하다

□ **greet** 맞이하다, 환영하다
→ to say hello or welcome 안녕이라고 말하거나 환영하다

□ **last** 계속되다, 지속되다
→ to keep happening for a certain amount of time 일정의 시간 동안 계속 발생하다

□ **palm** 손바닥
→ the inside part of the hand between the wrist and the fingers 손목과 손가락 사이의 손 안쪽 부분

□ **pillow** 베개
→ a soft thing to put your head on while you sleep 자는 동안에 머리를 놓는 부드러운 것

□ **protect** 보호하다
→ to keep something or someone safe from danger 위험으로부터 사람이나 사물을 안전하게 지키다

□ **remind** 생각나게 하다, 상기시키다
→ to make someone remember something 누군가에게 무엇인가를 기억나게 만들다

□ **represent** 나타내다, 상징하다
→ to stand for something else 다른 무엇인가를 상징하다

□ **rooster** 수탉
→ a male chicken 수컷 닭

□ **scary** 무서운, 두려운, 겁나는
→ making people feel afraid, frightening 사람들을 두려워하고 겁나게 만드는

□ **separation** 분리, 이별
→ the act of moving two things or people apart 두 개의 사물이나 사람을 떨어지도록 움직이는 행위

□ **symbol** 상징(물), 기호
→ an object that represents something 무엇인가를 나타내는 물체

□ **traditional** 전통의, 전통적인
→ being part of something that people have done for a long time 오랜 시간 동안 사람들이 해 왔던 어떤 것의 일부인

□ **valuable** 값비싼, 귀중한, 가치 있는
→ very important or expensive 매우 중요하거나 비싼

□ **victory** 승리, 성공
→ success in defeating an opponent 상대방을 물리치는 데 있어서의 성공

01 다음 빈칸에 들어갈 말로 적절한 것은?

> In some cases, hiccups can _____ for days or even weeks!

① cause
② bring
③ invite
④ produce
⑤ last

[02~03] 다음 밑줄 친 부분과 의미가 가장 가까운 것은?

02

> All of us need to go out to meet and greet them.

① welcome
② face
③ mean
④ try
⑤ say

03

> The olive wreath stands for peace and it is still sometimes used today!

① shows
② represents
③ suggests
④ stays
⑤ makes use of

04 다음 중 밑줄 친 부분의 뜻풀이가 바르지 않은 것은?

① I don't understand what you mean. (의미하다)
② A full moon is 9 times brighter than a half moon. (반달)
③ He tried praying, but that didn't ease his mind. (노력하다)
④ Meditation is helpful in training your body and spirit. (영혼, 정신)
⑤ I have to apologize to you for being rude. (무례한)

05 다음 빈칸에 공통으로 들어갈 말로 알맞은 것은?

> • Be sure to _____ the door before you leave.
> • He observed the thief open the _____ of the door.

① lock
② turn
③ fix
④ pull
⑤ rock

서답형
06 다음 빈칸에 들어갈 알맞은 단어를 〈보기〉에서 찾아 쓰시오. (형태 변화 가능)

> ┌─ 보기 ─┐
> traditional   scary   international

(1) She told me some _____ stories.
(2) Export law became a key factor in _____ trade.
(3) She is wearing _____ Korean clothes.

서답형
07 다음 우리말과 일치하도록 괄호 안의 어구를 바르게 배열하시오.

(1) 토니는 어둠 속으로 사라졌다. (the darkness, in, got, Tony, lost)
➡ _____

(2) 그 소녀들은 베개 싸움을 하고 있다. (having, fight, the girls, a pillow, are)
➡ _____

08 다음 영영풀이에 해당하는 것은?

> in the direction of something

① against
② directly
③ far
④ toward
⑤ within

01 다음 〈보기〉와 같은 관계가 주어진 빈칸에 알맞은 말을 쓰시오. (주어진 철자로 시작할 것)

┌─ 보기 ─┐
good – nice
└────────┘

(1) impolite ➡ r_____
(2) attempt ➡ t_____
(3) wicked ➡ e_____
(4) success ➡ v_____

02 다음 빈칸에 알맞은 단어를 〈보기〉에서 골라 쓰시오.

┌─ 보기 ─┐
arrive   celebrate   experience   mean
└────────┘

(1) Staying curious allows me to continuously _____ the excitement of learning something new.
(2) That doesn't _____ that I'm lazy.
(3) What time does the next train _____?
(4) They _____ Christmas and New Year's Day together.

03 다음 주어진 우리말에 맞게 빈칸을 채우시오.

(1) 그 방은 해변을 향해 있나요?
  ➡ Does the room _____ the beach?
(2) 2년간의 이별 후에 그 부부는 다시 만날 수 있었다.
  ➡ After two years of _____, the couple was _____ to meet again.

04 다음 우리말에 맞게 주어진 단어를 이용해 빈칸을 완성하시오.

┌────────────────────────────┐
그는 항아리를 색깔이 있는 물로 채웠습니다.
└────────────────────────────┘

➡ He filled a jar with _____ water. (color)

05 다음 〈보기〉에서 빈칸에 공통으로 들어갈 단어를 골라 쓰시오.

┌─ 보기 ─┐
in   about   at   from   of
└────────┘

(1) • I usually stay _____ home on Sundays.
   • It is rude to point _____ a person.
(2) • I am afraid _____ dogs when they bark.
   • Lemons remind people _____ things that are fresh and clean.

06 다음 우리말에 맞게 주어진 단어를 바르게 배열하시오.

(1) 그녀는 다정한 미소로 우리를 맞았다.
  (with, a, greeted, smile, kind, she, us)
  ➡ _____
(2) 그 회의는 세 시간 동안 계속되었다.
  (three, the, meeting, hours, lasted)
  ➡ _____
(3) 나는 그 동전을 그녀의 손바닥에 놓았다. (the, coin, I, her, put, palm, in)
  ➡ _____
(4) 붉은 깃발은 위험을 나타낸다.
  (a, danger, flag, represents, red)
  ➡ _____

Conversation

교과서

1 의미 묻고 답하기

> **A** What does that mean in Korea? 한국에서는 그게 어떤 의미니?
> **B** It means good luck. 행운을 뜻해.

■ 'What does that mean?'은 상대방의 말의 의도나 의미를 잘 이해하지 못할 때, 그 의도나 의미를 물어보는 표현이다. 대답할 때는 'It means ~.'로 의미를 설명해 준다.

의미를 묻는 표현

- What does that mean (in Korea)? (한국에서는) 그게 어떤 의미니?
- What is that exactly? 그것이 정확히 뭐니?
- I'd like to know what that means. 그것이 무슨 의미인지 알고 싶어.
- Could[Would/Will] you explain what that means? 그것이 무슨 의미인지 설명해 줄 수 있어?

■ Could[Can/Would/Will] you ~?'로 시작하는 의문문은 질문을 할 때도 쓰지만, 요청이나 부탁을 하는 경우에도 사용한다. 요청이나 부탁을 받았을 경우 꼭 Yes나 No로 대답할 필요는 없다.

ex) A: Would you tell me what this sign means? (이 표지판이 무슨 의미인지 말해 줄래?)
　　 B: It means "no smoking." ('금연'이라는 뜻이야.)

핵심 Check

1. 주어진 문장에 이어질 대화의 순서를 바르게 배열하시오.

   I don't understand what this means.
   (A) Yes. What does that mean?
   (B) It means "very important person."
   (C) Are you talking about VIP?

   ➡ _____

2. 다음 우리말과 일치하도록 빈칸에 알맞은 말을 쓰시오.

   A: Could you _____ _____ the sign _____? (그 표지판이 무슨 의미인지 설명해 줄 수 있니?)
   B: It means "no parking." ('주차 금지'라는 의미야.)

3. 주어진 단어를 배열하여 대화를 완성하시오.

   A: It's about English sayings. Do you know the saying, "Look before you leap."?
   B: No. _____ (that, what, to, I'd, means, like, know)
   A: Sure. _____ before you do something. (you, it, think, carefully, means, should)

❷ 경험 묻고 답하기

> **A** Have you ever been to Brazil? 너는 브라질 가 봤니?
>
> **B** Yes, I have. / No, I haven't. 응, 가 봤어. / 아니, 못 가 봤어.

- 상대방의 경험에 대해 물어볼 때는, 현재완료 시제를 사용하여 'Have you 과거분사 ~?'라고 묻는다. 경험을 묻는 말에 긍정으로 대답할 경우에는 'Yes, I have.'로, 부정으로 대답할 때는 'No, I haven't.'로 대답한다.
- 완료 시제를 사용할 때는 ago, yesterday, when 등과 같이 명백한 과거를 나타내는 말과 같이 사용되지 않는다. ex) When have you met him? (✕)   When did you meet him? (○)
- 경험을 나타내는 현재완료와 잘 사용하는 표현은 never(결코 ~ 않는), ever(어느 때고, 한 번이라도), once(한 번), twice(두 번), three times(세 번), before(전에) 등이 있다.
  ex) I have met him three times. (나는 그를 세 번 만난 적이 있다.)
- 'have been to 장소'는 '~에 가 본 경험이 있다'의 의미이고, 'have gone to 장소'는 '~에 갔다(그래서 지금 없다)'는 의미이다. ex) Have you gone to New York? (✕)

경험을 묻는 표현

- Have you ever 과거분사 ~? (~해 본 적 있니?)
- Is this your first time -ing ~? (~해 보는 것이 처음이니?)
- Do you have any experience of –ing ~? (~해 본 경험이 있니?)

경험을 묻는 질문에 대답하는 표현

- I have never 과거분사. (한 번도 ~해 본 적이 없어.)
- I have a lot of experience. (나는 경험이 풍부해.)

핵심 Check

4. 다음 우리말과 일치하도록 빈칸에 알맞은 말을 쓰시오.
   A: _____ the movie *Aquaman*? (너는 영화 아쿠아맨을 본 적 있니?)
   B: Yes, I _____. _____ you? (응. 봤어. 너는 봤니?)

5. 대화의 순서를 바르게 배열하시오.
   (A) That sounds like fun.
   (B) No, I haven't.
   (C) I'm going to Japan with my friends this winter.
   (D) Have you been there before?
   ➡ _____

6. 주어진 단어를 배열하여 대화를 완성하시오.
   A: _____ (before, had, have, *gimchi*, you)
   B: Yes, I have.

A. Listen and Talk 1 A

G: ❶Have you ever been to Brazil?

B: No, I haven't. ❷Have you?

G: Yes, I have. I went there ❸last year. ❹There was a big samba festival.

B: That sounds interesting. I ❺hope to go there someday.

G: 너는 브라질 가 봤니?
B: 아니, 못 가 봤어. 너는 가 봤니?
G: 응. 가 봤어. 작년에 거기 갔었어. 큰 삼바 축제가 있었어.
B: 재미있게 들린다. 나도 언젠가 거기 가고 싶어.

❶ 'Have you ever p.p ~?'는 경험을 묻는 표현이다. 특히 'Have you ever been to 장소?'는 '~에 가 본 적 있니?'라는 뜻으로 어떤 곳에 가 본 경험에 대해 말할 때 사용하는 표현이다. 응답은 'Yes, I have.'또는 'No, I haven't.'로 하면 된다.

❷ Have you 뒤에 'ever been to Brazil'이 생략되어 있다.

❸ last year(작년)는 과거의 특정 시점이므로 과거형 동사를 사용해야 한다.

❹ There+be동사의 과거형(was, were): ~가 있었다 festival: 축제

❺ hope는 to부정사를 목적어로 받는다.

Check(√) True or False

(1) The boy has never been to Brazil.　　　　　　　　　　　　　T ☐ F ☐

(2) There was a samba festival in Brazil last year.　　　　　　　T ☐ F ☐

B. Listen and Talk 1 B

W: ❶Welcome to the International Games Festival. ❷You can play many different traditional games here.

B: Wow! ❸It looks exciting! Which game should I play first?

W: Let's see. ❹Have you ever played *gorodki*?

B: No, I haven't. What is it?

W: It's a traditional game ❺from Russia.

B: How do I play it?

W: Put five sticks on the ground. Then ❻throw a bat at them.

B: That ❼sounds fun. I'll try that first.

W: 국제 게임 축제에 오신 걸 환영합니다. 당신은 여기서 많은 종류의 전통 게임을 할 수 있습니다.
B: 와! 재미있을 것 같아요! 어떤 게임 먼저 해야 하나요?
W: 한번 봅시다. 고로드키 게임 해 본 적 있나요?
B: 아니요. 그게 무엇인가요?
W: 러시아의 전통 게임이에요.
B: 어떻게 하나요?
W: 바닥에 다섯 개의 막대기를 놓으세요. 그리고 그것들을 향해 배트를 던지세요.
B: 재미있겠네요. 그거 먼저 할게요.

❶ welcome to ~: ~에 오신 걸 환영합니다

❷ can+동사원형: ~할 수 있다 traditional: 전통적인

❸ look + 형용사: ~하게 보이다 exciting: 흥미로운

❹ Have you ever p.p ~?: ~한 적 있니?

❺ from: (출처·기원) ~출신의[에서 온]

❻ throw: ~을 던지다 at: (방향) ~으로

❼ sound+형용사: ~하게 들리다

Check(√) True or False

(3) *Gorodki* is from France.　　　　　　　　　　　　　　　T ☐ F ☐

(4) The boy is in the International Games Festival.　　　　　　T ☐ F ☐

Listen and Talk 1 C

B: There is a Holi festival in Busan ❶this year.

G: A Holi festival? What is ❷that?

B: It's a traditional Indian festival. ❸People throw colored powder and water at each other.

G: That sounds exciting. ❹Have you ever been to a Holi festival?

B: No, I haven't. But my Indian friend told me a lot about it.

G: When is the festival?

B: ❺It's on the last full moon of the Hindu calendar. This year, it's ❻on March 21.

G: I'd like to go. ❼Should I bring anything?

B: No, but you should wear white clothes. Then the colored powder on your clothes will look more beautiful.

G: Okay. Thank you for the information.

❶ this year: 올해
❷ that은 'a Holi festival'을 의미한다.
❸ colored: 채색된, 색깔이 있는 at each other: 서로에게
❹ Have you ever been to 장소?: ~에 가 본 적 있니? festival: 축제
❺ Holi 축제가 언제인지에 대한 설명을 하고 있다 the last full moon: 마지막 보름달(이 뜨는 날)
❻ 날짜 앞에는 전치사 on을 사용한다.
❼ should+동사원형: ~해야 한다 Should I bring ~?: ~을 가져가야 하니?

Listen and Talk 2 A

G: Jinwoo, my Korean friend, ❶gave me *Yeot* as a gift. ❷What does that mean in Korea?

B: ❸It means good luck on a test.

❶ give는 4형식 동사로 간접목적어(~에게)와 직접목적어(~을[를]) 두 개를 받을 수 있다. as: ~으로
❷ What does that mean?: 그게 어떤 의미니? in Korea: 한국에서
❸ It은 Yeot을 의미한다. 주어 mean ~: 주어는 ~을 의미한다 good luck: 행운

Listen and Talk 2 B

B: Ling's birthday is ❶this Wednesday, ❷isn't it?

G: Yes. ❸I'm going to buy a book for her. What about you?

B: Well, ❹I'm thinking about buying her an

umbrella. I found a cute ❺one in a gift shop.

G: Oh, that's not a good gift for Chinese people. It means ❻something bad.

B: Really? What does an umbrella mean in China?

G: It means ❼separation. The words for *separation* and *umbrella* sound the same in Chinese.

B: I see. Then how about chocolate?

G: That's a good idea.

❶ this 요일: 이번 주 ~요일
❷ 부가의문문으로 말하는 이가 듣는 이에게 말한 내용을 확인하거나 동의를 구할 때 쓰며 '동사+주어(인칭대명사)'의 형태로 쓰인다. 앞 문장에 쓰인 동사가 be동사나 조동사이면 그대로, 일반동사이면 do동사로 쓰며, 앞 문장이 긍정이면 부정, 앞 문장이 부정이면 긍정으로 쓴다.
❸ be going to 동사원형: ~할 것이다, ~할 예정이다
❹ think about: ~에 대해 생각하다 about은 전치사이므로 뒤에 명사나 동명사가 올 수 있다. buy는 4형식 동사로 '~에게 …를 사 주다'의 의미로 사용되었다.
❺ one = umbrella
❻ -thing으로 끝나는 부정대명사(something, anything, nothing 등)는 보통의 다른 명사들과 달리 형용사가 뒤에서 수식한다.
❼ separation: 분리, 이별

Listen and Talk 2 C

G: ❶What a nice picture! Are these your friends?

B: Yes. We ❷took this picture at the beach. ❸ We had a lot of fun.

G: Oh, ❹look at that boy. That's really ❺rude.

B: Which boy?

G: The boy ❻who is making the V sign. ❼His palm is facing toward himself.

B: What's wrong with that?

G: It has a bad meaning in England. But showing your palm and making a V sign is okay.

B: What does that mean?

G: It means victory or peace.

❶ 'What+a+형용사+명사!'(감탄문) What a nice picture!: 이 사진 정말 멋지다!
❷ take a picture: 사진을 찍다
❸ have fun: 재미있다, 즐거운 시간을 보내다
❹ look at: ~을 보다
❺ rude: 무례한
❻ who는 주격 관계대명사로 who is making the V sign은 앞의 the boy를 수식하고 있다.
❼ palm: 손바닥 face: ~을 향하다 toward: ~쪽으로

● 다음 우리말과 일치하도록 빈칸에 알맞은 말을 쓰시오.

Listen and Talk 1 A

G: _____ _____ ever _____ to Brazil?

B: No, I _____. _____ you?

G: Yes, I _____. I went there _____ _____. There _____ a big samba festival.

B: That _____ interesting. I hope _____ _____ there _____.

Listen and Talk 1 B

W: Welcome _____ the International Games _____. You can play _____ _____ _____ _____ here.

B: Wow! It _____ exciting! _____ game _____ I play first?

W: Let's see. _____ _____ _____ played *gorodki*?

B: _____, _____ _____. What is it?

W: It's a traditional game _____ Russia.

B: _____ do I play it?

W: Put five sticks _____ the ground. Then _____ a bat _____ them.

B: That _____ _____. I'll try that first.

Listen and Talk 1 C

B: _____ _____ a Holi festival _____ Busan _____ year.

G: A Holi festival? What is that?

B: It's _____ _____ _____ _____. People throw _____ _____ and water at _____ other.

G: That _____ _____. _____ _____ _____ to a Holi festival?

B: No, I haven't. But my Indian friend _____ _____ a lot about it.

G: _____ is the festival?

B: It's _____ the last full moon of the Hindu calendar. This year, it's _____ March 21.

G: I'd _____ to go. _____ I bring anything?

B: No, but you should wear white _____. Then _____ _____ _____ on your _____ will look more beautiful.

G: Okay. Thank you _____ the information.

Listen and Talk 2 A

G: Jinwoo, my Korean friend, _____ _____ *Yeot* as a gift. _____ _____ _____ _____ _____ _____ _____ ?

B: It _____ good luck on a test.

Listen and Talk 2 B

B: Ling's birthday is _____ Wednesday, _____ _____ ?

G: Yes. I'm going to buy a book for her. What about you?

B: Well, I'm thinking _____ _____ her an umbrella. I found a cute _____ in a gift shop.

G: Oh, that's not a good gift for Chinese people. It means _____ _____.

B: Really? _____ _____ an umbrella _____ _____ _____ _____ ?

G: It _____ _____. The words for _____ and *umbrella* sound the same in Chinese.

B: I see. Then how _____ chocolate?

G: That's a good idea.

Listen and Talk 2 C

G: _____ _____ nice picture! _____ these your friends?

B: Yes. We _____ this picture at the beach. We had a lot of fun.

G: Oh, _____ _____ that boy. That's really _____.

B: Which boy?

G: The boy _____ _____ _____ the V sign. His _____ _____ _____ _____ himself.

B: What's wrong with that?

G: It has a bad _____ _____ England. But showing your palm and making a V sign is okay.

B: _____ _____ _____ _____ ?

G: It means _____ _____ _____ .

Do It Yourself

G: Hello, Santiago! What _____ you here today?

B: *Bienvenido*, Cathy. I came _____ see the Spanish festival.

G: Me, too. But what did you just say?

B: *Bienvenido*! It _____ "welcome" in Spanish. Look at those dancers. Their dance moves are so great.

G: Yes, they are.

B: _____ _____ _____ _____ _____ _____ a Spanish festival before?

G: No, _____ _____. Santiago, can you see the big letters on the stage? _____ _____ that mean?

B: Oh, gracias. That _____ "thank you."

G: 내 한국인 친구인 진우가 선물로 엿을 줬어. 한국에서는 이게 어떤 의미니?

B: 시험 잘 보라는 뜻이야.

B: Ling의 생일이 이번 수요일이야, 그렇지 않니?

G: 응. 나는 그녀에게 책을 사 줄 거야. 너는?

B: 음, 나는 우산을 사려고 생각하고 있어. 선물 가게에서 귀여운 걸 찾았거든.

G: 어, 그건 중국 사람들에게 좋은 선물이 아니야. 뭔가 나쁜 걸 뜻하거든.

B: 진짜? 중국에서 우산이 뭘 의미하는데?

G: 이별을 뜻해. 중국에서는 이별을 뜻하는 단어와 우산을 뜻하는 단어의 발음이 같거든.

B: 알겠어. 그러면 초콜릿 어때?

G: 좋은 생각이야.

G: 이 사진 정말 멋지다! 네 친구들이니?

B: 응. 우리는 해변에서 이 사진을 찍었어. 정말 재미있었어.

G: 어, 저 남자애 봐. 정말 무례하다.

B: 누구?

G: V사인을 하고 있는 애. 손바닥이 자기 쪽을 향하고 있어.

B: 그게 뭐 잘못됐어?

G: 영국에서는 나쁜 뜻을 갖고 있어. 하지만 손바닥을 보여 주면서 V사인을 만드는 건 괜찮아.

B: 그건 무슨 뜻인데?

G: 승리나 평화를 뜻해.

G: 안녕, Santiago! 오늘 여기 어쩐 일이야?

B: Bienvenido, Cathy. 나는 스페인 축제를 보러 왔어.

G: 나도. 그런데 방금 뭐라고 말했니?

B: Bienvenido! 스페인어로 "환영합니다."라는 뜻이야. 저 무용수들을 봐. 그들의 춤 움직임은 정말 멋지다.

G: 응, 그렇네.

B: 전에 스페인 축제에 가 본 적 있니?

G: 아니, 가 본 적 없어. Santiago, 무대에 있는 큰 글씨를 볼 수 있니? 무슨 뜻이야?

B: 아, gracias. 저건 "감사합니다."라는 뜻이야.

Conversation 시험대비 기본평가

[01~02] 다음 대화의 빈칸에 알맞은 것으로 짝지어진 것은?

01

> G: _____ you ever been to Brazil?
> B: Yes, I _____.

① Have/have ② Can/can ③ Did /did ④ Are/am ⑤ Do/do

02

> A: What does that _____ in Korea?
> B: It _____s good luck.

① make ② mean ③ stay ④ find ⑤ keep

03 다음 대화의 밑줄 친 부분의 의도로 알맞은 것은?

> A: Have you ever listened to Spanish music?
> B: Yes, I have.

① Asking about memories ② Giving advice
③ Asking about experiences ④ Requesting
⑤ Asking about the meanings

04 다음 대화의 순서를 바르게 배열한 것은?

> (A) No, I haven't. What is it?
> (B) It's a traditional game from Russia.
> (C) Have you ever played *gorodki*?

① (A) - (C) - (B) ② (B) - (A) - (C)
③ (B) - (C) - (A) ④ (C) - (A) - (B)
⑤ (C) - (B) - (A)

05 다음 대화에서 어법상 어색한 것을 고르시오.

> G: ①Have you ever gone to a Holi festival?
> B: ②No, I haven't. ③But my Indian friend told me a lot about it.
> G: ④When is the festival?
> B: ⑤It's on the last full moon of the Hindu calendar. This year, it's on March 21.

① ② ③ ④ ⑤

01 빈칸 (A)와 (B)에 알맞은 말을 고르시오.

> G: Jinwoo, my Korean friend, (A)_____ *Yeot* as a gift. (B)_____ does that mean in Korea?
> B: It means good luck on a test.

	(A)	(B)
①	gave	How
②	gave me	How
③	gave me	What
④	gave to me	How
⑤	gave to me	What

 02 주어진 문장에 이어질 대화의 순서로 가장 적절한 것은?

> Have you ever been to Brazil?

> (A) Yes, I have. I went there last year. There was a big samba festival.
> (B) No, I haven't. Have you?
> (C) That sounds interesting. I hope to go there someday.

① (A) - (C) - (B)　　② (B) - (A) - (C)
③ (B) - (C) - (A)　　④ (C) - (A) - (B)
⑤ (C) - (B) - (A)

[03~06] 다음 대화를 읽고, 물음에 답하시오.

> B: ⓐLing's birthday is this Wednesday, isn't it? (①)
> G: Yes. ⓑI'm going to buy a book for her. (②)
> B: Well, ⓒI'm thinking about buying her an umbrella. I found a cute one in a gift shop. (③)

> G: Oh, that's not a good gift for Chinese people. ⓓIt means bad something. (④)
> B: Really? (an, mean, in, what, umbrella, China, does, ?)
> G: It means separation. ⓔThe words for *separation* and *umbrella* sounds the same in Chinese. (⑤)
> B: I see. Then how about chocolate?
> G: That's a good idea.

03 위 대화의 ①~⑤ 중 주어진 문장이 들어갈 알맞은 곳은?

> What about you?

①　　②　　③　　④　　⑤

04 위 대화의 괄호 안에 주어진 단어들을 바르게 배열하여 문장을 완성하시오.

➡ _____

05 위 대화의 밑줄 친 ⓐ~ⓔ 중 어법상 틀린 개수를 고르시오.

① 1개　② 2개　③ 3개　④ 4개　⑤ 5개

06 위 대화를 읽고 답할 수 <u>없는</u> 질문을 <u>모두</u> 고르시오.

① What is the girl going to buy for Ling?
② What does a book mean in China?
③ When is Ling's birthday?
④ Where is the boy going to go to buy chocolate?
⑤ Is an umbrella a good present for Chinese people?

[07~08] 다음 대화를 읽고, 물음에 답하시오.

B: There is a Holi festival in Busan this year.
G: A Holi festival? (A)_____
B: It's a traditional Indian festival. People throw colored powder and water at each other.
G: That sounds exciting. (B)_____
B: No, I haven't. But my Indian friend told me a lot about it.
G: (C)_____
B: It's on the last full moon of the Hindu calendar. This year, it's on March 21.
G: I'd like to go. (D)_____
B: No, but you should wear white clothes. Then the colored powder on your clothes will look more beautiful.
G: Okay. Thank you for the information.

서답형
07 위 대화의 빈칸 (A)~(D)에 들어갈 말을 〈보기〉에서 골라 쓰시오.

┌─── 보기 ───
• Have you ever been to a Holi festival?
• What is Holi?
• What is that?
• When is the festival?
• Should I bring anything?
• Should I bring white clothes?
• What should I bring?
└

➡ (A) _____
　 (B) _____
　 (C) _____
　 (D) _____

08 위 대화의 내용과 일치하지 <u>않는</u> 것을 고르시오.

① A Holi festival will be held on March 21.
② At a Holi festival, people throw colored powder and water at each other.
③ The boy has an Indian friend.
④ At a Holi festival, people should wear colored clothes.
⑤ The boy has not been to a Holi festival.

[09~12] 다음 대화를 읽고, 물음에 답하시오.

W: Welcome to the International Games Festival. (①) You can play many different traditional games here.
B: Wow! ⓐIt looks (A)_____ (excite)! Which game should I play first? (②)
W: Let's see. (③)
B: No, I haven't. What is ⓑit? (④)
W: ⓒIt's a traditional game from Russia. (⑤)
B: How do I play ⓓit?
W: Put five sticks on the ground. Then throw a bat at them.
B: That sounds fun. I'll try ⓔthat first.

09 위 대화의 ①~⑤ 중 주어진 문장이 들어갈 알맞은 곳은?

┌─────────────────────────────┐
│ Have you ever played *gorodki*? │
└─────────────────────────────┘

① ② ③ ④ ⑤

서답형
10 위 대화의 빈칸 (A)에 주어진 단어를 이용하여 빈칸을 완성하시오.

➡ _____

11 위 대화의 밑줄 친 ⓐ~ⓔ 중에서 가리키는 대상이 <u>다른</u> 하나는?

① ⓐ ② ⓑ ③ ⓒ ④ ⓓ ⑤ ⓔ

서답형
12 위 대화의 내용에 맞게 빈칸을 완성하시오.

┌─────────────────────────────┐
│ *Gorodki* is _____ _____ │
│ _____ _____ Russia. The way │
│ to _____ *gorodki* is _____ │
│ _____ _____ on the ground │
│ and _____ _____ _____ at │
│ them. │
└─────────────────────────────┘

[01~04] 다음 대화를 읽고, 물음에 답하시오.

G: ①What a nice picture! Are these your friends?
B: Yes. ②We took this picture at the beach. We had a lot of fun.
G: Oh, look at that boy. That's really rude.
B: Which boy?
G: ③The boy which is making the V sign. (A)
_____
B: ④What's wrong with that?
G: It has a bad (B)_____(mean) in England. But showing your palm and making a V sign is okay.
B: ⑤What does that mean?
G: (C)It means victory or peace.

01 그림을 참고하고, 주어진 단어를 이용하여 빈칸 (A)에 알맞은 말을 쓰시오.

➡ _____

(toward, himself, palm, face)

02 주어진 단어를 이용하여 빈칸 (B)를 채우시오.

➡ _____

03 ①~⑤ 중 어법상 어색한 부분을 찾아 고치시오.

_____ ➡ _____

04 밑줄 친 (C)가 가리키는 것을 본문에서 찾아 쓰시오.

➡ _____

[05~07] 다음 대화를 읽고, 물음에 답하시오.

A: (A)_____ do you see in this picture?
B: The girl is ⓐ_____.
A: (B)_____ does ⓑ_____ mean in India?
B: 불운을 뜻해.

05 빈칸 (A)와 (B)에 공통으로 들어갈 단어를 쓰시오.

➡ _____

06 그림을 참고하고, 주어진 단어를 이용해 빈칸 ⓐ와 ⓑ에 공통으로 들어갈 말을 쓰시오. (7단어) (cut, on, hair, get)

➡ _____

07 밑줄 친 우리말을 영작하시오.

➡ _____

08 다음 대화의 밑줄 친 우리말을 영작하시오.

G: 너는 브라질에 가 봤니?
B: No, I haven't.

➡ _____

Grammar

교과서

① 현재완료

> • For a long time, Koreans **have thought** that fish are good guards.
> 오랜 세월 동안, 한국인들은 물고기가 훌륭한 파수꾼이라고 생각해 왔다.
>
> • **Have** you ever **visited** Paris before? 너는 전에 파리에 가 본 적이 있니?

■ 현재완료는 'have[has] + 과거분사'의 형태로 과거의 일이 현재까지 영향을 주는 동작·상태의 의미를 나타낸다.

■ 부정형은 'have[has] not + 과거분사'이며, 의문형은 'Have[Has] + 주어 + 과거분사 ~?'로 나타낸다.

• I **haven't completed** the work yet. 나는 일이 아직 안 끝났다.

• How long **have** you **lived** together? 당신들은 얼마 동안 함께 살았습니까?

■ 현재완료는 '완료(지금[막] …했다), 경험(…해 본 적이 있다), 계속((지금까지) …해 왔다), 결과(…해서 (그 결과) 지금 ~하다)'의 네 가지 용법으로 쓰인다.
완료 용법은 보통 'just, already, yet'과 같은 부사와 함께 쓰이며, 경험 용법은 'ever, never, once, before' 등과 같은 부사와 함께 쓰인다.

계속 용법은 보통 'for+기간 명사'나 'since+시간 명사'와 함께 쓰이며 결과 용법은 과거에 발생한 사건이 현재 미치고 있는 결과를 포함한다.

• They **have** already **finished** their lunch. 〈완료〉 그들은 이미 점심식사를 끝마쳤다.

• I **have** never **been** here before. 〈경험〉 저는 이곳이 처음입니다.

• He **has been** missing since last month. 〈계속〉 그는 지난달부터 실종되었다.

• She **has lost** her purse. 〈결과〉 그녀는 지갑을 잃어버렸다. (그 결과 (지갑이) 지금 없다.)

*have[has] been to vs. have[has] gone to

have[has] been to는 '~에 가 본적이 있다'는 경험을 나타내고, have[has] gone to는 '~에 가고 없다'는 결과를 나타낸다. 그러므로 have[has] gone to는 3인칭만 주어로 쓸 수 있다.

■ 현재완료는 과거의 일이 현재까지 영향을 주는 동작·상태를 나타내므로 과거를 나타내는 어구와 함께 쓸 수 없다.

• We **ate** lunch an hour ago.　　　(○)

• We have eaten lunch an hour ago. (×)

핵심 Check

1. 주어진 동사를 어법에 맞게 쓰시오.

(1) They _____ _____ to Seoul. So you cannot meet them now. (go)

(2) I _____ never _____ Seoul. (visit)

(3) _____ you ever _____ *The Little Prince*? (read)

② 결과를 나타내는 so ... that 구문

- It's **so** old **that** I can't really tell, but is it a fish?
  그것은 매우 오래되어서 정말 알 수가 없는데, 그건 물고기인가요?
- This book was **so** sad **that** I cried. 이 책이 매우 슬퍼서 나는 울었어.

■ 'so+형용사[부사]+that+주어+동사'의 형태로 '매우 …해서 ~하다'라는 의미이며 원인과 그에 따른 결과를 서술할 때 쓰인다.

■ so 뒤의 형용사나 부사는 원인을 나타내며, 접속사 that 뒤에 나오는 내용은 그에 따른 결과를 나타낸다.

- I was **so** tired **that** I couldn't exercise. 나는 너무 피곤해서 운동할 수 없었다.
- He was **so** happy **that** he danced. 그는 너무 기뻐 춤을 추었다.

■ 'so … that' 구문에서 that 앞에 형용사나 부사 대신 명사가 오면 so 대신 such를 쓴다.
- He was **such** a good runner **that** I couldn't catch him. 그가 너무 빨리 달려 나는 그를 따라잡을 수가 없었다.

■ 'so+형용사[부사]+that+주어+can ~'는 '형용사[부사]+enough+to 동사원형'으로 바꿔 쓸 수 있으며, 'so+형용사[부사]+that+주어+can't ~'는 'too+형용사[부사]+to 동사원형'으로 바꿔 쓸 수 있다.

- She is **so** kind **that** she can help her friends.
  = She is kind **enough to** help her friends.
- He was **so** sick **that** he couldn't go out.
  = He was **too** sick **to** go out.

핵심 Check

2. 다음 우리말에 맞게 빈칸에 알맞은 말을 쓰시오.
  (1) 나는 오늘 너무 바빠서 갈 수가 없어.
    ➡ I'm _____ _____ _____ I can't go today.
  (2) 그의 모자는 너무 커서 그것은 그의 눈을 가렸다.
    ➡ His hat was _____ _____ _____ it covered his eyes.

Grammar 시험대비 기본평가

01 다음 문장에서 어법상 어색한 부분을 바르게 고쳐 쓰시오.

(1) I have visit there many times.

_____ ➡ _____

(2) She has finished the work yesterday.

_____ ➡ _____

(3) Do you have cleaned your room?

_____ ➡ _____

(4) I'm so busy what I can't go out today.

_____ ➡ _____

(5) The room was very dirty that it smelled bad.

_____ ➡ _____

(6) Sam has lived with his pet dog for 2015.

_____ ➡ _____

(7) The man have lived with them for a long time.

_____ ➡ _____

02 다음 중 어법상 어색한 것은?

① I've never heard that before.
② Have you finished your homework?
③ Joel has work for 6 hours straight.
④ The bus has just arrived.
⑤ Linda has lost her smartphone.

03 다음 대화의 빈칸에 들어갈 말로 알맞은 것은?

M: How was your trip to Vietnam?
W: It was great!
M: Did you visit Danang?
W: Yes, of course. The place was _____ beautiful that I stayed a few more days.

① so   ② such   ③ very
④ too   ⑤ enough

01 다음 빈칸에 알맞은 말이 순서대로 바르게 짝지어진 것은?

> • _____ you ever visited Tibet?
> • I have never _____ to Rome.

① Were – gone
② Were – been
③ Have – gone
④ Have – been
⑤ Did – being

02 ^{중요} 다음 문장의 밑줄 친 부분 중에서 어법상 잘못된 곳을 고르시오.

> Amy was ①too ②sick yesterday ③that she ④couldn't take part ⑤in the meeting.

03 다음 질문에 대한 응답으로 알맞은 것은?

> Has Chris ever visited Seoul?

① Yes, he is.
② Yes, he does.
③ No, he isn't.
④ No, he doesn't.
⑤ No, he hasn't.

04 다음 빈칸에 알맞은 말이 바르게 짝지어진 것은?

> Steve was _____ hungry _____ he ate all the food on the table.

① as – as
② such – as
③ so – that
④ too – to
⑤ enough – to

05 서답형 다음 괄호 안에서 알맞은 말을 고르시오.

(1) I have (visited / visit) Phuket, Thailand.
(2) She (have / has) gone to Jeju.
(3) You can't meet her now. She has (been / gone) to China.
(4) Ann has been to Paris (before / ago).
(5) He (doesn't have / hasn't) read *The Little Prince*.

06 ^{중요} 다음 중 어법상 바르지 않은 것은?

① Dad's explanation was too clear that we could understand it easily.
② They have lived there since 2010.
③ The math problems were so easy that we could solve them.
④ Evan has just finished his homework.
⑤ Emma felt so sick that she couldn't even breathe.

07 다음 우리말을 영어로 바르게 옮긴 것은?

> 나는 전에 스페인 음식을 먹어본 적이 없다.

① I didn't eat Spanish food ago.
② I don't eat Spanish food before.
③ I have never eat Spanish food before.
④ I don't have eaten Spanish food before.
⑤ I have never eaten Spanish food before.

서답형

08 다음 괄호 안에서 알맞은 말을 고르시오.

(1) Jack was (so / such) witty that he became popular among us.

(2) *Mona Lisa* is so wonderful (that / what) people love it.

(3) It gave him (so / such) a shock that his face turned white.

(4) The boxes were so heavy that I (wouldn't / couldn't) carry them.

중요

09 다음 빈칸에 알맞은 말이 순서대로 짝지어진 것은?

• Ben has lived in Jeonju _____ 5 years.
• Ben has lived in Jeonju _____ 2005.

① after – for
② for – after
③ since – for
④ for – since
⑤ as – for

10 다음 두 문장을 한 문장으로 바르게 연결한 것은?

• Amanda studied very hard.
• So she got an A⁺.

① Amanda studied very hard that she got an A⁺.

② Amanda studied so hard that she got an A⁺.

③ Amanda studied hard so that she got an A⁺.

④ Amanda studied hard enough that she got an A⁺.

⑤ Amanda studied too hard that she could get an A⁺.

중요

11 다음 중 밑줄 친 부분의 용법이 다른 하나는?

① I have already eaten dinner.

② Have you ever played golf before?

③ Harry has not written his report yet.

④ The train has just left the platform.

⑤ Emily has just finished her homework.

서답형

12 다음 문장을 주어진 어휘를 이용하여 같은 의미가 되도록 바꿔 쓰시오.

(1) Julia got so angry that she couldn't speak. (too)
➡ _____

(2) Sean is so rich that he can buy the expensive car. (enough)
➡ _____

(3) The panda is so cute that I can't take my eyes off him. (to)
➡ _____

(4) The house was so nice that Melanie wanted to live there. (to)
➡ _____

13 다음 두 문장을 한 문장으로 바르게 바꾼 것은?

• Paulinya went to Russia.
• And she still stays there.

① Paulinya went to Russia.

② Paulinya has been to Russia.

③ Paulinya hasn't gone to Russia.

④ Paulinya has gone to Russia.

⑤ Paulinya hasn't come back yet.

14 다음 우리말을 영어로 바르게 옮긴 것은?

> 차가 너무 막혀서 나는 학교에 늦었다.

① Traffic was too heavy that I was late for school.
② Traffic was very heavy that I was late for school.
③ Traffic was enough heavy that I was late for school.
④ Traffic was so heavy that I was late for school.
⑤ Traffic was heavy too that I was late for school.

15 다음 문장에서 어법상 <u>어색한</u> 것을 고쳐 다시 쓰시오.

(1) Suyeon has just arrived at Busan Station an hour ago.

➡ _____

(2) Ron and his sisters have been to England. They are there now.

➡ _____

(3) Grace was too fat that she wore the beautiful dress.

➡ _____

➡ _____

(4) The drama was very boring that I turned off the TV.

➡ _____

(5) He has lived in Busan for 2010.

➡ _____

16 다음 글의 밑줄 친 ⓐ, ⓑ를 알맞은 형태로 바꿔 쓰시오.

> Ian ⓐhas visited Vietnam last week. But I have never ⓑgone there.

➡ ⓐ _____ ⓑ _____

17 다음 우리말을 영작했을 때 <u>어색한</u> 것을 찾아 고치시오.

(1) 나는 지난 월요일 이후로 그를 보지 못했다.
→ I have not seen him for last Monday.
(2) Cathy는 전에 부산에 가 본 적이 있다.
→ Cathy has gone to Busan before.
(3) 영화가 너무 지루해 나는 잠이 들어 버렸다.
→ The movie was too boring that I fell asleep.
(4) Eric은 너무 가난해서 그 차를 살 수 없었다.
→ Eric was poor enough that he couldn't buy the car.
(5) 그녀는 어제 시계를 지하철 역에서 잃어버렸다.
→ She has lost her watch at the subway station yesterday.

➡ _____
_____

18 다음 빈칸에 공통으로 들어갈 단어는?

> • Joe ran too fast for his brother _____ catch him.
> • The girl was clever enough _____ solve the problem by herself.

① so ② to ③ of
④ as ⑤ for

01 주어진 두 문장을 한 문장으로 바꿔 쓰시오.

(1) • Laura began to live in Chicago in 1998.
 • She still lives there.

➡ _____

(2) • Dan lost his cell phone.
 • So he doesn't have it now.

➡ _____

02 다음 문장을 so ~ that ... 구문으로 바꾸어 쓰시오.

(1) Kate is too young to drive a car.

➡ _____

(2) Stefanie is wise enough to give advice to her friends.

➡ _____

03 괄호 안에 주어진 어구를 이용하여 다음 우리말을 영어로 옮기시오.

(1) James는 그가 어릴 때부터 축구를 해 왔다. (soccer, since, a child)

➡ _____

(2) 비가 너무 많이 와서 우리는 밖에 나갈 수 없다. (rain, heavily, that, go outside)

➡ _____

(3) Charlie는 6개월 동안 한국어를 공부해 오고 있다. (has, study)

➡ _____

04 다음 문장을 어법에 맞게 고쳐 쓰시오.

(1) Mr. Brown has lived in New York for 2015.

➡ _____

(2) We have gone to Sydney.

➡ _____

(3) Elle hasn't taken a walk yesterday.

➡ _____

(4) My long padding coat is enough warm for me to endure the winter.

➡ _____

(5) Lylian was very afraid that she couldn't open her eyes.

➡ _____

05 괄호 안의 단어를 사용하여 주어진 문장을 같은 의미가 되도록 다시 쓰시오.

(1) Mike was so sick that he couldn't go to work yesterday. (too)

➡ _____

(2) The *samgyetang* was too hot for Amy to eat. (so, can)

➡ _____

(3) His essay was so nice that his teacher was satisfied. (enough)

➡ _____

(4) Tom ran fast enough to catch the last bus. (so, can)

➡ _____

06 우리말과 일치하도록 괄호 안의 단어를 바르게 배열하여 문장을 완성하시오.

(1) 그의 이웃집의 파티가 너무 시끄러워서 그는 잠을 전혀 잘 수 없었다. (he, his, party, neighbor's, sleep, was, couldn't, noisy, that, all, so, at)

➡ _____

_____

(2) Rose는 아직 도서실에 도착하지 않았다. (Rose, library, the, arrived, not, has, yet, at)

➡ _____

(3) 그 남자는 너무 친절해서 즉시 나를 도와주었다. (man, he, me, helped, kind, right, was, so, the, that, away)

➡ _____

(4) 나는 Paris에 한 번 다녀왔다. (I, Paris, been, once, have, to)

➡ _____

(5) Andrew는 그의 스마트폰을 기차에 놓고 내렸다. (Andrew, the, smartphone, train, left, his, has, in)

➡ _____

07 Bella가 경험한 일과 경험하지 않은 일에 관한 표를 보고, 〈보기〉와 같이 문장을 완성하시오.

What	Yes/No
learn to play the piano	Yes
drive a car	No
visit Angkor Wat	Yes
taste Vietnamese food	No
practice yoga	Yes

┌─ 보기 ─┐

Bella has learned to play the piano before.

➡ (1) _____
(2) _____
(3) _____
(4) _____

08 다음 두 문장을 〈보기〉와 같이 'so ... that ~' 구문을 사용하여 한 문장으로 연결하시오.

┌─ 보기 ─┐

I was very sick. I had to stay in bed all day.

→ I was so sick that I had to stay in bed all day.

(1) • The flowers are very beautiful.
• Many people come to see them.

➡ _____

_____

(2) • The house was very expensive.
• We decided not to buy it.

➡ _____

_____

(3) • This dish is too spicy.
• I need to drink a lot of milk.

➡ _____

_____

(4) • The movie was really sad.
• I cried a lot.

➡ _____

(5) • You are truly smart.
• You always get A's.

➡ _____

09 두 문장의 의미가 같도록 빈칸에 알맞은 말을 쓰시오.

Stephanie went to Australia, so she isn't here now.

= Stephanie _____ _____ to Australia.

Reading

Traditional Korean Symbols

Peter is visiting Korea to meet a friend, Mina, from a sister school.
to meet은 목적을 나타내는 부사적 용법의 to부정사이다.
Peter is going to stay at her grandfather's house for a week. When he
~할 예정이다
arrives, Mina shows him the guest room.
= Mina shows the guest room to him. (3형식)

Mina: Peter, you will stay here. This guest room is full of traditional
~으로 가득 차다
Korean things. Look at this pillow.
~을 보다

Peter: What are these things?
지시형용사

Mina: They're bats.

Peter: Bats on my pillow? That's scary!
내 베개 위에 박쥐가 있는 것

Mina: Not really. In Korea, bats are symbols of luck and a long life.
그렇지 않아.

Peter: That's surprising. In many Western countries, bats remind
앞 문장의 내용을 가리킨다.   *remind … of ~는 '…에게 ~을 상기시키다'라는 의미이다.*
people of darkness and scary things.

Mina shows Peter her grandfather's room. Peter and Mina's
= Mina shows her grandfather's room to Peter. (3형식)
grandfather meet and greet each other.

Grandfather: Hi, Peter! Have you ever seen this kind of lock before?
현재완료 시제로 경험 용법

Peter: No, I haven't. It's so old that I can't really tell, but is it a fish?
don't(×)   so … that ~ can't 구문으로 '너무 …해서 ~할 수 없다'라는 의미이다.

Grandfather: Yes. For a long time, Koreans have thought that fish are
have thought는 현재완료 시제로, 여기서는 과거의 일이 현재까지 계속됨을 나타낸다.
good guards. Fish don't close their eyes, even when they sleep.
its(×)

Peter: That's interesting.
앞 문장의 내용을 가리킨다.

Grandfather: We think fish can watch over valuable things. That's
'That's why …는' '…인 이유가 바로 그것이다'라는 뜻으로, 앞에서 언급한 것이 why 이하의 어떤 행위나 현상의 원인임을 말할 때 쓴다.
why this lock looks like a fish.
look like+명사: ~처럼 보이다

Peter: Now I understand.

---

traditional 전통의, 전통적인
symbol 상징, 기호
be full of ~으로 가득 차다
pillow 베개
remind 생각나게 하다, 상기시키다
darkness 어둠, 암흑
scary 무서운, 두려운
greet 맞이하다, 환영하다
watch over ~을 주시하다, 지키다
valuable 값비싼, 귀중한

확인문제

● 다음 문장이 본문의 내용과 일치하면 T, 일치하지 않으면 F를 쓰시오.

1 Peter is going to stay at Mina's grandfather's house for a week. ☐

2 The guest room is full of modern Korean things. ☐

3 In Korea, bats are symbols of luck and a long life. ☐

4 Recently Koreans think that fish are good guards. ☐

5 Fish don't close their eyes, even when they sleep. ☐

They go outside and walk around the garden.

Peter: What is on that piece of paper? It looks scary.
　　　　　　　= sheet　　　　감각동사 look 뒤에는 형용사가 온다.

Grandfather: Do you mean this painting of a rooster?
　　　　　　　　　　　　　　목적격 관계를 나타내는 전치사. …을, …의

Peter: Oh, is it a rooster?

Grandfather: Yes, it is. Roosters crow every morning.

Their crowing means that a new day is beginning. For many years,
= Roosters'　　　　　　접속사

Koreans have believed evil spirits go away when a rooster crows.
　　　　have believed는 현재완료 시제로, 여기서는 과거의 일이 현재까지 계속됨을 나타낸다.
　　　　evil spirits go away는 목적어로 쓰인 명사절이고, evil 앞에 접속사 that이 생략되어 있다.

Mina: Really? I've never heard that before.

Peter: Actually, I'm afraid of darkness and evil spirits. Could you
　　　= In fact　　　 be afraid of: ~을 무서워하다

draw a rooster for me, Mina?

Mina: Sure. I'll draw a big rooster for you!

Grandfather: Put the drawing above your door. Then it will protect

you.

Peter: Yes, I will.

Peter's Diary　　　　　　　　　　　　　　　　　　　　May 28

　I'm enjoying this trip so much that I want to stay longer. I love
　　　　　원인과 결과를 나타내는 so … that 구문으로, so 다음에 부사 much가 쓰였다. '너무 …해서 ~하다'라는 의미이다.

all the traditional Korean symbols in this house. Now I understand

a lot of them. I want to visit Korea again with my family.

rooster 수탉
crow (닭이) 울다
evil 사악한, 악마의
spirit 정신, 영혼
go away 사라지다. 떠나가다
protect 보호하다

확인문제

● 다음 문장이 본문의 내용과 일치하면 T, 일치하지 않으면 F를 쓰시오.

1　Peter asks what is on that piece of paper. ☐

2　Roosters' crowing means that a new day is ending. ☐

3　Koreans have believed evil spirits appear when a rooster crows. ☐

4　Peter is afraid of darkness and evil spirits. ☐

5　Mina will draw a big rooster for Peter. ☐

6　Peter wants to visit Korea again with his friends. ☐

● 우리말을 참고하여 빈칸에 알맞은 말을 쓰시오.

1 _____ Korean Symbols

2 Peter is visiting Korea to meet a friend, Mina, _____ _____ _____ _____.

3 Peter is going to _____ _____ her grandfather's house _____ _____ _____.

4 When he arrives, Mina shows _____ _____ _____ _____.

5 Peter, you will _____ _____.

6 This guest room _____ _____ _____ traditional Korean things.

7 _____ _____ this pillow.

8 What are _____ _____?

9 _____ bats.

10 Bats _____ _____ _____? That's _____!

11 _____ _____. In Korea, bats are _____ _____ luck and a long life.

12 That's _____. In many Western countries, bats _____ people _____ darkness and scary things.

13 Mina _____ Peter her grandfather's room.

14 Peter and Mina's grandfather _____ and _____ _____.

15 Hi, Peter! _____ _____ _____ _____ this kind of lock before?

16 No, I _____. It's _____ old _____ I can't really tell, but is it a fish?

17 Yes. _____ _____ _____ _____, Koreans have thought that fish are _____ _____.

1	전통적인 한국의 상징물
2	피터는 자매 학교 친구인 미나를 만나기 위해 한국을 방문 중이다.
3	피터는 일주일간 미나네 할아버지 댁에 머무를 것이다.
4	그가 도착하자, 미나가 그에게 손님방을 보여준다.
5	피터, 넌 여기에 머무르게 될 거야.
6	이 손님방은 한국의 전통 물건들로 가득 차 있어.
7	이 베개를 봐.
8	이것들은 뭐야?
9	그건 박쥐들이야.
10	내 베개 위에 박쥐가? 그거 겁나는데!
11	그렇지 않아. 한국에서는 박쥐가 행운과 장수의 상징이거든.
12	그거 놀라운 일인데. 서구의 많은 나라들에서 박쥐는 사람들에게 어둠과 무서운 것들을 상기시키거든.
13	미나는 피터에게 할아버지의 방을 보여준다.
14	피터와 미나의 할아버지가 만나서 서로 인사한다.
15	안녕, 피터! 너는 이런 종류의 자물쇠를 전에 본 적 있니?
16	아니요, 본 적 없어요. 그 자물쇠는 너무 오래되어서 사실 알아볼 수가 없는데, 그건 물고기인가요?
17	맞아. 오랜 세월 동안, 한국인들은 물고기가 훌륭한 파수꾼이라고 생각해 왔단다.

18 Fish don't _____ _____ _____, even when they sleep.

19 That's _____.

20 We think fish can _____ _____ valuable things. _____ _____ this lock looks _____ a fish.

21 Now I _____.

22 They go outside and _____ _____ the garden.

23 What is on _____ _____ _____ _____? It looks scary.

24 _____ _____ _____ this painting of a rooster?

25 Oh, is it _____ _____?

26 Yes, it is. Roosters _____ every morning.

27 Their crowing means that _____ _____ _____ is beginning.

28 For many years, Koreans have believed evil spirits _____ _____ when a rooster _____.

29 Really? _____ _____ _____ that before.

30 _____, I'm _____ of darkness and evil spirits.

31 Could you draw a rooster _____ _____, Mina?

32 Sure. I'll _____ _____ _____ _____ for you!

33 _____ the drawing _____ your door. Then it will _____ you.

34 Yes, I _____.

35 I'm enjoying this trip _____ _____ _____ I want to stay longer.

36 I love all the _____ _____ _____ in this house.

37 Now I understand _____ _____ _____ _____.

38 I want to visit Korea again _____ _____ _____.

18 물고기는 잘 때도 눈을 감지 않거든.

19 그거 재미있군요.

20 우리는 물고기가 귀중품을 지킬 수 있다고 생각해. 그것이 이 자물쇠가 물고기 모양으로 생긴 이유란다.

21 이제 이해가 되는군요.

22 그들은 밖에 나가서 정원을 걷는다.

23 저 종이에는 무엇이 그려져 있는 거죠? 무서워 보여요.

24 이 수탉 그림을 말하는 거니?

25 오, 그게 수탉이에요?

26 응, 그렇단다. 수탉은 매일 아침 울지.

27 수탉의 울음은 새로운 날이 시작하는 것을 의미해.

28 오랫동안 한국인들은 수탉이 울때 악령이 물러간다고 믿어 왔단다.

29 정말요? 전 그런 말을 들어본 적이 없어요.

30 사실 전 어둠과 악령을 무서워해요.

31 미나야, 날 위해 수탉을 그려 줄 수 있니?

32 물론이지. 내가 널 위해 커다란 수탉을 그려줄게!

33 그 그림을 네 문 위에 걸어 놓으렴. 그러면 그게 널 지켜 줄 거야.

34 네, 그럴게요.

35 난 이번 여행이 매우 즐거워서 더 오래 머무르고 싶다.

36 난 이 집의 모든 전통적인 한국의 상징물들이 아주 마음에 든다.

37 나는 이제 그것들을 많이 알게 되었다.

38 난 우리 가족과 함께 한국을 다시 방문하고 싶다.

● 우리말을 참고하여 본문을 영작하시오.

1 전통적인 한국의 상징물
➡ _____

2 피터는 자매 학교 친구인 미나를 만나기 위해 한국을 방문 중이다.
➡ _____

3 피터는 일주일간 미나네 할아버지 댁에 머무를 것이다.
➡ _____

4 그가 도착하자, 미나가 그에게 손님방을 보여준다.
➡ _____

5 피터, 넌 여기에 머무르게 될 거야.
➡ _____

6 이 손님방은 한국의 전통 물건들로 가득 차 있어.
➡ _____

7 이 베개를 봐.
➡ _____

8 이것들은 뭐야?
➡ _____

9 그건 박쥐들이야.
➡ _____

10 내 베개 위에 박쥐가? 그거 겁나는데!
➡ _____

11 그렇지 않아. 한국에서는 박쥐가 행운과 장수의 상징이거든.
➡ _____

12 그거 놀라운 일인데. 서구의 많은 나라들에서 박쥐는 사람들에게 어둠과 무서운 것들을 상기시키거든.
➡ _____

13 미나는 피터에게 할아버지의 방을 보여준다.
➡ _____

14 피터와 미나의 할아버지가 만나서 서로 인사한다.
➡ _____

15 안녕, 피터! 너는 이런 종류의 자물쇠를 전에 본 적 있니?
➡ _____

16 아니요, 본 적 없어요. 그 자물쇠는 너무 오래되어서 사실 알아볼 수가 없는데, 그건 물고기인가요?
➡ _____

17 맞아. 오랜 세월 동안, 한국인들은 물고기가 훌륭한 파수꾼이라고 생각해 왔단다.
➡ _____

18 물고기는 잘 때도 눈을 감지 않거든.

➡ _____

19 그거 재미있군요.

➡ _____

20 우리는 물고기가 귀중품을 지킬 수 있다고 생각해. 그것이 이 자물쇠가 물고기 모양으로 생긴 이유란다.

➡ _____

21 이제 이해가 되는군요.

➡ _____

22 그들은 밖에 나가서 정원을 걷는다.

➡ _____

23 저 종이에는 무엇이 그려져 있는 거죠? 무서워 보여요.

➡ _____

24 이 수탉 그림을 말하는 거니?

➡ _____

25 오, 그게 수탉이에요?

➡ _____

26 응, 그렇단다. 수탉은 매일 아침 울지.

➡ _____

27 수탉의 울음은 새로운 날이 시작하는 것을 의미해.

➡ _____

28 오랫동안 한국인들은 수탉이 울 때 악령이 물러간다고 믿어 왔단다.

➡ _____

29 정말요? 전 그런 말을 들어본 적이 없어요.

➡ _____

30 사실 전 어둠과 악령을 무서워해요.

➡ _____

31 미나야, 날 위해 수탉을 그려 줄 수 있니?

➡ _____

32 물론이지. 내가 널 위해 커다란 수탉을 그려줄게!

➡ _____

33 그 그림을 네 문 위에 걸어 놓으렴. 그러면 그게 널 지켜 줄 거야.

➡ _____

34 네, 그럴게요.

➡ _____

35 난 이번 여행이 매우 즐거워서 더 오래 머무르고 싶다.

➡ _____

36 난 이 집의 모든 전통적인 한국의 상징물들이 아주 마음에 든다.

➡ _____

37 나는 이제 그것들을 많이 알게 되었다.

➡ _____

38 난 우리 가족과 함께 한국을 다시 방문하고 싶다.

➡ _____

[01~03] 다음 글을 읽고, 물음에 답하시오.

Peter is visiting Korea to meet a friend, Mina, from a sister school. Peter is going to stay at her grandfather's house for a week. When he arrives, Mina shows him the guest room.

Mina: Peter, you will stay here. This guest room is full of traditional Korean things. Look at this pillow.

Peter: What are these things?

Mina: They're bats.

Peter: Bats on my pillow? ⓐThat's scary!

Mina: ⓑNot really. In Korea, bats are symbols of luck and a long life.

Peter: That's surprising. In many Western countries, bats remind people of darkness and scary things.

서답형

01 위 글의 밑줄 친 ⓐThat이 가리키는 것을 우리말로 쓰시오.

➡ _____

서답형

02 미나가 밑줄 친 ⓑ처럼 말한 이유를 우리말로 쓰시오.

➡ _____

03 위 글의 내용과 일치하지 <u>않는</u> 것은?

① 피터는 자매 학교 친구인 미나를 만나기 위해 한국을 방문 중이다.

② 피터는 한 달 동안 미나네 할아버지 댁에 머무를 것이다.

③ 미나의 할아버지 댁의 손님방은 한국의 전통 물건들로 가득 차 있다.

④ 한국에서는 박쥐가 행운과 장수의 상징이다.

⑤ 서구의 많은 나라들에서, 박쥐는 사람들에게 어둠과 무서운 것들을 상기시켜 준다.

[04~06] 다음 글을 읽고, 물음에 답하시오.

Grandfather: Hi, Peter! ⓐ<u>Have</u> you ever <u>seen</u> this kind of lock before?

Peter: ⓑ<u>아니, 없어요.</u> It's so old that I can't really tell, but is it a fish?

Grandfather: Yes. For a long time, Koreans have thought that fish are good guards. Fish don't close their eyes, even when they sleep.

Peter: That's interesting.

Grandfather: We think fish can __(A)__ valuable things. That's why this lock looks like a fish.

Peter: Now I understand.

04 위 글의 빈칸 (A)에 들어갈 알맞은 말을 고르시오.

① show around
② wait for
③ look into
④ watch over
⑤ look forward to

중요

05 위 글의 밑줄 친 ⓐ와 현재완료의 용법이 같은 것을 <u>모두</u> 고르시오.

① She <u>has lost</u> her handbag.
② How long <u>have</u> you <u>stayed</u> here?
③ How many times <u>have</u> you <u>read</u> it?
④ I <u>have</u> just <u>finished</u> my work.
⑤ She <u>has been</u> to New York.

서답형

06 위 글의 밑줄 친 ⓑ의 우리말에 맞게 3단어로 영작하시오.

➡ _____

[07~09] 다음 글을 읽고, 물음에 답하시오.

Peter is visiting Korea to meet a friend, Mina, from a ___ⓐ___ . Peter is going to stay at her grandfather's house for a week. When he arrives, Mina shows him the guest room.

Mina: Peter, you will stay here. This guest room is full of traditional Korean things. Look at this pillow.

Peter: What are these things?

Mina: They're bats.

Peter: Bats on my pillow? That's scary!

Mina: ___ⓑ___ In Korea, bats are symbols of luck and a long life.

Peter: That's surprising. In many Western countries, bats remind people of darkness and scary things.

서답형

07 주어진 영영풀이를 참고하여 빈칸 ⓐ에 철자 s로 시작하는 단어를 쓰시오.

> a school which is financially, historically or socially linked to another

➡ _____

08 위 글의 빈칸 ⓑ에 들어갈 알맞은 말을 고르시오.

① That's right.
② Why not?
③ You can say that again.
④ You said it.
⑤ Not really.

중요

09 위 글에서 베개에 있는 박쥐 디자인에 대한 'Peter'의 심경 변화로 가장 알맞은 것을 고르시오.

① surprised → excited
② disappointed → scared
③ bored → disappointed
④ scared → surprised
⑤ ashamed → depressed

[10~12] 다음 글을 읽고, 물음에 답하시오.

Grandfather: Hi, Peter! Have you ever seen this ⓐkind of lock before?

Peter: No, I haven't. ⓑIt's so old that I can't really tell, but is it a fish?

Grandfather: Yes. For a long time, Koreans have thought that fish are good guards. Fish don't close their eyes, even when they sleep.

Peter: That's interesting.

Grandfather: We think fish can watch over valuable things. ⓒ그것이 이 자물쇠가 물고기 모양으로 생긴 이유란다.

Peter: Now I understand.

10 위 글의 밑줄 친 ⓐkind와 같은 의미로 쓰인 것을 고르시오.

① You've been very kind.
② Thank you for your kind invitation.
③ What kind of house do you live in?
④ It was really kind of you to help me.
⑤ He was a very kind and helpful man.

서답형

11 위 글의 밑줄 친 ⓑIt이 가리키는 것을 다음 빈칸에 쓰시오.

➡ the _____ that Mina's grandfather showed Peter

서답형

12 위 글의 밑줄 친 ⓒ의 우리말에 맞게 한 단어를 보충하여, 주어진 어휘를 알맞게 배열하시오.

> fish / lock / that's / like / this / a / looks

➡ _____

[13~15] 다음 글을 읽고, 물음에 답하시오.

They go outside and walk around the garden.

Peter: What is on that piece of paper? ⓐIt looks like scary.

Grandfather: Do you mean this painting of a rooster?

Peter: Oh, is it a rooster?

Grandfather: Yes, it is. Roosters crow every morning. Their crowing means that a new day is beginning. For many years, Koreans have believed evil spirits go away when a rooster crows.

Mina: Really? I've never heard that before.

Peter: Actually, I'm afraid of darkness and evil spirits. Could you draw a rooster for me, Mina?

Mina: Sure. I'll draw a big rooster for you!

Grandfather: Put the drawing above your door. Then it will protect you.

Peter: Yes, I will.

서답형

13 위 글의 밑줄 친 ⓐ에서 어법상 틀린 부분을 찾아 고치시오.

_____ ➡ _____

14 위 글의 제목으로 알맞은 것을 고르시오.

① Enjoy Walking around the Garden
② Look at the Scary Painting of a Rooster
③ What Does the Painting of a Rooster Mean?
④ The Reason Roosters Crow Every Morning
⑤ Why Is Peter Afraid of Darkness and Evil Spirits?

15 위 글을 읽고 대답할 수 없는 질문은?

① Who goes outside and walks around the garden?
② Does Peter know what is on the piece of paper?
③ What's the meaning of the roosters' crowing?
④ What will Mina draw for Peter?
⑤ Why does Grandfather tell Peter to put the drawing above his door, not below the door?

[16~17] 다음 일기를 읽고, 물음에 답하시오.

Peter's Diary

May 28

ⓐI'm enjoying this trip so much that I want to stay longer. I love all the traditional Korean symbols in this house. Now I understand a lot of them. I want to visit Korea again with my family.

서답형

16 위 일기의 밑줄 친 ⓐ를 다음과 같이 바꿔 쓸 때 빈칸 (A)와 (B)에 들어갈 알맞은 말을 〈보기〉에서 골라 쓰시오.

┌ 보기 ┐
Such/such, So/so, For/for, As/as, But/but

• (A)_____ I'm enjoying this trip very much, I want to stay longer.
• I'm enjoying this trip very much, (B)_____ I want to stay longer.

17 위 일기의 내용과 일치하지 않는 것은?

① 피터는 이번 여행이 매우 즐거워서 더 오래 머무르고 싶어 한다.
② 피터는 방문한 집의 전통적인 한국의 상징물들이 모두 마음에 든다.
③ 이제 피터는 전통적인 한국의 상징물들을 많이 알게 되었다.
④ 피터는 전통적인 한국의 상징물들에 대해 계속 공부하고 싶어 한다.
⑤ 피터는 가족들과 함께 한국을 다시 방문하고 싶어 한다.

[18~19] 다음 글을 읽고, 물음에 답하시오.

Do you know about traditional Chinese dances? There are many kinds. ⓐ , there are a lion dance, a fan dance, and an umbrella dance. One of the most famous dances is the lion dance. In this dance, two dancers dress and act like lions. They usually dance on special days, such as New Year's Day. I think their dance moves are great. I hope to practice this dance someday.

18 위 글의 빈칸 ⓐ에 들어갈 알맞은 말을 고르시오.

① However   ② In other words
③ Therefore   ④ In addition
⑤ For example

서답형
19 다음 문장에서 위 글의 내용과 다른 부분을 찾아서 고치시오. (두 군데)

A lion dance is a traditional Chinese dance and people usually perform it at any time. In this dance, three dancers dress and act like lions.

➡ (1) _____
   (2) _____

[20~21] 다음 글을 읽고, 물음에 답하시오.

My trip to Korea was great. My friend Mina and her grandfather were very kind to me. (A)[During / For] my trip, I learned (B)[a lot / a lot of] about traditional Korean symbols. That was so (C)[interesting / interested] that I want to visit Korea again with my family.
                       I: Peter

서답형
20 위 글의 괄호 (A)~(C)에서 어법상 알맞은 낱말을 골라 쓰시오.

➡ (A)_____ (B)_____ (C)_____

중요
21 위 글을 읽고 피터의 여행에 대해 알 수 없는 것을 고르시오.

① 여행 장소   ② 여행 기간
③ 같이 지낸 사람들   ④ 여행에서 배운 것
⑤ 여행에 대한 느낌

[22~24] 다음 글을 읽고, 물음에 답하시오.

Peter: What is on that piece of paper? It looks scary.
Grandfather: Do you mean this painting of a rooster?
Peter: Oh, is it a rooster?
Grandfather: Yes, it is. Roosters crow every morning. Their crowing means that a new day is (A)[beginning / ending]. For many years, Koreans have believed evil spirits go away when a rooster crows.
Mina: Really? I've never heard that before.
Peter: ⓐActually, I'm afraid of darkness and evil spirits. ⓑCould you draw a rooster for me, Mina?
Mina: Sure. I'll draw a big rooster for you!
Grandfather: Put the drawing above your door. Then it will (B)[prevent / protect] you.
Peter: Yes, I (C)[do / will].

서답형
22 위 글의 괄호 (A)~(C)에서 문맥이나 어법상 알맞은 낱말을 골라 쓰시오.

➡ (A)_____ (B)_____ (C)_____

23 위 글의 밑줄 친 ⓐActually와 바꿔 쓸 수 있는 말을 모두 고르시오.

① As a result   ② In fact
③ Above all   ④ In other words
⑤ As a matter of fact

서답형
24 다음 빈칸 (A)와 (B)에 들어갈 알맞은 단어를 본문에서 찾아, Peter가 밑줄 친 ⓑ처럼 말한 이유를 완성하시오.

Because Peter is (A)_____ of darkness and evil spirits and he wants them to (B)_____ _____ thanks to the painting of a rooster.

[01~03] 다음 글을 읽고, 물음에 답하시오.

Peter is visiting Korea to meet a friend, Mina, from a sister school. Peter is going to stay at her grandfather's house for a week. When he arrives, ⓐ<u>Mina shows him the guest room.</u>

Mina: Peter, you will stay here. This guest room is full of traditional Korean things. Look at this pillow.

Peter: What are these things?

Mina: They're bats.

Peter: Bats on my pillow? That's scary!

Mina: Not really. In Korea, bats are symbols of luck and a long life.

Peter: That's surprising. In many Western countries, bats remind people of darkness and scary things.

01 위 글의 밑줄 친 ⓐ를 3형식 문장으로 고치시오.

➡ _____

02 다음 질문에 대한 알맞은 대답을 주어진 단어로 시작하여 쓰시오. (5 단어)

Q: What do bats symbolize in Korea?

A: They symbolize _____.

03 다음 문장에서 위 글의 내용과 <u>다른</u> 부분을 찾아서 고치시오.

Bats remind people of happiness and pleasant things in many Western countries.

➡ _____ _____

[04~07] 다음 글을 읽고, 물음에 답하시오.

Mina shows Peter her grandfather's room. ⓐ<u>Peter and Mina's grandfather meet and greet to each other.</u>

Grandfather: Hi, Peter! ⓑ너는 이런 종류의 자물쇠를 전에 본 적 있니?

Peter: No, I haven't. It's so old that I can't really tell, but is it a fish?

Grandfather: Yes. For a long time, Koreans have thought that fish are good guards. Fish don't close their eyes, even when they sleep.

Peter: That's interesting.

Grandfather: We think fish can watch over valuable things. That's why this lock looks like a fish.

Peter: Now I understand.

04 위 글의 밑줄 친 ⓐ에서 어법상 틀린 부분을 찾아 고치시오.

_____ ➡ _____

05 위 글의 밑줄 친 ⓑ의 우리말에 맞게 한 단어를 보충하여, 주어진 어휘를 알맞게 배열하시오.

seen / lock / this / you / kind / ever / of / have

➡ _____

06 다음 질문에 대한 알맞은 대답을 주어진 단어로 시작하여 쓰시오. (9 단어)

Q: Why have Koreans thought that fish are good guards?

A: Because _____

_____ .

07 본문의 내용과 일치하도록 다음 빈칸에 알맞은 단어를 쓰시오.

> The lock that Mina's grandfather shows Peter looks like _____ _____ .

[08~10] 다음 글을 읽고, 물음에 답하시오.

> They go outside and walk around the garden.
>
> **Peter:** What is on that piece of paper? It looks scary.
>
> **Grandfather:** Do you mean this painting of a rooster?
>
> **Peter:** Oh, is it a rooster?
>
> **Grandfather:** Yes, it is. Roosters crow every morning. Their crowing means that a new day is beginning. For many years, Koreans have believed evil spirits go away when a rooster crows.
>
> **Mina:** Really? ⓐ전 그런 말을 들어본 적이 없어요.
>
> **Peter:** Actually, I'm afraid of darkness and evil spirits. Could you draw a rooster for me, Mina?
>
> **Mina:** Sure. I'll draw a big rooster for you!
>
> **Grandfather:** Put the drawing above your door. Then it will protect you.
>
> **Peter:** Yes, I will.

08 다음 질문에 대한 알맞은 대답을 5 단어로 쓰시오.

> **Q:** What is on the piece of paper that Peter is pointing to?

➡ _____

09 위 글을 읽고 (1) 수탉의 울음소리의 의미와 (2) 그에 대한 한국 사람들의 믿음이 무엇인지를 우리말로 쓰시오.

➡ (1) _____

(2) _____

10 위 글의 밑줄 친 ⓐ의 우리말에 맞게 주어진 어휘를 이용하여 5단어로 영작하시오.

> that

➡ _____

[11~13] 다음 글을 읽고, 물음에 답하시오.

> Peter is ①visiting Korea to meet a friend, Mina, from a sister school. Peter is going to stay at her grandfather's house for a week. When he arrives, Mina ②shows him the guest room.
>
> **Mina:** Peter, you will ③stay here. This guest room ⓐis full of traditional Korean things. Look at this pillow.
>
> **Peter:** What are these things?
>
> **Mina:** They're bats.
>
> **Peter:** Bats on my pillow? That's scary!
>
> **Mina:** ④Not really. In Korea, bats are symbols of luck and a long life.
>
> **Peter:** That's ⑤reasonable. In many Western countries, bats remind people of darkness and scary things.

11 위 글의 밑줄 친 ⓐ와 바꿔 쓸 수 있는 말을 쓰시오. (3단어)

➡ _____

12 위 글의 밑줄 친 ①~⑤에서 문맥상 낱말의 쓰임이 적절하지 않은 것을 찾아 알맞게 고치시오.

➡ _____

13 본문의 내용과 일치하도록 다음 빈칸 (A)와 (B)에 알맞은 단어를 쓰시오. (한 칸에 여러 단어를 쓸 수 있음.)

> In Korea, bats remind people of positive things such as (A)_____ and (B)_____ . On the other hand, in many Western countries, bats are symbols of (C)_____ things such as darkness and scary things.

해석

Project Link

We made our own class flag. The flag is a triangle. It means we always work
together. There is a tiger on the flag. It shows that we are powerful. The red
represents our energy.

구문해설 • work together: 함께 일하다

우리는 우리 반의 깃발을 만 들었다. 깃발은 삼각형이다. 그것은 우리가 항상 함께 일 하는 것을 의미한다. 깃발에 호랑이 한 마리가 있다. 그것 은 우리가 강력하다는 것을 보여준다. 빨간색은 우리의 에너지를 나타낸다.

Think and Write

Do you know about traditional Chinese dances? There are many kinds. For
example, there are a lion dance, a fan dance, and an umbrella dance. One of
the most famous dances is the lion dance. In this dance, two dancers dress and
act like lions. They usually dance on special days, such as New Year's Day. I
think their dance moves are great.
I hope to practice this dance someday.

구문해설 • traditional: 전통적인 • kind: 종류 • fan dance: 부채춤 • usually: 대개
• dance move: 춤 동작 • someday: 언젠가

당신은 전통적인 중국 춤에 대해 아는가? 많은 종류들이 있다. 예를 들면, 사자춤, 부 채춤, 그리고 우산춤이 있다. 가장 유명한 춤들 중의 하나 가 사자춤이다. 이 춤에서, 두 명의 댄서들이 사자처럼 옷을 입고 행동한다. 사람들은 사 자춤을 대개 설날과 같은 특 별한 날에 춘다. 나는 그들의 춤 동작들이 멋지다고 생각한 다. 나는 언젠가 이 춤을 연습 하기를 바란다.

Presentation Time

Do you want to have a good time in Korea? Then follow these steps. First,
please take off your shoes when you go into people's homes. Next, bow when
you greet others. Also, use two hands when you give something to older
people. And do not blow your nose at the table and do not point at people.
Lastly, do not call older people by their first names.

구문해설 • follow: 따르다 • take off: 벗다 • bow: 절하다 • greet: 인사하다
• point at: ~을 가리키다, 손가락질하다

한국에서 즐거운 시간을 보내고 싶은가요? 그러면 다음 단계를 따르세요. 먼저 사람들의 집에 들 어갈 때는 신발을 벗으세요. 다음 에 다른 사람들에게 인사할 때 절 을 하세요. 또한 나이가 많은 사 람들에게 무언가를 줄 때는 두 손 을 사용하세요. 그리고 식탁에서 코를 풀지 말고 사람들을 가리키 지 마세요. 마지막으로 나이가 많은 사람들을 이름으로 부르지 마세요.

Words & Expressions

01 다음 대화의 빈칸에 들어갈 말을 고르시오.

> A: Have you ever _____ Chinese food?
> B: Yes, I have.

① got　　② took　　③ tried
④ served　　⑤ tied

02 다음 대화에서 밑줄 친 'face'와 같은 의미로 쓰인 것을 모두 고르시오.

> G: Oh, look at that boy. That's really rude.
> B: Which boy?
> G: The boy who is making the V sign. His palm is <u>facing</u> toward himself.

① The palms should <u>face</u> the ceiling.
② His <u>face</u> was covered with wrinkles.
③ It's a brush used for soaping your <u>face</u>.
④ Be sure that the photos you want to scan are <u>facing</u> up.
⑤ The garden <u>faces</u> south.

[03~04] 다음 빈칸에 공통으로 들어갈 단어를 주어진 철자로 시작하여 쓰시오.

03
> • A pear drops when a c_____ flies from the tree.
> • They c_____ at the same time every morning when the sun rises.

04
> • He cupped her chin in the p_____ of his hand.
> • They can climb up p_____ trees easily.

Conversation

[05~06] 다음 대화를 읽고, 물음에 답하시오.

> G: ①Have you ever been to Brazil?
> B: No, I haven't. Have you?
> G: ②Yes, I have. ③I have been there last year. ④There was a big samba festival.
> B: That sounds interesting. ⑤I hope to go there someday.

05 대화의 밑줄 친 ①~⑤ 중에서 어색한 곳을 고르고 바르게 고치시오.

➡ _____

06 〈보기〉에서 대화의 내용과 일치하는 <u>않는</u> 것의 개수를 고르시오.

> ┌─ 보기 ┐
> ⓐ The boy has never been to Brazil.
> ⓑ The girl visited Brazil last year.
> ⓒ The girl wants to go to Brazil.
> ⓓ The girl has ever been to Brazil.
> ⓔ There was a samba festival in Brazil last year.
> ⓕ The boy had a fun time in Brazil.

① 1개　② 2개　③ 3개　④ 4개　⑤ 5개

07 다음 중 어색한 대화를 고르시오.

① A: Have you ever played *gorodki*?
　 B: No, I haven't. What is it?
② A: What does that mean?
　 B: It means victory or peace.
③ A: Should I bring anything?
　 B: No, but please wear white clothes.
④ A: Have you ever gone to Brazil?
　 B: No. Have you?
⑤ A: What is that?
　 B: It's a traditional Indian festival.

[08~11] 다음 대화를 읽고, 물음에 답하시오.

> G: Hello, Santiago! What brings you here today?
> B: *Bienvenido*, Cathy. (①)
> G: Me, too. But what did you just say?
> B: *Bienvenido*! It (A)_____ "welcome" in Spanish. (②) Look at those dancers. Their dance moves are so great. (③)
> G: Yes, they are.
> B: 전에 스페인 축제에 가 본 적 있니?
> G: No, I haven't. Santiago, can you see the big letters on the stage? (④) What does that mean? (⑤)
> B: Oh, *gracias*. That (B)_____ "thank you."

08 위 대화의 ①~⑤ 중 주어진 문장이 들어갈 알맞은 곳은?

> I came to see the Spanish festival.

①   ②   ③   ④   ⑤

09 빈칸 (A)와 (B)에 공통으로 들어갈 말을 대화의 어휘 중에서 찾아 어법에 맞게 쓰시오.

➡ _____

10 위 대화의 밑줄 친 우리말을 영작하시오.

➡ _____

11 위 대화의 내용과 일치하지 <u>않는</u> 것을 고르시오.

① Santiago knows the meaning of some Spanish words.
② Cathy didn't know the meaning of *gracias*.
③ Cathy has never been to Spain.
④ There are small letters, *gracias*, on the stage.
⑤ Cathy came to see the Spanish festival.

[12~13] 다음 대화를 읽고, 물음에 답하시오.

> W: Welcome (A)_____ the International Games Festival. You can play many different traditional games here.
> B: Wow! It looks exciting! Which game should I play first?
> W: Let's see. Have you ever played *gorodki*?
> B: No, I haven't. What is it?
> W: It's a traditional game (B)_____ Russia.
> B: How do I play it?
> W: Put five sticks (C)_____ the ground. Then throw a bat (D)_____ them.
> B: That sounds fun. I'll try that first.

12 빈칸 (A)~(D)에 알맞은 것을 〈보기〉에서 골라 쓰시오.

> ┤ 보기 ├
> on   from   at   to

➡ (A)_____   (B)_____
   (C)_____   (C)_____

13 주어진 영영풀이에 해당하는 단어를 대화에서 찾아 쓰시오.

> being part of something that people have done for a long time

➡ _____

Grammar

14 다음 중 밑줄 친 부분의 쓰임이 〈보기〉와 같은 것을 <u>모두</u> 고르면?

> ┤ 보기 ├
> <u>Have</u> you ever <u>been</u> to America?

① Nolan <u>has learned</u> English for 6 years.
② The train <u>has</u> just <u>left</u> the station.
③ I <u>have watched</u> *Avatar* three times.
④ I <u>haven't met</u> a famous movie star.
⑤ My smartphone <u>has broken</u>.

15 다음 우리말을 영어로 바르게 옮긴 것은?

> 그는 너무 천천히 걸어서 회의에 늦었다.

① He walked too slowly as he was late for the meeting.
② He walked slowly so that he was late for the meeting.
③ He walked so slowly that he was late for the meeting.
④ He walked slowly enough that he was late for the meeting.
⑤ He walked too slowly to be late for the meeting.

16 다음 중 어법상 <u>어색한</u> 것은?

① When have you visited London?
② Have you watched *The Wizard of Oz*?
③ Lindsay has visited Korea twice.
④ We have known her since she was a little girl.
⑤ Jake has been sick for two weeks.

17 다음 두 문장을 한 문장으로 바르게 연결한 것은?

> • Mom became very angry.
> • Mom yelled at me.

① Mom became very angry that she yelled at me.
② Mom became enough angry to yell at me.
③ Mom became too angry to yell at me.
④ Mom became angry as that she yelled at me.
⑤ Mom became so angry that she yelled at me.

18 다음 우리말에 맞게 빈칸에 알맞은 말을 쓰시오.

> Sonya는 너무 피곤해서 곧 잠이 들었다.

➡ Sonya was _____ tired _____ she fell asleep in a moment.

19 다음 우리말과 의미가 같도록 빈칸에 알맞은 말을 쓰시오.

(1) 그는 인도를 방문해 본 적이 없다.
  ➡ He _____ never _____ to India.
(2) Shirley는 영국에 가서 여기 없다.
  ➡ Shirley _____ _____ to England.

20 다음 중 어법상 <u>어색한</u> 것은?

① He is so smart that he can solve all these math problems without a calculator.
② Nicole was very tired that she couldn't go shopping.
③ Ms. Winslet is such a nice teacher that she gives all her students gifts.
④ The little boy was too short to reach the shelf.
⑤ Edan studied hard enough to pass the math test.

21 괄호 안에 주어진 어휘를 이용하여 다음을 영작하시오.

(1) 그 차는 너무 빨라서 경찰은 그것을 잡을 수 없었다. (the car, fast, that, the police, catch)
  ➡ _____
(2) 그 콘서트는 너무 좋아서 많은 사람들이 그것을 다시 보러 갔다. (the concert, good, that, see, again)
  ➡ _____

22 주어진 두 문장을 현재완료를 이용해 한 문장으로 만드시오.

(1) Lin spent all the money for shopping.
So she doesn't have any money now.

➡ _____

(2) Jeremy started to play the piano six years ago. And he still plays the piano.

➡ _____

Reading

[23~24] 다음 글을 읽고, 물음에 답하시오.

Peter is visiting Korea ⓐto meet a friend, Mina, from a sister school. Peter is going to stay at her grandfather's house for a week. When he arrives, Mina shows him the guest room.

Mina: Peter, you will stay here. This guest room is full of (A)[modern / traditional] Korean things. Look at this pillow.

Peter What are these things?

Mina: They're bats.

Peter: Bats on my pillow? That's (B)[scary / terrific]!

Mina: Not really. In Korea, bats are symbols of luck and a long life.

Peter: That's surprising. In many Western countries, bats (C)[remind / remain] people of darkness and scary things.

23 위 글의 밑줄 친 ⓐto meet과 to부정사의 용법이 같은 것을 모두 고르시오.

① I went to the store to buy some eggs.
② It wasn't easy to solve the problem.
③ He wanted to get a good grade.
④ I have some questions to ask her.
⑤ He studied hard to be a scientist.

24 위 글의 괄호 (A)~(C)에서 문맥상 알맞은 낱말을 골라 쓰시오.

➡ (A)_____ (B)_____ (C)_____

[25~27] 다음 글을 읽고, 물음에 답하시오.

Mina shows Peter her grandfather's room. Peter and Mina's grandfather meet and greet each other.

Grandfather: Hi, Peter! Have you ever seen this kind of lock before?

Peter: No, I haven't. It's ___ⓐ___ old ___ⓑ___ I can't really tell, but is it a fish?

Grandfather: Yes. For a long time, Koreans have thought that fish are good guards. Fish don't close their eyes, even when they sleep.

Peter: ⓒThat's interesting.

Grandfather: We think fish can watch over valuable things. That's why this lock looks like a fish.

Peter: Now I understand.

25 위 글의 빈칸 ⓐ와 ⓑ에 들어갈 알맞은 말을 고르시오.

① such – that ② too – as
③ enough – that ④ so – that
⑤ so – as

26 위 글의 밑줄 친 ⓒThat이 가리키는 것을 본문에서 찾아 쓰시오.

➡ _____

27 위 글의 주제로 알맞은 것을 고르시오.

① the reason Mina shows Peter her grandfather's room
② the most popular kind of lock in Korea
③ the reason fish don't close their eyes
④ various kinds of locks in traditional Korean houses
⑤ the reason the lock looks like a fish

[28~30] 다음 글을 읽고, 물음에 답하시오.

Peter: What is on that piece of paper? It looks scary.

Grandfather: Do you mean this painting of a rooster?

Peter: Oh, is it a rooster?

Grandfather: Yes, it is. Roosters crow every morning. Their crowing means that a new day is beginning. For many years, Koreans have believed ⓐ____ when a rooster crows.

Mina: Really? I've never heard that before.

Peter: Actually, I'm afraid ⓑ____ darkness and evil spirits. Could you draw a rooster ⓒ____ me, Mina?

Mina: Sure. I'll draw a big rooster ⓒ____ you!

Grandfather: Put the drawing above your door. Then it will protect you.

Peter: Yes, I will.

28 위 글의 빈칸 ⓐ에 들어갈 알맞은 말을 고르시오.

① evil spirits go away
② darkness follows
③ people go to sleep
④ evil spirits arrive
⑤ it gets dark

29 위 글의 빈칸 ⓑ와 ⓒ에 들어갈 전치사가 바르게 짝지어진 것은?

① in – to   ② of – at
③ of – for   ④ for – to
⑤ in – for

30 위 글의 내용과 일치하지 <u>않는</u> 것은?

① 피터는 종이 위에 있는 그림을 무서워한다.
② 피터는 종이 위에 수탉 그림이 있는 것을 알고 있었다.
③ 수탉의 울음은 새로운 날이 시작하는 것을 의미한다.
④ 피터는 어둠과 악령을 무서워한다.
⑤ 미나는 피터를 위해 커다란 수탉을 그려줄 것이다.

[31~32] 다음 일기를 읽고, 물음에 답하시오.

Peter's Diary

May 28

I'm enjoying this trip so much that I want ⓐto stay longer. I love all the traditional Korean symbols in this house. ⓑNow I understand a lot of it. I want to visit Korea again with my family.

31 아래 〈보기〉에서 위 일기의 밑줄 친 ⓐto stay와 문법적 쓰임이 같은 것의 개수를 고르시오.

┌─ 보기 ─┐
① It is time to go to bed.
② She decided to meet him again.
③ I worked hard to pass the test.
④ He is the last man to tell a lie.
⑤ It is good to help the old.
└────────┘

① 1개   ② 2개   ③ 3개   ④ 4개   ⑤ 5개

32 위 일기의 밑줄 친 ⓑ에서 어법상 <u>틀린</u> 부분을 찾아 고치시오.

_____ ➡ _____

[01~02] 주어진 문장의 뒤에 나올 대화의 순서를 알맞게 쓰시오.

출제율 90%

01

> There is a Holi festival in Busan this year.

> (A) That sounds exciting. Have you ever been to a Holi festival?
>
> (B) It's a traditional Indian festival. People throw colored powder and water at each other.
>
> (C) A Holi festival? What is that?
>
> (D) No, I haven't. But my Indian friend told me a lot about it.

➡ _____

출제율 85%

02

> Oh, look at that boy. That's really rude.

> (A) What's wrong with that?
>
> (B) It has a bad meaning in England. But showing your palm and making a V sign is okay.
>
> (C) It means victory or peace.
>
> (D) Which boy?
>
> (E) What does that mean?
>
> (F) The boy who is making the V sign. His palm is facing toward himself.

➡ _____

[03~04] 다음 대화를 읽고, 물음에 답하시오.

> G: Have you ever been to Brazil?
>
> B: No, I (A)_____. (B)_____ you?

> G: Yes, I (C)_____. I went there last year. There (D)_____ a big samba festival.
>
> B: That (E)_____ interesting. I hope (F)_____ there someday.

출제율 100%

03 빈칸 (A)~(C)에 들어갈 단어를 쓰시오. (각 1 단어)

➡ (A)_____ (B)_____ (C)_____

출제율 90%

04 빈칸 (D)~(F)에 들어갈 말이 바르게 짝지어진 것은?

	(D)	(E)	(F)
①	is	sounds	go
②	is	sounds like	to go
③	was	sounds like	going
④	was	sounds	to go
⑤	were	sounds like	going

[05~07] 다음 대화를 읽고, 물음에 답하시오.

> B: Ling's birthday is this Wednesday, isn't it?
>
> G: Yes. I'm going to buy a book for her. (①) What about you?
>
> B: Well, I'm thinking about buying her an umbrella. I found a cute one in a gift shop. (②)
>
> G: Oh, that's not a good gift for (A)_____ people. (③) It means something bad.
>
> B: Really? What does an umbrella mean in China?
>
> G: (④) The words for *separation* and *umbrella* sound the same in (B)_____.
>
> B: I see. (⑤) Then how about chocolate?
>
> G: That's a good idea.

출제율 85%

05 위 대화의 ①~⑤ 중 주어진 문장이 들어갈 알맞은 곳은?

> It means separation.

①   ②   ③   ④   ⑤

출제율 95%

06 (A)와 (B)에 공통으로 들어갈 말을 쓰시오. (대화의 단어를 이용해서 쓸 것)

➡ _____

출제율 90%

07 주어진 영영풀이에 해당하는 단어를 대화에서 찾아 쓰시오.

> the act of moving two things or people apart

➡ _____

출제율 100%

08 빈칸에 공통으로 알맞은 단어를 쓰시오.

> • Have you heard _____ the Flower Fair?
> • I'm thinking _____ buying her an umbrella.
> • People like to talk _____ the leisure time.

출제율 90%

09 다음 제시된 의미에 맞는 단어를 주어진 철자로 시작하여 빈칸에 쓰고, 알맞은 것을 골라 문장을 완성하시오. (형태 변화 가능)

> • b_____ : to lower your head or bend your body
> • c_____ : to make the loud sound that a rooster makes
> • l_____ : to keep happening for a certain amount of time

(1) The meeting _____ three hours yesterday.

(2) The rooster _____ about once an hour.

(3) I always _____ to my teacher.

출제율 90%

10 다음 대화의 빈칸 (A)와 (B)를 주어진 단어를 이용해 완성하시오.

> A: Have you ever (A)_____ (listen) to (B)_____ (Spain) music?
> B: Yes, I have.

출제율 90%

11 다음 대화의 밑줄 친 우리말을 주어진 단어를 써서 영작하시오.

> A: What does eating 12 grapes on New Year's Day mean in Spain?
> B: 12개월 동안 행운을 의미한다. (luck, for)

➡ _____

출제율 95%

12 다음 중 어법상 올바른 문장을 모두 고르시오.

① I have met him several times.

② Mary has lived here since 10 years.

③ Have you ever gone to Malaysia?

④ Scarlet has moved to Los Angeles 5 years ago.

⑤ He has been sick for two days.

출제율 90%

13 다음 우리말과 일치하도록 괄호 안의 어구를 바르게 배열하여 문장을 완성하시오.

(1) 그는 너무 뚱뚱해서 맞는 셔츠가 거의 없다.
(hardly / so / he / him / shirt / there / is / is / fits / fat / that / that / any).

➡ _____

(2) 그의 목소리가 너무 작아서 나는 그가 말하는 것을 듣지 못했다.
(I / couldn't / his voice / talk / so / was / hear / small / him / that).

➡ _____

(3) Jenny는 Sunny를 한 시간 동안 기다려 왔다.
(Jenny / Sunny / waited / hour / has / an / for / for).

➡ _____

14 출제율 95%

다음 중 어법상 <u>어색한</u> 문장을 고르시오.

① Taylor was so hungry that he has eaten all the food on the table.

② Jonathan woke up so late that he missed the first train to London.

③ After cleaning her home, she was so tired that she couldn't take a walk.

④ The table was so heavy that I couldn't move it by myself.

⑤ The cell phone was so expensive that I couldn't buy it.

15 출제율 90%

다음 두 문장을 한 문장으로 바꾸시오.

(1) It started to rain a week ago. And it still rains.

➡ _____

(2) Elvis went to Wien. And he is there now.

➡ _____

[16~18] 다음 글을 읽고, 물음에 답하시오.

Mina: Peter, you will stay here. (A)<u>이 손님방은 한국 전통 물건들로 가득 차 있어.</u> Look at this pillow.

Peter: What are these things?

Mina: They're bats.

Peter: Bats on my pillow? That's scary!

Mina: Not really. In Korea, bats are ___ⓐ___ of luck and a long life.

Peter: That's surprising. In many Western countries, bats remind people ___ⓑ___ darkness and scary things.

16 출제율 90%

위 글의 빈칸 ⓐ에 들어갈 가장 알맞은 말을 고르시오.

① subjects　　　② traditions

③ opinions　　　④ symbols

⑤ cultures

17 출제율 85%

위 글의 빈칸 ⓑ에 들어갈 알맞은 전치사를 쓰시오.

➡ _____

18 출제율 95%

위 글의 밑줄 친 (A)의 우리말에 맞게 한 단어를 보충하여, 주어진 어구를 알맞게 배열하시오.

Korean / full / this / things / guest room / traditional / is

➡ _____

[19~21] 다음 글을 읽고, 물음에 답하시오.

Mina shows Peter her grandfather's room. Peter and Mina's grandfather meet and greet each other.

Grandfather: Hi, Peter! Have you ever seen this kind of lock before?

Peter: No, I (A)[don't / haven't]. ⓐ<u>It's so old that I can't really tell</u>, but is it a fish?

Grandfather: Yes. For a long time, Koreans have thought that fish (B)[is / are] good guards. Fish don't close their eyes, even when they sleep.

Peter: That's interesting.

Grandfather: We think fish can watch over valuable things. That's (C)[because / why] this lock looks like a fish.

Peter: Now I understand.

19 출제율 95%

위 글의 괄호 (A)~(C)에서 어법상 알맞은 낱말을 골라 쓰시오.

➡ (A)_____ (B)_____ (C)_____

✎ 출제율 90%

20 위 글의 밑줄 친 ⓐ를 우리말로 옮기시오.

➡ _____

✎ 출제율 85%

21 위 글의 내용과 일치하지 <u>않는</u> 것은?

① 피터와 미나의 할아버지가 만나서 서로 인사한다.
② 피터는 미나의 할아버지가 보여주신 종류의 자물쇠를 전에 본 적이 없다.
③ 오랜 세월 동안, 한국인들은 물고기가 훌륭한 파수꾼이라고 생각해 왔다.
④ 물고기는 잘 때 그들의 눈을 감는다.
⑤ 한국인들은 물고기가 귀중품을 지킬 수 있다고 생각한다.

[22~24] 다음 글을 읽고, 물음에 답하시오.

Peter: What is on that ⓐpiece of paper? It looks scary.
Grandfather: Do you mean this painting of a rooster?
Peter: Oh, is it a rooster?
Grandfather: Yes, it is. Roosters crow every morning. Their crowing means that a new day is beginning. For many years, Koreans have believed evil spirits go away when a rooster crows.
Mina: Really? I've never heard that before.
Peter: Actually, I'm afraid of darkness and evil spirits. Could you draw a rooster for me, Mina?
Mina: Sure. I'll draw a big rooster for you!
Grandfather: Put the drawing above your door. Then ⓑit will protect you.
Peter: Yes, I will.

✎ 출제율 95%

22 위 글의 밑줄 친 ⓐpiece와 바꿔 쓸 수 있는 말을 쓰시오.

➡ _____

✎ 출제율 90%

23 위 글의 밑줄 친 ⓑit이 가리키는 것을 본문에서 찾아 쓰시오.

➡ _____

✎ 출제율 95%

24 위 글의 요지로 알맞은 것을 고르시오.

① 종이 위에 그린 부적은 미신이다.
② 수탉이 매일 아침 울어야 새로운 날이 시작한다.
③ 오랫동안 한국인들은 수탉이 울 때 악령이 물러간다고 믿고 문 위에 수탉 그림을 걸어놓았다.
④ 미나는 피터를 위해 큰 수탉을 그려줄 것이다.
⑤ 수탉 그림은 문 위에 붙여놓아야 한다.

[25~26] 다음 일기를 읽고, 물음에 답하시오.

Peter's Diary

May 28

I'm enjoying this trip so much that I want to stay longer. I love all the traditional Korean symbols in this house. Now I understand a lot of them. ⓐI want visiting Korea again with my family.

✎ 출제율 95%

25 다음 질문에 대한 알맞은 대답을 주어진 단어로 시작하여 쓰시오. (7 단어)

Q: Why does Peter want to stay longer?
A: Because _____.

✎ 출제율 90%

26 위 일기의 밑줄 친 ⓐ에서 어법상 틀린 부분을 찾아 고치시오.

➡ _____ ➡ _____

[01~03] 다음 대화를 읽고, 물음에 답하시오.

B: Ling's birthday is this Wednesday, isn't it?

G: Yes. I'm going (A)_____ a book for her. What about you?

B: Well, I'm thinking about (B)_____ her an umbrella. I found a cute (C)one in a gift shop.

G: Oh, ①that's a good gift for Chinese people. It means something bad.

B: Really? ②What does an umbrella mean in China?

G: ③It means separation. ④The words for *separation* and *umbrella* sound the same in Chinese.

B: I see. Then how about chocolate?

G: ⑤That's a good idea.

01 buy를 이용하여 빈칸 (A)와 (B)에 들어갈 말을 쓰시오.

➡ (A)_____ (B)_____

02 ①~⑤ 중 대화의 흐름상 어색한 것을 고르고 바르게 고치시오.

_____ ➡ _____

03 밑줄 친 (C)가 가리키는 것을 본문에서 찾아 쓰시오.

➡ _____

04 주어진 두 문장을 현재완료를 이용해 한 문장으로 만드시오.

(1) Charlie started to study Korean six months ago. He still studies Korean.

➡ _____

(2) I lost my umbrella. So I don't have it now.

➡ _____

05 다음 우리말을 괄호 안에 주어진 어구를 이용하여 영작하시오.

(1) 나의 삼촌은 2007년 이래로 그 회사에서 일해 오고 있다. (work for, company, since)

➡ _____
_____

(2) 나는 그렇게 아름다운 다리를 본 적이 없다. (such, never, see, beautiful)

➡ _____
_____

(3) 그 산은 너무 높아서 나는 꼭대기까지 걸어갈 수가 없다. (high, that, to the top)

➡ _____

(4) 나의 부모님은 너무 현명하셔서 나는 보통 그분들의 조언을 따른다. (wise, follow, usually)

➡ _____

06 다음 두 문장을 접속사 that을 사용하여 한 문장으로 연결하시오.

(1) • The dogs are really cute.
• I can't take my eyes off them.

➡ _____

(2) • The weather was very nice.
• They went on a picnic.

➡ _____

Peter is visiting Korea to meet a friend, Mina, from a sister school. Peter is going to stay at her grandfather's house (A)[during / for] a week. When he arrives, Mina shows (B)[him / to him] the guest room.

Mina: Peter, you will stay here. This guest room is full of traditional Korean things. Look at this pillow.

Peter: What are these things?

Mina: They're bats.

Peter: Bats on my pillow? That's scary!

Mina: Not really. In Korea, bats are symbols of luck and a long life.

Peter: ⓐThat's (C)[surprising / surprised]. In many Western countries, bats remind people of darkness and scary things.

07 위 글의 괄호 (A)~(C)에서 어법상 알맞은 낱말을 골라 쓰시오.

➡ (A)_____ (B)_____ (C)_____

08 위 글의 밑줄 친 ⓐThat이 가리키는 것을 본문에서 찾아 쓰시오.

➡ _____

09 위 글을 읽고, 한국과 서구의 많은 나라들에서 박쥐가 상징하는 것이 어떻게 다른지 우리말로 쓰시오.

➡ 한국: _____

　서구의 많은 나라들: _____

_____

Peter: What is on that piece of paper? It looks scary.

Grandfather: ⓐ이 수탉 그림을 말하는 거니?

Peter: Oh, is it a rooster?

Grandfather: Yes, it is. Roosters crow every morning. Their crowing means that a new day is beginning. For many years, Koreans have believed evil spirits go away when a rooster crows.

Mina: Really? I've never heard ⓑthat before.

Peter: Actually, I'm afraid of darkness and evil spirits. Could you draw a rooster for me, Mina?

Mina: Sure. I'll draw a big rooster for you!

Grandfather: Put the drawing above your door. Then it will protect you.

Peter: Yes, I will.

10 위 글의 밑줄 친 ⓐ의 우리말에 맞게 한 단어를 보충하여, 주어진 어휘를 알맞게 배열하시오.

mean / painting / you / rooster / this / do / a

➡ _____

11 다음 문장에서 위 글의 내용과 다른 부분을 찾아서 고치시오. (본문의 단어를 사용하시오.)

The meaning of roosters' crowing is that the sun is setting. For many years, Koreans have believed evil spirits disappear with the crowing of roosters.

_____ ➡ _____

12 위 글의 밑줄 친 ⓑthat이 가리키는 것을 본문에서 찾아 쓰시오.

➡ _____

01 다음 주어진 단어와 그림을 참고하여 대화를 완성하시오.

visit a Spanish festival

A: Have you ever _____?

B: No, _____. Have you?

A: Yes, I have. I _____ last year. (visit) There was a La Tomatina festival.

B: What is La Tomatina festival?

A: It's _____ festival. People _____.

B: _____?

A: It's the last Tuesday in August.

B: I'd like to go. It sounds interesting.

02 다음 내용을 바탕으로 학급 신문에 다른 나라의 전통 문화를 소개하는 글을 쓰시오.

1. Q: What do you want to talk about?

   A: I want to talk about traditional Chinese dances.

2. Q: What are some examples?

   A: There are a lion dance, a fan dance, and an umbrella dance.

3. Q: Choose one and search for more information about it.

   A: In the lion dance, two dancers dress and act like lions. They do the dance on special days.

4. Q: What do you think of it?

   A: I think their dance moves are great.

An Amazing Traditional Chinese Dance

Do you know about (A)_____ Chinese dances? There are many kinds. For example, there are a lion dance, a fan dance, and an umbrella dance. One of the most famous dances (B)_____ the lion dance. In this dance, two dancers dress and act (C)_____ lions. They usually dance on (D)_____ days, such as New Year's Day. I think their dance moves are great. I hope (E)_____ this dance someday.

단원별 모의고사

[01~03] 다음 대화를 읽고, 물음에 답하시오.

> G: ⓐ<u>How a nice picture!</u> Are these your friends?
> B: Yes. (①) We took this picture at the beach. We had a lot of fun.
> G: Oh, look at that boy. (②) That's really rude.
> B: ⓑ<u>Who boy?</u>
> G: ⓒ<u>The boy whose is making the V sign.</u> ⓓ<u>His palm is facing toward him.</u> (③)
> B: What's wrong with that?
> G: (④) But ⓔ<u>showing your palm and making a V sign is okay.</u>
> B: What does that mean?
> G: (⑤) It means victory or peace.

01 위 대화의 ①~⑤ 중 주어진 문장이 들어갈 알맞은 곳은?

> It has a bad meaning in England.

①   ②   ③   ④   ⑤

02 위 대화의 밑줄 친 ⓐ~ⓔ 중 어법상 틀린 개수를 고르시오.

① 1개   ② 2개   ③ 3개   ④ 4개   ⑤ 5개

03 주어진 영영풀이에 해당하는 단어를 위 대화에서 찾아 쓰시오.

(1)

> the inside part of the hand between the wrist and the fingers

➡ _____

(2)

> to have the front part toward something

➡ _____

[04~05] 다음 대화를 읽고, 물음에 답하시오.

> G: Hello, Santiago! What ① _____ you here today?
> B: *Bienvenido*, Cathy. I came ② _____ the Spanish festival.
> G: Me, too. But what did you just say?
> B: *Bienvenido*! It means "welcome" ③ _____. Look at those dancers. Their dance ④ _____ are so great.
> G: Yes, they are.
> B: Have you ever been to a Spanish festival before?
> G: No, I ⑤ _____. Santiago, can you see the big letters on the stage? <u>무슨 뜻이야?</u>
> B: Oh, *gracias*. That means "thank you."

04 위 대화의 빈칸 ①~⑤에 들어갈 말이나 설명으로 적절하지 <u>않은</u> 것은?

① brings
② to see, to부정사의 부사적 용법으로 '보기 위해서'의 의미로 사용되었다.
③ in Spain, '스페인어로'의 의미로 사용되었다.
④ moves
⑤ haven't

05 위 대화의 밑줄 친 우리말을 영작하시오.

➡ _____

06 다음 대화에서 <u>어색한</u> 부분을 <u>모두</u> 찾아 고치시오. (2개)

> G: Have you ever been to Brazil?
> B: No, I haven't. Do you?
> G: Yes, I do. I went there last year. There was a big samba festival.
> B: That sounds interesting. I hope to go there someday.

(1) _____ ➡ _____
(2) _____ ➡ _____

[07~09] 다음 대화를 읽고, 물음에 답하시오.

W: ①Welcome to the International Games Festival. ②You can play many different traditional games here.

B: Wow! ③It looks exciting! (A)_____ game should I play first?

W: Let's see. 고로드키(*gorodki*) 게임 해 본 적 있나요?

B: No, I haven't. (B)_____ is it?

W: ④It's a traditional game from Russia.

B: (C)_____ do I play it?

W: ⑤Putting five sticks on the ground. Then throw a bat at them.

B: That sounds fun. I'll try that first.

07 (A)~(C)에 알맞은 의문사를 〈보기〉에서 골라 쓰시오.

┌─ 보기 ─┐
Who   Which   What   Why   How

➡ (A)_____   (B)_____   (C)_____

08 위 대화의 밑줄 친 우리말을 영작하시오.

➡ _____

09 ①~⑤ 중 문법상 어색한 부분을 고르고 바르게 고치시오.

_____ ➡ _____

[10~12] 다음 대화를 읽고, 물음에 답하시오.

B: There is a Holi festival in Busan this year. (①)

G: A Holi festival? What is that?

B: (②) ⓐPeople throw colored powder and water at each other.

G: That sounds exciting. (③) ⓑHave you ever been to a Holi festival?

B: ⓒYes, I have. But my Indian friend told me a lot about it.

G: When is the festival?

B: (④) ⓓIt's on the last full moon of the Hindu calendar. This year, it's on March 21.

G: ⓔI'd like to go. Should I bring anything?

B: No, but you should wear white clothes. (⑤) Then the colored powder on your clothes will look more beautiful.

G: Okay. Thank you for the information.

10 위 대화의 ①~⑤ 중 주어진 문장이 들어갈 알맞은 곳은?

┌──────────────────────────┐
It's a traditional Indian festival.
└──────────────────────────┘

①   ②   ③   ④   ⑤

11 ⓐ~ⓔ 중 대화의 흐름상 어색한 부분을 고르시오.

① ⓐ   ② ⓑ   ③ ⓒ   ④ ⓓ   ⑤ ⓔ

12 위 대화의 내용과 일치하도록 빈칸을 채우시오.

┌──────────────────────────┐
A Holi festival is _____.
It will be held in _____ this year.
In a Holi festival, people _____
_____. When people
wear _____, the colored
powder on the white clothes can
_____.
└──────────────────────────┘

13 〈보기〉의 밑줄 친 'has swum'과 같은 용법으로 쓰인 것은?

┌─ 보기 ─┐
Evan has never swum in this lake before.

① Amy has just finished her homework.
② Chuck has lived in Seoul since 2002.
③ The concert has already started.
④ Rosalind has gone to France.
⑤ I have watched the movie twice.

14 다음 문장과 같은 뜻의 문장을 to부정사를 이용하여 쓰시오.

(1) The soup smelled so bad that I couldn't have it.

➡ _____

(2) Einstein was so clever that he could understand the theory.

➡ _____

15 다음 문장의 틀린 곳을 고쳐 다시 쓰시오.

(1) When have you gone there?

➡ _____

(2) I have studied English since 5 years.

➡ _____

(3) I was so busy to help her.

➡ _____

_____

(4) The bunjee jump was scary so that we screamed a lot.

➡ _____

16 다음 문장의 빈칸에 for나 since 중 알맞은 것을 쓰시오.

(1) Christine has stayed in Seoul _____ five years.

(2) We have known her _____ 2002.

17 다음 두 문장을 접속사 that을 사용하여 한 문장으로 연결하시오.

• Phillip has lived in China for a long time.

• He can speak Chinese very well.

➡ _____

_____

[18~20] 다음 글을 읽고, 물음에 답하시오.

Mina: Peter, you will stay here. This guest room is full of traditional Korean things. Look at this pillow.

Peter: What are these things?

Mina: They're bats.

Peter: ⓐBats on my pillow? That's scary!

Mina: Not really. In Korea, bats are symbols of luck and a long life.

Peter: That's surprising. In many Western countries, ⓑ박쥐는 사람들에게 어둠과 무서운 것들을 상기시키거든.

18 위 글의 밑줄 친 ⓐ에서 알 수 있는 피터의 심경으로 알맞지 않은 것을 고르시오.

① terrified   ② grateful
③ frightened   ④ afraid
⑤ scared

19 위 글의 밑줄 친 ⓑ의 우리말에 맞게 주어진 어휘를 이용하여 8 단어로 영작하시오.

remind, of

➡ _____

20 위 글의 목적으로 알맞은 것을 고르시오.

① 자매학교 친구를 방문하는 방법을 설명하기 위한 글이다.
② 손님방을 한국 전통 물건들로 가득 채우는 방법을 설명하기 위한 글이다.
③ 베개에 있는 박쥐 디자인에 대한 피터의 반응을 소개하기 위한 글이다.
④ 전통적인 한국의 상징물들 중 박쥐의 의미를 소개하기 위한 글이다.
⑤ 서구의 많은 나라들에서 박쥐들이 상징하는 것을 소개하기 위한 글이다.

[21~23] 다음 글을 읽고, 물음에 답하시오.

Grandfather: Hi, Peter! Have you ever seen this kind of lock before?

Peter: No, I haven't. It's so old that I can't really tell, but is it a fish?

Grandfather: Yes. For a long time, Koreans have thought that fish are good ____ⓐ____. Fish don't close their eyes, even when they sleep.

Peter: That's interesting.

Grandfather: We think fish can watch over valuable things. That's why this lock looks ⓑlike a fish.

Peter: Now I understand.

21 주어진 영영풀이를 참고하여 빈칸 ⓐ에 철자 g로 시작하는 단어를 쓰시오.

> people who watch over something or someone

➡ _____

22 위 글의 밑줄 친 ⓑlike와 같은 의미로 쓰인 것을 고르시오.

① Do you like this music?
② How did you like the movie?
③ I like my coffee strong.
④ She sounds like a serious person.
⑤ I like to hear the boy singing.

23 빈칸 (A)와 (B)에 알맞은 단어를 넣어, 위 글에서 자물쇠가 물고기처럼 생긴 이유를 완성하시오.

> Fish (A)_____ _____ their eyes even when they sleep, so people think fish can (B)_____ _____ valuable things. For that reason, this lock looks like a fish.

(A) _____   (B) _____

[24~25] 다음 글을 읽고, 물음에 답하시오.

Peter: What is on that piece of paper? It looks scary.

Grandfather: Do you mean this painting of a rooster?

Peter: Oh, is it a rooster?

Grandfather: Yes, it is. Roosters crow every morning. Their crowing means that a new day is beginning. For many years, Koreans ⓐhave believed evil spirits go away when a rooster crows.

Mina: Really? I've never heard that before.

Peter: Actually, I'm afraid of darkness and evil spirits. Could you draw a rooster for me, Mina?

Mina: Sure. I'll draw a big rooster for you!

Grandfather: Put the drawing above your door. ⓑThen it will protect you.

Peter: Yes, I will.

24 아래 〈보기〉에서 위 글의 밑줄 친 ⓐ와 현재완료의 용법이 다른 것의 개수를 고르시오.

> ┤ 보기 ├
> ① She has gone to America.
> ② It has been fine since last week.
> ③ Have you solved it yet?
> ④ I have visited New York three times.
> ⑤ They have already seen it.

① 1개   ② 2개   ③ 3개   ④ 4개   ⑤ 5개

25 다음 빈칸에 알맞은 단어를 넣어 ⓑThen에 대한 설명을 완성하시오.

> _____ you put the drawing above your door,

➡ _____

Lesson 4

Go Green Together

 의사소통 기능

- 걱정 표현하기
  I'm worried about the Earth.
- 방법 묻기
  Can you tell me how to make the bag?

 언어 형식

- 수동태
  The waste **is turned** into food for the plants by bacteria.
- 비교급 강조
  The plants grow **much** faster than plants in soil.

Words & Expressions

Key Words

- □ **air conditioner** 에어컨
- □ **amazing** [əméiziŋ] 형 놀라운
- □ **any** [əni] 형 어떤, 무슨
- □ **anywhere** [énihwɛər] 부 어디든
- □ **article** [ɑ́:rtikl] 명 (신문) 기사
- □ **bottom** [bátəm] 명 바닥, 맨 아래
- □ **chemical** [kémikəl] 명 화학 물질
- □ **clay** [klei] 명 점토
- □ **connect** [kənékt] 동 연결하다
- □ **consume** [kənsú:m] 동 섭취하다, 먹다, 소모하다
- □ **difficult** [dífkʌlt] 형 어려운
- □ **disappear** [dìsəpíər] 동 사라지다
- □ **documentary** [dkjuméntəri] 명 다큐멘터리, 기록물
- □ **enough** [inʌf] 형 충분한 부 충분히
- □ **environment** [inváiərənmənt] 명 환경
- □ **experiment** [ikspérəmənt] 명 실험
- □ **fan** [fæn] 명 선풍기, 부채
- □ **feed**(–fed–fed) [fi:d] 동 먹이를 주다, 먹이다
- □ **fix** [fiks] 동 고정하다
- □ **gardening** [gɑ́:rdniŋ] 명 정원 가꾸기, 원예
- □ **global** [glóubəl] 형 지구의
- □ **grow** [grou] 동 재배하다
- □ **hang** [hæŋ] 동 매달려 있다
- □ **healthy** [hélθi] 형 건강한, 건강에 좋은
- □ **helpful** [hélpfəl] 형 도움이 되는, 유용한
- □ **hole** [houl] 명 구멍
- □ **information** [infərméiʃən] 명 정보
- □ **instead** [instéd] 부 대신에
- □ **interesting** [íntərəstiŋ] 형 흥미로운
- □ **island** [áilənd] 명 섬
- □ **leave** [li:v] 동 남기다, ~을 떠나다
- □ **lid** [lid] 명 뚜껑
- □ **nervous** [nə́:rvəs] 형 초조한, 긴장된
- □ **plate** [pleit] 명 접시
- □ **pot** [pɑt] 명 화분, 그릇
- □ **pollution** [pəlú:ʃən] 명 오염
- □ **problem** [práblem] 명 문제
- □ **process** [práses] 명 과정
- □ **produce** [prədjú:s] 동 생산하다, 만들다
- □ **productive** [prədʌ́ktiv] 형 생산적인
- □ **put** [put] 동 두다, 놓다
- □ **raise** [reiz] 동 기르다, 키우다
- □ **repeat** [ripí:t] 동 반복하다
- □ **say** [sei] 동 ~라고 쓰여 있다
- □ **sea level** 해수면
- □ **sew** [sou] 동 바느질하다
- □ **should** [ʃəd] 조 ~해야 한다
- □ **speech contest** 말하기 대회
- □ **solution** [səlú:ʃən] 명 해결책
- □ **soil** [sɔil] 명 토양, 흙
- □ **solve** [sɑlv] 동 해결하다
- □ **space** [speis] 명 공간
- □ **terrible** [térəbl] 형 끔찍한
- □ **too** [tu:] 부 너무, 지나치게
- □ **traditional** [trədíʃənl] 형 전통적인
- □ **warming** [wɔ́:rmiŋ] 명 온난화
- □ **waste** [weist] 동 낭비하다 명 쓰레기, 폐기물
- □ **water** [wɔ́:tər] 동 물을 주다

Key Expressions

- □ **be about** ~ ~에 관한 것이다
- □ **be worried about** ~에 관해 걱정하다
- □ **cut A into B** A를 B로 자르다
- □ **fill A with B** A를 B로 채우다
- □ **get**+비교급 점점 ~해지다
- □ **go up** 올라가다, 상승하다
- □ **how to**+동사원형 ~하는 방법
- □ **in danger** 위험에 처한
- □ **in place** 제자리에
- □ **look**+형용사 ~처럼 보이다
- □ **right away** 즉시, 당장(=**at once**)
- □ **remind A of B** A에게 B를 상기시키다
- □ **run out** (시간이) 다 되다
- □ **throw away** 버리다
- □ **try to**+동사원형 ~하려고 노력하다[애쓰다]
- □ **turn A into B** A를 B로 바꾸다
- □ **turn off** (전기, 가스, 수도 등을) 끄다
- □ **turn on** (전기, 가스, 수도 등을) 켜다
- □ **What[How] about** ~? ~은 어때?
- □ **Why don't you**+동사원형 ~? ~하는 게 어때?

Word Power

※ 서로 반대되는 뜻을 가진 단어

- ☐ **waste** (낭비하다) ↔ **save** (절약하다)
- ☐ **disappear** (사라지다) ↔ **appear** (나타나다)
- ☐ **turn off** (끄다) ↔ **turn on** (켜다)
- ☐ **near** (가까운) ↔ **far** (먼)
- ☐ **fill** (채우다) ↔ **empty** (비우다)
- ☐ **bottom** (바닥) ↔ **top** (꼭대기)

- ☐ **much** (양이 많은) ↔ **little** (양이 적은)
- ☐ **lose** (잃다) ↔ **gain** (얻다)
- ☐ **enough** (충분한) ↔ **short; lacking** (부족한)
- ☐ **difficult** (어려운) ↔ **easy** (쉬운)
- ☐ **without** (~ 없이) ↔ **with** (~이 있는, ~을 가지고)
- ☐ **productive** (생산적인) ↔ **unproductive** (비생산적인)

※ 서로 비슷한 뜻을 가진 단어

- ☐ **nervous : anxious** (초조한, 걱정하는)
- ☐ **danger : jeopardy** (위험)
- ☐ **connect : link** (연결하다)
- ☐ **produce : create** (만들어 내다)
- ☐ **solution : answer** (해결책, 해답)

- ☐ **raise : rear** (키우다, 기르다)
- ☐ **consume : eat** (섭취하다, 먹다)
- ☐ **choose : select** (고르다, 선택하다)
- ☐ **disappear : vanish** (사라지다)
- ☐ **amazing : astonishing** (놀라운)

English Dictionary

- ☐ **chemical** 화학 물질
  - → a substance used in chemistry or produced by a chemical process 화학에서 사용되거나 화학 과정에서 만들어지는 물질
- ☐ **connect** 연결하다
  - → to join or be joined with something else 다른 무언가와 연결하거나 연결되다
- ☐ **consume** 먹다
  - → to eat or drink, especially a lot of something 어떤 것을 많이 먹거나 마시다
- ☐ **documentary** 다큐멘터리
  - → a film or a television or radio programme that gives detailed information about a particular subject 특별한 주제에 관해 상세한 정보를 제공하는 영화나 TV 또는 라디오 프로그램
- ☐ **feed** 먹이를 주다
  - → to give food to a person or animal 사람이나 동물에게 먹이를 주다
- ☐ **fix** 고정시키다
  - → to fasten something in position so that it cannot move

    움직이지 못하도록 무언가를 자리에 고정시키다

- ☐ **hole** 구멍
  - → an empty space in an object, usually with an opening to the object's surface 물체의 빈 공간, 대개 물체의 표면에 있는 틈
- ☐ **raise** 기르다, 키우다
  - → to take care of a person, or an animal or plant, until they are completely grown 완전히 자랄 때까지 사람이나 동물, 또는 식물을 돌보다
- ☐ **produce** 생산하다
  - → to make something or bring something into existence

    어떤 것을 만들거나 존재하게 하다
- ☐ **productive** 생산적인
  - → producing or achieving a lot

    많은 것을 생산하거나 성취[달성]하는
- ☐ **repeat** 반복하다
  - → to happen, or to do something, more than once

    한 번 이상 어떤 일이 일어나거나 어떤 것을 하다
- ☐ **water** 물을 주다
  - → to pour water onto plants or the soil that they are growing in 식물이 자라고 있는 토양이나 식물에 물을 붓다

서답형

01 다음 짝지어진 두 단어의 관계가 같도록 빈칸에 알맞은 단어를 주어진 글자로 시작하여 쓰시오.

> nervous : anxious – eat : c_____

02 다음 빈칸에 공통으로 들어갈 말은?

> • They turn off their lights for an hour to _____ people of our environmental problems.
> • This song _____s me of my first date.

① hang ② remind ③ make
④ fill ⑤ leave

중요
03 다음 중 밑줄 친 단어의 우리말 뜻이 잘못된 것은?

① Why don't you make a bag?
　왜 하지 않았니
② In some countries, people are in danger.
　　　　　　　　　　　　　위험에 처한
③ I am worried about my homework.
　　~에 관해 걱정하다
④ I want to talk about soil pollution.
　　　　　　　　토양 오염
⑤ We should also use fans instead of air conditioners.　　　　~ 대신에

[04~05] 다음 영영풀이에 해당하는 단어를 고르시오.

04
> to happen, or to do something, more than once

① fix ② produce
③ repeat ④ connect
⑤ waste

05
> to fasten something in position so that it cannot move

① water ② produce
③ sew ④ fix
⑤ feed

서답형
06 다음 우리말에 맞게 빈칸에 알맞은 단어를 쓰시오.

> 그것을 사용하는 법을 말해 줄 수 있니?

➡ Can you tell me _____ _____ _____ it?

07 다음 빈칸에 들어갈 말이 알맞게 짝지어진 것은?

> • Cut them _____ small pieces.
> • We should not put too much food _____ our plates.

① with – for ② into – in
③ from – at ④ to – on
⑤ into – on

중요
08 다음 우리말에 맞게 빈칸에 들어갈 말이 알맞게 짝지어진 것은?

> 한 가지 장치만으로도 식물과 물고기를 동시에 키울 수 있어.
> We can _____ plants and _____ fish in just one system.

① rise – raise ② produce – fix
③ grow – raise ④ consume – raise
⑤ grow – try

01 다음 빈칸에 들어갈 말을 〈보기〉에서 찾아 쓰시오. (필요하면 변형하여 쓰시오.)

---| 보기 |---
article   turn   consume   water
appear   produce

(1) The plants clean the water by _____ the food.
(2) I'm reading an _____ about aquaponics.
(3) Aquaponics is a much more _____ way of growing food.
(4) The waste is _____ into food for the plants by bacteria.

02 다음 문장에 어울리는 단어를 〈보기〉에서 찾아 쓰시오. (필요하면 변형하여 쓰시오.)

---| 보기 |---
connect   feed   bottom   solution

(1) After you _____ the fish, they produce waste.
(2) The speeches are about environmental problems and their _____.
(3) I used the tube to _____ the pump to the pot.
(4) I made holes in the _____ of a pot.

03 다음 우리말과 같은 표현이 되도록 문장의 빈칸을 채우시오.

(1) 나 다음 주에 있을 웅변대회 때문에 걱정이야.
 ➡ I'm _____ _____ the speech contest next week.
(2) 사람들은 한 시간 동안 불을 끈다.
 ➡ People _____ _____ their lights for an hour.
(3) 지구가 점점 더워지고 있어.
 ➡ The Earth is _____ _____.

04 다음 그림에 해당하는 단어를 주어진 철자로 시작하여 쓰시오.

(1) ➡ g_____ _____
(2) ➡ t_____ _____
(3) ➡ _____ d_____
(4) ➡ h_____

05 다음 영영풀이에 알맞은 단어를 〈보기〉에서 찾아 쓰시오.

---| 보기 |---
chemical   disappear   raise

(1) _____ : to take care of a person, or an animal or plant, until they are completely grown
(2) _____ : to become impossible to see any longer

Conversation

1 걱정 표현하기

> **I'm worried about the Earth.** 나는 지구가 걱정돼.

- 'I'm worried about ~'은 걱정을 나타내는 표현으로 'I'm worried about' 뒤에 명사나 대명사, 동명사를 써서 '나는 ~에 대해 걱정한다.'라는 의미를 나타낸다.

■ 걱정이나 두려움을 표현할 때는 I'm worried about ~., I worry about ~., I'm concerned about[for] ~., I'm nervous about[of] ~., I'm anxious about[for] ~. 등으로 말할 수 있다

- I'm nervous about the exam. (나는 시험이 걱정돼.)
- I'm concerned about my health. (나는 내 건강이 걱정돼.)
- I feel uneasy about this matter. (나는 이 문제가 염려돼.)

■ 걱정을 표현한 상대에게 해 줄 수 있는 대답

- Don't worry. (걱정하지 마.)
- Try not to get worried. You'll do fine. (걱정하지 마. 넌 잘할 거야.)
- Take it easy. (마음 편히 가져.)
- Everything will be all right. (모든 게 괜찮아질 거야.)

핵심 Check

1. 다음 대화의 빈칸에 알맞은 말은?

   A: What's wrong?

   B: My math exam was very difficult. _____

   ① Don't worry.

   ② I'm worried about the result.

   ③ Mathematics is one of my favorites.

   ④ How about studying together?

   ⑤ I'm concerned about you.

2. 다음 우리말과 같은 의미가 되도록 주어진 단어를 이용하여 빈칸을 채우시오.

   음식 낭비가 걱정이야. (worry, waste)

   ➡ I'm _____ _____ _____ food.

2 방법 묻기

Can you tell me how to make the bag? 가방을 어떻게 만드는지 알려 줄 수 있니?

- 상대방에게 무엇인가를 하는 방법을 물을 때는 '~하는 방법'이라는 의미의 'how to+동사원형' 구문을 사용하여, 'Do you know how to+동사원형 ~?', 'Can you tell me how to+동사원형 ~?' 또는 'Can you explain (to me) how to+동사원형~?' 등과 같이 말할 수 있다.

- Do you know how to make a cake? (너는 케이크 만드는 방법을 아니?)
- Can you explain how to fix this radio? (이 라디오를 고치는 방법을 설명해 주겠니?)
- Can you tell me how to use a microwave? (전자레인지 사용하는 법을 나한테 말해 주겠니?)
- Do you know how to play the violin? (너는 바이올린을 연주하는 법을 아니?)

- 'how+to부정사'는 'how+주어+should+동사원형'으로 바꿔 쓸 수 있다.

- Do you know how to swim? (너는 수영하는 방법을 아니?)
  = Do you know how you should swim?
- Can you tell me how to make the bag? 가방을 어떻게 만드는지 알려 줄 수 있니?
  = Can you tell me how I should make the bag?

핵심 Check

3. 다음 대화의 밑줄 친 부분과 바꾸어 쓸 수 있는 것은?

A: Are you good at cooking?

B: Yes, I know <u>how I should make</u> cookies and sandwiches.

① how to should make　　② how to making

③ what to make　　④ how to make

⑤ how I to make

4. 다음 빈칸에 들어갈 알맞은 것은?

Do you know _____ to make cheese?

① what　② why　③ when

④ where　⑤ how

5. 다음 우리말에 맞게 주어진 단어를 이용하여 빈칸을 채우시오.

눈사람 그리는 방법을 말해 주겠니? (how, draw)

Can you tell me _____ _____ _____ a snowman?

Listen and Talk 1 Get Ready

B: In my school, ❶students leave so much food on their plates. ❷I'm worried about wasting food.

G: Right, that's a big problem. ❸We should not put too much food on our plates.

B: You're right. ❹We shouldn't.

B: 우리 학교에서, 학생들이 그릇에 너무 많은 음식을 남겨. 나는 음식 낭비가 걱정이야.

G: 맞아, 큰 문제야. 우리가 접시에 너무 많은 음식을 담으면 안 돼.

B: 맞아. 우리는 그러면 안 돼.

❶ leave는 '~을 남기다'는 뜻이고, so는 부사로 much를 수식한다.
❷ be worried about은 '~에 대해 걱정하다'는 뜻이고, 전치사 about 뒤에는 명사나 동명사를 사용한다.
❸ should not은 '~해서는 안 된다'는 의미고, put A on B는 'A를 B에 놓다[두다]'는 뜻이다.
❹ We shouldn't.는 We shouldn't put too much food on our plates.를 줄인 말이다.

Check(√) True or False

(1) The boy is worried about wasting food. T ☐ F ☐

(2) The girl doesn't agree with the boy's opinion. T ☐ F ☐

Listen and Talk 1 Listen and Check

G: Did you watch the documentary last night?

B: No, I didn't. What was it about?

G: ❶It was about global warming. ❷The Earth is getting hotter, and sea levels are going up. I'm worried about the Earth.

B: Oh, I've heard about that problem before. ❸Some islands are disappearing, so people are losing their homes.

G: Yes. It is terrible.

B: ❹Is there any way to stop it?

G: We can save energy. We should turn off the lights when we don't need them. ❺We should also use fans instead of air conditioners.

B: Those are great ideas. I'll try to do those things right away.

G: 어젯밤에 다큐멘터리 봤어?

B: 아니, 못봤어. 무슨 내용이었어?

G: 지구 온난화에 대한 내용이었어. 지구가 점점 더워지면서, 해수면이 올라가고 있대. 나는 지구가 걱정돼.

B: 어, 나도 그 문제에 대해 들어본 적 있어. 몇몇 섬들이 사라져서, 사람들이 자기 집을 잃고 있대.

G: 맞아. 끔찍해.

B: 그걸 막을 방법이 있을까?

G: 에너지를 아끼는 방법이 있지. 우리는 전등을 필요하지 않을 때 꼭 꺼야 해. 그리고 우리는 또한 에어컨보다는 선풍기를 써야 해.

B: 좋은 생각이다. 그것들을 바로 시도해 봐야겠다.

❶ be about은 '~에 관한 것이다'라는 뜻이다.
❷ 'get+비교급' 형태로 '점점 ~해지다'는 뜻이다.
❸ so는 결과를 나타내는 접속사로 '그래서'의 의미이다. 앞 문장에는 원인이 나온다.
❹ to stop은 명사 way를 수식하는 형용사적 용법이다.
❺ instead of는 '~ 대신에'라는 뜻이다.

Check(√) True or False

(3) The boy watched the documentary about global warming. T ☐ F ☐

(4) Because of global warming, people are losing their homes. T ☐ F ☐

Listen and Talk 1 Listen and Speak

B: You ❶look nervous. What's wrong?

G: I'm worried about the speech contest next week. ❷The speeches are about environmental problems and their solutions.

B: What are you going to talk about?

G: ❸I want to talk about soil pollution, but I can't find enough information.

B: ❹What about water problems instead? I read an article, and ❺it said we don't have enough water. I'm really worried about it. I think we have to do something about that problem.

G: But isn't there enough water for everyone?

B: No. In some countries, ❻people are in danger because they don't have enough water. Our country could have this problem in the near future.

G: Oh, I didn't know that. I will talk about that problem and its solutions. Thank you for your advice!

❶ look+형용사: ~하게 보이다. look nervous는 '걱정스러워 보인다'로 해석한다.

❷ be about ~: ~에 관한 것이다

❸ want to+동사원형: ~하기를 원하다. enough는 명사를 수식하는 형용사로 '충분한'의 의미이다.

❹ What about ~?: ~은 어때?, instead는 부사로 '대신에'라는 의미이다.

❺ it은 an article를 가리키고, 여기서 said는 '~라고 쓰여 있다'는 뜻이다.

❻ be in danger: 위험에 처해 있다

Listen and Talk 2 Get Ready

G: Look at this ball. ❶Can you tell me how to use it?

M: Just play soccer for thirty minutes, and the light will turn on. ❷You can use the light anywhere.

G: Wow, that's interesting.

❶ '의문사+to 동사원형' 형태로 how to use it은 '그것을 사용하는 방법'으로 해석한다.

❷ anywhere는 부사로 '어디서든'의 의미이다.

Listen and Talk 2 Listen and Write

B: I like your bag, Jenny. ❶Where did you get it?

G: ❷I made it myself.

B: You made it yourself? That's amazing!

G: ❸Why don't you make one? It's not difficult.

B: Really? ❹Can you tell me how to make it?

G: Sure. Find some old jeans. Cut them into small pieces. Then sew the pieces together.

B: That sounds easy. I'll make one as a birthday present for my sister.

❶ 여기서 get은 '사다(buy)'의 의미로 사용되었다.

❷ myself는 재귀대명사로 강조 용법으로 사용되었다. '내가 직접 그것을 만들었어.'의 의미이다.

❸ Why don't you+동사원형 ~?: '~하는 게 어때?'

❹ '의문사+to 동사원형' 형태로 how to make it은 '그것을 만드는 방법'으로 해석한다.

Listen and Talk 2 Listen and Speak

G: ❶Have you heard of Earth Hour before?

B: No, I haven't. What is it?

G: It's a global environmental event. ❷People turn off their lights for an hour.

B: Why do they do that?

G: They do it ❸to remind people of our environmental problems. They believe ❹such a small action can change the world.

B: Oh, I see. Can you tell me how to join it?

G: Sure. Just turn off your lights from 8:30 p.m. to 9:30 p.m. on the last Saturday in March.

B: That's easy. I will join the next Earth Hour.

❶ Have+주어+과거분사 ~?: 현재완료 의문문으로 '~해 본 적이 있니?'의 의미다.

❷ turn off: (불, 전기, 가스 등을) 끄다, for+시간은 '~ 동안'으로 해석한다.

❸ to remind는 부정사의 부사적 용법의 목적으로 '~하기 위해'라는 뜻이다. remind A of B: A에게 B를 상기시키다

❹ 'such+관사(a/an)+형용사+명사' 어순으로 사용한다.

Do It Yourself

G: ❶ You look upset. What's going on?

B: ❷I am worried about my science homework. I need to make a short video ❸about saving the environment. But ❹making a video is difficult.

G: Well, ❺how about using this application? It's easy.

B: Can you tell me how to use it?

G: Sure! Open the application. Add your photos and choose some music. Then it will make a video with your photos.

B: Wow, that sounds easy. I'll try it now. Thanks.

❶ look+형용사: ~하게 보이다, look upset은 '기분이 안 좋아 보인다'로 해석한다.

❷ be worried about은 '~에 대해 걱정하다'는 뜻이고, 전치사 about 뒤에는 명사나 동명사를 사용한다.

❸ 전치사 about 뒤에 동명사 saving을 사용했다.

❹ making은 주어로 사용된 동명사이다.

❺ how about+명사/동명사 ~? '~하는 게 어때?'

● 다음 우리말과 일치하도록 빈칸에 알맞은 말을 쓰시오.

Listen and Talk 1 A

B: In my school, students _____ so much food _____ their plates. I'm _____ _____ _____ food.

G: Right, that's a big problem. We should not _____ too much food _____ our plates.

B: You're right. We _____.

Listen and Talk 1 B

G: Did you watch the documentary last night?

B: No, I didn't. _____ was it _____?

G: It _____ _____ global warming. The Earth is _____ _____, and sea levels are _____ _____. I'm _____ about the Earth.

B: Oh, I've heard _____ that problem _____. Some islands are _____, so people are _____ their homes.

G: Yes. It is _____.

B: Is there any way _____ _____ it?

G: We can save energy. We should _____ _____ the lights when we don't need _____. We should also use fans _____ _____ air conditioners.

B: Those are great ideas. I'll _____ _____ do those things.

Listen and Talk 1 C

B: You look _____. What's wrong?

G: I'm _____ about the speech contest next week. The speeches are _____ environmental problems and their _____.

B: What are you going to _____ _____?

G: I want to talk about soil pollution, but I can't find _____ _____.

B: What about water problems _____? I read an article, and it _____ we don't have enough water. I'm really worried about it. I think we _____ _____ do something about that problem.

G: But _____ there enough water for everyone?

B: No. In some countries, people are _____ _____ _____ they don't have enough water. Our country could have this problem in the _____ future.

G: Oh, I didn't know that. I will _____ _____ that problem and its solutions. Thank you _____ your _____!

해석

B: 우리 학교에서, 학생들이 그릇에 너무 많은 음식을 남겨. 나는 음식 낭비가 걱정이야.

G: 맞아, 큰 문제야. 우리가 접시에 너무 많은 음식을 담으면 안 돼.

B: 맞아. 우리는 그러면 안 돼.

G: 어젯밤에 다큐멘터리 봤어?

B: 아니, 못봤어. 무슨 내용이었어?

G: 지구 온난화에 대한 내용이었어. 지구가 점점 더워지면서, 해수면이 올라가고 있대. 나는 지구가 걱정돼.

B: 어, 나도 그 문제에 대해 들어 본 적 있어. 몇몇 섬들이 사라져서, 사람들이 자기 집을 잃고 있대.

G: 맞아. 끔찍해.

B: 그걸 막을 방법이 있을까?

G: 에너지를 아끼는 방법이 있지. 우리는 전등을 필요하지 않을 때 꼭 꺼야 해. 그리고 우리는 또한 에어컨보다는 선풍기를 써야 해.

B: 좋은 생각이다. 그것들을 바로 시도해 봐야겠다.

B: 너 걱정스러워 보인다. 무슨 일이야?

G: 나 다음 주에 있을 웅변대회 때문에 걱정이야. 환경 문제와 그 해결책에 관한 대회거든.

B: 너 뭐에 대해 말할 건데?

G: 토양 오염에 대해 얘기하고 싶었는데, 충분한 정보를 찾지 못했어.

B: 그러면 대신 수질 문제에 대해 이야기하는 게 어때? 나 기사를 읽었는데, 우리에게 물이 충분하지 않대. 나는 정말 그게 걱정돼. 우리 그 문제를 해결하기 위해 뭔가 해야 한다고 생각해.

G: 하지만 모든 사람한테 충분한 물이 있지 않아?

B: 아니. 몇몇 국가에서는 물이 부족해서, 사람들이 위험에 처하기도 해. 우리나라도 조만간 그런 일이 일어날 수 있어.

G: 어, 나 그건 몰랐어. 나 그러면 그 문제와 해결책에 대해 얘기할래. 조언 고마워!

Listen and Talk 2 A

G: Look at this ball. Can you tell me _____ _____ _____ it?

M: Just play soccer for thirty minutes, and the light will _____ _____. You can use the light _____.

G: Wow, that's _____.

Listen and Talk 2 B

B: I like your bag, Jenny. Where did you _____ it?

G: I made it _____.

B: You made it yourself? That's _____.

G: _____ _____ _____ make one? It's not difficult.

B: Really? Can you tell me _____ _____ it?

G: Sure. Find some old jeans. _____ them _____ small pieces. Then _____ the pieces _____.

B: That sounds _____. I'll make one as a birthday present for my sister.

Listen and Talk 2 C

G: _____ you _____ _____ Earth Hour before?

B: No, I haven't. What is it?

G: It's a global environmental event. People _____ _____ their lights _____ an hour.

B: Why do they do that?

G: They do it _____ _____ people _____ our environmental problems. They believe _____ a small action can change the world.

B: Oh, I see. Can you tell me _____ _____ _____ it?

G: Sure. Just _____ _____ your lights _____ 8:30 p.m. _____ 9:30 p.m. _____ the last Saturday _____ March.

B: That's easy. I will join the next Earth Hour.

Do It Yourself

G: You _____ _____. What's going on?

B: I _____ _____ _____ my science homework. I need to make a short video about _____ the environment. But _____ a video is difficult.

G: Well, _____ _____ _____ this application? It's easy.

B: Can you tell me how _____ _____ it?

G: Sure! Open the application. _____ your photos and choose some music. Then it will make a video with your photos.

B: Wow, that _____ _____. I'll try it now. Thanks.

해석

G: 이 공 좀 보세요. 어떻게 사용하는지 말해 주실래요?
M: 30분 동안 축구를 하면 전구가 켜질 거예요. 당신은 전구를 어디서든 이용할 수 있어요.
G: 와, 그거 참 재미있네요.

B: 네 가방 예쁘다, Jenny. 어디서 샀어?
G: 내가 만들었어.
B: 네가 만들었다고? 놀랍다.
G: 너도 하나 만들어 보는 게 어때? 안 어려워.
B: 그래? 어떻게 만드는지 알려 줄 수 있니?
G: 그럼. 오래된 청바지를 찾아. 그걸 작은 조각으로 잘라. 그런 다음 조각들을 함께 꿰매면 돼.
B: 쉬울 것 같아. 내 여동생 생일 선물로 하나 만들어야겠어.

G: 지구촌 전등 끄기 행사에 대해 들어 봤니?
B: 아니, 들어 본 적이 없어. 그게 뭔데?
G: 지구촌 환경 행사야. 사람들은 한 시간 동안 불을 끄지.
B: 그걸 왜 하는데?
G: 사람들에게 환경문제에 대해서 상기시키기 위해서지. 이런 작은 행동이 세상을 바꿀 수 있다고 생각하는 거야.
B: 아, 이제 알겠어. 그거 어떻게 참여하는지 말해 줄 수 있니?
G: 그럼. 그냥 3월의 마지막 토요일에 오후 8시 반부터 9시 반까지 불을 끄기만 하면 돼.
B: 쉽네. 다음 번 행사 때 참여해야겠어.

G: 너 기분이 안 좋아 보인다. 무슨 일 있니?
B: 나는 내 과학 숙제를 걱정하고 있어. 나는 환경 지키기에 대한 짧은 비디오를 만들어야 해. 그런데 영상 만드는 게 어려워.
G: 음, 이 앱을 사용해 보는 게 어때? 쉬워.
B: 어떻게 사용하는지 말해 주겠니?
G: 물론. 앱을 열어. 사진들을 추가하고 음악을 골라. 그러면 이 앱이 너의 사진들을 이용해서 영상을 만들 거야.
B: 와, 그거 쉽다. 지금 시도해 볼게. 고마워.

01 다음 우리말에 맞도록 빈칸에 들어갈 알맞은 말을 쓰시오.

> 나는 과학 숙제가 걱정이 돼.

➡ I'm _____ _____ my science homework.

02 다음 대화의 빈칸에 들어갈 말로 알맞은 것은?

> G: Look at this ball. _____
> M: Just play soccer for thirty minutes, and the light will turn on.

① What are you going to do?
② Can you tell me what it is?
③ What ball do you like?
④ What are you going to talk about?
⑤ Can you tell me how to use it?

03 다음 대화의 빈칸에 들어갈 말로 가장 적절한 것은?

> B: I like your bag, Jenny. Where did you get it?
> G: I made it myself.
> B: You made it yourself? That's amazing.
> G: _____ make one? It's not difficult.
> B: Really?

① How about   ② Why don't you
③ Where do you   ④ What about
⑤ What do you say to

04 다음 대화의 밑줄 친 우리말에 맞게 주어진 단어를 알맞은 순서로 배열하시오.

> A: I made a money box with a plastic cup.
> B: <u>어떻게 만드는지 말해 줄 수 있니?</u> (can, how, tell, me, you, to, it, make)
> B: Sure.

➡ _____

[01~02] 다음 대화를 읽고 물음에 답하시오.

G: You look upset. What's going on?

B: (A)_____ I need to make a short video about saving the environment. But making a video is difficult.

G: Well, how about using this application? It's easy.

B: (B)Can you tell me how to use it?

G: Sure! Open the application. Add your photos and choose some music. Then it will make a video with your photos.

B: Wow, that sounds easy. I'll try it now. Thanks.

01 위 대화의 빈칸 (A)에 들어갈 말로 알맞은 것은?

① I'm worried about using an application.
② Do you know how to write it?
③ I am worried about my science homework.
④ Why don't you go see a doctor?
⑤ I am worried about the environment.

02 위 대화의 밑줄 친 (B)와 같은 의미가 되도록 문장의 빈칸을 채우시오.

➡ Can you tell me _____?

[03~05] 다음 대화를 읽고 물음에 답하시오.

B: I like your bag, Jenny. Where did you get it?

G: (A)내가 직접 만들었어.

B: You made it yourself? That's amazing.

G: Why don't you make ⓐone? It's not difficult.

B: Really? Can you tell me (B)_____?

G: Sure. Find some old jeans. Cut them into small pieces. Then sew the pieces together.

B: That sounds easy. I'll make ⓐone as a birthday present for my sister.

03 위 대화의 밑줄 친 (A)를 영어로 바르게 나타낸 것을 모두 고르시오.

① I myself made it.
② I was making it to me.
③ I made me it.
④ I made it myself.
⑤ I made myself to it.

04 위 대화의 빈칸 (B)에 들어갈 말로 알맞은 것은?

① how easy it is   ② what to make
③ where to get it   ④ how to use it
⑤ how to make it

05 위 대화의 밑줄 친 ⓐ가 공통으로 가리키는 것을 찾아 두 단어로 쓰시오.

➡ _____

06 다음 대화의 빈칸에 공통으로 들어갈 말은?

G: Did you watch the documentary last night?

B: No, I didn't. What was it _____?

G: It was _____ global warming.

① about   ② for   ③ at   ④ in   ⑤ on

[07~08] 다음 대화를 읽고 물음에 답하시오.

> B: In my school, students leave so much food on their plates. I'm worried about (A)_____.
> G: Right, that's a big problem. We should not put too much food on our plates.
> B: You're right. (B)We shouldn't.

07 위 대화의 빈칸 (A)에 들어갈 말로 알맞은 것은?

① saving energy
② wasting food
③ eating too much
④ plastic waste
⑤ the trash in cafeteria

08 위 대화의 밑줄 친 (B)의 의도로 알맞은 것은?

① 음식물 쓰레기를 버리지 말자.
② 음식물 잔반 처리를 잘하자.
③ 먹을 수 있는 만큼만 음식을 담자.
④ 식판 대신에 다른 식기를 사용하자.
⑤ 음식을 많이 담는 것은 큰 문제가 아니다.

09 다음 중 짝지어진 대화가 <u>어색한</u> 것을 고르시오.

① A: I'm worried about soil pollution.
   B: Me, too.
② A: I made a bag with some old jeans.
   B: Can you tell me how to make it?
③ A: What does it mean?
   B: It means we are wasting paper.
④ A: Can you tell me how to use it?
   B: Sure.
⑤ A: How much chocolate is produced in a day?
   B: Our chocolate is made by robots.

[10~12] 다음 대화를 읽고 물음에 답하시오.

> G: Have you heard of Earth Hour before?
> B: No, I haven't. What is it?
> G: It's a global environmental event. People (a)_____ their lights for an hour.
> B: Why do they do that?
> G: (A)<u>사람들에게 환경문제에 대해서 상기시키기 위해서지</u>. They believe such a small action can change the world.
> B: Oh, I see. Can you tell me how to join it?
> G: Sure. Just turn off your lights from 8:30 p.m. to 9:30 p.m. on the last Saturday in March.
> B: That's easy. I will join the next Earth Hour.

서답형

10 위 대화의 빈칸 (a)에 들어갈 단어에 대한 영어 설명을 읽고 알맞은 단어를 쓰시오.

> to make a machine, a television, an engine, or a light etc. stop operating by pushing a button

➡ _____

서답형

11 위 대화의 우리말 (A)에 맞게 주어진 문장의 빈칸을 채우시오.

➡ They do it _____ _____ people _____ our environmental problems.

12 위 대화의 Earth Hour에 관한 내용으로 <u>어색한</u> 것은?

① Earth Hour는 세계 환경 행사다.
② 참가자들은 1시간 동안 불을 끈다.
③ 참가자들은 그들의 행동이 세상을 바꿀 수 있다고 믿는다.
④ 매달 8시 30분부터 9시 30분까지 참가 가능하다.
⑤ Earth Hour는 1년에 한 번 열린다.

[01~02] 다음 대화를 읽고 물음에 답하시오.

B: I like your bag, Jenny. Where did you get it?

G: I made it myself.

B: You made it yourself? That's amazing.

G: Why don't you make one? It's not difficult.

B: Really? (A)어떻게 만드는지 알려줄 수 있니?(can, tell, me, how, to)

G: Sure. Find some old jeans. Cut them into small pieces. Then sew the pieces together.

B: That sounds easy.

01 위 대화의 밑줄 친 (A)의 우리말에 맞게 주어진 단어를 이용하여 영어로 쓰시오.

➡ _____

02 위 대화를 읽고 아래 그림의 빈칸을 채우시오.

(1) ____ ____ ____ a bag

Find some (2)____ jeans.　(3) ____ the jeans ____ small pieces.　(4) ____ the pieces together.

➡ (1) _____
➡ (2) _____ (3) _____ , _____
　 (4) _____

[03~04] 다음 대화를 읽고 물음에 답하시오.

G: Did you watch the documentary last night?

B: No, I didn't. What was it about?

G: It was about global warming. The Earth is getting hotter, and sea levels are going up. (A)나는 지구가 걱정이 돼. (am, worry, the Earth)

B: Oh, I've heard about that problem before. Some islands are disappearing, so people are losing their homes.

G: Yes. It is terrible.

B: Is there any way to stop it?

G: We can save energy. We should turn off the lights when we don't need them. We should also use fans instead of air conditioners.

B: Those are great ideas. I'll try to do those things.

03 위 대화의 밑줄 친 (A)의 우리말에 맞게 주어진 단어를 이용하여 영작하시오.

➡ _____

04 위 대화에서 두 사람이 나누는 문제점과 그것의 해결책을 찾아 아래 문장을 완성하시오.

• Problem
Because the Earth is _____ _____ and sea levels are _____ _____, some islands are _____.
• Solutions
_____ _____ the lights when you _____ _____ them. And _____ fans _____ _____ air conditioners.

05 다음 대화의 밑줄 친 (A)를 완전한 문장으로 다시 쓰시오.

B: In my school, students leave so much food on their plates. I'm worried about wasting food.

G: Right, that's a big problem. We should not put too much food on our plates.

B: You're right. (A)We shouldn't.

➡ _____

Grammar

① 수동태

> • He found the treasure. <능동태> 그가 그 보물을 발견했다.
> • The treasure **was found** by him. <수동태> 그 보물은 그에 의해 발견되었다.

■ 수동태는 '주어+be동사+동사의 과거분사+by+행위자'의 형식을 가지며 '…에 의해 ~되다[당하다]'라는 의미로 주어가 동사가 나타내는 행위를 당하거나 행동의 영향을 받는 것을 나타낸다. 수동태 문장의 주어 자리에는 능동태 문장의 목적어가 오고, by 다음에는 능동태 문장의 주어를 쓴다. 누가 그 동작을 했는지 중요하지 않거나 잘 모를 때, 수동태 문장으로 표현한다. 수동태는 현재, 과거, 미래 시제로 쓸 수 있고, 'be동사+동사의 과거분사'에서 be동사로 시제를 표현한다.

  • This process **is repeated** again and again! 이러한 과정이 계속해서 반복된다!

■ 4형식 문장의 수동태는 간접목적어와 직접목적어 각각을 주어로 하는 수동태가 가능하다. 직접목적어를 주어로 한 수동태에서는 간접목적어 앞에 특정한 전치사를 써야 한다.

  전치사 to를 쓰는 동사는 'give, send, tell, teach, show, bring' 등이고, 전치사 for를 쓰는 동사는 'buy, make, choose, cook, get' 등이며, 전치사 of를 쓰는 동사는 'ask' 등이 있다. 또한 make, buy, read, write 등은 직접목적어를 주어로 하는 수동태만 가능하다.

  • A computer **was bought** for me by Mom. 컴퓨터가 엄마에 의해 나에게 사주어졌다.

■ 조동사가 있는 문장의 수동태는 '조동사+be+p.p.' 형식을 갖는다.

  • A book **will be read** to us by Mom. 책이 엄마에 의해 우리에게 읽힐 것이다.

■ 목적격보어가 원형부정사인 경우, 수동태 문장에서는 to부정사로 바뀐다.

  • Ted **was made** to clean the car by his dad. Ted는 그의 아빠에 의해 세차하도록 시켜졌다.

■ by 이외의 전치사를 사용하는 수동태에 유의한다.

  • be interested in: ~에 흥미가 있다   • be filled with: ~로 가득 차다

  • be covered with: ~로 덮여 있다   • be surprised at: ~에 놀라다

  • be made of: ~로 만들어지다(물리적 변화)   • be made from: ~로 만들어지다(화학적 변화)

  • be satisfied with: ~에 만족하다   • be pleased with: ~에 기뻐하다

핵심 Check

1. 다음 괄호 안에서 알맞은 말을 고르시오.

(1) The ring (found / was found) by them.

(2) A letter was written (for / to) her by Jim.

(3) The room was filled (by / with) many books.

② 비교급 강조

> • The plants grow **much** faster than plants in soil.
> 그 식물들은 흙에서 자라는 식물들보다 훨씬 빨리 자란다.
>
> • It will get **even** bigger. 그것은 한층 더 커질 것이다.

■ 비교급을 강조할 때는 비교급 앞에 much, still, even, far, a lot 등의 부사를 쓰며 '(…보다) 훨씬 더 ~한'이라는 의미를 갖는다.

- A tiger is stronger than a cat. 호랑이는 고양이보다 더 강하다.

- A tiger is **much** stronger than a cat. 호랑이는 고양이보다 훨씬 더 강하다.

- Mary is prettier than Kim. Mary가 Kim보다 더 예쁘다.

- Mary is **a lot** prettier than Kim. Mary가 Kim보다 훨씬 더 예쁘다.

■ very는 원급의 형용사[부사]를 수식하며, 비교급은 수식하지 않는다.

- She is **very** beautiful. 〈원급 강조〉 그녀는 매우 예쁘다

- She is **much** more beautiful than her sister. 〈비교급 강조〉 그녀는 자기 여동생보다 훨씬 더 예쁘다.

cf. She is very more beautiful than her sister. (×)

핵심 Check

2. 다음 괄호 안에서 알맞은 말을 고르시오.

(1) Dan is (very / far) wiser than Josh.

(2) This computer is (lot / even) newer than that one.

(3) My smartphone is (much / many) nicer than yours.

Grammar 시험대비 기본평가

01 다음 빈칸에 알맞은 것은?

> He built the house.
> → The house _____ by him.

① builds   ② built   ③ has built
④ is built   ⑤ was built

02 다음 빈칸에 들어갈 말로 적절하지 <u>않은</u> 것은?

> They choose aquaponics because it is _____ easier than traditional gardening.

① even   ② very   ③ a lot
④ still   ⑤ far

03 다음 우리말에 맞게 빈칸에 알맞은 말을 쓰시오.

productive: 생산적인
source: 공급원

(1) 그 창문은 Mike에 의해 깨졌다.
➡ The window _____ _____ by Mike.
(2) 노인과 바다는 Hemingway에 의해 쓰여졌다.
➡ *The Old Man and the Sea* _____ _____ by Hemingway.
(3) 그것은 식량을 재배하는 훨씬 더 생산적인 방법이다.
➡ It is a _____ more productive way of growing food.
(4) 인터넷은 훨씬 더 좋은 뉴스 공급원이다.
➡ The Internet is a _____ better source for news.

04 다음 문장에서 어법상 어색한 부분을 바르게 고쳐 쓰시오.

(1) Laura is very kinder than Bill.
_____ ➡ _____
(2) Her room cleans every day by her.
_____ ➡ _____

01 다음 빈칸에 알맞은 것은?

| *The Kiss* _____ by Gustav Klimt. |

① paints　　　② painted
③ to paint　　④ was painting
⑤ was painted

02 다음 중 밑줄 친 부분이 어법상 <u>어색한</u> 것을 고르시오.

① This is a <u>far more difficult</u> problem to solve than that one.
② My computer is <u>much more expensive</u> than yours.
③ It is <u>very nicer</u> than that car.
④ We need <u>a far larger</u> place to play.
⑤ He bought an <u>even newer</u> car for his family.

03 다음 중 수동태로의 전환이 <u>어색한</u> 것은?

① He makes a cake.
　→ A cake is made by him.
② They built the beautiful bridge long time ago.
　→ The beautiful bridge was built long time ago by them
③ Her mother chose her a dress.
　→ A dress was chosen for her by her mother.
④ Ella sent me a book bought at the shop.
　→ A book was sent for me yesterday by Ella.
⑤ She asked him to arrive home early.
　→ He was asked to arrive home early by her.

04 다음 우리말을 바르게 영작한 것은?

| 그 콘서트 티켓은 Christine을 위해 그녀의 언니에 의해 구매되었다. |

① The concert ticket was bought to Christine by her sister.
② The concert ticket was bought for Christine by her sister.
③ The concert ticket was bought of Christine by her sister.
④ Christine was bought for the concert ticket by her sister.
⑤ The concert ticket was bought for her sister by Christine.

05 다음 중 어법상 올바른 것은?

① It was still simpler than it looked.
② *Romeo and Juliet* wrote Shakespeare.
③ There are planets which are much big than the sun.
④ The letter will be sent yesterday by Mr. Green.
⑤ Roald Dahl was written by the book, *Charlie and the Chocolate Factory*.

06 다음 괄호 안에서 알맞은 것을 고르시오.

(1) Many photos were shown [to / for] him by the police.
(2) A model plane was made [to / for] Jack by his dad.
(3) Some questions were asked [to / of] the teacher by students.

07 다음 밑줄 친 부분의 쓰임이 나머지 넷과 다른 것은?

① Stephanie is <u>much</u> more beautiful than other girls.

② His new movie was <u>much</u> nicer than the previous one.

③ I spent too <u>much</u> time looking up the examples.

④ Harry is <u>much</u> wiser than we expected.

⑤ The actual price is <u>much</u> higher than that.

08 다음 빈칸에 공통으로 들어갈 알맞은 것은?

- You can have as _____ as you like.
- People tend to be _____ more friendly in small towns.

① still   ② well   ③ very
④ much   ⑤ many

09 다음 중 밑줄 친 부분의 의미가 〈보기〉와 같은 것은?

> ┤ 보기 ├
> Kate taught him <u>even</u> more difficult problems.

① I don't <u>even</u> know what happened to Jim.

② Two and four are <u>even</u> numbers.

③ This dictionary is <u>even</u> more useful than that.

④ So now the score is <u>even</u>.

⑤ The surface of the road is <u>even</u>.

10 다음 중 태의 변화가 어색한 것은?

① The phonograph was invented by Thomas Edison.
→ Thomas Edison invented the phonograph.

② My father made this chair last year.
→ This chair was made by my father last year.

③ Mom bought me a new smartphone.
→ A new smartphone was bought for me by Mom.

④ The doctor advised him to do more exercise.
→ He was advised to do more exercise by the doctor.

⑤ They made Dan finish the work by next Monday.
→ Dan was made finish the work by next Monday by them.

11 다음 빈칸에 공통으로 들어갈 말로 가장 적절한 것은?

- Are you satisfied _____ your new car?
- His heart was filled _____ pride at that time.

① at   ② with   ③ in
④ by   ⑤ of

12 다음 문장을 수동태로 바르게 바꾼 것은?

> They throw away much paper.

① Much paper throw away them.

② Much paper thrown away by them.

③ Much paper is thrown away them.

④ Much paper is thrown by them.

⑤ Much paper is thrown away by them.

13 다음 문장을 수동태로 바르게 바꾼 것은?

> We should turn off the lights when we leave our classrooms.

① The lights should turn off us when we leave our classrooms.

② The lights should be turned off by us when we leave our classrooms.

③ The lights should turned by us when we leave our classrooms.

④ The lights should be turned off us when we leave our classrooms.

⑤ The lights should be turned by us when we leave our classrooms.

서답형
14 주어진 단어를 이용하여 다음 우리말을 영어로 쓰시오.

(1) *Sunflower*는 Van Gogh에 의해 그려졌다. (paint)

➡ _____

(2) 그 사진들은 Mel에 의해 찍힌 것이 아니었다. (take, pictures)

➡ _____

(3) 그 건물은 돌로 만들어졌다. (make)

➡ _____

(4) 건강이 돈보다 훨씬 중요하다. (health, important, far)

➡ _____

(5) 내가 사기를 원했던 컴퓨터는 예전 것보다 훨씬 더 쌌다. (lot, the old one)

➡ _____
_____

서답형
15 주어진 단어의 형태를 알맞게 바꿔 문장을 완성하시오.

> Jupiter is much _____ than Mars. (big)

서답형
16 괄호 안에 주어진 어휘를 어법에 맞게 빈칸에 쓰시오.

> • The classroom _____ _____ by some students. (clean)
> • Many cars _____ _____ in the factory. (make)
> • Ann runs fast, but her brother runs even _____. (fast)
> • The refrigerator is a lot _____ _____ than the telephone. (important)

[17~18] 다음 두 문장이 같은 의미가 되도록 빈칸에 알맞은 말을 고르시오.

중요
17
> She chose Jenny a hairpin.
> = A hairpin _____ Jenny by her.

① chose
② was choosing
③ was chosen to
④ was chosen
⑤ was chosen for

18
> Wendy saw Peter Pan flying high.
> = Peter Pan _____ high by Wendy.

① is seen fly
② was seen fly
③ is seen flying
④ was seen flying
⑤ was seen to fly

서답형
19 다음 문장에서 어법상 어색한 부분을 찾아 바르게 고치시오.

(1) The accident was happened last night.

_____ ➡ _____

(2) The refrigerator invented by James Harrison in 1862.

_____ ➡ _____

(3) His essay is many better than mine.

_____ ➡ _____

01 다음 문장을 수동태는 능동태로, 능동태는 수동태로 고치시오.

(1) Solutions to this problem were discovered by our scientists.

➡ _____

(2) This song will be sung by me.

➡ _____

(3) Dan made her the cookies.

➡ _____

(4) We must do something to help him.

➡ _____

(5) Who invented the telephone in 1876?

➡ _____

02 다음 문장의 비교급을 강조하여 다시 쓰시오. (서로 다른 강조 어휘를 사용할 것.)

(1) Cars are more expensive than bicycles.

➡ _____

(2) It was more beautiful than I had imagined.

➡ _____

(3) Manchester United is hoping to do better this year.

➡ _____

(4) It'll be cheaper than buying a new jacket.

➡ _____

(5) Jane is cleverer than her twin brother.

➡ _____

03 다음 문장에서 어법상 어색한 부분을 찾아 바르게 고쳐 다시 쓰시오.

(1) When we waste paper, we are destroyed so many trees.

➡ _____
_____

(2) How much chocolate is producing in a day?

➡ _____

(3) Wine is made of grapes.

➡ _____

(4) Matt was seen dance on the stage by his friends.

➡ _____

(5) *Bibimbap* will be cooked to Mariel by Minjun tomorrow.

➡ _____

(6) His little brother will be read a storybook by Robert.

➡ _____
_____

04 주어진 단어의 형태를 알맞게 바꾸어 빈칸을 채우시오.

You look so much _____ than usual. (nice)

05 다음 우리말을 괄호 안에 주어진 어구를 이용하여 영작하시오.

(1) 이 드레스는 내 친구에 의해 디자인되었다. (this dress)

➡ _____

(2) *Charlie and the Chocolate Factory*는 William Shakespeare에 의해 쓰여지지 않았다. (write)

➡ _____

(3) 인터뷰는 한국어와 영어로 진행됐다. (the interview, carry, both, in, out)

➡ _____

(4) 이러한 항목들이 각 응답자에게 물어졌다. (items, ask, each respondent)

➡ _____

(5) 그는 그녀에게 긴 편지를 썼다. (write) (수동 태로 쓸 것.)

➡ _____

(6) Annabel은 그녀의 서울에서의 생활에 만족했다. (satisfy, her life in Seoul)

➡ _____

06 🌟 중요 다음 문장에서 어법상 어색한 부분을 찾아 바르게 고치시오.

(1) The problem of control is many more important.

(2) You look too smarter than your picture.

(3) It seemed ever more difficult than I had expected.

(4) Was it very bigger than your dog?

(5) This hat is lots cheaper than that.

➡ _____

_____

07 다음 우리말을 괄호 안에 주어진 어구를 이용하여 영작하시오.

(1) 이 탑은 저 탑보다 훨씬 더 높다. (this tower, high, lot)

➡ _____

(2) 내 남동생은 나보다 훨씬 더 높게 뛴다. (jump, even, I)

➡ _____

(3) 그녀는 그녀의 오빠보다 훨씬 더 활동적이다. (much, active, her brother)

➡ _____

(4) Brenda는 전보다 훨씬 더 친절하다. (kinder, far, before)

➡ _____

(5) 민주주의는 공산주의보다 훨씬 더 낫다. (democracy, communism, good, still)

➡ _____

08 🏠 고난이도 다음 문장을 수동태로 바꿔 쓰시오.

(1) Amanda taught me math last year. (두 가지로 쓸 것.)

➡ _____

_____

(2) Teresa chose us a chocolate cake.

➡ _____

(3) Ann asked me a question.

➡ _____

09 다음 그림을 보고 주어진 단어를 이용하여 비교하는 문장을 쓰시오. (fast, much)

Yuri

Sumi

➡ _____

My Science Project: Home Aquaponics

Jennifer: What are you reading?

Eric: I'm reading an article about aquaponics. It's a way of growing
plants without soil. We can also grow plants and raise fish in just one
system.

Jennifer: Is that possible?

Eric: We'll see. I'm going to try it at home for my science project.
Fish, bacteria, and plants are the main parts of aquaponics.
After you feed the fish, they produce waste. The waste is turned
into food for the plants by bacteria. The plants clean the water by
consuming the food. This process is repeated again and again!

raise 기르다
bacteria 박테리아, 세균
produce 생산하다
turn into ∼이 되다, ∼로 변하다
consume 먹다, 소비하다, 소모하다

확인문제

● 다음 문장이 본문의 내용과 일치하면 T, 일치하지 않으면 F를 쓰시오.

1 Aquaponics is a way of growing plants without soil. ☐
2 We can grow plants and raise fish in two systems. ☐
3 Fish, bacteria, and plants are the main parts of aquaponics. ☐
4 The waste is turned into food for the plants by fish. ☐

Home Aquaponics   by Eric Jackson

Questions: How can I make an aquaponics system at home?

Why is aquaponics good?

Period: From May 15 to August 15

Materials: a pot & small stones, a fish tank, a plastic tube, a water
pump, plants, some fish, a box cutter, clay

Steps:

1. I made holes in the bottom of a pot. Then I put small stones and
   plants in it.
2. I made a big hole in the lid of the fish tank and put the pot in the
   hole.

hole 구멍
lid 뚜껑
fix 고정하다, 수리하다
connect 연결하다

3. I fixed the pot in place with clay.
제자리에

4. I made another hole in the lid and put a tube through it.
another+단수명사

5. I put a water pump in the fish tank. I used the tube to connect the
=the hole / 부사적 용법(목적)
pump to the pot.

6. I filled the fish tank with water and put some fish in it. Then I
fill A with B: A를 B로 채우다
turned on the pump.
turn on: 켜다, 작동하다

확인문제

● 다음 문장이 본문의 내용과 일치하면 T, 일치하지 <u>않으면</u> F를 쓰시오.

1 Eric made holes in the bottom of a pot. ☐
2 Eric put a water pump in the pot. ☐
3 Eric used a tube to connect the pump to the pot. ☐

Results: From this experiment, I grew my plants and raised fish with
aquaponics. I just fed the fish, but the plants have grown 17 centimeters
단지, 그저   have grown은 현재완료로 '…해서 그 결과 ~하다'라는 의미이다.
in three months. The fish stay healthy and the water is clean all the time.
stay+형용사 보어   항상
Conclusion: Some important things about aquaponics were learned
수동태 문장으로 주어가 복수이고 시제는 과거이므로 be동사는 were를 쓴다.
from this experiment. First, water is saved because the plants don't
need watering. Second, it is good for the environment because no
need watering=need to be watered   ~에 좋다
chemicals are used. Finally, you can do aquaponics anywhere because
수동태
it doesn't need much space.

I found out...

Some farmers use aquaponics to produce vegetables and raise
부사적 용법(목적)
fish. They choose aquaponics because it is far easier than traditional
far가 비교급 easier의 의미를 강조하여 '훨씬 더 …한'이라는 뜻이다.
gardening. Also, it is a much more productive way of growing food.
much가 비교급 more productive의 의미를 강조하여 '훨씬 더 …한'이라는 뜻이다.
The plants grow much faster than plants in soil, and it saves space.
절약한다
I hope more food is produced in this way in the future because it is
수동태
healthy for us and the environment.

result 결과
water (식물 등에) 물을 주다
chemical 화학 물질, 화학 제품
productive 생산적인, 생산력 있는
future 미래

확인문제

● 다음 문장이 본문의 내용과 일치하면 T, 일치하지 <u>않으면</u> F를 쓰시오.

1 The fish stay healthy and the water is clean all the time. ☐
2 Water is wasted because the plants need watering. ☐
3 The plants in soil grow faster than the plants in aquaponics. ☐

● 우리말을 참고하여 빈칸에 알맞은 말을 쓰시오.

1 My _____ _____ : Home Aquaponics

2 _____ are you reading?

3 I'm reading _____ _____ about aquaponics.

4 It's a way of growing plants _____ _____ .

5 We can also grow plants and raise fish _____ _____ _____ _____ .

6 Is that _____ ?

7 We'll see. I'm _____ _____ _____ it at home for my science project.

8 Fish, bacteria, and plants are _____ _____ _____ of aquaponics.

9 After you _____ the fish, they produce _____ .

10 The waste _____ _____ _____ food for the plants by bacteria.

11 The plants clean the water _____ _____ the food.

12 This process _____ _____ again and again!

13 _____ _____ by Eric Jackson

14 Questions: _____ can I make an aquaponics system at home?

15 _____ is aquaponics good?

16 Period: _____ May 15 _____ August 15

17 _____ : a pot & small stones, a fish tank, a plastic tube, a water pump, plants, some fish, _____ _____ _____ , clay

1	나의 과학 프로젝트: 가정용 아쿠아포닉스
2	무엇을 읽고 있니?
3	아쿠아포닉스에 관한 기사를 읽고 있어.
4	흙 없이 식물을 재배할 수 있는 방법이야.
5	또 한 가지 장치만으로도 식물과 물고기를 동시에 키울 수 있어.
6	그게 가능하니?
7	곧 알게 될 거야. 내가 과학 프로젝트로 집에서 해 볼 예정이거든.
8	물고기, 박테리아, 식물이 아쿠아포닉스의 주요 부분이다.
9	물고기에게 먹이를 주면, 그것들은 배설물을 만들어 낸다.
10	이 배설물은 박테리아에 의해 식물의 먹이로 바뀐다.
11	식물은 그 먹이를 먹음으로써 물을 정화한다.
12	이러한 과정이 계속해서 반복된다!
13	가정용 아쿠아포닉스 에릭 잭슨
14	질문: 집에서 아쿠아포닉스 장치를 어떻게 만들 수 있을까?
15	아쿠아포닉스가 왜 좋은가?
16	기간: 5월 15일부터 8월 15일까지
17	재료: 화분과 작은 돌들, 어항, 플라스틱 관, 수중 펌프, 식물, 물고기, 커터칼, 찰흙

18 _____ : I made holes in the _____ of a pot.

19 _____ I _____ small stones and plants _____ it.

20 I made a big hole in _____ _____ of the fish tank and _____ the pot _____ the hole.

21 I _____ the pot in place _____ clay.

22 I made _____ _____ in the lid and put a tube _____ it.

23 I _____ a water pump _____ the fish tank.

24 I used the tube _____ _____ the pump _____ the pot.

25 I _____ the fish tank _____ water and put some fish in it.

26 Then I _____ _____ the pump.

27 Results: From this experiment, I grew my plants and raised fish _____ _____ .

28 I just _____ the fish, but the plants _____ _____ 17 centimeters _____ three months.

29 The fish stay _____ and the water is clean _____ _____ _____ .

30 Conclusion: Some important things about aquaponics _____ _____ from this experiment.

31 First, water _____ _____ because the plants don't need watering.

32 Second, it is good for the environment because no chemicals _____ _____ .

33 _____ , you can do aquaponics _____ because it doesn't need much space.

34 *I found out...* Some farmers use aquaponics _____ _____ vegetables and raise fish.

35 They choose aquaponics because it is _____ _____ _____ traditional gardening.

36 Also, it is a _____ _____ _____ way of growing food.

37 The plants grow _____ _____ _____ plants in soil, and it saves space.

38 I hope more food _____ _____ in this way in the future because it is _____ _____ us and the environment.

18 절차: 화분 바닥에 구멍들을 뚫었다.

19 그런 후에 화분에 작은 돌들을 넣고 식물을 심었다.

20 어항 덮개에 큰 구멍을 내고 구멍에 그 화분을 넣었다.

21 찰흙으로 화분을 제자리에 고정하였다.

22 덮개에 또 다른 구멍을 하나 만들고 그 안에 관을 넣었다.

23 어항에 수중 펌프를 넣었다.

24 관을 이용하여 펌프를 화분에 연결하였다.

25 어항에 물을 채우고 물고기 몇 마리를 거기에 넣었다.

26 그러고 나서 펌프를 작동하였다.

27 결과: 이 실험으로 나는 아쿠아포닉스로 식물과 물고기를 키웠다.

28 나는 그저 물고기에 먹이만 주었는데도 식물은 석 달 동안 17cm나 자랐다.

29 물고기는 건강을 유지하며 물은 항상 깨끗하다.

30 결론: 아쿠아포닉스에 관한 몇 가지 중요한 사항이 이 실험에서 발견되었다.

31 첫째, 식물에 물을 줄 필요가 없으므로 물이 절약된다.

32 둘째, 화학 물질이 사용되지 않으므로 아쿠아포닉스는 환경에 이롭다.

33 끝으로, 넓은 공간이 필요하지 않으므로 당신은 어디에서나 아쿠아포닉스를 쉽게 할 수 있다.

34 나는 알게 되었다... 몇몇 농부들은 채소를 생산하고 물고기를 키우는 데 아쿠아포닉스를 이용한다.

35 그들은 아쿠아포닉스가 전통 재배 방식보다 훨씬 더 쉽기 때문에 그것을 선택한다.

36 또한, 아쿠아포닉스는 식량을 재배하는 훨씬 더 생산적인 방법이다.

37 식물들이 흙에서 자라는 식물보다 훨씬 빠르게 자라고 공간도 절약한다.

38 그것은 우리와 환경에 훨씬 건강하기 때문에 나는 미래에 더 많은 식량이 이런 방식으로 생산되기를 희망한다.

• 우리말을 참고하여 본문을 영작하시오.

1 나의 과학 프로젝트: 가정용 아쿠아포닉스

➡ _____

2 무엇을 읽고 있니?

➡ _____

3 아쿠아포닉스에 관한 기사를 읽고 있어.

➡ _____

4 흙 없이 식물을 재배할 수 있는 방법이야.

➡ _____

5 또 한 가지 장치만으로도 식물과 물고기를 동시에 키울 수 있어.

➡ _____

6 그게 가능하니?

➡ _____

7 곧 알게 될 거야. 내가 과학 프로젝트로 집에서 해 볼 예정이거든.

➡ _____

8 물고기, 박테리아, 식물이 아쿠아포닉스의 주요 부분이다.

➡ _____

9 물고기에게 먹이를 주면, 그것들은 배설물을 만들어 낸다.

➡ _____

10 이 배설물은 박테리아에 의해 식물의 먹이로 바뀐다.

➡ _____

11 식물은 그 먹이를 먹음으로써 물을 정화한다.

➡ _____

12 이러한 과정이 계속해서 반복된다!

➡ _____

13 가정용 아쿠아포닉스   에릭 잭슨

➡ _____

14 질문: 집에서 아쿠아포닉스 장치를 어떻게 만들 수 있을까?

➡ _____

15 아쿠아포닉스가 왜 좋은가?

➡ _____

16 기간: 5월 15일부터 8월 15일까지

➡ _____

17 재료: 화분과 작은 돌들, 어항, 플라스틱 관, 수중 펌프, 식물, 물고기, 커터칼, 찰흙

➡ _____

18 절차: 화분 바닥에 구멍들을 뚫었다.
➡ _____

19 그런 후에 화분에 작은 돌들을 넣고 식물을 심었다.
➡ _____

20 어항 덮개에 큰 구멍을 내고 구멍에 그 화분을 넣었다.
➡ _____

21 찰흙으로 화분을 제자리에 고정하였다.
➡ _____

22 덮개에 또 다른 구멍을 하나 만들고 그 안에 관을 넣었다.
➡ _____

23 어항에 수중 펌프를 넣었다.
➡ _____

24 관을 이용하여 펌프를 화분에 연결하였다.
➡ _____

25 어항에 물을 채우고 물고기 몇 마리를 거기에 넣었다.
➡ _____

26 그러고 나서 펌프를 작동하였다.
➡ _____

27 결과: 이 실험으로 나는 아쿠아포닉스로 식물과 물고기를 키웠다.
➡ _____

28 나는 그저 물고기에 먹이만 주었는데도 식물은 석 달 동안 17cm나 자랐다.
➡ _____

29 물고기는 건강을 유지하며 물은 항상 깨끗하다.
➡ _____

30 결론: 아쿠아포닉스에 관한 몇 가지 중요한 사항이 이 실험에서 발견되었다.
➡ _____

31 첫째, 식물에 물을 줄 필요가 없으므로 물이 절약된다.
➡ _____

32 둘째, 화학 물질이 사용되지 않으므로 아쿠아포닉스는 환경에 이롭다.
➡ _____

33 끝으로, 넓은 공간이 필요하지 않으므로 당신은 어디에서나 아쿠아포닉스를 쉽게 할 수 있다.
➡ _____

34 나는 알게 되었다... 몇몇 농부들은 채소를 생산하고 물고기를 키우는 데 아쿠아포닉스를 이용한다.
➡ _____

35 그들은 아쿠아포닉스가 전통 재배 방식보다 훨씬 더 쉽기 때문에 그것을 선택한다.
➡ _____

36 또한, 아쿠아포닉스는 식량을 재배하는 훨씬 더 생산적인 방법이다.
➡ _____

37 식물들이 흙에서 자라는 식물보다 훨씬 빠르게 자라고 공간도 절약한다.
➡ _____

38 그것은 우리와 환경에 훨씬 건강하기 때문에 나는 미래에 더 많은 식량이 이런 방식으로 생산되기를 희망한다.
➡ _____

[01~03] 다음 글을 읽고 물음에 답하시오.

> **Jennifer:** What are you reading?
> **Eric:** I'm ⓐreading an article about aquaponics. ⓑIt's a way of ⓒgrowing plants without soil. We can also grow plants and raise fish in just one system.
> **Jennifer:** Is that possible?
> **Eric:** We'll see. I'm going to try it at home for my science project.

서답형

01 위 글의 밑줄 친 ⓐ, ⓒ와 문법적 쓰임이 같은 것을 각각 아래 〈보기〉에서 모두 골라 쓰시오.

> ┤ 보기 ├
> ① Studying English is interesting.
> ② I heard him crying in the room.
> ③ The girl standing at the door is my sister.
> ④ Have you finished cleaning the room?
> ⑤ His hobby is collecting stamps.

➡ ⓐ와 쓰임이 같은 것: _____
　 ⓒ와 쓰임이 같은 것: _____

서답형

02 위 글의 밑줄 친 ⓑIt이 가리키는 것을 본문에서 찾아 쓰시오.

➡ _____

03 위 글의 내용과 일치하지 않는 것은?

① 에릭은 아쿠아포닉스에 관한 기사를 읽고 있다.
② 아쿠아포닉스는 흙 없이 식물을 재배할 수 있는 방법이다.
③ 아쿠아포닉스는 두 가지 장치로 식물과 물고기를 동시에 키울 수 있다.
④ 제니퍼는 아쿠아포닉스가 가능한지를 묻고 있다.
⑤ 에릭은 과학 프로젝트로 아쿠아포닉스를 집에서 해 볼 예정이다.

[04~06] 다음 글을 읽고 물음에 답하시오.

> Fish, (A)[bacteria / bacterias], and plants are the main parts of aquaponics. After you feed the fish, they produce waste. The waste is turned (B)[by / into] food for the plants by bacteria. The plants clean the water by (C) [consuming / saving] the food. This process is repeated ⓐagain and again!

서답형

04 위 글의 괄호 (A)~(C)에서 문맥이나 어법상 알맞은 낱말을 골라 쓰시오.

➡ (A)_____ (B)_____ (C)_____

서답형

05 본문의 내용과 일치하도록 다음 빈칸 (A)와 (B)에 알맞은 단어를 쓰시오.

> The main parts of aquaponics are (A)_____, (B)_____ and (C)_____.

중요

06 위 글의 밑줄 친 ⓐagain and again과 바꿔 쓸 수 없는 말을 고르시오.

① repeatedly　　② time after time
③ relatively　　④ over and over
⑤ time and time again

[07~09] 다음 글을 읽고 물음에 답하시오.

> Home Aquaponics　　　　　by Eric Jackson
> **Questions:** How can I make an aquaponics system at home?
> 　　　　　Why is aquaponics good?
> **Period:** From May 15 to August 15
> **Materials:** a pot & small stones, a fish tank, a plastic tube, a water pump, plants, some fish, a box cutter, clay

Steps:

1. I made holes in the bottom of a pot. Then I put small stones and plants in it.
2. I made a big hole in the lid of the fish tank and put the pot in the hole.
3. I fixed the pot in place with clay.
4. I made another ____ⓐ____ in the lid and put a ____ⓑ____ through it.
5. I put a water pump in the fish tank. I used the tube to connect the pump to the pot.
6. I filled the fish tank with water and put some fish in it. Then I turned on the pump.

07 위 글의 종류로 알맞은 것을 고르시오.

① summary   ② manual
③ review   ④ experiment report
⑤ book report

08 다음 그림을 참조하여 위 글의 빈칸 ⓐ와 ⓑ에 들어갈 알맞은 말을 쓰시오.

➡ ⓐ _____ , ⓑ _____

09 위 글을 읽고 대답할 수 없는 질문은?

① What did Eric use to make his home aquaponics system?
② What did Eric put in the pot?
③ With what did Eric fix the pot in place?
④ How did Eric connect a water pump to the pot?
⑤ What plants are suitable for the home aquaponics system?

[10~12] 다음 글을 읽고 물음에 답하시오.

Results:

From this experiment, I grew my plants and raised fish with aquaponics. I just ⓐ _____, but the plants have grown 17 centimeters in three months. The fish stay healthy and the water is clean all the time.

Conclusion:

Some important things about aquaponics were learned from this experiment. First, water is saved because the plants don't need watering. Second, it is good for the environment because no chemicals are used. ⓑFinally, you can do aquaponics anywhere because it doesn't need much space.

10 위 글의 빈칸 ⓐ에 들어갈 가장 알맞은 말을 고르시오.

① used an aquaponics system
② cleaned a fish tank
③ fed the fish
④ turned on the pump
⑤ used some chemicals

11 위 글의 밑줄 친 ⓑFinally와 바꿔 쓸 수 있는 말을 고르시오.

① In addition   ② Therefore
③ At first   ④ Moreover
⑤ Lastly

12 위 글에서 필자가 주장하는 바로 가장 적절한 것은?

① 아쿠아포닉스는 비용이 많이 든다.
② 아쿠아포닉스에는 많은 장점이 있다.
③ 아쿠아포닉스는 물고기를 기르기에 가장 좋은 방법이다.
④ 아쿠아포닉스를 실천하기가 어렵다.
⑤ 과학 과제로 아쿠아포닉스 실험이 적합하다.

[13~15] 다음 글을 읽고 물음에 답하시오.

I found out...

(①) Some farmers use aquaponics ⓐto produce vegetables and raise fish. (②) They choose aquaponics because it is ⓑfar easier than traditional gardening. (③) The plants grow much faster than plants in soil, and it saves space. (④) I hope more food is produced in this way in the future because it is healthy for us and the environment. (⑤)

13 위 글의 흐름으로 보아, 주어진 문장이 들어가기에 가장 적절한 곳은?

> Also, it is a much more productive way of growing food.

① ② ③ ④ ⑤

14 아래 〈보기〉에서 위 글의 밑줄 친 ⓐto produce와 문법적 쓰임이 같은 것의 개수를 고르시오.

┌─── 보기 ───┐
① I don't know what to do next.
② I got up early to catch the train.
③ He has many children to look after.
④ He is the last man to tell a lie.
⑤ He promised to read the book.
└───────────┘

① 1개 ② 2개 ③ 3개 ④ 4개 ⑤ 5개

15 위 글의 밑줄 친 ⓑfar와 바꿔 쓸 수 없는 말을 고르시오.

① much   ② very
③ even   ④ still
⑤ a lot

[16~18] 다음 글을 읽고 물음에 답하시오.

Home Aquaponics   by Eric Jackson

  ⓐ : How can I make an aquaponics system at home?
        Why is aquaponics good?
  ⓑ : From May 15 to August 15
  ⓒ : a pot & small stones, a fish tank, a plastic tube, a water pump, plants, some fish, a box cutter, clay
  ⓓ :
1. I made holes in the bottom of a pot. Then I put small stones and plants in it.

(A) I filled the fish tank with water and put some fish in it. Then I turned on the pump.
(B) I made another hole in the lid and put a tube through it. I put a water pump in the fish tank. I used the tube to connect the pump to the pot.
(C) I made a big hole in the lid of the fish tank and put the pot in the hole. I fixed the pot in place with clay.

16 다음 중 가정용 아쿠아포닉스 시스템을 만들기 위해 필요한 준비물이 아닌 것을 모두 고르시오.

① 플라스틱 관   ② 꽃삽
③ 수중 펌프   ④ 찰흙
⑤ 물뿌리개

서답형
17 위 글의 빈칸 ⓐ~ⓓ에 들어갈 알맞은 말을 쓰시오.

➡ ⓐ _____ ⓑ _____
   ⓒ _____ ⓓ _____

18 위 글의 ⓓ에 대한 설명에서 주어진 글 다음에 이어질 글의 순서로 가장 적절한 것은?

① (A)-(C)-(B)   ② (B)-(A)-(C)
③ (B)-(C)-(A)   ④ (C)-(A)-(B)
⑤ (C)-(B)-(A)

[19~21] 다음 글을 읽고 물음에 답하시오.

> Jennifer: What are you reading?
> Eric: I'm reading an article about aquaponics. It's a way of growing plants ___ⓐ___. We can also grow plants and ⓑraise fish in just one system.
> Jennifer: Is that possible?
> Eric: We'll see. I'm going to try it at home for my science project.

19 위 글의 제목으로 알맞은 것을 고르시오.

① Let's Read an Article Together!
② What Is Aquaponics?
③ Various Ways of Growing Plants
④ How to Raise Fish Successfully
⑤ Do You Want to Write a Science Project?

20 위 글의 빈칸 ⓐ에 들어갈 알맞은 말을 고르시오.

① without water   ② in the soil
③ with chemicals   ④ without soil
⑤ on the ground

21 위 글의 밑줄 친 ⓑraise와 같은 의미로 쓰인 것을 고르시오.

① I raise various kinds of roses.
② Please raise my salary.
③ We raise money for a charity.
④ They raise many important questions.
⑤ Raise up your arms!

[22~24] 다음 글을 읽고 물음에 답하시오.

> Let's Make Our School Green!
> Lots of energy is wasted around us. To solve ⓐthis problem, let's do these things. First, we should turn off the lights when we leave our classrooms. Next, we should turn off the classroom computers when we are not using ⓑthem. Lastly, we should close the doors and windows when we use air conditioners. ⓒDoing these things will be helpful to our school and the environment.

서답형

22 위 글의 밑줄 친 ⓐthis problem과 ⓑthem이 가리키는 것을 본문에서 찾아 쓰시오.

➡ ⓐ _____ ,
   ⓑ _____

서답형

23 위 글의 밑줄 친 ⓒ를 다음과 같이 바꿔 쓸 때 빈칸에 알맞은 말을 쓰시오.

➡ _____ these things will be helpful to our school and the environment.

24 위 글의 내용과 일치하지 <u>않는</u> 것은?

① 위 글은 우리 학교를 친환경적으로 만드는 방법에 관한 글이다.
② 우리 주변에서 많은 에너지가 낭비되고 있다.
③ 우리는 교실을 나갈 때 전깃불을 꺼야 한다.
④ 우리는 교실 컴퓨터를 사용하지 않을 때 그것들을 꺼야 한다.
⑤ 에어컨을 사용할 때는 환기를 위해 교실 문과 창문을 열어야 한다.

[01~02] 다음 글을 읽고 물음에 답하시오.

Jennifer: What are you reading?

Eric: I'm reading an ⓐ about aquaponics. It's a way of growing plants without soil. We can also grow plants and raise fish in just one system.

Jennifer: Is that possible?

Eric: We'll see. I'm going to try it at home for my science project.

01 주어진 영영풀이를 참고하여 빈칸 ⓐ에 철자 a로 시작하는 단어를 쓰시오.

a piece of writing that is published in a newspaper or magazine

➡ _____

02 다음 빈칸 (A)와 (B)에 알맞은 단어를 넣어 아쿠아포닉스에 대한 소개를 완성하시오.

With aquaponics we can grow plants and raise fish in just (A)_____ system (B)_____ soil.

➡ (A) _____ (B) _____

[03~05] 다음 글을 읽고 물음에 답하시오.

Fish, bacteria, and plants are the main parts of aquaponics. After you ⓐ the fish, they produce waste. The waste is turned into food for the plants by bacteria. The plants clean the water by ⓑ the food. ⓒThis process is repeated again and again!

03 본문의 한 단어를 변형하여 위 글의 빈칸 ⓐ에 들어갈 알맞은 말을 쓰시오.

➡ _____

04 위 글의 빈칸 ⓑ에 consume을 알맞은 형태로 쓰시오.

➡ _____

05 다음 빈칸 (A)~(C)에 알맞은 단어를 본문에서 찾아 넣어 ⓒThis process에 대한 설명을 완성하시오.

1. Fish eat the food you give to them and produce (A)_____.
2. (B)_____ turn the waste into food for the plants.
3. The (C)_____ consume the food and clean the water.

➡ (A)_____ (B)_____ (C)_____

[06~08] 다음 글을 읽고 물음에 답하시오.

Home Aquaponics   by Eric Jackson

Steps:

1. I made holes in the bottom of a pot. Then I put small stones and plants in ⓐit.
2. I made a big hole in the lid of the fish tank and put the pot in the hole.
3. I fixed the pot in place with clay.
4. I made another hole in the lid and put a tube through ⓑit.
5. I put a water pump in the fish tank. I used the tube to connect the pump to the pot.
6. I filled the fish tank with water and put some fish in ⓒit. Then I turned on the pump.

06 다음 질문에 대한 알맞은 대답을 주어진 단어로 시작하여 쓰시오. (6 단어)

Q: At first, where did Eric make holes?
A: He made them _____.

07 위 글의 밑줄 친 ⓐ~ⓒ의 <u>it</u>이 가리키는 것을 본문에서 찾아 각각 쓰시오.

➡ ⓐ _____ ⓑ _____

ⓒ _____

08 다음 문장에서 위 글의 내용과 <u>다른</u> 부분 <u>두</u> 군데를 찾아서 고치시오.

> • Eric put a water pump in the pot and connected it to the fish tank by using the tube.

➡ _____

[09~10] 다음 글을 읽고 물음에 답하시오.

Results:

From this experiment, I grew my plants and raised fish with aquaponics. ⓐ<u>나는 그저 물고기 에 밥만 주었는데도 식물은 석 달 동안 17cm나 자랐다.</u> The fish stay healthy and the water is clean all the time.

Conclusion:

Some important things about aquaponics were learned from this experiment. First, water is saved because the plants don't need watering. Second, it is good for the environment because no chemicals are used. Finally, you can do aquaponics anywhere because it doesn't need much space.

I = Eric

09 위 글의 밑줄 친 ⓐ의 우리말에 맞게 한 단어를 보충하여, 주어진 어구를 알맞게 배열하시오.

> have grown / fed / the fish / just / 17 centimeters / three months / the plants / but / I

➡ _____
_____

10 위 글을 읽고 아쿠아포닉스의 장점 세 가지를 우리말로 쓰 시오.

➡ (1) _____

(2) _____

(3) _____

[11~13] 다음 글을 읽고, 물음에 답하시오.

Home Aquaponics   by Eric Jackson

Questions: How can I make an aquaponics system at home?

Why is aquaponics good?

Period: From May 15 to August 15

Materials: a pot & small stones, a fish tank, a plastic tube, a water pump, plants, some fish, a box cutter, clay

Steps:

1. I made holes in the ⓐ(top, bottom) of a pot. Then I put small stones and plants in it.
2. I made a big hole in the lid of the fish tank and put the pot in the hole.
3. I fixed the pot in place with clay.
4. I made another hole in the lid and put a tube through it.
5. I put a water pump in the fish tank. ⓑ<u>관을 이용하여 펌프를 화분에 연결하였다.</u>
6. I filled the fish tank with water and put some fish in it. Then I turned on the pump.

11 다음 질문에 대한 알맞은 대답을 빈칸에 쓰시오.

> Q: How long did Eric do the experiment?
> A: About _____ months.

12 위 글의 괄호 ⓐ에서 알맞은 것을 고르시오.

➡ _____

13 위 글의 밑줄 친 ⓑ의 우리말에 맞게 주어진 어휘를 이용하 여 11 단어로 영작하시오.

> connect, to

➡ _____

해석

After You Read

Window Farming

Do you want to grow plants in your house? Then try window farming! You
want는 부정사(to+동사원형)를 목적어로 취하는 동사이다.   시도하다

can do it anywhere near a window with plastic bottles. Each bottle hangs from
=window farming (전) ~ 가까이   each는 단수 명사를 취하며 단수 동사가 온다.

the one above, so you don't need much space.

구문해설 · farming 농업. 농사 · anywhere 어디에서나 · hang 매달리다 · above 위에 · space 공간

창문 농경
집에서 식물을 기르고 싶나
요? 그렇다면 창문 농경을 해
보세요! 플라스틱 병으로 창
문 근처 어디에서나 그것을
할 수 있습니다. 각각의 병은
위에 매달려 있어서 많은 공
간을 필요로 하지 않아요.

Think and Write

Let's Make Our School Green!

Lots of energy is wasted around us. To solve this problem, let's do these
= Much   수동태   부사적 용법(목적)

things. First, we should turn off the lights when we leave our classrooms.
~을 끄다   접속사

Next, we should turn off the classroom computers when we are not using
~을 끄다

them.
= the classroom computers

Lastly, we should close the doors and windows when we use air conditioners.
= Finally   닫다(동사)

Doing these things will be helpful to our school and the environment.
동명사(주어)   ~에 도움이 되다

구문해설 · waste: 낭비하다. · leave: 떠나다. · helpful: 도움이 되는, · environment: 환경

우리 학교를 친환경적으로 만
듭시다!
우리 주변에서 많은 에너지가
낭비되고 있습니다. 이 문제
를 해결하기 위해, 다음과 같
은 일들을 해 봅시다. 먼저 우
리가 교실을 나갈 때 전깃불
을 꺼야 합니다. 다음 우리가
교실 컴퓨터를 사용하지 않을
때 그것들을 꺼야 합니다. 마
지막으로 에어컨을 사용할 때
교실 문과 창문을 닫아야 합
니다. 이런 일들을 하는 것은
우리 학교와 환경에 도움이
될 것입니다.

Culture Link

This refrigerator works without electricity. It is powered by dirty water. It is
작동하다 ~이 없이   수동태

useful for countries that have little electricity.
~에 유용하다   거의 없는(부정문)

When you need water, just have this water drop! It reduces the use of plastic
명령문   물방울

bottles.

This special tower is the Warka Water Tower. Thanks to this tower, people can
= because of

get water from the air. It saves water.
~부터 …를 얻다

구문해설 · power: ~에 동력을 공급하다 · thanks to: ~ 덕분에

이 냉장고는 전력 없이 작동된다.
그것은 더러운 물에 의해 동력을
공급받는다. 이것은 전력이 거의
없는 나라에 유용하다.
당신이 물이 필요할 때. 그냥 이
물방울을 마셔라! 이것은 플라스
틱 병의 사용을 줄인다.
이 특별한 탑은 와카 워터 타워이
다. 이 탑 덕분에 사람들은 공기
로부터 물을 얻을 수 있다. 이것
은 물을 절약한다.

영역별 핵심문제

01 다음 짝지어진 두 단어의 관계가 같도록 빈칸에 알맞은 단어를 쓰시오.

> waste : save – far : _____

02 다음 대화의 빈칸 ⓐ와 ⓑ에 들어갈 말이 바르게 짝지어진 것은?

> G: Look at this ball. Can you tell me how
> ⓐ _____ it?
> M: Just play soccer for thirty minutes, and
> the light will ⓑ _____ . You can use
> the light anywhere.
> G: Wow, that's interesting.

① using – turn up
② to use – turn off
③ to make – go up
④ making – run out
⑤ to use – turn on

[03~04] 다음 영영풀이에 해당하는 것을 고르시오.

03

> to make something or bring something
> into existence

① fix   ② sew
③ produce   ④ connect
⑤ feed

04

> to pour water onto plants or the soil that
> they are growing in

① water   ② waste
③ reuse   ④ use
⑤ solve

05 다음 빈칸에 들어갈 말이 바르게 짝지어진 것은?

> • _____ the cup with water.
> • Time is running _____ for the Earth.

① Put – on   ② Fill – out
③ Make – in   ④ Put – to
⑤ Fill – of

06 다음 밑줄 친 부분의 뜻이 잘못된 것은?

① It's a way of growing plants without soil.
토양, 흙
② This process is repeated again and again.
반복되다
③ I feed the fish. ~을 먹다
④ I fixed the pot in place with clay.
고정시켰다
⑤ Each bottle hangs from the one above.
매달려 있다

[07~08] 다음 대화를 읽고 물음에 답하시오.

> Jenny: You look upset. What's going on?
> Ben: (A)나는 과학 숙제가 걱정이 돼. I need to
> make a short video about saving the
> environment. But making a video is
> difficult.
> Jenny: Well, how about using this application?
> It's easy.
> Ben: Can you tell me how to use it?
> Jenny: (1)_____
> Ben: Wow, that sounds easy. I'll try it now.
> Thanks.

07 위 대화의 (A)의 우리말에 맞게 영어로 쓰시오.

➡ _____

08 Ben의 질문에 대한 Jenny의 대답을 빈칸 (1)에 넣을 때 알맞은 순서는?

> (A) Then it will make a video with your photos.
> (B) Add your photos and choose some music.
> (C) Sure! Open the application.

① (A)-(B)-(C)   ② (B)-(A)-(C)
③ (B)-(C)-(A)   ④ (C)-(A)-(B)
⑤ (C)-(B)-(A)

[09~11] 다음 대화를 읽고 물음에 답하시오.

G: Have you heard of Earth Hour before?
B: No, I ⓐhaven't. What is it?
G: It's a global environmental event. People ⓑ turn off their lights for an hour.
B: Why do they do that?
G: They do it to ⓒremind people of our environmental problems. They believe (A) such a small action can ⓓexchange the world.
B: Oh, I see. (B)_____
G: Sure. Just turn off your lights from 8:30 p.m. to 9:30 p.m. on the last Saturday in March.
B: ⓔThat's easy. I will join the next Earth Hour.

09 위 대화의 밑줄 친 (A)에 해당하는 행동을 우리말로 구체적으로 쓰시오.

➡ _____

_____

10 위 대화의 빈칸 (B)에 들어갈 알맞은 것은?

① Do you know how to use it?
② Can you explain how to make it?
③ Can you tell me how to join it?
④ Can you tell me where to join it?
⑤ Can you tell me when to begin?

11 위 대화의 흐름상 밑줄 친 ⓐ~ⓔ 중, 어휘의 쓰임이 어색한 것은?

① ⓐ   ② ⓑ   ③ ⓒ   ④ ⓓ   ⑤ ⓔ

[12~13] 다음 대화를 읽고 물음에 답하시오.

G: Did you watch the documentary last night?
B: No, I didn't. What was it about?
G: It was about global warming. (A)지구가 점점 더워지면서, 해수면이 올라가고 있대. I'm worried about the Earth.
B: Oh, I've heard about that problem before. Some islands are disappearing, so people are losing their homes.
G: Yes. It is terrible.
B: Is there any way to stop it?
G: We can save energy. We should turn off the lights when we don't need them. We should also use fans (B)_____ air conditioners.
B: Those are great ideas. I'll try to do those things.

12 위 대화의 밑줄 친 (A)의 우리말에 맞게 주어진 문장의 빈칸을 채우시오.

➡ The Earth is _____ _____,
and sea levels are _____ _____.

13 위 대화의 빈칸 (B)에 들어갈 알맞은 것은?

① because of   ② instead of
③ thanks to   ④ during
⑤ despite

14 다음 중 어법상 올바른 것은?

① The cat was more bigger than yours.
② Blue whales are considered to be the biggest animals.
③ The car in the show room was far expensive than I thought.
④ My brother wasn't made wash the car by my dad.
⑤ The waste turned into food for the plants by bacteria.

15 다음 밑줄 친 부분과 바꿔 쓸 수 있는 것은?

> The line on the blackboard is <u>much</u> longer than the line on the desk.

① very   ② so   ③ lot
④ even   ⑤ too

16 다음 빈칸에 들어갈 말을 순서대로 바르게 짝지은 것을 고르시오.

> • This scarf looks _____ on you than that one.
> • Many dolls _____ in the factory by them.

① too nice – made
② very nicer – were made
③ far nicer – were made
④ far nicer – made
⑤ very nicer – made

17 다음 문장에서 어법상 <u>틀린</u> 것을 고쳐 다시 쓰시오.

(1) I heard 17 trees use to make one ton of paper.
➡ _____

(2) A car accident was happened a few days ago in front of the school.
➡ _____
_____

(3) A beautiful dress is being made to her daughter by Angie.
➡ _____
_____

(4) The tree is planted her grandfather right after he bought the house.
➡ _____
_____

(5) Yesterday Don was seen cross the road by Bella.
➡ _____
_____

(6) The expensive car will buy by someone for whom money grows on trees.
➡ _____
_____

18 다음 빈칸에 들어갈 전치사가 나머지와 <u>다른</u> 것은?

① Our chocolate is made _____ robots.
② The telephone was invented _____ Alexander Bell.
③ *Romeo and Juliet* was written _____ Shakespeare.
④ The pictures in this album were taken _____ Sam.
⑤ Are you satisfied _____ your job as a tour guide?

19 다음 우리말을 괄호 안에 주어진 어구를 이용하여 영작하시오.

(1) 낮은 여름보다 겨울에 훨씬 짧다. (days, much, in winter, 9 단어)

➡ _____

(2) Ann은 코미디언보다 훨씬 더 유머가 있다. (far, humorous, comedians, 7 단어)

➡ _____

(3) 한국에서 축구는 야구보다 훨씬 인기 있다. (soccer, even, popular, 9 단어)

➡ _____

Reading

[20~22] 다음 글을 읽고 물음에 답하시오.

Fish, bacteria, and plants are the main parts of aquaponics. After you feed the fish, they produce ⓐwaste. ⓑThe waste is turned into food for the plants by bacteria. The plants clean the water by consuming the food. This process ⓒ _____ again and again!

20 위 글의 밑줄 친 ⓐwaste와 같은 의미로 쓰인 것을 고르시오.

① Don't waste your time trying it.

② It's a waste of time to do the thing.

③ I didn't waste a good opportunity.

④ We must use waste talents.

⑤ Let's recycle the industrial waste.

21 위 글의 밑줄 친 ⓑ를 능동태로 고치시오.

➡ _____

22 위 글의 빈칸 ⓒ에 repeat를 알맞은 형태로 쓰시오.

➡ _____

[23~24] 다음 글을 읽고 물음에 답하시오.

Home Aquaponics   by Eric Jackson

Questions: How can I make an aquaponics system at home?

Why is aquaponics good?

Period: From May 15 to August 15

Materials: a pot & small stones, a fish tank, a plastic tube, a water pump, plants, some fish, a box cutter, clay

Steps:

1. I made holes in the bottom of a pot. Then I put small stones and plants in it.

2. I made a big hole in the lid of the fish tank and put the pot in the hole.

3. I fixed the pot in place with clay.

4. I made another hole in the lid and put a tube through it.

5. I put a water pump in the fish tank. I used the tube ⓐto connect the pump to the pot.

6. I filled the fish tank with water and put some fish in it. Then I turned on the pump.

23 위 글의 밑줄 친 ⓐto connect와 to부정사의 용법이 다른 것을 모두 고르시오.

① He smiled to see the puppy.

② It is necessary to use the dictionary.

③ She must be honest to say so.

④ I have some letters to write.

⑤ This water is not good to drink.

24 위 글의 내용과 일치하지 않는 것은?

① 에릭은 집에서 아쿠아포닉스 장치를 어떻게 만들 수 있을지와 아쿠아포닉스가 왜 좋은지를 알기 위해 실험을 했다.

② 에릭은 5월 15일부터 8월 15일까지 실험을 했다.

③ 어항 바닥에 큰 구멍을 내고 구멍에 화분을 넣었다.

④ 어항에 수중 펌프를 넣고 관을 이용하여 펌프를 화분에 연결하였다.

⑤ 어항에 물을 채우고 물고기 몇 마리를 거기에 넣었다.

[25~26] 다음 글을 읽고 물음에 답하시오.

Results:

From this experiment, I grew my plants and raised fish with aquaponics. I just fed the fish, but the plants have grown 17 centimeters ⓐ_____ three months. The fish stay healthy and the water is clean all the time.

Conclusion:

Some important things about aquaponics were learned from this experiment. First, water is saved because the plants don't need watering. Second, it is good ⓑ_____ the environment because no chemicals are used. Finally, you can do aquaponics anywhere because it doesn't need much space.

I = Eric

25 위 글의 빈칸 ⓐ와 ⓑ에 들어갈 전치사가 바르게 짝지어진 것은?

① in – for
② for – at
③ at – for
④ for – to
⑤ in – at

26 위 글을 읽고 대답할 수 없는 질문은?

① Did Eric grow his plants and raise fish at the same time?
② How is the water quality with aquaponics?
③ Why is water saved with aquaponics?
④ Why is aquaponics good for the environment?
⑤ What do you need to do aquaponics?

[27~29] 다음 글을 읽고 물음에 답하시오.

I found out...

Some farmers use aquaponics to produce vegetables and raise fish. They choose aquaponics because it is far ⓐ_____ than traditional gardening. Also, it is a much ⓑ_____ way of growing food. The plants grow much ⓒ_____ than plants in soil, and it saves space. I hope ⓓ_____ food is produced in ⓔthis way in the future because it is healthy for us and the environment.

27 위 글의 빈칸 ⓐ~ⓓ에 각각 easy, productive, fast, much의 비교급을 쓰시오.

➡ ⓐ _____ ⓑ _____
ⓒ _____ ⓓ _____

28 위 글의 밑줄 친 ⓔthis way가 가리키는 것을 본문에서 찾아 쓰시오.

➡ _____

29 위 글을 읽고 아쿠아포닉스의 장점이 아닌 것을 고르시오.

① 전통적인 재배 방식보다 훨씬 쉽다.
② 식량을 재배하는 훨씬 더 생산적인 방법이다.
③ 화학 물질의 사용을 줄여준다.
④ 식물들이 흙에서 자라는 식물보다 훨씬 빠르게 자라고 공간도 절약한다.
⑤ 우리와 환경에 훨씬 건강하다.

단원별 예상문제

출제율 95%

01 다음 짝지어진 단어의 관계가 같도록 빈칸에 알맞은 말을 쓰시오.

> choose : select = link : _____

출제율 90%

02 다음 영영풀이에 해당하는 단어는?

> an empty space in an object, usually with an opening to the object's surface

① plant   ② system   ③ hole
④ space   ⑤ bottle

출제율 85%

03 다음 빈칸에 우리말에 맞게 알맞은 단어를 쓰시오.

> • 나는 찰흙으로 화분을 제자리에 고정하였다 .
> (A) I _____ the pot in _____ with clay.
> • 식물에 물을 줄 필요가 없으므로 물이 절약된다.
> (B) Water is saved because the plants don't need _____.

출제율 90%

04 다음은 Home Aquaponics에 관한 글이다. 알맞은 단어를 골라 쓰시오.

> Fish, bacteria, and plants are the main parts of aquaponics. After you (A)[feed / consume] the fish, they produce waste. The waste is turned into food for the (B)[fish / plants] by bacteria. The plants clean the water by consuming the food. This (C)[process / produce] is repeated again and again.

➡ (A)_____ (B)_____ (C)_____

[05~06] 다음 대화를 읽고 물음에 답하시오.

> G: Did you watch the documentary last night?
> B: No, I didn't. What was it about?
> G: It was about global warming. The Earth is getting hotter, and sea levels are going up. (A)_____
> B: Oh, I've heard about that problem before. Some islands are (B)_____, so people are losing their homes.
> G: Yes. It is terrible.

출제율 90%

05 위 대화의 빈칸 (A)에 들어갈 말로 가장 적절한 것은?

① I'm worried about the trash on the street.
② I'm worried about the Earth.
③ The documentary was very interesting.
④ How high are sea levels going up?
⑤ How is the weather?

출제율 100%

06 위 대화의 빈칸 (B)에 들어갈 말로 알맞은 것은?

① appearing   ② expanding
③ warming   ④ developing
⑤ disappearing

[07~09] 다음 대화를 읽고 물음에 답하시오.

> Boy: You look nervous. What's wrong?
> Girl: I'm worried about the speech contest next week. The speeches are about environmental problems and their solutions.
> Boy: What are you going to talk about?
> Girl: I want to talk about soil pollution, but I can't find enough information.

Boy: What about water problems (A)_____? I read an article, and it said we don't have enough water. I'm really worried about it. I think we have to do something about that problem.

Girl: But isn't there enough water for everyone?

Boy: No. In some countries, people are in danger (B)_____ they don't have enough water. Our country could have this problem in the near future.

Girl: Oh, I didn't know that. I will talk about that problem and its solutions. Thank you for your advice!

출제율90%

07 What topic did the girl want to talk about at first? (Write a full sentence.)

➡ _____

출제율95%

08 위 대화의 빈칸 (A)와 (B)에 들어갈 말이 알맞게 짝지어진 것은?

① however – though ② instead – so
③ instead – because ④ however – so
⑤ therefore – because

출제율95%

09 위 대화의 내용과 일치하지 않는 것은?

① The girl looks nervous because she has the speech contest next week.
② The girl doesn't have enough information about soil pollution.
③ The boy is worried about not having enough water.
④ The girl knew that there isn't enough water for everyone.
⑤ The girl will talk about water shortage instead of soil pollution.

출제율90%

10 다음 대화의 빈칸 ⓐ와 ⓑ에 들어갈 단어가 알맞게 짝지어진 것은?

Boy: In my school, students ⓐ_____ so much food on their plates. I'm worried about wasting food.

Girl: Right, that's a big problem. We should not ⓑ_____ too much food on our plates.

Boy: You're right. We shouldn't.

① leave – put   ② put – put
③ take – turn   ④ make – leave
⑤ leave – fill

출제율95%

11 다음 중 밑줄 친 부분이 어법상 잘못된 것은?

① Jake was chosen as our class leader.
② The work must be finished before noon.
③ He was given a reward by the king.
④ The children looked after by their mother.
⑤ The kids are surprised at his grades.

출제율90%

12 다음 빈칸에 들어갈 수 없는 것을 고르시오.

Tigers are _____ faster than pigs.

① very   ② much   ③ far
④ still   ⑤ a lot

13 다음 중 수동태로 바꿔 쓴 것이 잘못된 것은?

① A cake was eaten by Joe.
= Joe ate a cake.

② A cat chases a mouse.
= A mouse is chased by a cat.

③ They take good care of old people at home.
= Old people are taken good care by them at home.

④ The police found the missing boy last Saturday.
= The missing boy was found by the police last Saturday.

⑤ Marc Chagall painted *I and the Village* in 1911.
= *I and the Village* was painted by Marc Chagall in 1911.

14 다음 주어진 단어들을 이용하여 빈칸을 알맞게 채우시오.

• (fast, cheap)
(1) Light travels _____ _____ than sound.
(2) Vegetables are _____ _____ than beef.

➡ (1) _____

(2) _____

15 다음 문장과 같은 뜻이 되도록 빈칸을 채우시오.

(1) Sandra will see the movie *Avatar* tonight.
➡ The movie *Avatar* _____
_____.

(2) John Logie Baird invented the TV in 1925.
➡ The TV _____
_____.

16 우리말 의미에 맞도록 괄호 안의 어구를 알맞게 배열하시오.

(1) laptop이 컴퓨터보다 훨씬 더 유용하다.
(the laptop, the computer, more, is, useful, much, than).
➡ _____

(2) 그녀는 여동생보다 훨씬 더 젊어 보인다. (she, even, sister, her, younger, little, looks, than)
➡ _____

[17~19] 다음 글을 읽고 물음에 답하시오.

Fish, bacteria, and plants are the main parts of aquaponics. After you feed the fish, ⓐthey produce waste. The waste is turned into food for the plants by bacteria. The plants clean the water by consuming ⓑthe food. This process is repeated again and again!

17 위 글의 밑줄 친 ⓐthey가 가리키는 것을 본문에서 찾아 쓰시오.

➡ _____

18 다음 빈칸에 알맞은 단어를 넣어 ⓑthe food에 대한 소개를 완성하시오.

After _____ is produced by the fish, bacteria turn it into food for the plants.

➡ _____

19 위 글의 내용과 일치하지 <u>않는</u> 것은?

① 물고기, 박테리아, 식물이 아쿠아포닉스의 주요 부분이다.

② 물고기에게 먹이를 주면, 그것들은 배설물을 만들어 낸다.

③ 이 배설물은 물고기에 의해 식물의 먹이로 바뀐다.

④ 식물은 그 먹이를 먹음으로써 물을 정화한다.

⑤ 이러한 과정이 계속해서 반복된다.

[20~22] 다음 글을 읽고 물음에 답하시오.

Steps:

1. I made holes in the bottom of a pot. @Then I put small stones and plants in it.
2. I made a big hole in the lid of the fish tank and put the pot in the hole.
3. I (A)[fixed / repaired] the pot in place ⓑ_____ clay.
4. I made another hole in the lid and put a tube (B)[threw / through] it.
5. I put a water pump in the fish tank. I used the tube to connect the pump to the pot.
6. I filled the fish tank ⓒ_____ water and put some fish in it. Then I turned (C)[on / off] the pump.

20 위 글의 밑줄 친 @Then을 다음과 같이 바꿔 쓸 때 빈칸에 들어갈 알맞은 말을 쓰시오.

➡ After _____

21 위 글의 괄호 (A)~(C)에서 문맥상 알맞은 낱말을 골라 쓰시오.

➡ (A)_____ (B)_____ (C)_____

22 위 글의 빈칸 ⓑ와 ⓒ에 공통으로 들어갈 알맞은 전치사를 고르시오.

① to   ② on   ③ at
④ by   ⑤ with

[23~25] 다음 글을 읽고 물음에 답하시오.

Results:

From this experiment, I grew my plants and raised fish with aquaponics. I just fed the fish, but the plants ①<u>have grown</u> 17 centimeters in three months. The fish stay ②<u>healthily</u> and the water is clean all the time.

Conclusion:

Some important things about aquaponics ③<u>was</u> learned from this experiment. First, water ⓐ_____ because the plants don't need ④<u>being watered</u>. Second, it is good for the environment because no chemicals are used. Finally, you can do aquaponics ⑤<u>anywhere</u> because it doesn't need much space.

I = Eric

23 위 글의 밑줄 친 ①~⑤ 중 어법상 <u>틀린</u> 것의 개수를 고르시오.

① 1개   ② 2개   ③ 3개   ④ 4개   ⑤ 5개

24 위 글의 빈칸 ⓐ에 save를 알맞은 형태로 쓰시오.

➡ _____

25 다음 문장에서 위 글의 내용과 <u>다른</u> 부분을 찾아서 고치시오.

• From this experiment, the plants have grown 17 centimeters in three months because Eric watered the plants.

➡ _____
_____

01 다음 그림을 보고 대화의 빈칸을 완성하시오.

flower pot

1. Make holes in the bottom.
2. Fill the cup with soil and plants.

A: I made _____ _____ _____ with a plastic cup.

B: Can you tell me _____ _____ _____ it?

A: Sure. Make holes in _____ _____. Then _____ the cup _____ soil and plants.

02 다음은 수질 오염에 관한 그림이다. 〈보기〉에서 알맞은 해결책을 골라 대화를 완성하시오.

water pollution

보기
recycle   plant many trees
use less water   use less soap

A: I am worried about (A)_____ these days.

B: Me, too. We should (B)_____ to solve this problem.

➡ (A) _____
  (B) _____

03 다음은 어떤 환경 문제에 관한 대화이다. 빈칸 (A)에는 언급하고 있는 문제를, (B)에는 해결책을 주어진 단어를 이용하여 쓰시오.

G: Did you watch the documentary last night?

B: No, I didn't. What was it about?

G: It was about (A)_____. The Earth is getting hotter, and sea levels are going up. I'm worried about the Earth.

B: Is there any way to stop it?

G: We can save energy. We should (B)_____ (the lights) when we don't need them. We should also use fans instead of air conditioners.

B: Those are great ideas. I'll try to do those things.

➡(A) _____   (B) _____

04 다음 주어진 문장을 능동태는 수동태로, 수동태는 능동태로 바꾸시오.

(1) What did he do last weekend?

  ➡ _____

(2) Van Gogh painted these paintings.

  ➡ _____

(3) My father gave me that watch years ago.

  ➡ _____

05 다음 문장에서 틀린 것을 고쳐 다시 쓰시오.

(1) He is very tall than his son.

➡ _____

(2) Sue uses too much water than Nick.

➡ _____

[06~08] 다음 글을 읽고 물음에 답하시오.

Home Aquaponics   by Eric Jackson

Questions: ⓐ   can I make an aquaponics system at home?

Why is aquaponics good?

Steps:

1. I made holes in the bottom of a pot. Then I put small stones and plants in it.
2. I made a big hole in the lid of the fish tank and put the pot in the hole.
3. I fixed the pot in place with clay.
4. I made another hole in the lid and put a tube through it.
5. I put a water pump in the fish tank. I used the tube ⓑ_____.

6. I filled the fish tank with water and put some fish in it. ⓒThen I turned on the pump.

06 위 글의 빈칸 ⓐ에 들어갈 알맞은 말을 쓰시오.

➡ _____

07 그림을 참조하여 위 글의 빈칸 ⓑ에 들어갈 알맞은 말을 쓰시오. (7 단어)

➡ _____

08 위 글의 밑줄 친 ⓒThen을 다음과 같이 바꿔 쓸 때 빈칸에 들어갈 알맞은 말을 쓰시오.

➡ _____ I filled the fish tank with water and put some fish in it

[09~11] 다음 글을 읽고 물음에 답하시오.

Conclusion:

ⓐSome important things about aquaponics were learned from this experiment. First, water is saved because the plants don't need ⓑwatering. Second, it is good for the environment because no chemicals are used. Finally, you can do aquaponics anywhere because it doesn't need much space.

09 위 글의 밑줄 친 ⓐ를 I를 주어로 하여 능동태로 고치시오.

➡ _____

_____

10 위 글의 밑줄 친 ⓑ를 to부정사를 사용하여 고치시오.

➡ _____

11 본문의 내용과 일치하도록 다음 빈칸 (A)~(C)에 알맞은 단어를 넣어 아쿠아포닉스의 장점을 정리하시오.

(1) You need not water the plants in aquaponics.

➡ You can (A)_____.

(2) You need not (B)_____ in aquaponics.

➡ Aquaponics is good for the environment.

(3) You don't need (C)_____ in aquaponics.

➡ You can do aquaponics anywhere.

01 다음은 일상생활에서 발생할 수 있는 문제와 해결책에 관한 문장이다. 〈보기〉를 참고하여, 문제점과 그에 대한 해결책으로 알맞은 두 문장 이상의 대화를 완성하시오.

<문제점>

a park in my town – It is full of trash. / my brother – He always buys too many things. / my cat – He is missing. / my friend – She uses her smartphone too often.

<해결책>

We should clean up the park together. / He should make a shopping list.
You should put up posters to find him. / She should find a new hobby.

<보기>

A: I'm worried about a park in my town. It is full of trash.
  Can you tell me how to solve this problem?
B: I think we should clean up the park together.

---

02 다음 내용을 바탕으로 학교에서 환경을 보호하는 방법을 친구들에게 제안하는 글을 쓰시오.

Problem
Lots of energy is wasted.
Solutions
• Turn off the lights.
• Turn off the classroom computers.
• Close the doors and windows when we use air conditioners.

Let's Make Our School Green!

  Lots of energy (A)_____ around us. To solve this problem, let's do these things. First, we should (B)_____ the lights when we leave our classrooms. Next, we should turn off the classroom computers when we are not (C)_____ them. Lastly, we should (D)_____ the doors and windows when we use air conditioners. Doing these things will be (E)_____ to our school and the environment.

단원별 모의고사

01 다음 단어에 대한 영어 설명이 어색한 것은?

① in place: in the correct position

② productive: producing or achieving a lot

③ consume: to eat or drink, especially a lot of something

④ reuse: to use something again

⑤ remind: to make someone forget something that they must do

02 다음 짝지어진 단어의 관계가 같도록 빈칸에 알맞은 말을 쓰시오.

turn off : turn on = appear : _____

03 다음 영영풀이에 해당하는 단어를 고르시오.

a cover for the open part of a pot, box, or container, etc.

① lid   ② tank

③ article   ④ cup

⑤ project

04 다음 글의 빈칸에 들어갈 말이 바르게 짝지어진 것은?

Time is (A)_____ for the Earth. Remember the Earth is (B)_____. Keep the Earth green!

① getting – dangerous

② polluting – clean

③ making up – safe

④ turning on – going up

⑤ running out – in danger

[05~06] 다음 대화를 읽고 물음에 답하시오.

B: I like your bag, Jenny. Where did you get ⓐit?

G: I made ⓑit myself.

B: You made ⓒit yourself? That's amazing.

G: Why don't you make one? ⓓIt's not difficult.

B: Really? Can you tell me how to make ⓔit?

G: Sure. Find some old jeans. (A)그걸 작은 조각으로 잘라. Then sew the pieces together.

B: That sounds easy. I'll make one as a birthday present for my sister.

05 위 대화의 밑줄 친 ⓐ~ⓔ 중, 가리키는 대상이 다른 하나는?

① ⓐ   ② ⓑ   ③ ⓒ   ④ ⓓ   ⑤ ⓔ

06 위 대화의 밑줄 친 (A)의 우리말에 맞게 주어진 단어를 이용하여 영어로 쓰시오.

➡ _____

(cut, into, pieces)

07 다음 대화의 빈칸 (A)에 들어갈 말을 주어진 단어를 이용하여 영어로 쓰시오.

G: Earth Hour is a global environmental event. People turn off their lights for an hour.

B: Why do they do that?

G: They do it to remind people of our environmental problems.

B: Oh, I see. (A)_____ (can, tell, how, join, it)

G: Sure. Just turn off your lights from 8:30 p.m. to 9:30 p.m. on the last Saturday in March.

B: That's easy.

➡ _____

[08~10] 다음 대화를 읽고 물음에 답하시오.

Ben: You look nervous. What's wrong?

Jenny: I'm worried about the speech contest next week. The speeches are about environmental problems and their solutions.

Ben: What are you going to talk about?

Jenny: I want to talk about soil pollution, but I can't find enough information.

Ben: What about water problems instead? I read an article, and ⓐit said we don't have enough water. I'm really worried about ⓑit. I think we have to do something about ⓒthat problem.

Jenny: But isn't there enough water for everyone?

Ben: No. In some countries, (A)물이 부족해서 사람들이 위험에 처하기도 해. Our country could have ⓓthis problem in the near future.

Jenny: Oh, I didn't know that. I will talk about ⓔthat problem and its solutions. Thank you for your advice!

08 위 대화를 읽고 답할 수 없는 질문은?

① What topic will Jenny talk about?
② Why is Jenny going to talk about soil pollution?
③ What is Ben worried about?
④ When is the speech contest?
⑤ Is there enough water for everyone?

09 위 대화의 밑줄 친 ⓐ~ⓔ 중, 가리키는 대상이 다른 하나는?

① ⓐ　　② ⓑ　　③ ⓒ　　④ ⓓ　　⑤ ⓔ

10 위 대화의 밑줄 친 (A)의 우리말에 맞게 주어진 어구를 이용하여 영어로 쓰시오.

(are, danger, because, they, enough water)

➡ _____

_____

11 다음 밑줄 친 부분 중 생략할 수 있는 것은?

① The airplane was invented by the Wright brothers in 1903.
② *Harry Potter* was written by J. K. Rowling.
③ The bike was fixed by my elder brother.
④ English is spoken in Australia by them.
⑤ The children weren't taught by him.

12 다음 〈보기〉의 표현이 빈칸에 들어갈 수 없는 문장은?

보기
much　　far

① This dictionary is _____ heavier than that book.
② Taking a bus is _____ cheaper than taking a taxi.
③ She felt _____ great after taking a sound sleep.
④ My brother jumps _____ higher than I.
⑤ Lisa dances _____ harder than me.

13 다음 밑줄 친 부분의 쓰임이 나머지 넷과 다른 것은?

① The bike was repaired by my brother.

② This chocolate cake was cooked for me by my mother.

③ Water is saved because the plants don't need watering.

④ She often avoided replying to our comments.

⑤ The pictures were drawn by my daughter.

14 다음 그림을 보고 주어진 단어를 이용하여 비교하는 문장을 쓰시오.

➡ _____

(feather, stone, much)

15 다음 문장에서 틀린 것을 고쳐 다시 쓰시오.

(1) Paper is made of wood.

➡ _____

(2) Olivia was cooked the chicken soup by her mother.

➡ _____

(3) A man was appeared on the stage slowly.

➡ _____

(4) I didn't know you were interested by Latin dance.

➡ _____

(5) Some birds were heard sing on the tree.

➡ _____

[16~17] 다음 글을 읽고 물음에 답하시오.

Jennifer: What are you reading?

Eric: I'm reading an article about aquaponics. It's a way of growing plants (A)[with / without] soil. We can also grow plants and (B)[rise / raise] fish in just one system.

Jennifer: Is ⓐthat possible?

Eric: We'll (C)[see / show]. I'm going to try it at home for my science project.

16 위 글의 괄호 (A)~(C)에서 문맥이나 어법상 알맞은 낱말을 골라 쓰시오.

➡ (A)_____ (B)_____ (C)_____

17 위 글의 밑줄 친 ⓐthat이 가리키는 것을 본문에서 찾아 쓰시오.

➡ _____

_____

[18~19] 다음 글을 읽고 물음에 답하시오.

Steps:

1. I made holes in the bottom of a pot. Then I put small stones and plants ①_____ it.

2. I made a big hole ②_____ the lid of the fish tank and put the pot in the hole.

3. ⓐ찰흙으로 화분을 제자리에 고정하였다.

4. I made another hole in the lid and put a tube through it.

5. I put a water pump ③_____ the fish tank. I used the tube to connect the pump ④_____ the pot.

6. I filled the fish tank with water and put some fish ⑤_____ it. Then I turned on the pump.

18 위 글의 빈칸 ①~⑤에 들어갈 전치사가 나머지 넷과 <u>다른</u> 것은?

①   ②   ③   ④   ⑤

19 위 글의 밑줄 친 ⓐ의 우리말에 맞게 한 단어를 보충하여, 주어진 어휘를 알맞게 배열하시오.

> with / the / fixed / I / clay / pot / in

➡ _____

[20~21] 다음 글을 읽고 물음에 답하시오.

> **Results:**
>
> From this experiment, I grew my ⓐ_____ and raised ⓑ_____ with aquaponics. I just fed the fish, but the plants have grown 17 centimeters in three months. The fish stay healthy and the water is clean all the time.
>
> **Conclusion:**
>
> Some important things about aquaponics were learned from this experiment. First, water is saved because the plants don't need watering. Second, it is good for the environment because no chemicals are used. Finally, you can do aquaponics anywhere because it doesn't need much space.
>
> I = Eric

20 다음 그림을 참조하여 위 글의 빈칸 ⓐ와 ⓑ에 들어갈 알맞은 말을 쓰시오.

➡ ⓐ _____ ⓑ _____

21 위 글의 내용과 일치하지 <u>않는</u> 것은?

① 에릭은 그저 물고기에 밥만 주었는데도 식물은 석 달 동안 17cm나 자랐다.

② 아쿠아포닉스로 물고기는 건강을 유지하며 물은 항상 깨끗하다.

③ 아쿠아포닉스에서는 식물에 물을 자주 주어야 하므로 물이 많이 소비된다.

④ 화학 물질이 사용되지 않으므로 아쿠아포닉스는 환경에 이롭다.

⑤ 넓은 공간이 필요하지 않으므로 당신은 어디에서나 아쿠아포닉스를 쉽게 할 수 있다.

[22~23] 다음 글을 읽고 물음에 답하시오.

> *I found out...*
>
> Some farmers use aquaponics to produce vegetables and raise fish. They choose aquaponics because it is ⓐ<u>far</u> easier than traditional gardening. Also, it is a much more productive way of growing food. The plants grow much faster than plants in soil, and it saves space. I hope more food is produced in this way in the future because it is healthy for us and the environment.

22 위 글의 밑줄 친 ⓐ와 바꿔 쓸 수 있는 것은?

① so   ② very   ③ too
④ much   ⑤ lot

23 다음 문장에서 위 글의 내용과 <u>다른</u> 부분을 찾아서 고치시오.

> The plants in soil grow much faster than the plants in aquaponics system.

➡ _____

_____

Middle School 2-1
1학기 전과정

중간 + 기말
적중100 plus
영어 기출문제집

영어 중 2

능률 | 김성곤

Best Collection

내용문의 중등영어발전소 적중100 편집부 TEL 070-7707-0457
인터넷 서비스 www.jj100.co.kr

INSIGHT
on the textbook

교과서 파헤치기

영어 기출 문제집

적중 100 plus
1학기 전과정

영어 중 2

능률 | 김성곤

INSIGHT
on the textbook

교과서 파헤치기

※ 다음 영어를 우리말로 쓰시오.

01 personal		22 subject
02 carefully		23 solve
03 appropriate		24 incorrect
04 comment		25 interesting
05 bring		26 report
06 dictionary		27 teens
07 awesome		28 surprisingly
08 filter		29 environment
09 understand		30 recipe
10 finally		31 prepare
11 impossible		32 outdoors
12 share		33 sometimes
13 borrow		34 nervous
14 exciting		35 from A to B
15 hurt		36 keep in mind
16 part		37 break the law
17 silly		38 spend 시간 -ing
18 etiquette		39 have fun
19 bother		40 in front of
20 restroom		41 just like
21 public		42 check out
		43 find out

※ 다음 우리말을 영어로 쓰시오.

01 (법률 · 약속 등을) 어기다		
02 캐리어, 운반[이동] 장치		
03 사진술		
04 올리다, 게시하다		
05 복사하다		
06 사실		
07 포스터		
08 주제		
09 준비하다		
10 건강에 좋은, 건강한		
11 완벽한		
12 (작품을) 전시하다, 보여주다		
13 남기다		
14 긴장되는, 불안해하는		
15 야외에서, 옥외에서		
16 환경		
17 고르다		
18 가끔		
19 아마도		
20 놀랍게도		
21 결과		

22 셀피		
23 조리법		
24 무례한		
25 옷		
26 조사		
27 적절한		
28 빌리다		
29 불가능한		
30 괴롭히다		
31 이해하다		
32 사전		
33 화장실		
34 ~을 보다		
35 ~에 관심[흥미]이 있다		
36 법을 어기다		
37 무엇보다도		
38 명심하다		
39 ~에 동의하다		
40 ~ 앞에		
41 확인하다		
42 발견하다, 찾아보다		
43 세계 곳곳에		

※ 다음 영영풀이에 알맞은 단어를 <보기>에서 골라 쓴 후, 우리말 뜻을 쓰시오.

1 _____ : good for your body: _____

2 _____ : available for anyone to use: _____

3 _____ : to have or use something with other people: _____

4 _____ : correct or suitable for a particular time, situation, or purpose: _____

5 _____ : to find or provide a way of dealing with a problem: _____

6 _____ : an opinion that you express about someone or something: _____

7 _____ : a piece of information that is known to be true: _____

8 _____ : a set of instructions for cooking a particular type of food: _____

9 _____ : the formal rules for polite behavior in society or in a particular group: _____

10 _____ : to make plans or arrangements for something that will happen in the future: _____

11 _____ : the art, profession, or method of producing photographs or the scenes in films: _____

12 _____ : speaking or behaving in a way that is not polite and is likely to offend or annoy people: _____

13 _____ : to put a message or computer document on the Internet so that other people can see it: _____

14 _____ : something that happens or exists because of something that happened before: _____

15 _____ : to take something or someone with you to the place where you are now, or to the place you are talking about: _____

16 _____ : to take and use something that belongs to someone else for a period of time before returning it: _____

보기			
etiquette	comment	healthy	post
solve	prepare	recipe	result
share	bring	fact	public
borrow	photography	rude	appropriate

※ 다음 우리말과 일치하도록 빈칸에 알맞은 말을 쓰시오.

Listen & Talk 1 A

G: _____ _____ these club posters . What are you _____ _____?

B: I'm interested _____ _____. _____ _____ you?

G: I'm _____ _____ photography.

G: 동아리 포스터들을 봐. 너는 어떤 것에 관심이 있니?
B: 나는 요리에 관심이 있어. 너는 어때?
G: 나는 사진에 관심이 있어.

Listen & Talk 1 B

B: What _____ you _____ _____ do this weekend?

G: I'm _____ _____ _____ to a baseball game _____ my brother.

B: _____ you _____ _____ baseball?

G: Not really. I'm _____ to the baseball game _____ my brother likes baseball.

B: You're so nice! Then _____ are you _____ in?

G: I'm _____ _____ in soccer. I _____ _____ _____ to a soccer game _____ .

B: 이번 주말에 뭐 할 거야?
G: 나는 동생하고 야구 보러 갈 거야.
B: 너는 야구에 관심 있니?
G: 사실은 좋아하지 않아. 나는 내 동생이 좋아해서 야구 보러 가는 거야.
B: 너 정말 착하다! 그럼 너는 어떤 것에 관심 있니?
G: 나는 축구에 더 관심 있어. 언젠가 축구 경기를 보러 가고 싶어.

Listen & Talk 1 C

G: _____ are you _____ _____?

B: I'm looking at TV program _____. What show _____ I _____?

G: Well, what are you _____ _____?

B: _____ _____ in music.

G: Then how _____ _____ the *Friday Pop Music Show*?

B: I'm actually not _____ _____ _____ _____ pop music. I like to _____ _____ rap music.

G: Then _____ _____ you watch *Hit the Beat*?

B: Good idea.

G: 뭐 보고 있니?
B: TV 프로그램 편성표 보고 있어. 어떤 걸 봐야 할까?
G: 음, 너 어떤 분야에 관심이 있니?
B: 나는 음악에 관심이 있어.
G: 그러면 "Friday Pop Music Show"를 보는 게 어때?
B: 사실 팝 음악을 많이 좋아하지는 않아. 나는 랩 음악 듣는 걸 좋아해.
G: 그러면 "Hit the Beat"을 보는 건 어때?
B: 좋은 생각이야.

Listen & Talk 1 D

A: _____ are you _____ _____?

B: I'm interested _____ games and social media. _____ _____ you?

A: I'm _____ _____ music and _____ _____.

B: _____ are _____ interested in social media.

A: 너는 무엇에 관심이 있니?
B: 나는 게임과 소셜 미디어에 관심이 있어. 너는 어때?
A: 나는 음악과 소셜 미디어에 관심이 있어.
B: 우리는 둘 다 소셜 미디어에 관심이 있구나.

Listen & Talk 2 A

B: May I _____ my dog _____ the bus?

W: Yes, you _____ . But you _____ _____ your dog in the carrier.

B: 버스에 제 개를 데리고 타도 되나요?
W: 네, 됩니다. 하지만 당신은 개를 캐리어에 넣어야 해요.

Listen & Talk 2 B

G: Hi. _____ I _____ in now?

M: Sure. _____ me _____ your ticket, please.

G: _____ it is. _____ I _____ the music in the concert hall?

M: _____, you _____ _____.

G: Okay. May I _____ _____ _____ the band?

M: No, you _____ _____. You can only _____ pictures _____ _____ the concert hall. Please _____ the concert.

G: Oh, okay. Thank you.

Listen & Talk 2 C

B: _____ me.

W: Hello. _____ can I do _____ you?

B: _____ I _____ this new science book?

W: No, _____ _____ _____. Students _____ _____ new books _____.

B: Then _____ I _____ some pages from the book? I need them for my science report.

W: _____, _____ _____. But please _____ _____ them online.

B: Okay, I _____. Thank you!

Let's communicate 1

A: What _____ you interested _____?

B: _____ _____ _____ music.

A: _____ _____ you go to a concert hall this weekend?

B: _____ good. _____ I _____ the music there?

A: Yes, you _____. / No, you _____ _____.

Do It Yourself A

M: Hey, Yumi. What _____ you _____?

G: Hello, Mr. King. I'm _____ for tomorrow's _____. It is about _____ _____ my interests .

M: That _____ _____! What _____ you _____ _____?

G: I'm _____ _____ photography. I will _____ _____ it tomorrow.

M: Oh, I'm _____ _____ photography, _____.

G: Really? Then _____ I _____ you for some advice for my presentation?

M: Sure.

G: 안녕하세요. 지금 안에 들어가도 되나요?

M: 그럼요. 티켓을 보여 주시겠어요?

G: 여기 있어요. 콘서트홀 안에서 노래 녹음해도 되나요?

M: 아니요, 안 됩니다.

G: 알겠습니다. 밴드 사진은 찍어도 되나요?

M: 아니요, 안 됩니다. 콘서트홀 밖에 서만 사진을 찍을 수 있어요. 즐거운 관람되세요.

G: 아, 알겠습니다. 감사합니다.

B: 실례합니다.

W: 안녕하세요. 무엇을 도와드릴까요?

B: 이 새로 출시된 과학책 빌려도 될까요?

W: 아뇨, 불가능합니다. 학생들은 새로 출시된 책을 집으로 가져갈 수 없어요.

B: 그러면 책에서 몇 장 정도 복사해도 될까요? 과학 보고서 쓰는 데 필요해서요.

W: 네, 그러세요. 하지만 그걸 인터넷상에 공유하지는 마세요.

B: 네, 안 그럴게요. 감사합니다!

A: 너는 무엇에 관심이 있니?

B: 나는 음악에 관심이 있어.

A: 이번 주에 콘서트홀에 가는 건 어때?

B: 그거 좋겠다. 거기서 음악을 녹음해도 될까?

A: 그래, 돼. / 아니, 안 돼.

M: 유미야. 뭐 하고 있니?

G: 안녕하세요, King씨. 저는 내일 발표를 준비하고 있어요. 제 관심사 중 하나에 대한 거예요.

M: 그거 재미있겠다! 너는 어떤 것에 관심이 있니?

G: 저는 사진에 관심이 있어요. 저는 그것에 대해 내일 이야기할 거예요.

M: 오, 나도 역시 사진에 관심이 있어.

G: 정말요? 그렇다면 제 발표에 대해 몇 가지 조언을 부탁해도 될까요?

M: 물론이지.

대화문 Test

※ 다음 우리말에 맞도록 대화를 영어로 쓰시오.

 해석

Listen & Talk 1 A

G: _____

B: _____

G: _____

G: 동아리 포스터들을 봐. 너는 어떤 것에 관심이 있니?
B: 나는 요리에 관심이 있어. 너는 어때?
G: 나는 사진에 관심이 있어.

Listen & Talk 1 B

B: _____

G: _____

B: _____

G: _____

B: _____

G: _____

B: 이번 주말에 뭐 할 거야?
G: 나는 동생하고 야구 보러 갈 거야.
B: 너는 야구에 관심 있니?
G: 사실은 좋아하지 않아. 나는 내 동생이 좋아해서 야구 보러 가는 거야.
B: 너 정말 착하다! 그럼 너는 어떤 것에 관심 있니?
G: 나는 축구에 더 관심 있어. 언젠가 축구 경기를 보러 가고 싶어.

Listen & Talk 1 C

G: _____

B: _____

G: _____

B: _____

G: _____

B: _____

G: _____

B: _____

G: 뭐 보고 있니?
B: TV 프로그램 편성표 보고 있어. 어떤 걸 봐야 할까?
G: 음, 너 어떤 분야에 관심이 있니?
B: 나는 음악에 관심이 있어.
G: 그러면 "Friday Pop Music Show"를 보는 게 어때?
B: 사실 팝 음악을 많이 좋아하지는 않아. 나는 랩 음악 듣는 걸 좋아해.
G: 그러면 "Hit the Beat"을 보는 건 어때?
B: 좋은 생각이야.

Listen & Talk 1 D

A: _____

B: _____

A: _____

B: _____

A: 너는 무엇에 관심이 있니?
B: 나는 게임과 소셜 미디어에 관심이 있어. 너는 어때?
A: 나는 음악과 소셜 미디어에 관심이 있어.
B: 우리는 둘 다 소셜 미디어에 관심이 있구나.

Listen & Talk 2 A

B: _____

W: _____

B: 버스에 제 개를 데리고 타도 되나요?
W: 네, 됩니다. 하지만 당신은 개를 캐리어에 넣어야 해요.

Listen & Talk 2 B

G: _____

M: _____

G: _____

M: _____

G: _____

M: _____

G: _____

Listen & Talk 2 C

B: _____

W: _____

B: _____

W: _____

B: _____

W: _____

B: _____

Let's communicate 1

A: _____

B: _____

A: _____

B: _____

A: _____

Do It Yourself A

M: _____

G: _____
_____

M: _____

G: _____

M: _____

G: _____

M: _____

G: 안녕하세요. 지금 안에 들어가도 되나요?

M: 그럼요. 티켓을 보여 주시겠어요?

G: 여기 있어요. 콘서트홀 안에서 노래 녹음해도 되나요?

M: 아니요, 안 됩니다.

G: 알겠습니다. 밴드 사진은 찍어도 되나요?

M: 아니요, 안 됩니다. 콘서트홀 밖에서만 사진을 찍을 수 있어요. 즐거운 관람되세요.

G: 아, 알겠습니다. 감사합니다.

B: 실례합니다.

W: 안녕하세요. 무엇을 도와드릴까요?

B: 이 새로 출시된 과학책 빌려도 될까요?

W: 아뇨, 불가능합니다. 학생들은 새로 출시된 책을 집으로 가져갈 수 없어요.

B: 그러면 책에서 몇 장 정도 복사해도 될까요? 과학 보고서 쓰는 데 필요해서요.

W: 네, 그러세요. 하지만 그걸 인터넷상에 공유하지는 마세요.

B: 네, 안 그럴게요. 감사합니다!

A: 너는 무엇에 관심이 있니?

B: 나는 음악에 관심이 있어.

A: 이번 주에 콘서트홀에 가는 건 어때?

B: 그거 좋겠다. 거기서 음악을 녹음해도 될까?

A: 그래, 돼. / 아니, 안 돼.

M: 유미야. 뭐 하고 있니?

G: 안녕하세요, King씨. 저는 내일 발표를 준비하고 있어요. 제 관심사 중 하나에 대한 거예요.

M: 그거 재미있겠다! 너는 어떤 것에 관심이 있니?

G: 저는 사진에 관심이 있어요. 저는 그것에 대해 내일 이야기할 거예요.

M: 오, 나도 역시 사진에 관심이 있어.

G: 정말요? 그렇다면 제 발표에 대해 몇 가지 조언을 부탁해도 될까요?

M: 물론이지.

※ 다음 우리말과 일치하도록 빈칸에 알맞은 것을 골라 쓰시오.

1 _____ _____ Selfies!
A. About　　　　B. All

2 #_____ _____
A. Facts　　　　B. Selfie

3 _____ you _____ _____ selfies?
A. in　　　　B. interested　　　　C. are

4 You _____ like to _____ selfies on social media, but how _____ do you know about selfies?
A. much　　　　B. post　　　　C. probably

5 _____ are some interesting _____.
A. facts　　　　B. here

6 Robert Cornelius _____ the world's _____ selfie _____ 1839.
A. in　　　　B. first　　　　C. took

7 *Selfie* _____ a new _____ in the _____ in 2013.
A. word　　　　B. became　　　　C. dictionary

8 Buzz Aldrin _____ the first _____ _____ in 1966.
A. selfie　　　　B. space　　　　C. took

9 #_____ _____
A. Survey　　　　B. Selfie

10 _____ selfies is part of _____ life for many teens, but do teens really _____ it?
A. enjoy　　　　B. daily　　　　C. taking

11 _____ find _____, we did a _____.
A. survey　　　　B. out　　　　C. to

12 We asked three _____ to 300 students from _____ 14 _____ 16.
A. to　　　　B. questions　　　　C. ages

13 _____ look _____ the results.
A. at　　　　B. let's

14 _____, 90 _____ of the girls take selfies, but _____ 15 percent of the boys take selfies.
A. only　　　　B. percent　　　　C. surprisingly

15 _____, 93 percent of these students said _____ they use _____.
A. filters　　　　B. that　　　　C. also

16 The _____ also _____ that the students _____ selfies at school the most.
A. take　　　　B. showed　　　　C. survey

17 _____ _____ some of the students' _____.
A. comments　　　　B. out　　　　C. check

18 Lewis, 14, _____ Selfies are _____.
A. awesome　　　　B. England

1 셀피에 대한 모든 것!

2 셀피와 관련된 사실들

3 당신은 셀피에 관심이 있는가?

4 당신은 아마 소셜 미디어에 셀피를 게시하기를 좋아할지도 모르지만, 셀피에 대해 얼마나 많이 알고 있는가?

5 여기 몇 가지 재미있는 사실들이 있다.

6 로버트 코닐리어스가 1839년에 전 세계 최초의 셀피를 찍었다.

7 selfie는 2013년에 사전에 신조어로 등재되었다.

8 버즈 올드린이 1966년에 최초의 우주 셀피를 찍었다.

9 셀피 설문 조사

10 셀피 찍기는 많은 십대들에게 일상생활의 한 부분인데, 십대들은 정말로 그것을 즐기고 있는가?

11 알아보기 위해 우리는 설문 조사를 했다.

12 우리는 14세에서 16세 사이의 학생 300명에게 세 가지를 질문했다.

13 그 결과를 보자.

14 놀랍게도, 소녀들의 90퍼센트가 셀피를 찍지만, 소년들의 15퍼센트만이 셀피를 찍는다.

15 또한 이 학생들의 93퍼센트는 필터를 사용한다고 대답했다.

16 설문은 또한 학생들이 학교에서 가장 많이 셀피를 찍는다는 것을 보여 주었다.

17 학생들의 의견 몇 가지를 확인해 보라.

18 루이스, 14세, 영국: 셀피는 굉장하다.

19 Making _____ faces is _____ fun!
A. really   B. silly

20 Minwoo, 16, Korea I enjoy _____ selfies, but some students _____ too much time _____ it.
A. doing   B. taking   C. spend

21 Kate, 15, Denmark My pictures _____ _____ when I _____ filters.
A. use   B. good   C. look

22 But _____ my selfies don't _____ _____ me.
A. like   B. sometimes   C. look

23 #_____ _____
A. Etiquette   B. Selfie

24 You should follow _____ for _____.
A. selfies   B. etiquette

25 Ask _____ these questions _____ you take, _____, or look at selfies.
A. post   B. before   C. yourself

26 1. _____ _____ I?
A. am   B. where

27 Choose _____ places to take _____.
A. selfies   B. appropriate

28 _____ take selfies in _____ or public _____.
A. hospitals   B. don't   C. restrooms

29 It may _____ _____ people.
A. other   B. bother

30 2. _____ can see _____?
A. this   B. who

31 _____ in mind that _____ can _____ your selfies.
A. see   B. anyone   C. keep

32 _____ carefully _____ you _____ them.
A. post   B. choose   C. when

33 3. What _____ of _____ should I _____?
A. leave   B. comments   C. kinds

34 _____ nice _____ on _____ people's selfies.
A. other   B. leave   C. comments

35 _____ be rude. That _____ easy, _____ it?
A. doesn't   B. sounds   C. don't

36 _____ these _____ and have _____ with your selfies.
A. tips   B. follow   C. fun

19 우스꽝스러운 표정을 짓는 것은 정말로 재미있다!

20 민우, 16세, 한국: 나는 셀피 찍는 것을 즐기지만 몇몇 학생들은 그것을 하는 데 너무 많은 시간을 쓴다.

21 케이트, 15세, 덴마크: 내 사진은 필터를 사용할 때 멋져 보인다.

22 하지만 가끔 나의 셀피가 나처럼 보이지 않는다.

23 셀피 예절

24 당신은 셀피 예절을 따라야 한다.

25 셀피를 찍고, 게시하거나 보기 전에 스스로 이 질문들을 물어보라.

26 1. 내가 어디에 있는가?

27 셀피를 찍기에 적합한 장소를 선택하라.

28 병원이나 공중화장실에서 셀피를 찍지 마라.

29 그것은 다른 사람들을 신경 쓰이게 할 수 있다.

30 2. 누가 이것을 볼 수 있는가?

31 누구나 당신의 셀피를 볼 수 있다는 것을 명심하라.

32 그것들을 게시할 때 신중하게 골라라.

33 3. 어떤 코멘트를 남겨야 하는가?

34 다른 사람들의 셀피에 상냥한 코멘트를 남겨라.

35 무례하게 굴지 마라. 쉬운 것처럼 들린다, 그렇지 않은가?

36 이러한 조언들을 따라서 당신의 셀피와 즐거운 시간을 보내라!

※ 다음 우리말과 일치하도록 빈칸에 알맞은 말을 쓰시오.

1 All _____ Selfies!

2 #Selfie _____

3 Are you _____ _____ selfies?

4 You probably _____ _____ _____ selfies on social media, but _____ _____ do you know _____ selfies?

5 _____ _____ some interesting _____.

6 Robert Cornelius _____ the world's _____ _____ in 1839.

7 *Selfie* _____ a new word _____ _____ _____ in 2013.

8 Buzz Aldrin _____ the _____ _____ selfie in 1966.

9 #Selfie _____

10 _____ _____ is part of _____ _____ for many teens, _____ do teens really enjoy it?

11 _____ _____ _____, we did a _____.

12 We _____ three questions to 300 students _____ _____ 14 _____ 16.

13 _____ _____ _____ the results.

14 _____, 90 percent of the girls _____ _____, but only _____ _____ _____ _____ _____ take selfies .

15 Also, 93 percent of these students said _____ they _____ _____.

16 The _____ also _____ that the students _____ at school the most.

17 _____ _____ some of the students' _____.

18 Lewis, 14, England _____ are _____.

1 셀피에 대한 모든 것!

2 셀피와 관련된 사실들

3 당신은 셀피에 관심이 있는가?

4 당신은 아마 소셜 미디어에 셀피를 게시하기를 좋아할지도 모르지만, 셀피에 대해 얼마나 많이 알고 있는가?

5 여기 몇 가지 재미있는 사실들이 있다.

6 로버트 코닐리어스가 1839년에 전 세계 최초의 셀피를 찍었다.

7 selfie는 2013년에 사전에 신조어로 등재되었다.

8 버즈 올드린이 1966년에 최초의 우주 셀피를 찍었다.

9 셀피 설문 조사

10 셀피 찍기는 많은 십대들에게 일상생활의 한 부분인데, 십대들은 정말로 그것을 즐기고 있는가?

11 알아보기 위해 우리는 설문 조사를 했다.

12 우리는 14세에서 16세 사이의 학생 300명에게 세 가지를 질문했다.

13 그 결과를 보자.

14 놀랍게도, 소녀들의 90퍼센트가 셀피를 찍지만, 소년들의 15퍼센트만이 셀피를 찍는다.

15 또한 이 학생들의 93퍼센트는 필터를 사용한다고 대답했다.

16 설문은 또한 학생들이 학교에서 가장 많이 셀피를 찍는다는 것을 보여 주었다.

17 학생들의 의견 몇 가지를 확인해 보라.

18 루이스, 14세, 영국: 셀피는 굉장하다.

19 _____ silly _____ is really fun!

20 Minwoo, 16, Korea I _____ _____ _____, but some students _____ too much time _____ it .

21 Kate, 15, Denmark My pictures _____ _____ when I _____ _____.

22 But _____ my selfies _____ _____ _____ me.

23 #Selfie _____.

24 You _____ _____ _____ for selfies.

25 _____ _____ these questions before you _____, _____, or _____ _____ selfies.

26 1. _____ _____ I?

27 Choose _____ places _____ _____ _____.

28 _____ _____ selfies in hospitals or _____ _____.

29 It may _____ _____ people.

30 2. Who _____ _____ this ?

31 _____ _____ _____ that anyone can see your selfies.

32 _____ carefully _____ you _____ them.

33 3. _____ _____ _____ comments should I _____ ?

34 _____ nice comments on _____ _____ _____.

35 Don't _____ _____ . That sounds easy, _____ _____ ?

36 _____ these tips and _____ _____ with your selfies.

19 우스꽝스러운 표정을 짓는 것은 정말로 재미있다!

20 민우, 16세, 한국: 나는 셀피 찍는 것을 즐기지만 몇몇 학생들은 그것을 하는 데 너무 많은 시간을 쓴다.

21 케이트, 15세, 덴마크: 내 사진은 필터를 사용할 때 멋져 보인다.

22 하지만 가끔 나의 셀피가 나처럼 보이지 않는다.

23 셀피 예절

24 당신은 셀피 예절을 따라야 한다.

25 셀피를 찍고, 게시하거나 보기 전에 스스로 이 질문들을 물어보라.

26 1. 내가 어디에 있는가?

27 셀피를 찍기에 적합한 장소를 선택하라.

28 병원이나 공중화장실에서 셀피를 찍지 마라.

29 그것은 다른 사람들을 신경 쓰이게 할 수 있다.

30 2. 누가 이것을 볼 수 있는가?

31 누구나 당신의 셀피를 볼 수 있다는 것을 명심하라.

32 그것들을 게시할 때 신중하게 골라라.

33 3. 어떤 코멘트를 남겨야 하는가?

34 다른 사람들의 셀피에 상냥한 코멘트를 남겨라.

35 무례하게 굴지 마라. 쉬운 것처럼 들린다. 그렇지 않은가?

36 이러한 조언들을 따라서 당신의 셀피와 즐거운 시간을 보내라!

※ 다음 문장을 우리말로 쓰시오.

1 All About Selfies!
➡ _____

2 Selfie Facts
➡ _____

3 Are you interested in selfies?
➡ _____

4 You probably like to post selfies on social media, but how much do you know about selfies?
➡ _____

5 Here are some interesting facts.
➡ _____

6 Robert Cornelius took the world's first selfie in 1839.
➡ _____

7 *Selfie* became a new word in the dictionary in 2013.
➡ _____

8 Buzz Aldrin took the first space selfie in 1966.
➡ _____

9 Selfie Survey
➡ _____

10 Taking selfies is part of daily life for many teens, but do teens really enjoy it?
➡ _____

11 To find out, we did a survey.
➡ _____

12 We asked three questions to 300 students from ages 14 to 16.
➡ _____

13 Let's look at the results.
➡ _____

14 Surprisingly, 90 percent of the girls take selfies, but only 15 percent of the boys take selfies.
➡ _____

15 Also, 93 percent of these students said that they use filters.
➡ _____

16 The survey also showed that the students take selfies at school the most.
➡ _____

17 Check out some of the students' comments.
➡ _____

18 Lewis, 14, England   Selfies are awesome.
➡ _____

19 Making silly faces is really fun!
➡ _____

20 Minwoo, 16, Korea I enjoy taking selfies, but some students spend too much time doing it.
➡ _____

21 Kate, 15, Denmark My pictures look good when I use filters.
➡ _____

22 But sometimes my selfies don't look like me.
➡ _____

23 Selfie Etiquette
➡ _____

24 You should follow etiquette for selfies.
➡ _____

25 Ask yourself these questions before you take, post, or look at selfies.
➡ _____

26 Where am I?
➡ _____

27 Choose appropriate places to take selfies.
➡ _____

28 Don't take selfies in hospitals or public restrooms.
➡ _____

29 It may bother other people.
➡ _____

30 Who can see this?
➡ _____

31 Keep in mind that anyone can see your selfies.
➡ _____

32 Choose carefully when you post them.
➡ _____

33 What kinds of comments should I leave?
➡ _____

34 Leave nice comments on other people's selfies.
➡ _____

35 Don't be rude. That sounds easy, doesn't it?
➡ _____

36 Follow these tips and have fun with your selfies.
➡ _____

Step4

※ 다음 괄호 안의 단어들을 우리말에 맞도록 바르게 배열하시오.

1 (Selfies! / About / All)
➡ _____

2 (Facts / #Selfie)
➡ _____

3 (you / are / in / selfies? / interested)
➡ _____

4 (you / like / post / probably / selfies / to / media, / on / social / but / much / how / know / you / do / selfies? / about)
➡ _____
_____

5 (are / some / here / facts. / interesting)
➡ _____

6 (Cornelius / Robert / the / took / selfie / first / 1839. / world's / in)
➡ _____

7 (selfie / new / became / word / a / in / 2013. / dictionary / the / in)
➡ _____

8 (Aldrin / Buzz / first / took / the / selfie / 1966. / in / space)
➡ _____

9 (Survey / #Selfie)
➡ _____

10 (selfies / taking / part / is / life / daily / of / teens, / many / for / but / teens / do / it? / enjoy / really)
➡ _____
_____

11 (out, / find / to / did / we / survey. / a)
➡ _____

12 (we / three / asked / questions / 300 / to / ages / from / students / 16. / to / 14)
➡ _____

13 (look / at / let's / results. / the)
➡ _____

14 (surprisingly, / percent / of / 90 / girls / the / selfies, / take / but / 15 / only / percent / the / of / boys / selfies. / take)
➡ _____
_____

15 (percent / also, / of / 93 / students / these / said / they / filters. / use / that)
➡ _____
_____

16 (showed / survey / the / also / that / students / the / selfies / take / at / most. / the / school)
➡ _____
_____

17 (out / check / of / some / the / comments. / students')
➡ _____

18 (England / 14, / Lewis, // awesome. / are / selfies)
➡ _____

1 셀피에 대한 모든 것!

2 셀피와 관련된 사실들

3 당신은 셀피에 관심이 있는가?

4 당신은 아마 소셜 미디어에 셀피를 게시하기를 좋아할지도 모르지만, 셀피에 대해 얼마나 많이 알고 있는가?

5 여기 몇 가지 재미있는 사실들이 있다.

6 로버트 코닐리어스가 1839년에 전 세계 최초의 셀피를 찍었다.

7 selfie는 2013년에 사전에 신조어로 등재되었다.

8 버즈 올드린이 1966년에 최초의 우주 셀피를 찍었다.

9 셀피 설문 조사

10 셀피 찍기는 많은 십대들에게 일상생활의 한 부분인데, 십대들은 정말로 그것을 즐기고 있는가?

11 알아보기 위해 우리는 설문 조사를 했다.

12 우리는 14세에서 16세 사이의 학생 300명에게 세 가지를 질문했다.

13 그 결과를 보자.

14 놀랍게도, 소녀들의 90퍼센트가 셀피를 찍지만, 소년들의 15퍼센트만이 셀피를 찍는다.

15 또한 이 학생들의 93퍼센트는 필터를 사용한다고 대답했다.

16 설문은 또한 학생들이 학교에서 가장 많이 셀피를 찍는다는 것을 보여 주었다.

17 학생들의 의견 몇 가지를 확인해 보라.

18 루이스, 14세, 영국: 셀피는 굉장하다.

19 (faces / silly / making / fun! / really / is)
➡ _____

20 (Korea / 16, / Minwoo, // I / selfies, / taking / enjoy / but / too / spend / students / some / time / it. / doing / much)
➡ _____
_____

21 (Denmark / 15, / Kate, // my / look / pictures / good / I / when / filters. / use)
➡ _____

22 (sometimes / but / selfies / my / look / me. / don't / like)
➡ _____

23 (Etiquette / #Selfie)
➡ _____

24 (you / follow / etiquette / should / selfies. / for)
➡ _____

25 (ask / these / yourself / questions / you / before / post, / take, / or / selfies. / at / look)
➡ _____

26 (I? / am / where)
➡ _____

27 (choose / places / to / appropriate / selfies. / take)
➡ _____

28 (selfies / don't / take / hospitals / in / restrooms. / or / public)
➡ _____

29 (it / bother / people. / may / other)
➡ _____

30 (see / this? / can / who)
➡ _____

31 (mind / in / keep / that / can / anyone / see / selfies. / your)
➡ _____

32 (carefully / choose / you / when / them. / post)
➡ _____

33 (kinds / what / comments / of / leave? / I / should)
➡ _____

34 (nice / leave / comments / other / on / selfies. / people's)
➡ _____

35 (be / don't / rude. // that / easy, / it? / doesn't / sounds)
➡ _____

36 (these / follow / tips / and / fun / have / selfies. / your / with)
➡ _____

19 우스꽝스러운 표정을 짓는 것은 정말로 재미있다!

20 민우, 16세, 한국: 나는 셀피 찍는 것을 즐기지만 몇몇 학생들은 그것을 하는 데 너무 많은 시간을 쓴다.

21 케이트, 15세, 덴마크: 내 사진은 필터를 사용할 때 멋져 보인다.

22 하지만 가끔 나의 셀피가 나처럼 보이지 않는다.

23 셀피 예절

24 당신은 셀피 예절을 따라야 한다.

25 셀피를 찍고, 게시하거나 보기 전에 스스로 이 질문들을 물어보라.

26 1. 내가 어디에 있는가?

27 셀피를 찍기에 적합한 장소를 선택하라.

28 병원이나 공중화장실에서 셀피를 찍지 마라.

29 그것은 다른 사람들을 신경 쓰이게 할 수 있다.

30 2. 누가 이것을 볼 수 있는가?

31 누구나 당신의 셀피를 볼 수 있다는 것을 명심하라.

32 그것들을 게시할 때 신중하게 골라라.

33 3. 어떤 코멘트를 남겨야 하는가?

34 다른 사람들의 셀피에 상냥한 코멘트를 남겨라.

35 무례하게 굴지 마라. 쉬운 것처럼 들린다. 그렇지 않은가?

36 이러한 조언들을 따라서 당신의 셀피와 즐거운 시간을 보내라!

※ **다음 우리말을 영어로 쓰시오.**

1 셀피에 대한 모든 것!
➡ _____

2 셀피와 관련된 사실들
➡ _____

3 당신은 셀피에 관심이 있는가?
➡ _____

4 당신은 아마 소셜 미디어에 셀피를 게시하기를 좋아할지도 모르지만, 셀피에 대해 얼마나 많이 알고 있는가?
➡ _____

5 여기 몇 가지 재미있는 사실들이 있다.
➡ _____

6 로버트 코닐리어스가 1839년에 전 세계 최초의 셀피를 찍었다.
➡ _____

7 *selfie*는 2013년에 사전에 신조어로 등재되었다.
➡ _____

8 버즈 올드린이 1966년에 최초의 우주 셀피를 찍었다.
➡ _____

9 셀피 설문 조사
➡ _____

10 셀피 찍기는 많은 십대들에게 일상생활의 한 부분인데, 십대들은 정말로 그것을 즐기고 있는가?
➡ _____

11 알아보기 위해 우리는 설문 조사를 했다.
➡ _____

12 우리는 14세에서 16세 사이의 학생 300명에게 세 가지를 질문했다.
➡ _____

13 그 결과를 보자.
➡ _____

14 놀랍게도, 소녀들의 90퍼센트가 셀피를 찍지만, 소년들의 15퍼센트만이 셀피를 찍는다.
➡ _____

15 또한 이 학생들의 93퍼센트는 필터를 사용한다고 대답했다.
➡ _____

16 설문은 또한 학생들이 학교에서 가장 많이 셀피를 찍는다는 것을 보여 주었다.
➡ _____

17 학생들의 의견 몇 가지를 확인해 보라.
➡ _____

18 루이스, 14세, 영국: 셀피는 굉장하다.
➡ _____

19 우스꽝스러운 표정을 짓는 것은 정말로 재미있다!

➡ _____

20 민우, 16세, 한국: 나는 셀피 찍는 것을 즐기지만 몇몇 학생들은 그것을 하는 데 너무 많은 시간을 쓴다.

➡ _____

21 케이트, 15세, 덴마크: 내 사진은 필터를 사용할 때 멋져 보인다.

➡ _____

22 하지만 가끔 나의 셀피가 나처럼 보이지 않는다.

➡ _____

23 셀피 예절

➡ _____

24 당신은 셀피 예절을 따라야 한다.

➡ _____

25 셀피를 찍고, 게시하거나 보기 전에 스스로 이 질문들을 물어보라.

➡ _____

26 내가 어디에 있는가?

➡ _____

27 셀피를 찍기에 적합한 장소를 선택하라.

➡ _____

28 병원이나 공중화장실에서 셀피를 찍지 마라.

➡ _____

29 그것은 다른 사람들을 신경 쓰이게 할 수 있다.

➡ _____

30 누가 이것을 볼 수 있는가?

➡ _____

31 누구나 당신의 셀피를 볼 수 있다는 것을 명심하라.

➡ _____

32 그것들을 게시할 때 신중하게 골라라.

➡ _____

33 어떤 코멘트를 남겨야 하는가?

➡ _____

34 다른 사람들의 셀피에 상냥한 코멘트를 남겨라.

➡ _____

35 무례하게 굴지 마라. 쉬운 것처럼 들린다, 그렇지 않은가?

➡ _____

36 이러한 조언들을 따라서 당신의 셀피와 즐거운 시간을 보내라.

➡ _____

※ 다음 우리말과 일치하도록 빈칸에 알맞은 말을 쓰시오.

Project Link

1. Our group _____ _____ _____ dance.

2. We _____ a dance.

3. We _____ a dance video and _____ it online.

4. You _____ see it _____ www.yutu.com.

1. 우리 그룹은 춤에 관심이 있다.
2. 우리는 춤을 만들었다.
3. 우리는 춤 비디오를 녹화하고 그것을 온라인에 올렸다.
4. 너는 그것을 www.yutu.com.에서 볼 수 있다.

Think and Write

1. _____ a Great Internet _____!

2. _____ we use the internet, we _____ _____ some _____.

3. Then we _____ _____ the internet _____.

4. _____ of all, we _____ follow language rules _____ people _____ not understand us.

5. _____, we should _____ only _____ information.

6. People _____ believe our _____ information.

7. _____, we _____ _____ _____ rude comments.

8. We _____ hurt _____ feelings.

9. _____ these rules _____ _____.

10. Then you _____ _____ a great internet user!

1. 멋진 인터넷 사용자가 되어라!
2. 우리가 인터넷을 사용할 때, 우리는 몇 가지 규칙을 따라야 한다.
3. 그러면 우리는 인터넷을 더 즐길 수 있다.
4. 무엇보다, 사람들이 우리를 이해하지 못할 수도 있기 때문에 우리는 언어 규칙들을 따라야 한다.
5. 또한, 우리는 오직 사실인 정보만을 게시해야 한다.
6. 사람들은 우리의 부정확한 정보를 믿을지도 모른다.
7. 마지막으로, 무례한 코멘트를 남기지 말아야 한다.
8. 우리는 다른 사람들의 감정을 다치게 할 수 있다.
9. 이런 규칙들을 명심해라.
10. 그러면 너는 멋진 인터넷 사용자가 될 것이다!

Culture Link

1. A student _____ the United States is _____ in the _____.

2. He _____ a cartoon _____, *GoGreenMan*, and _____ it online.

3. He _____ helps the environment _____ _____ his character, *GoGreenMan*.

1. 미국 출신의 한 학생은 환경에 관심이 있다.
2. 그는 GoGreenMan이라는 만화의 수퍼 영웅을 만들어 인터넷에 게시했다.
3. 그는 또한 그의 캐릭터인 GoGreenMan과 꼭 같이 환경을 돕는다.

구석구석 지문 Test

※ 다음 우리말을 영어로 쓰시오.

Project Link

1. 우리 그룹은 춤에 관심이 있다.

   ➡ _____

2. 우리는 춤을 만들었다.

   ➡ _____

3. 우리는 춤 비디오를 녹화하고 그것을 온라인에 올렸다.

   ➡ _____

4. 너는 그것을 www.yutu.com.에서 볼 수 있다.

   ➡ _____

Think and Write

1. 멋진 인터넷 사용자가 되어라!

   ➡ _____

2. 우리가 인터넷을 사용할 때, 우리는 몇 가지 규칙을 따라야 한다.

   ➡ _____

3. 그러면 우리는 인터넷을 더 즐길 수 있다.

   ➡ _____

4. 무엇보다, 사람들이 우리를 이해하지 못할 수도 있기 때문에 우리는 언어 규칙들을 따라야 한다.

   ➡ _____

5. 또한, 우리는 오직 사실인 정보만을 게시해야 한다.

   ➡ _____

6. 사람들은 우리의 부정확한 정보를 믿을지도 모른다.

   ➡ _____

7. 마지막으로, 무례한 코멘트를 남기지 말아야 한다.

   ➡ _____

8. 우리는 다른 사람들의 감정을 다치게 할 수 있다.

   ➡ _____

9. 이런 규칙들을 명심해라.

   ➡ _____

10. 그러면 너는 멋진 인터넷 사용자가 될 것이다!

   ➡ _____

Culture Link

1. 미국 출신의 한 학생은 환경에 관심이 있다.

   ➡ _____

2. 그는 GoGreenMan이라는 만화의 수퍼 영웅을 만들어 인터넷에 게시했다.

   ➡ _____

3. 그는 또한 그의 캐릭터인 GoGreenMan과 꼭 같이 환경을 돕는다.

   ➡ _____

※ 다음 영어를 우리말로 쓰시오.

01 common

02 vegetable

03 meat

04 more

05 British

06 drop

07 else

08 mixed

09 fresh

10 slowly

11 sweet

12 other

13 traditional

14 sweets

15 as

16 fry

17 have

18 part

19 choice

20 contest

21 carrot

22 include

23 Indian

24 instead

25 always

26 Western

27 less

28 local

29 often

30 usually

31 onion

32 rule

33 side dish

34 celebrate

35 at least

36 be ready to+동사원형

37 check out

38 come with

39 for a long time

40 had better+동사원형

41 have ~ in common

42 heat ~ up

43 such as

※ 다음 우리말을 영어로 쓰시오.

01	식료품	
02	특별한	
03	아침 식사	
04	동양의	
05	더하다	
06	운동하다	
07	문화	
08	콩	
09	피곤한	
10	음식물을 제공하다[권하다]	
11	튀겨진	
12	카레	
13	맛있는	
14	스페인의	
15	식전 음식	
16	건강에 좋은	
17	칠면조	
18	제안	
19	균형이 잡힌	
20	가끔, 때때로	
21	건강	

22	과일	
23	주문하다	
24	국수	
25	추천하다	
26	베트남의	
27	또한	
28	주요리	
29	충분한	
30	특히	
31	전통적인	
32	섞인, 복합된	
33	대신에	
34	흔한	
35	～의 끝에	
36	A와 B 둘 다	
37	할인받다	
38	A를 B에 넣다	
39	머무르다	
40	～을 돌보다	
41	요즘, 최근	
42	버리다	
43	상을 받다	

※ 다음 영영풀이에 알맞은 단어를 <보기>에서 골라 쓴 후, 우리말 뜻을 쓰시오.

1 _____ : having been cooked in hot oil: _____

2 _____ : feeling that you want to sleep or rest: _____

3 _____ : the meal you have in the morning: _____

4 _____ : a small dish that you eat before a meal: _____

5 _____ : happening often and to many people or in many places: _____

6 _____ : consisting of several different types of things or people: _____

7 _____ : to ask for food or a drink in a restaurant, bar etc.: _____

8 _____ : food and other goods that are sold by a grocer or a supermarket: _____

9 _____ : a small piece of sweet food made of sugar or chocolate: _____

10 _____ : relating to the particular area you live in, or the area you are talking about: _____

11 _____ : an idea, plan, or possibility that someone mentions, or the act of mentioning it: _____

12 _____ : a plant that is eaten raw or cooked, such as a cabbage, a carrot, or peas: _____

13 _____ : a competition or a situation in which two or more people or groups are competing with each other: _____

14 _____ : to give someone food or drink, especially as part of a meal or in a restaurant, bar etc: _____

15 _____ : to advise someone to do something, especially because you have special knowledge of a situation or subject: _____

16 _____ : a long thin piece of food made from a mixture of flour, water, and eggs, usually cooked in soup or boiling water: _____

보기			
recommend	vegetable	noodle	sweets
breakfast	grocery	order	tired
serve	local	contest	common
fried	mixed	suggestion	appetizer

※ 다음 우리말과 일치하도록 빈칸에 알맞은 말을 쓰시오.

Listen & Talk 1 A

G: I _____ I _____ too many sweets _____ _____.

B: That's _____ _____ _____ your health. _____ _____ _____ fruit instead.

Listen & Talk 1 B

G: You _____ very _____ today. _____ you _____ well?

B: Yes, I did. But I _____ _____ _____ these days, _____ in the morning.

G: Do you _____ _____ breakfast?

B: No, I _____.

G: _____ _____ _____ _____ breakfast. Breakfast _____ you _____.

B: I _____ know that. Do you _____ any _____ _____?

G: Well, you _____ _____ _____ every day. That _____ _____ you.

B: Okay. I _____.

Listen & Talk 1 C

G: Justin, our school _____ _____ is tomorrow. What _____ you _____ _____ make?

B: I'm _____ _____ _____ sandwiches.

G: What do you _____ _____ _____ in them?

B: _____, cheese, and _____.

G: You'd _____ _____ vegetables _____ your sandwiches. _____ _____ onions and carrots?

B: No, I'm _____ _____ _____ add them. I _____ _____ those vegetables.

G: That's not a good _____. Mr. Kim said we _____ _____ food for the contest.

B: You're _____. I _____ _____ grocery shopping and _____ onions and carrots.

Listen and Talk 2 A

G: It's my _____ _____ here. _____ do you _____?

M: I _____ the pizza and salad.

Listen and Talk 2 B

B: Good morning, Jiwoo. _____ are you doing _____ _____?

G: I'm _____ _____ a restaurant _____ my class party.

B: Wow! _____ is the party?

G: It's next Friday. We _____ _____ _____ to Bella's Restaurant, _____ it is _____ _____.

B: _____ _____ you _____ _____ Chang's Restaurant? I went there _____. The food and _____ were _____.

G: _____ great. What do you _____ there?

B: I recommend the _____ _____.

G: I _____ we _____ _____ there. Thank you.

Listen and Talk 2 C

W: Hello. _____ you _____ _____ order?

B: It's my _____ here. What _____ you _____?

W: I _____ the chicken sandwich. It is the _____ _____ _____ at our restaurant.

B: Well, I _____ _____ chicken very much. _____ you _____ _____ _____?

W: _____ _____ the turkey sandwich?

B: Oh, I _____ turkey. I'll _____ that.

W: _____ _____ you _____ a drink with the sandwich? You can _____ _____ 500-won _____.

B: That's great. Then I'll _____ an orange juice, _____.

Do It Yourself A

G: _____ _____ lunch today?

B: We _____ four _____. _____ _____ do you want?

G: Well, I want _____ _____. What do you _____?

B: I recommend the _____ _____.

G: That _____ _____. I will _____ that. _____ _____ you?

B: I _____ know. I'm _____ _____.

G: _____ _____ your health, _____ _____ have some food. _____ you _____ some tomato soup?

B: All _____. I will.

B: 안녕, Jiwoo. 너 지금 뭐 하고 있니?
G: 학급 파티 때 갈 식당을 찾고 있어.
B: 와! 파티가 언제야?
G: 다음 주 금요일이야. 우리는 Bella 식당에 가고 싶은데, 너무 비싸.
B: Chang 식당을 찾아보는 건 어때? 나 거기 한번 간 적 있어. 음식이랑 가격 다 괜찮았어.
G: 좋을 것 같아. 거기서 어떤 것을 추천하니?
B: 나는 국수를 추천해.
G: 내 생각에 우리 거기 가야겠다. 고마워.

W: 안녕하세요. 주문하시겠어요?
B: 저 여기 처음 왔어요. 추천해주시겠어요?
W: 치킨 샌드위치 추천합니다. 그게 우리 식당에서 가장 인기 있는 메뉴에요.
B: 음, 제가 치킨을 별로 안 좋아해요. 다른 거 추천해주시겠어요?
W: 칠면조 샌드위치는 어떠세요?
B: 아, 저 칠면조 좋아해요. 그걸로 주세요.
W: 음료랑 샌드위치를 같이 주문하는 게 어떠세요? 500원 할인받을 수 있어요.
B: 좋네요. 그럼 오렌지 주스도 주세요.

G: 오늘 점심은 어떤 거야?
B: 우리에겐 네 개의 선택들이 있어. 너는 어떤 것을 원하니?
G: 글쎄, 나는 면을 원해. 너는 어떤 것을 추천하니?
B: 나는 볶음면을 추천해.
G: 그거 맛있겠다. 나는 그걸 먹을래. 너는 어때?
B: 나는 잘 모르겠어. 배가 고프지 않아.
G: 하지만, 너의 건강을 위해서는 음식을 좀 먹는 게 좋아. 토마토 수프를 먹어 보는 게 어떻겠니?
B: 그래. 그렇게 할게.

※ 다음 우리말에 맞도록 대화를 영어로 쓰시오.

Listen & Talk 1 A

G: _____

B: _____

G: 나 요즘 단 걸 너무 많이 먹는 것 같아.
B: 그건 건강에 좋지 않아. 대신에 과일을 먹는 게 좋아.

Listen & Talk 1 B

G: _____

B: _____

G: _____

B: _____

G: _____

B: _____

G: _____

B: _____

G: 너 오늘 매우 피곤해 보인다. 잠을 잘 못 잤니?
B: 아니, 잘 잤어. 그런데, 나 요즘 자주, 특히 아침에 쉽게 피곤해져.
G: 너 아침밥을 주로 먹니?
B: 아니, 먹지 않아.
G: 아침밥을 먹는 게 좋아. 아침밥은 너 한테 힘을 주거든.
B: 나 그건 몰랐어. 또 다른 제안해 줄 것 있니?
G: 음, 너는 또한 매일 운동해야 해. 그게 도움이 될 거야.
B: 알겠어. 그럴게.

Listen & Talk 1 C

G: _____

B: _____

G: _____

B: _____

G: _____

B: _____

G: _____

B: _____

G: Justin, 우리 학교 요리 대회가 내일이야. 뭐 만들 거니?
B: 샌드위치 만들 거야.
G: 뭐 넣을 거니?
B: 치킨이랑 치즈랑 계란.
G: 너 샌드위치에 채소 넣는 게 좋을 거야. 양파랑 당근은 어때?
B: 싫어. 안 넣을 거야. 나 그 채소들 싫어해.
G: 그건 좋은 생각이 아니야. 김 선생님은 요리 대회에서 건강에 좋은 음식을 만들어야 한다고 했어.
B: 네 말이 맞아. 나 식료품 쇼핑 가서 양파와 당근을 사야겠다.

Listen and Talk 2 A

G: _____

M: _____

G: 저 여기 처음 왔어요. 추천해 주시겠어요?
M: 저는 피자와 샐러드를 추천해요.

Listen & Talk 2 B

B: _____

G: _____

B: _____

G: _____

B: _____

_____

G: _____

B: _____

G: _____

B: 안녕, Jiwoo. 너 지금 뭐 하고 있니?

G: 학급 파티 때 갈 식당을 찾고 있어.

B: 와! 파티가 언제야?

G: 다음 주 금요일이야. 우리는 Bella 식당에 가고 싶은데, 너무 비싸.

B: Chang 식당을 찾아보는 건 어때? 나 거기 한번 간 적 있어. 음식이랑 가격 다 괜찮았어.

G: 좋을 것 같아. 거기서 어떤 것을 추천하니?

B: 나는 국수를 추천해.

G: 내 생각에 우리 거기 가야겠다. 고마워.

Listen and Talk 2 C

W: _____

B: _____

W: _____

B: _____

W: _____

B: _____

W: _____

B: _____

W: 안녕하세요. 주문하시겠어요?

B: 저 여기 처음 왔어요. 추천해주시겠어요?

W: 치킨 샌드위치 추천합니다. 그게 우리 식당에서 가장 인기 있는 메뉴에요.

B: 음, 제가 치킨을 별로 안 좋아해요. 다른 거 추천해주시겠어요?

W: 칠면조 샌드위치는 어떠세요?

B: 아, 저 칠면조 좋아해요. 그걸로 주세요.

W: 음료랑 샌드위치를 같이 주문하는 게 어떠세요? 500원 할인받을 수 있어요.

B: 좋네요. 그럼 오렌지 주스도 주세요.

Do It Yourself A

G: _____

B: _____

G: _____

B: _____

G: _____

B: _____

G: _____

B: _____

G: 오늘 점심은 어떤 거야?

B: 우리에겐 네 개의 선택들이 있어. 너는 어떤 것을 원하니?

G: 글쎄, 나는 면을 원해. 너는 어떤 것을 추천하니?

B: 나는 볶음면을 추천해.

G: 그거 맛있겠다. 나는 그걸 먹을래. 너는 어때?

B: 나는 잘 모르겠어. 배가 고프지 않아.

G: 하지만, 너의 건강을 위해서는 음식을 좀 먹는 게 좋아. 토마토 수프를 먹어 보는 게 어떻겠니?

B: 그래. 그렇게 할게.

※ 다음 우리말과 일치하도록 빈칸에 알맞은 것을 골라 쓰시오.

1 School Lunches _____ the _____
A. World   B. Around

2 Hello, _____ _____ food reporter Minjun _____ Korea.
A. from   B. is   C. this

3 For _____ students, lunch is the _____ _____ of the school day.
A. part   B. best   C. many

4 _____ Korea, we _____ eat rice and soup _____ lunch.
A. for   B. often   C. in

5 We also have _____ _____, such _____ *Bulgogi* or *Gimchi*.
A. as   B. dishes   C. side

6 _____ our school _____ special dish, _____ as pizza, *Bibimbap*, or pasta.
A. such   B. serves   C. sometimes

7 _____ do students _____ live in in _____ countries eat for lunch?
A. other   B. who   C. what

8 _____ hear _____ our food reporters!
A. from   B. let's

9 _____, _____
A. France   B. Belle

10 Our school _____ healthy and _____ _____.
A. meals   B. balanced   C. serves

11 We _____ eat a salad _____ an _____.
A. appetizer   B. as   C. usually

12 _____ dishes often _____ meat or _____.
A. fish   B. include   C. main

13 We also eat _____ fruit _____ the _____ of the lunch.
A. at   B. fresh   C. end

14 Oh, I _____ _____ forget about baguettes!
A. never   B. can

15 They're _____ _____ cheese.
A. with   B. great

16 _____ school _____ has a special _____.
A. rule   B. also   C. our

17 We must _____ _____ the lunch table _____ at _____ 30 minutes.
A. least   B. at   C. for   D. stay

---

1 세계 각국의 학교 급식

2 안녕하세요. 저는 한국에서 온 음식 취재 기자 민준입니다.

3 많은 학생들에게 점심시간은 학교 일과 중 가장 좋은 부분입니다.

4 한국에서는 점심으로 자주 밥과 국을 먹습니다.

5 우리는 불고기나 김치 같은 반찬도 먹습니다.

6 때때로 우리 학교는 피자, 비빔밥 또는 파스타 같은 특식을 제공합니다.

7 다른 나라에서 사는 학생들은 점심으로 무엇을 먹을까요?

8 우리 음식 취재 기자들에게서 들어보겠습니다!

9 벨, 프랑스

10 우리 학교는 건강하고 균형 잡힌 식사를 제공합니다.

11 우리는 보통 식전 음식으로 샐러드를 먹습니다.

12 주요리는 보통 고기나 생선을 포함합니다.

13 우리는 점심의 끝에 신선한 과일도 먹습니다.

14 오, 절대 바게트를 빠뜨릴 수는 없죠!

15 바게트는 치즈와 잘 어울립니다.

16 우리 학교에는 또한 특별한 규칙이 있습니다.

17 우리는 적어도 30분간 점심 식탁에 반드시 머물러야 합니다.

18 _____, _____

A. Brazil   B. Bruno

19 _____, we have _____ and rice for lunch.

A. beans   B. usually

20 _____ and vegetables are _____ in our _____ dishes.

A. side   B. common   C. meat

21 My _____ lunch _____ _____ plantains.

A. with   B. comes   C. favorite

22 A _____ is a fruit _____ looks _____ a banana.

A. plantain   B. like   C. which

23 We _____ _____ plantains.

A. fry   B. usually

24 Our school lunches are _____ _____ the vegetables and fruit _____ from _____ farms.

A. local   B. because   C. come   D. fresh

25 _____, _____

A. Singapore   B. Nicole

26 People who live in Singapore come from many _____ cultures, so we _____ both _____ and _____ dishes at lunch.

A. Western   B. have   C. different   D. Eastern

27 Students can _____ _____ many dishes, _____ _____ curry, noodle soup, or pasta, each day.

A. as   B. from   C. such   D. choose

28 My school won an _____ for _____ school food _____ year.

A. last   B. healthy   C. award

29 Our lunches are always _____, and they _____ good, _____!

A. too   B. taste   C. healthy

30 _____ school lunch do you _____ to _____?

A. try   B. which   C. want

31 Does it _____ anything _____ _____ with your school lunch?

A. have   B. common   C. in

32 Please _____ your comments _____ www.chopchoplunch.com.

A. at   B. leave

18 브루노, 브라질

19 보통, 우리는 점심으로 콩과 밥을 먹습니다.

20 우리의 곁들임 음식에는 고기와 채소가 흔히 나옵니다.

21 내가 가장 좋아하는 점심에는 플랜테인이 나옵니다.

22 플랜테인은 바나나처럼 생긴 과일입니다.

23 우리는 보통 플랜테인을 튀깁니다.

24 채소와 과일이 현지 농장에서 오기 때문에 우리 학교 급식은 신선합니다.

25 니콜, 싱가포르

26 싱가포르에 사는 사람들은 매우 다양한 문화권에서 오기 때문에, 우리는 점심에 동양식과 서양식을 모두 먹습니다.

27 학생들은 매일 카레, 국수 또는 파스타와 같이 많은 요리 중에서 선택할 수 있습니다.

28 우리 학교는 작년에 건강한 학교 음식 상을 받았습니다.

29 우리의 점심은 항상 건강에 좋고, 맛 또한 좋습니다!

30 여러분은 어떤 학교 급식을 먹어 보고 싶나요?

31 그것이 여러분의 학교 급식과 공통되는 것이 있습니까?

32 여러분의 의견을 www.chopchoplunch.com에 남겨 주세요.

※ 다음 우리말과 일치하도록 빈칸에 알맞은 말을 쓰시오.

1 School Lunches _____ the _____

2 Hello, _____ _____ food _____ Minjun _____ Korea.

3 _____ many students, lunch is _____ _____ _____ _____ the school day.

4 In Korea, we _____ _____ rice and soup _____ _____.

5 We also have _____ _____, such _____ *Bulgogi* or *Gimchi*.

6 Sometimes our school _____ special _____, _____ pizza, *Bibimbap*, or pasta.

7 What do _____ _____ _____ in _____ _____ eat for lunch?

8 _____ _____ _____ _____ our food reporters!

9 Belle, _____

10 Our school serves _____ and _____ _____.

11 We _____ _____ a salad _____ an appetizer.

12 Main dishes _____ _____ meat or _____.

13 We _____ _____ fresh fruit _____ _____ _____ _____ the lunch.

14 Oh, I _____ _____ _____ about baguettes!

15 They're _____ _____ cheese.

16 Our school _____ _____ a _____ _____.

17 We _____ _____ _____ the lunch table for _____ _____ 30 minutes.

---

1 세계 각국의 학교 급식

2 안녕하세요, 저는 한국에서 온 음식 취재 기자 민준입니다.

3 많은 학생들에게 점심시간은 학교 일과 중 가장 좋은 부분입니다.

4 한국에서는 점심으로 자주 밥과 국을 먹습니다.

5 우리는 불고기나 김치 같은 반찬도 먹습니다.

6 때때로 우리 학교는 피자, 비빔밥 또는 파스타 같은 특식을 제공합니다.

7 다른 나라에서 사는 학생들은 점심으로 무엇을 먹을까요?

8 우리 음식 취재 기자들에게서 들어보겠습니다!

9 벨, 프랑스

10 우리 학교는 건강하고 균형 잡힌 식사를 제공합니다.

11 우리는 보통 식전 음식으로 샐러드를 먹습니다.

12 주요리는 보통 고기나 생선을 포함합니다.

13 우리는 점심의 끝에 신선한 과일도 먹습니다.

14 오, 절대 바게트를 빠뜨릴 수는 없죠!

15 바게트는 치즈와 잘 어울립니다.

16 우리 학교에는 또한 특별한 규칙이 있습니다.

17 우리는 적어도 30분간 점심 식탁에 반드시 머물러야 합니다.

18 Bruno, _____

19 Usually, we _____ _____ and _____ for lunch.

20 Meat and vegetables are _____ _____ our _____ _____.

21 My _____ lunch _____ _____ plantains.

22 A plantain is a _____ which _____ _____ a banana.

23 We _____ _____ plantains.

24 Our school lunches are _____ _____ the vegetables and fruit _____ _____ _____ _____.

25 Nicole, _____

26 People _____ _____ _____ Singapore _____ _____ many different cultures, so we have _____ Eastern _____ Western dishes at lunch.

27 Students _____ _____ _____ many dishes, _____ _____ curry, noodle soup, or pasta, _____ _____.

28 My school _____ _____ _____ for healthy school food _____ _____.

29 Our lunches are _____ _____, and they _____ _____, too!

30 _____ school lunch do you _____ _____ _____?

31 Does it _____ anything _____ _____ _____ your school lunch?

32 Please _____ _____ _____ at www.chopchoplunch.com.

18	브루노, 브라질
19	보통, 우리는 점심으로 콩과 밥을 먹습니다.
20	우리의 곁들임 음식에는 고기와 채소가 흔히 나옵니다.
21	내가 가장 좋아하는 점심에는 플랜테인이 나옵니다.
22	플랜테인은 바나나처럼 생긴 과일입니다.
23	우리는 보통 플랜테인을 튀깁니다.
24	채소와 과일이 현지 농장에서 오기 때문에 우리 학교 급식은 신선합니다.
25	니콜, 싱가포르
26	싱가포르에 사는 사람들은 매우 다양한 문화권에서 오기 때문에, 우리는 점심에 동양식과 서양식을 모두 먹습니다.
27	학생들은 매일 카레, 국수 또는 파스타와 같이 많은 요리 중에서 선택할 수 있습니다.
28	우리 학교는 작년에 건강한 학교 음식 상을 받았습니다.
29	우리의 점심은 항상 건강에 좋고, 맛 또한 좋습니다!
30	여러분은 어떤 학교 급식을 먹어 보고 싶나요?
31	그것이 여러분의 학교 급식과 공통되는 것이 있습니까?
32	여러분의 의견을 www.chopchoplunch.com에 남겨 주세요.

※ 다음 문장을 우리말로 쓰시오.

1 School Lunches Around the World
➡ _____

2 Hello, this is food reporter Minjun from Korea.
➡ _____

3 For many students, lunch is the best part of the school day.
➡ _____

4 In Korea, we often eat rice and soup for lunch.
➡ _____

5 We also have side dishes, such as *Bulgogi* or *Gimchi* .
➡ _____

6 Sometimes our school serves special dishes, such as pizza, *Bibimbap* , or pasta.
➡ _____

7 What do students who live in other countries eat for lunch?
➡ _____

8 Let's hear from our food reporters!
➡ _____

9 Belle, France
➡ _____

10 Our school serves healthy and balanced meals.
➡ _____

11 We usually eat a salad as an appetizer.
➡ _____

12 Main dishes often include meat or fish.
➡ _____

13 We also eat fresh fruit at the end of the lunch.
➡ _____

14 Oh, I can never forget about baguettes!
➡ _____

15 They're great with cheese.
➡ _____

16 Our school also has a special rule.
➡ _____

17 We must stay at the lunch table for at least 30 minutes.
➡ _____

18 Bruno, Brazil

➡ _____

19 Usually, we have beans and rice for lunch.

➡ _____

20 Meat and vegetables are common in our side dishes.

➡ _____

21 My favorite lunch comes with plantains.

➡ _____

22 A plantain is a fruit which looks like a banana.

➡ _____

23 We usually fry plantains.

➡ _____

24 Our school lunches are fresh because the vegetables and fruit come from local farms.

➡ _____

25 Nicole, Singapore

➡ _____

26 People who live in Singapore come from many different cultures, so we have both Eastern and Western dishes at lunch.

➡ _____

27 Students can choose from many dishes, such as curry, noodle soup, or pasta, each day.

➡ _____

28 My school won an award for healthy school food last year.

➡ _____

29 Our lunches are always healthy, and they taste good, too!

➡ _____

30 Which school lunch do you want to try?

➡ _____

31 Does it have anything in common with your school lunch?

➡ _____

32 Please leave your comments at www.chopchoplunch.com.

➡ _____

본문 Test

※ 다음 괄호 안의 단어들을 우리말에 맞도록 바르게 배열하시오.

1 (Around / Lunches / the / School / World)
➡ _____

2 (hello, / is / this / reporter / food / Korea. / from / Minjun)
➡ _____

3 (students, / many / for / lunch / is / best / part / the / of / day. / school / the)
➡ _____

4 (Korea, / in / we / eat / often / soup / and / rice / lunch. / for)
➡ _____

5 (also / we / side / have / dishes, / or / such *Gimchi*. / as / *Bulgogi*)
➡ _____

6 (our / sometimes / school / serves / dishes, / special / as / pizza, / such / or / pasta. / *Bibimbap*,)
➡ _____

7 (students / do / what / live / who / countries / in / other / lunch? / for / eat)
➡ _____

8 (hear / let's / from / reporters! / food / our)
➡ _____

9 (France / Belle,)
➡ _____

10 (school / serves / our / healthy / meals. / balanced / and)
➡ _____

11 (we / eat / usually / salad / as / a / appetizer. / an)
➡ _____

12 (dishes / main / include / often / fish. / or / meat)
➡ _____

13 (also / we / eat / fruit / fresh / at / end / the / of / lunch. / the)
➡ _____

14 (oh, / can / I / forget / never / baguettes! / about)
➡ _____

15 (great / with / they're / cheese.)
➡ _____

16 (school / our / has / a / rule. / also / special)
➡ _____

17 (must / we / at / stay / the / table / lunch / for / least / minutes. / at / 30)
➡ _____

1   세계 각국의 학교 급식

2   안녕하세요. 저는 한국에서 온 음식 취재 기자 민준입니다.

3   많은 학생들에게 점심시간은 학교 일과 중 가장 좋은 부분입니다.

4   한국에서는 점심으로 자주 밥과 국을 먹습니다.

5   우리는 불고기나 김치 같은 반찬도 먹습니다.

6   때때로 우리 학교는 피자, 비빔밥 또는 파스타 같은 특식을 제공합니다.

7   다른 나라에서 사는 학생들은 점심으로 무엇을 먹을까요?

8   우리 음식 취재 기자들에게서 들어보겠습니다!

9   벨, 프랑스

10   우리 학교는 건강하고 균형 잡힌 식사를 제공합니다.

11   우리는 보통 식전 음식으로 샐러드를 먹습니다.

12   주요리는 보통 고기나 생선을 포함합니다.

13   우리는 점심의 끝에 신선한 과일도 먹습니다.

14   오, 절대 바게트를 빠뜨릴 수는 없죠!

15   바게트는 치즈와 잘 어울립니다.

16   우리 학교에는 또한 특별한 규칙이 있습니다.

17   우리는 적어도 30분간 점심 식탁에 반드시 머물러야 합니다.

18 (Brazil / Bruno,)
➡ _____

19 (we / usually, / beans / have / rice / and / lunch. / for)
➡ _____

20 (vegetables / and / meat / are / in / common / our / dishes. / side)
➡ _____

21 (favorite / my / lunch / plantains. / with / comes)
➡ _____

22 (plantain / a / fruit / is / a / which / a / banana. / like / looks)
➡ _____

23 (usually / plantains. / we / fry)
➡ _____

24 (school / are / our / lunches / fresh / because / vegetables / the / fruit / and / from / farms. / local / come)
➡ _____

25 (Singapore / Nicole,)
➡ _____

26 (live / who / people / Singapore / in / from / come / different / many / cultures, / so / have / we / and / Eastern / both / dishes / Western / lunch. / at)
➡ _____

27 (can / students / from / choose / dishes, / many / as / such / noodle soup, / or / curry, / day. / pasta, / each)
➡ _____

28 (school / my / won / award / an / healthy / for / food / year. / school / last)
➡ _____

29 (lunches / are / our / healthy, / always / and / taste / too! / they / good,)
➡ _____

30 (school / which / lunch / you / do / try? / to / want)
➡ _____

31 (it / does / have / anything / with / common / in / lunch? / school / your)
➡ _____

32 (your / leave / please / at / comments / www.chopchoplunch.com.)
➡ _____

18 브루노, 브라질

19 보통, 우리는 점심으로 콩과 밥을 먹습니다.

20 우리의 곁들임 음식에는 고기와 채소가 흔히 나옵니다.

21 내가 가장 좋아하는 점심에는 플랜테인이 나옵니다.

22 플랜테인은 바나나처럼 생긴 과일입니다.

23 우리는 보통 플랜테인을 튀깁니다.

24 채소와 과일이 현지 농장에서 오기 때문에 우리 학교 급식은 신선합니다.

25 니콜, 싱가포르

26 싱가포르에 사는 사람들은 매우 다양한 문화권에서 오기 때문에, 우리는 점심에 동양식과 서양식을 모두 먹습니다.

27 학생들은 매일 카레, 국수 또는 파스타와 같이 많은 요리 중에서 선택할 수 있습니다.

28 우리 학교는 작년에 건강한 학교 음식 상을 받았습니다.

29 우리의 점심은 항상 건강에 좋고, 맛 또한 좋습니다!

30 여러분은 어떤 학교 급식을 먹어 보고 싶나요?

31 그것이 여러분의 학교 급식과 공통되는 것이 있습니까?

32 여러분의 의견을 www.chopchoplunch.com에 남겨 주세요.

※ 다음 우리말을 영어로 쓰시오.

1 세계 각국의 학교 급식

➡ _____

2 안녕하세요, 저는 한국에서 온 음식 취재 기자 민준입니다.

➡ _____

3 많은 학생들에게 점심시간은 학교 일과 중 가장 좋은 부분입니다.

➡ _____

4 한국에서는 점심으로 자주 밥과 국을 먹습니다.

➡ _____

5 우리는 불고기나 김치 같은 반찬도 먹습니다.

➡ _____

6 때때로 우리 학교는 피자, 비빔밥 또는 파스타 같은 특식을 제공합니다.

➡ _____

7 다른 나라에서 사는 학생들은 점심으로 무엇을 먹을까요?

➡ _____

8 우리 음식 취재 기자들에게서 들어보겠습니다!

➡ _____

9 벨, 프랑스

➡ _____

10 우리 학교는 건강하고 균형 잡힌 식사를 제공합니다.

➡ _____

11 우리는 보통 식전 음식으로 샐러드를 먹습니다.

➡ _____

12 주요리는 보통 고기나 생선을 포함합니다.

➡ _____

13 우리는 점심의 끝에 신선한 과일도 먹습니다.

➡ _____

14 오, 절대 바게트를 빠뜨릴 수는 없죠!

➡ _____

15 바게트는 치즈와 잘 어울립니다.

➡ _____

16 우리 학교에는 또한 특별한 규칙이 있습니다.

➡ _____

17 우리는 적어도 30분간 점심 식탁에 반드시 머물러야 합니다.

➡ _____

18 브루노, 브라질

➡ _____

19 보통, 우리는 점심으로 콩과 밥을 먹습니다.

➡ _____

20 우리의 곁들임 음식에는 고기와 채소가 흔히 나옵니다.

➡ _____

21 내가 가장 좋아하는 점심에는 플랜테인이 나옵니다.

➡ _____

22 플랜테인은 바나나처럼 생긴 과일입니다.

➡ _____

23 우리는 보통 플랜테인을 튀깁니다.

➡ _____

24 채소와 과일이 현지 농장에서 오기 때문에 우리 학교 급식은 신선합니다.

➡ _____

25 니콜, 싱가포르

➡ _____

26 싱가포르에 사는 사람들은 매우 다양한 문화권에서 오기 때문에, 우리는 점심에 동양식과 서양식을 모두 먹습니다.

➡ _____

27 학생들은 매일 카레, 국수 또는 파스타와 같이 많은 요리 중에서 선택할 수 있습니다.

➡ _____

28 우리 학교는 작년에 건강한 학교 음식 상을 받았습니다.

➡ _____

29 우리의 점심은 항상 건강에 좋고, 맛 또한 좋습니다!

➡ _____

30 여러분은 어떤 학교 급식을 먹어 보고 싶나요?

➡ _____

31 그것이 여러분의 학교 급식과 공통되는 것이 있습니까?

➡ _____

32 여러분의 의견을 www.chopchoplunch.com에 남겨 주세요.

➡ _____

※ 다음 우리말과 일치하도록 빈칸에 알맞은 말을 쓰시오.

Think and Write

1. _____ of My _____ Restaurant

2. _____ favorite _____ is Antonio's Restaurant.

3. It is a _____ restaurant.

4. It is _____ my home.

5. Mixed paella is the _____ _____ _____ at this restaurant.

6. _____ of the food _____ really fresh and _____, and the prices are _____.

7. I _____ this restaurant!

1. 내가 가장 좋아하는 음식점 방문 후기
2. 내가 가장 좋아하는 음식점은 Antonio's Restaurant이야.
3. 그곳은 스페인 음식점이야.
4. 그곳은 나의 집에서 가까워.
5. 이 음식점에서 가장 인기 있는 음식은 혼합 파엘라야.
6. 모든 음식이 정말 신선하고 맛있으며 가격도 싸.
7. 나는 이 음식점을 추천해.

Culture Link

1. _____ China, people eat noodles _____ their birthday.

2. Chinese people don't want _____ _____ the noodles _____ _____ a long life.

3. Doro wat is a chicken _____ _____ Ethiopia.

4. There are _____ _____ _____ vegetables in it.

5. People eat this _____ for New Year's _____.

6. Bánh xu xê is a _____ _____ cake.

7. People eat this cake _____ _____.

8. _____ the cake _____ the husbands and wife will _____ _____ _____ _____ together.

9. In the United States, people _____ _____ _____ _____ Thanksgiving.

10. They _____ _____ _____ the food and their health.

1. 중국에서 사람들은 그들의 생일에 국수를 먹는다.
2. 중국 사람들은 장수하려고 국수를 자르려 하지 않는다.
3. Doro wat은 에티오피아의 치킨카레 요리이다.
4. 그 안에 많은 야채가 들어 있다.
5. 사람들은 이 음식을 새해 만찬으로 먹는다.
6. Bánh xu xê는 전통적인 베트남 케이크이다.
7. 사람들은 이 케이크를 결혼식에서 먹는다.
8. 이 케이크를 먹는 것은 남편과 아내가 함께 행복한 삶을 살 것을 의미한다.
9. 미국에서 사람들은 추수감사절을 기념하기 위해 칠면조 요리를 먹는다.
10. 그들은 음식과 그들의 건강에 대해 감사한다.

※ 다음 우리말을 영어로 쓰시오.

Think and Write

1. 내가 가장 좋아하는 음식점 방문 후기
➡ _____

2. 내가 가장 좋아하는 음식점은 Antonio's Restaurant이야.
➡ _____

3. 그곳은 스페인 음식점이야.
➡ _____

4. 그곳은 나의 집에서 가까워.
➡ _____

5. 이 음식점에서 가장 인기 있는 음식은 혼합 파엘라야.
➡ _____

6. 모든 음식이 정말 신선하고 맛있으며 가격도 싸.
➡ _____

7. 나는 이 음식점을 추천해.
➡ _____

Culture Link

1. 중국에서 사람들은 그들의 생일에 국수를 먹는다.
➡ _____

2. 중국 사람들은 장수하려고 국수를 자르려 하지 않는다.
➡ _____

3. Doro wat은 에티오피아의 치킨카레 요리이다.
➡ _____

4. 그 안에 많은 야채가 들어 있다.
➡ _____

5. 사람들은 이 음식을 새해 만찬으로 먹는다.
➡ _____

6. Bánh xu xê는 전통적인 베트남 케이크이다.
➡ _____

7. 사람들은 이 케이크를 결혼식에서 먹는다.
➡ _____

8. 이 케이크를 먹는 것은 남편과 아내가 함께 행복한 삶을 살 것을 의미한다.
➡ _____

9. 미국에서 사람들은 추수감사절을 기념하기 위해 칠면조 요리를 먹는다.
➡ _____

10. 그들은 음식과 그들의 건강에 대해 감사한다.
➡ _____

※ 다음 영어를 우리말로 쓰시오.

01 rude	_____	22 sister school	_____
02 last	_____	23 scary	_____
03 Chinese	_____	24 shake	_____
04 calendar	_____	25 protect	_____
05 evil	_____	26 symbol	_____
06 lock	_____	27 valuable	_____
07 face	_____	28 good luck	_____
08 colored	_____	29 crow	_____
09 full moon	_____	30 pillow	_____
10 try	_____	31 remind	_____
11 bow	_____	32 traditional	_____
12 separation	_____	33 peace	_____
13 represent	_____	34 darkness	_____
14 guard	_____	35 talk about	_____
15 international	_____	36 blow one's nose	_____
16 last year	_____	37 watch over	_____
17 Vietnamese	_____	38 take off	_____
18 guest	_____	39 be afraid of	_____
19 greet	_____	40 have been to 장소	_____
20 palm	_____	41 be full of	_____
21 spirit	_____	42 go away	_____
		43 remind A of B	_____

※ 다음 우리말을 영어로 쓰시오.

01 해변, 바닷가 _____

02 가루, 분말 _____

03 옷, 의복 _____

04 (닭이) 울다 _____

05 경험 _____

06 축제 _____

07 박쥐 _____

08 우산 _____

09 선물 가게 _____

10 어둠, 암흑 _____

11 베개 _____

12 인도의, 인도 사람의 _____

13 자물쇠; 잠그다 _____

14 반달 _____

15 도착하다 _____

16 뮤지컬 _____

17 운 _____

18 전통의, 전통적인 _____

19 지불하다 _____

20 의미하다 _____

21 평화, 화해 _____

22 수탉 _____

23 생각나게 하다 _____

24 말하다, (정확히) 알다 _____

25 승리 _____

26 ~쪽으로 _____

27 영혼, 정신 _____

28 손바닥 _____

29 나타내다, 상징하다 _____

30 무례한 _____

31 보호하다 _____

32 채색된 _____

33 사악한, 악마의 _____

34 흔들다, 흔들리다 _____

35 사라지다, 떠나가다 _____

36 (옷 등을) 벗다 _____

37 A에게 B를 생각나게 하다 _____

38 ~을 가리키다 _____

39 ~에 대해 이야기하다 _____

40 ~으로 가득 차다 _____

41 ~을 듣다 _____

42 ~을 주시하다, 지키다 _____

43 ~을 두려워하다 _____

※ 다음 영영풀이에 알맞은 단어를 <보기>에서 골라 쓴 후, 우리말 뜻을 쓰시오.

1 _____ : a male chicken: _____

2 _____ : no light: _____

3 _____ : morally bad or wicked: _____

4 _____ : a soft thing to put your head on while you sleep: _____

5 _____ : to say hello or welcome: _____

6 _____ : to have the front part toward something: _____

7 _____ : to stand for something else: _____

8 _____ : to make the loud sound that a rooster makes: _____

9 _____ : success in defeating an opponent: _____

10 _____ : very important or expensive: _____

11 _____ : the inside part of the hand between the wrist and the fingers: _____

12 _____ : to keep something or someone safe from danger: _____

13 _____ : to make someone remember something: _____

14 _____ : making people feel afraid, frightening: _____

15 _____ : to lower your head or bend your body: _____

16 _____ : an object that represents something: _____

보기			
scary	greet	protect	bow
face	palm	evil	symbol
darkness	crow	represent	valuable
remind	victory	rooster	pillow

※ 다음 우리말과 일치하도록 빈칸에 알맞은 말을 쓰시오.

Listen & Talk 1 A

G: _____ you ever _____ _____ Brazil?

B: No, I _____. _____ you?

G: Yes, I _____. I went there _____ year. There _____ a big samba festival.

B: That _____ interesting. I hope _____ _____ there _____.

Listen & Talk 1 B

W: _____ _____ the International Games Festival. You can play many _____ _____ games here.

B: Wow! It _____ _____! _____ game _____ I play first?

W: _____ see. _____ you ever _____ *gorodki*?

B: No, I _____. What is it?

W: It's a _____ game _____ Russia.

B: _____ do I _____ it?

W: _____ five sticks _____ the ground. Then _____ a bat _____ them.

B: That _____ _____. I'll _____ that first.

Listen & Talk 1 C

B: There _____ a Holi festival in Busan _____ _____.

G: A Holi _____? _____ is that?

B: It's a _____ _____ festival. People _____ colored powder and water _____ _____ _____.

G: That _____ _____. _____ you ever _____ _____ a Holi festival?

B: No, I _____. But my Indian friend _____ me _____ about it.

G: _____ is the festival?

B: It's _____ the last _____ _____ of the Hindu calendar. This year, it's _____ _____ _____.

G: I'd like to go. _____ I _____ anything?

B: No, but you _____ _____ white clothes. Then the _____ powder on your clothes will _____ more _____.

G: Okay. _____ _____ the information.

Listen and Talk 2 A

G: Jinwoo, my Korean friend, _____ me *Yeot* _____ a gift. _____ does that _____ in Korea?

B: It _____ good luck _____ _____ _____.

Listen and Talk 2 B

B: Ling's birthday is _____ Wednesday, _____ _____?

G: Yes. I'm _____ _____ _____ a book _____ her. What _____ you?

B: Well, I'm _____ _____ buying her an umbrella. I found a _____ _____ in a gift shop.

G: Oh, that's not a _____ _____ _____ Chinese people. It means _____ _____.

B: Really? What _____ an umbrella _____ in _____?

G: It _____ _____. The words for separation and *umbrella* sound the same _____ _____.

B: I see. Then _____ _____ chocolate?

G: That's a good _____.

Listen and Talk 2 C

G: _____ _____ _____ picture! Are these your friends?

B: Yes. We _____ this picture at the beach. We had _____ _____ _____ fun.

G: Oh, _____ _____ that boy. That's really _____.

B: _____ boy?

G: The boy who _____ _____ the V sign. His palm is _____ _____ himself.

B: What's _____ _____ that?

G: It has a _____ _____ in England. But _____ your palm and _____ a V sign is okay.

B: What _____ that _____?

G: It _____ victory or _____.

Do It Yourself A

G: Hello, Santiago! What _____ you here today?

B: *Bienvenido*, Cathy. I came _____ _____ the _____ festival.

G: Me, _____. But what _____ you just _____?

B: *Bienvenido*! It _____ "welcome" in Spanish. _____ _____ those dancers. Their dance _____ are so great.

G: Yes, _____ are.

B: _____ you ever _____ a Spanish festival _____?

G: No, I _____. Santiago, can you see the big letters _____ the stage? _____ does that _____?

B: Oh, gracias. That _____ "thank you."

B: Ling의 생일이 이번 수요일이야, 그렇지 않니?

G: 응. 나는 그녀에게 책을 사 줄 거야. 너는?

B: 음, 나는 우산을 사려고 생각하고 있어. 선물 가게에서 귀여운 걸 찾았거든.

G: 어, 그건 중국 사람들에게 좋은 선물이 아니야. 뭔가 나쁜 걸 뜻하거든.

B: 진짜? 중국에서 우산이 뭘 의미하는데?

G: 이별을 뜻해. 중국에서는 이별을 뜻하는 단어와 우산을 뜻하는 단어의 발음이 같거든.

B: 알겠어. 그러면 초콜릿 어때?

G: 좋은 생각이야.

G: 이 사진 정말 멋지다! 네 친구들이니?

B: 응. 우리는 해변에서 이 사진을 찍었어. 정말 재미있었어.

G: 어, 저 남자애 봐. 정말 무례하다.

B: 누구?

G: V사인을 하고 있는 애. 손바닥이 자기 쪽을 향하고 있어.

B: 그게 뭐 잘못됐어?

G: 영국에서는 나쁜 뜻을 갖고 있어. 하지만 손바닥을 보여 주면서 V사인을 만드는 건 괜찮아.

B: 그건 무슨 뜻인데?

G: 승리나 평화를 뜻해.

G: 안녕, Santiago! 오늘 여기 어쩐 일이야?

B: Bienvenido, Cathy. 나는 스페인 축제를 보러 왔어.

G: 나도. 그런데 방금 뭐라고 말했니?

B: Bienvenido! 스페인어로 "환영합니다."라는 뜻이야. 저 무용수들을 봐. 그들의 춤 움직임은 정말 멋지다.

G: 응, 그렇네.

B: 전에 스페인 축제에 가 본 적 있니?

G: 아니, 가 본 적 없어. Santiago, 무대에 있는 큰 글씨들 볼 수 있니? 무슨 뜻이야?

B: 아, gracias. 저건 "감사합니다."라는 뜻이야.

※ 다음 우리말에 맞도록 대화를 영어로 쓰시오.

해석

Listen & Talk 1 A

G: _____

B: _____

G: _____

B: _____

G: 너는 브라질 가 봤니?
B: 아니, 못 가 봤어. 너는 가 봤니?
G: 응. 가 봤어. 작년에 거기 갔었어. 큰 삼바 축제가 있었어.
B: 재미있게 들린다. 나도 언젠가 거기 가고 싶어.

Listen & Talk 1 B

W: _____

B: _____

W: _____

B: _____

W: _____

B: _____

W: _____

B: _____

W: 국제 게임 축제에 오신 걸 환영합니다. 당신은 여기서 많은 종류의 전통 게임을 할 수 있습니다.
B: 와! 재미있을 것 같아요! 어떤 게임 먼저 해야 하나요?
W: 어디 봅시다. 고로드키 게임 해 본 적 있나요?
B: 아니요. 그게 무엇인가요?
W: 러시아의 전통 게임이에요.
B: 어떻게 하나요?
W: 바닥에 다섯 개의 막대기를 놓으세요. 그리고 그것들을 향해 배트를 던지세요.
B: 재미있겠네요. 그거 먼저 할게요.

Listen & Talk 1 C

B: _____

G: _____

B: _____

G: _____

B: _____

G: _____

B: _____

G: _____

B: _____

G: _____

B: 올해에는 부산에서 Holi Festival이 있어.
G: Holi Festival? 그게 뭐야?
B: 인도의 전통 축제야. 사람들은 서로에게 색 파우더와 물을 던지지.
G: 재미있겠다. Holi festival에 가 본 적 있니?
B: 아니, 없어. 근데 인도 친구가 그것에 대해 많이 이야기해 줬어.
G: 축제가 언제야?
B: 힌두교 달력으로 마지막 보름달이 뜨는 날이야. 올해는 3월 21일이네.
G: 가고 싶다. 나 뭐 가져야 하니?
B: 아니, 하지만 하얀 옷을 입어야 돼. 그러면 네 옷에 묻은 색 파우더가 더 예쁘게 보일 거야.
G: 알겠어. 정보 알려줘서 고마워.

Listen and Talk 2 A

G: _____

B: _____

G: 내 한국인 친구인 진우가 선물로 엿을 줬어. 한국에서는 이게 어떤 의미니?
B: 시험 잘 보라는 뜻이야.

Listen and Talk 2 B

B: _____

G: _____

B: _____

G: _____

B: _____

G: _____
_____

B: _____

G: _____

Listen and Talk 2 C

G: _____

B: _____

G: _____

B: _____

G: _____

B: _____

G: _____

B: _____

G: _____

Do It Yourself A

G: _____

B: _____

G: _____

B: _____

G: _____

B: _____

G: _____
_____

B: _____

B: Ling의 생일이 이번 수요일이야, 그렇지 않니?

G: 응. 나는 그녀에게 책을 사 줄 거야. 너는?

B: 음, 나는 우산을 사려고 생각하고 있어. 선물 가게에서 귀여운 걸 찾았거든.

G: 어, 그건 중국 사람들에게 좋은 선물이 아니야. 뭔가 나쁜 걸 뜻하거든.

B: 진짜? 중국에서 우산이 뭘 의미하는데?

G: 이별을 뜻해. 중국에서는 이별을 뜻하는 단어와 우산을 뜻하는 단어의 발음이 같거든.

B: 알겠어. 그러면 초콜릿 어때?

G: 좋은 생각이야.

G: 이 사진 정말 멋지다! 네 친구들이니?

B: 응. 우리는 해변에서 이 사진을 찍었어. 정말 재미있었어.

G: 어, 저 남자애 봐. 정말 무례하다.

B: 누구?

G: V사인을 하고 있는 애. 손바닥이 자기 쪽을 향하고 있어.

B: 그게 뭐 잘못됐어?

G: 영국에서는 나쁜 뜻을 갖고 있어. 하지만 손바닥을 보여 주면서 V사인을 만드는 건 괜찮아.

B: 그건 무슨 뜻인데?

G: 승리나 평화를 뜻해.

G: 안녕, Santiago! 오늘 여기 어쩐 일이야?

B: Bienvenido, Cathy. 나는 스페인 축제를 보러 왔어.

G: 나도. 그런데 방금 뭐라고 말했니?

B: Bienvenido! 스페인어로 "환영합니다."라는 뜻이야. 저 무용수들을 봐. 그들의 춤 움직임은 정말 멋지다.

G: 응, 그렇네.

B: 전에 스페인 축제에 가 본 적 있니?

G: 아니, 가 본 적 없어. Santiago, 무대에 있는 큰 글씨들 볼 수 있니? 무슨 뜻이야?

B: 아, gracias. 저건 "감사합니다."라는 뜻이야.

※ 다음 우리말과 일치하도록 빈칸에 알맞은 것을 골라 쓰시오.

1 _____ Korean _____
A. symbols   B. traditional

2 Peter is _____ Korea _____ meet a friend, Mina, _____ a sister school.
A. from   B. to   C. visiting

3 Peter is going to _____ _____ her grandfather's house _____ a week.
A. at   B. stay   C. for

4 When he _____, Mina _____ him the _____ room.
A. guest   B. shows   C. arrives

5 Peter, you will _____ _____.
A. here   B. stay

6 This _____ room is _____ of _____ Korean things.
A. traditional   B. full   C. guest

7 Look _____ this _____.
A. pillow   B. at

8 What _____ these _____?
A. things   B. are

9 _____ _____.
A. bats   B. they're

10 Bats _____ my _____? That's _____!
A. scary   B. pillow   C. on

11 Not really. In Korea, bats are _____ of _____ and a long _____.
A. life   B. symbols   C. luck

12 That's _____. In many Western countries, bats _____ people of _____ and scary things.
A. darkness   B. surprising   C. remind

13 Mina _____ Peter _____ _____ room.
A. grandfather's   B. her   C. shows

14 Peter and Mina's grandfather _____ and _____ each _____.
A. other   B. greet   C. meet

15 Hi, Peter! _____ you ever _____ this _____ of lock before?
A. kind   B. seen   C. have

16 No, I _____. It's _____ old _____ I can't really tell, but is it a fish?
A. that   B. haven't   C. so

17 Yes. _____ a long time, Koreans have _____ that fish are good _____.
A. guards   B. thought   C. for

1 전통적인 한국의 상징물

2 피터는 자매 학교 친구인 미나를 만나기 위해 한국을 방문 중이다.

3 피터는 일주일간 미나네 할아버지 댁에 머무를 것이다.

4 그가 도착하자, 미나가 그에게 손님방을 보여준다.

5 피터, 넌 여기에 머무르게 될 거야.

6 이 손님방은 한국의 전통 물건들로 가득 차 있어.

7 이 베개를 봐.

8 이것들은 뭐야?

9 그건 박쥐들이야.

10 내 베개 위에 박쥐가? 그거 겁나는데!

11 그렇지 않아. 한국에서는 박쥐가 행운과 장수의 상징이거든.

12 그거 놀라운 일인데. 서구의 많은 나라들에서 박쥐는 사람들에게 어둠과 무서운 것들을 상기시키거든.

13 미나는 피터에게 할아버지의 방을 보여준다.

14 피터와 미나의 할아버지가 만나서 서로 인사한다.

15 안녕, 피터! 너는 이런 종류의 자물쇠를 전에 본 적 있니?

16 아니요, 본 적 없어요. 그 자물쇠는 너무 오래되어서 사실 알아볼 수가 없는데, 그건 물고기인가요?

17 맞아. 오랜 세월 동안, 한국인은 물고기가 훌륭한 파수꾼이라고 생각해 왔단다.

18 Fish don't _____ their eyes, _____ when they _____.
A. sleep   B. even   C. close

19 _____ _____.
A. interesting   B. that's

20 We think fish can watch _____ valuable things. That's _____ this lock looks _____ a fish.
A. like   B. why   C. over

21 _____ I _____.
A. understand   B. now

22 They go _____ and _____ _____ the garden.
A. around   B. walk   C. outside

23 What is _____ that _____ of paper ? It looks _____.
A. piece   B. scary   C. on

24 Do you _____ this _____ of a rooster?
A. painting   B. mean

25 Oh, is _____ a _____ ?
A. rooster   B. it

26 Yes, it is. Roosters _____ _____ morning.
A. every   B. crow

27 Their _____ means _____ a new day is _____.
A. beginning   B. that   C. crowing

28 For many years, Koreans have believed _____ spirits go _____ when a rooster _____.
A. away   B. crows   C. evil

29 Really? I've _____ _____ that _____.
A. before   B. heard   C. never

30 _____, I'm _____ of darkness and evil _____.
A. spirits   B. actually   C. afraid

31 Could you _____ a rooster _____ me, Mina?
A. for   B. draw

32 Sure. I'll _____ a big _____ for you!
A. rooster   B. draw

33 _____ the drawing _____ your door. Then it will _____ you.
A. protect   B. above   C. put

34 _____, I _____.
A. will   B. yes

35 I'm enjoying this trip _____ much _____ I want to stay _____.
A. longer   B. that   C. so

36 I love _____ the _____ Korean symbols _____ this house.
A. in   B. traditional   C. all

37 Now I _____ a _____ of them.
A. lot   B. understand

38 I _____ to _____ Korea again _____ my family.
A. with   B. visit   C. want

---

18 물고기는 잘 때도 눈을 감지 않거든.

19 그거 재미있군요.

20 우리는 물고기가 귀중품을 지킬 수 있다고 생각해. 그것이 이 자물쇠가 물고기 모양으로 생긴 이유란다.

21 이제 이해가 되는군요.

22 그들은 밖에 나가서 정원을 걷는다.

23 저 종이에는 무엇이 그려져 있는 거죠? 무서워 보여요.

24 이 수탉 그림을 말하는 거니?

25 오, 그게 수탉이에요?

26 응, 그렇단다. 수탉은 매일 아침 울지.

27 수탉의 울음은 새로운 날이 시작하는 것을 의미해.

28 오랫동안 한국인들은 수탉이 울 때 악령이 물러간다고 믿어 왔단다.

29 정말요? 전 그런 말을 들어본 적이 없어요.

30 사실 전 어둠과 악령을 무서워해요.

31 미나야, 날 위해 수탉을 그려 줄 수 있니?

32 물론이지. 내가 널 위해 커다란 수탉을 그려줄게!

33 그 그림을 네 문 위에 걸어 놓으렴. 그러면 그게 널 지켜 줄 거야.

34 네, 그럴게요.

35 난 이번 여행이 매우 즐거워서 더 오래 머무르고 싶다.

36 난 이 집의 모든 전통적인 한국의 상징물들이 아주 마음에 든다.

37 나는 이제 그것들을 많이 알게 되었다.

38 난 우리 가족과 함께 한국을 다시 방문하고 싶다.

※ 다음 우리말과 일치하도록 빈칸에 알맞은 말을 쓰시오.

1 _____ Korean _____

2 Peter is _____ Korea _____ _____ a friend, Mina, _____ a sister school.

3 Peter is _____ _____ _____ _____ her grandfather's house _____ a week .

4 _____ he _____, Mina shows him the _____ _____.

5 Peter, you _____ _____ _____.

6 This guest room _____ _____ _____ _____ Korean things.

7 _____ _____ this pillow.

8 What are _____ _____?

9 They're _____.

10 _____ _____ my _____? That's _____!

11 Not really. In Korea, bats are _____ _____ _____ and a _____ _____.

12 That's surprising. In many _____ _____, bats _____ people _____ _____ and _____ things.

13 Mina _____ Peter her _____ _____.

14 Peter and Mina's grandfather _____ and _____ _____.

15 Hi, Peter! _____ you ever _____ this _____ _____ before?

16 No, I _____. It's _____ old _____ I _____ really tell, but is it a fish?

17 Yes. _____ _____ _____ _____ _____., Koreans _____ _____ that fish are good guards .

1 전통적인 한국의 상징물

2 피터는 자매 학교 친구인 미나를 만나기 위해 한국을 방문 중이다.

3 피터는 일주일간 미나네 할아버지 댁에 머무를 것이다.

4 그가 도착하자, 미나가 그에게 손님방을 보여준다.

5 피터, 넌 여기에 머무르게 될 거야.

6 이 손님방은 한국의 전통 물건들로 가득 차 있어.

7 이 베개를 봐.

8 이것들은 뭐야?

9 그건 박쥐들이야.

10 내 베개 위에 박쥐가? 그거 겁나는데!

11 그렇지 않아. 한국에서는 박쥐가 행운과 장수의 상징이거든.

12 그거 놀라운 일인데. 서구의 많은 나라들에서 박쥐는 사람들에게 어둠과 무서운 것들을 상기시키거든.

13 미나는 피터에게 할아버지의 방을 보여준다.

14 피터와 미나의 할아버지가 만나서 서로 인사한다.

15 안녕, 피터! 너는 이런 종류의 자물쇠를 전에 본 적 있니?

16 아니요, 본 적 없어요. 그 자물쇠는 너무 오래되어서 사실 알아볼 수가 없는데, 그건 물고기인가요?

17 맞아. 오랜 세월 동안, 한국인들은 물고기가 훌륭한 파수꾼이라고 생각해 왔단다.

18 Fish _____ _____ their eyes , even _____ they _____.

19 That's _____.

20 We think fish can _____ _____ valuable things. That's _____ this lock _____ _____ a fish.

21 _____ I _____.

22 They _____ _____ and _____ _____ the garden.

23 What is _____ _____ _____ of paper? It _____ _____.

24 Do you _____ this painting of a _____?

25 Oh, _____ _____ a rooster?

26 Yes, it is. Roosters _____ _____ _____.

27 Their crowing _____ that a new day is _____.

28 For many years, Koreans _____ _____ evil spirits _____ _____ _____ a rooster _____.

29 Really? I've _____ _____ that _____.

30 _____, I'm _____ _____ darkness and _____ _____.

31 _____ you _____ a rooster _____ me, Mina?

32 Sure. I'll _____ a big rooster _____ you!

33 _____ the drawing _____ your door. Then it _____ _____ you.

34 Yes, I _____.

35 I'm enjoying this trip _____ much _____ I want _____ _____ _____.

36 I love all the _____ _____ _____ in this house.

37 Now I understand _____ _____ _____ them.

38 I _____ _____ _____ Korea again _____ my family.

18 물고기는 잘 때도 눈을 감지 않 거든.

19 그거 재미있군요.

20 우리는 물고기가 귀중품을 지킬 수 있다고 생각해. 그것이 이 자 물쇠가 물고기 모양으로 생긴 이유란다.

21 이제 이해가 되는군요.

22 그들은 밖에 나가서 정원을 걷 는다.

23 저 종이에는 무엇이 그려져 있 는 거죠? 무서워 보여요.

24 이 수탉 그림을 말하는 거니?

25 오, 그게 수탉이에요?

26 응, 그렇단다. 수탉은 매일 아침 울지.

27 수탉의 울음은 새로운 날이 시 작하는 것을 의미해.

28 오랫동안 한국인들은 수탉이 울 때 악령이 물러간다고 믿어 왔 단다.

29 정말요? 전 그런 말을 들어본 적이 없어요.

30 사실 전 어둠과 악령을 무서워 해요.

31 미나야. 날 위해 수탉을 그려 줄 수 있니?

32 물론이지. 내가 널 위해 커다란 수탉을 그려줄게!

33 그 그림을 네 문 위에 걸어 놓으 렴. 그러면 그게 널 지켜 줄 거 야.

34 네. 그럴게요.

35 난 이번 여행이 매우 즐거워서 더 오래 머무르고 싶다.

36 난 이 집의 모든 전통적인 한국 의 상징물들이 아주 마음에 든 다.

37 나는 이제 그것들을 많이 알게 되었다.

38 난 우리 가족과 함께 한국을 다 시 방문하고 싶다.

※ 다음 문장을 우리말로 쓰시오.

1 Traditional Korean Symbols

➡ _____

2 Peter is visiting Korea to meet a friend, Mina, from a sister school.

➡ _____

3 Peter is going to stay at her grandfather's house for a week.

➡ _____

4 When he arrives, Mina shows him the guest room.

➡ _____

5 Peter, you will stay here.

➡ _____

6 This guest room is full of traditional Korean things.

➡ _____

7 Look at this pillow.

➡ _____

8 What are these things?

➡ _____

9 They're bats.

➡ _____

10 Bats on my pillow? That's scary!

➡ _____

11 Not really. In Korea, bats are symbols of luck and a long life.

➡ _____

12 That's surprising. In many Western countries, bats remind people of darkness and scary things.

➡ _____

13 Mina shows Peter her grandfather's room.

➡ _____

14 Peter and Mina's grandfather meet and greet each other.

➡ _____

15 Hi, Peter! Have you ever seen this kind of lock before?

➡ _____

16 No, I haven't. It's so old that I can't really tell, but is it a fish?

➡ _____

17 Yes. For a long time, Koreans have thought that fish are good guards.

➡ _____

18 Fish don't close their eyes, even when they sleep.

➡ _____

19 That's interesting.

➡ _____

20 We think fish can watch over valuable things. That's why this lock looks like a fish.

➡ _____

21 Now I understand

➡ _____

22 They go outside and walk around the garden.

➡ _____

23 What is on that piece of paper? It looks scary.

➡ _____

24 Do you mean this painting of a rooster?

➡ _____

25 Oh, is it a rooster?

➡ _____

26 Yes, it is. Roosters crow every morning.

➡ _____

27 Their crowing means that a new day is beginning.

➡ _____

28 For many years, Koreans have believed evil spirits go away when a rooster crows.

➡ _____

29 Really? I've never heard that before.

➡ _____

30 Actually, I'm afraid of darkness and evil spirits.

➡ _____

31 Could you draw a rooster for me, Mina?

➡ _____

32 Sure. I'll draw a big rooster for you!

➡ _____

33 Put the drawing above your door. Then it will protect you.

➡ _____

34 Yes, I will.

➡ _____

35 I'm enjoying this trip so much that I want to stay longer.

➡ _____

36 I love all the traditional Korean symbols in this house.

➡ _____

37 Now I understand a lot of them.

➡ _____

38 I want to visit Korea again with my family.

➡ _____

※ 다음 괄호 안의 단어들을 우리말에 맞도록 바르게 배열하시오.

1 (Symbols / Korean / Traditional)
➡ _____

2 (is / Peter / Korea / visiting / meet / to / friend, / a / Mina, / school. / a / from / sister)
➡ _____

3 (is / to / going / at / Peter / stay / grandfather's / her / house / week. / a / for)
➡ _____

4 (arrives, / he / when / Mina / the / shows / room. / him / guest)
➡ _____

5 (you / Peter, / here / will / stay)
➡ _____

6 (is / guest / this / room / of / full / things. / Korean / traditional)
➡ _____

7 (look / this / at / pillow.)
➡ _____

8 (are / things? / these / what)
➡ _____

9 (bats. / they're)
➡ _____

10 (my / bats / pillow? / on // scary! / that's)
➡ _____

11 (really. / not // Korea, / in / are / bats / of / symbols / luck / and / life. / long / a)
➡ _____

12 (surprising. / that's // many / countries, / in / Western / remind / bats / of / darkness / people / things. / and / scary)
➡ _____

13 (Peter / shows / Mina / room. / grandfather's / her)
➡ _____

14 (Mina's / and / Peter / grandfather / greet / and / other. / meet / each)
➡ _____

15 (Peter! / Hi, // you / have / seen / ever / this / lock / before? / of / kind)
➡ _____

16 (haven't. / no, / I // it's / that / old / so / I / really / can't / tell, / but / fish? / a / it / is)
➡ _____

17 (yes. // a / time, / for / long / Koreans / thought / have / that / are / guards. / good / fish)
➡ _____

1 전통적인 한국의 상징물

2 피터는 자매 학교 친구인 미나를 만나기 위해 한국을 방문 중이다.

3 피터는 일주일간 미나네 할아버지 댁에 머무를 것이다.

4 그가 도착하자, 미나가 그에게 손님방을 보여준다.

5 피터, 넌 여기에 머무르게 될 거야.

6 이 손님방은 한국의 전통 물건들로 가득 차 있어.

7 이 베개를 봐.

8 이것들은 뭐야?

9 그건 박쥐들이야.

10 내 베개 위에 박쥐가? 그거 겁나는데!

11 그렇지 않아. 한국에서는 박쥐가 행운과 장수의 상징이거든.

12 그거 놀라운 일인데. 서구의 많은 나라들에서 박쥐는 사람들에게 어둠과 무서운 것들을 상기시키거든.

13 미나는 피터에게 할아버지의 방을 보여준다.

14 피터와 미나의 할아버지가 만나서 서로 인사한다.

15 안녕, 피터! 너는 이런 종류의 자물쇠를 전에 본 적 있니?

16 아니요, 본 적 없어요. 그 자물쇠는 너무 오래되어서 사실 알아볼 수가 없는데. 그건 물고기인가요?

17 맞아. 오랜 세월 동안, 한국인들은 물고기가 훌륭한 파수꾼이라고 생각해 왔단다.

18 (don't / fish / eyes, / their / close / even / sleep. / they / when)
➡ _____

19 (interesting. / that's)
➡ _____

20 (we / fish / can / think / over / watch / things. / valuable // that's / this / why / lock / a / fish. / like / looks)
➡ _____

21 (understand. / I / now)
➡ _____

22 (outside / go / they / and / around / garden. / the / walk)
➡ _____

23 (is / what / that / on / paper? / of / piece // scary. / looks / it)
➡ _____

24 (mean / you / do / painting / this / rooster? / a / of)
➡ _____

25 (it / is / oh, / rooster? / a)
➡ _____

26 (is. / it / yes, / roosters / morning. / every / crow)
➡ _____

27 (crowing / their / means / that / a / beginning. / is / day / new)
➡ _____

28 (years, / many / for / Koreans / believed / have / spirits / evil / away / when / go / crows. / rooster / a)
➡ _____

29 (really? / never / I've / heard / before. / that)
➡ _____

30 (actually, / I'm / darkness / of / afraid / and / spirits. / evil)
➡ _____

31 (you / rooster / could / a / draw / Mina? / me, / for)
➡ _____

32 (sure. // draw / I'll / big / for / a / rooster / you!)
➡ _____

33 (the / put / above / drawing / door. / your // then / will / you. / it / protect)
➡ _____

34 (will. / I / yes,)
➡ _____

35 (I'm / this / enjoying / trip / much / so / that / longer. / I / stay / to / want)
➡ _____

36 (all / love / I / the / Korean / traditional / symbols / house. / in / this)
➡ _____

37 (I / now / understand / a / them. / of / lot)
➡ _____

38 (I / visit / to / want / again / Korea / family. / my / with)
➡ _____

18 물고기는 잘 때도 눈을 감지 않거든.

19 그거 재미있군요.

20 우리는 물고기가 귀중품을 지킬 수 있다고 생각해. 그것이 이 자물쇠가 물고기 모양으로 생긴 이유란다.

21 이제 이해가 되는군요.

22 그들은 밖에 나가서 정원을 걷는다.

23 저 종이에는 무엇이 그려져 있는 거죠? 무서워 보여요.

24 이 수탉 그림을 말하는 거니?

25 오, 그게 수탉이에요?

26 응. 그렇단다. 수탉은 매일 아침 울지.

27 수탉의 울음은 새로운 날이 시작하는 것을 의미해.

28 오랫동안 한국인들은 수탉이 울 때 악령이 물러간다고 믿어 왔단다.

29 정말요? 전 그런 말을 들어본 적이 없어요.

30 사실 전 어둠과 악령을 무서워해요.

31 미나야, 날 위해 수탉을 그려 줄 수 있니?

32 물론이지. 내가 널 위해 커다란 수탉을 그려줄게!

33 그 그림을 네 문 위에 걸어 놓으렴. 그러면 그게 널 지켜 줄 거야.

34 네, 그럴게요.

35 난 이번 여행이 매우 즐거워서 더 오래 머무르고 싶다.

36 난 이 집의 모든 전통적인 한국의 상징물들이 아주 마음에 든다.

37 나는 이제 그것들을 많이 알게 되었다.

38 난 우리 가족과 함께 한국을 다시 방문하고 싶다.

※ 다음 우리말을 영어로 쓰시오.

1 전통적인 한국의 상징물

➡ _____

2 피터는 자매 학교 친구인 미나를 만나기 위해 한국을 방문 중이다.

➡ _____

3 피터는 일주일간 미나네 할아버지 댁에 머무를 것이다.

➡ _____

4 그가 도착하자, 미나가 그에게 손님방을 보여준다.

➡ _____

5 피터, 넌 여기에 머무르게 될 거야.

➡ _____

6 이 손님방은 한국의 전통 물건들로 가득 차 있어.

➡ _____

7 이 베개를 봐.

➡ _____

8 이것들은 뭐야?

➡ _____

9 그건 박쥐들이야.

➡ _____

10 내 베개 위에 박쥐가? 그거 겁나는데!

➡ _____

11 그렇지 않아. 한국에서는 박쥐가 행운과 장수의 상징이거든.

➡ _____

12 그거 놀라운 일인데. 서구의 많은 나라들에서 박쥐는 사람들에게 어둠과 무서운 것들을 상기시키거든.

➡ _____

13 미나는 피터에게 할아버지의 방을 보여준다.

➡ _____

14 피터와 미나의 할아버지가 만나서 서로 인사한다.

➡ _____

15 안녕, 피터! 너는 이런 종류의 자물쇠를 전에 본 적 있니?

➡ _____

16 아니요, 본 적 없어요. 그 자물쇠는 너무 오래되어서 사실 알아볼 수가 없는데, 그건 물고기인가요?

➡ _____

17 맞아. 오랜 세월 동안, 한국인들은 물고기가 훌륭한 파수꾼이라고 생각해 왔단다.

➡ _____

18 물고기는 잘 때도 눈을 감지 않거든.
➡ _____

19 그거 재미있군요.
➡ _____

20 우리는 물고기가 귀중품을 지킬 수 있다고 생각해. 그것이 이 자물쇠가 물고기 모양으로 생긴 이유란다.
➡ _____

21 이제 이해가 되는군요.
➡ _____

22 그들은 밖에 나가서 정원을 걷는다.
➡ _____

23 저 종이에는 무엇이 그려져 있는 거죠? 무서워 보여요.
➡ _____

24 이 수탉 그림을 말하는 거니?
➡ _____

25 오, 그게 수탉이에요?
➡ _____

26 응, 그렇단다. 수탉은 매일 아침 울지.
➡ _____

27 수탉의 울음은 새로운 날이 시작하는 것을 의미해.
➡ _____

28 오랫동안 한국인들은 수탉이 울 때 악령이 물러간다고 믿어 왔단다.
➡ _____

29 정말요? 전 그런 말을 들어본 적이 없어요.
➡ _____

30 사실 전 어둠과 악령을 무서워해요.
➡ _____

31 미나야, 날 위해 수탉을 그려 줄 수 있니?
➡ _____

32 물론이지. 내가 널 위해 커다란 수탉을 그려줄게!
➡ _____

33 그 그림을 네 문 위에 걸어 놓으렴. 그러면 그게 널 지켜 줄 거야.
➡ _____

34 네, 그럴게요.
➡ _____

35 난 이번 여행이 매우 즐거워서 더 오래 머무르고 싶다.
➡ _____

36 난 이 집의 모든 전통적인 한국의 상징물들이 아주 마음에 든다.
➡ _____

37 나는 이제 그것들을 많이 알게 되었다.
➡ _____

38 난 우리 가족과 함께 한국을 다시 방문하고 싶다.
➡ _____

※ 다음 우리말과 일치하도록 빈칸에 알맞은 말을 쓰시오.

Think and Write

1. Do you know about _____ _____ _____?

2. _____ _____ many kinds.

3. _____ _____, there _____ a lion dance, a _____ dance, and an umbrella dance.

4. _____ _____ the most famous _____ _____ the lion dance.

5. In this dance, two dancers _____ and _____ lions.

6. They _____ dance _____ special days, _____ _____ New Year's Day.

7. I think their _____ _____ are _____.

8. I hope _____ _____ this dance _____.

1. 당신은 전통적인 중국 춤에 대해 아는가?
2. 많은 종류들이 있다.
3. 예를 들면, 사자춤, 부채춤, 그리고 우산 춤이 있다.
4. 가장 유명한 춤들 중의 하나가 사자춤이다.
5. 이 춤에서, 두 명의 댄서들이 사자처럼 옷을 입고 행동한다.
6. 사람들은 사자춤을 대개 설날과 같은 특별한 날에 춘다.
7. 나는 그들의 춤 동작들이 멋지다고 생각한다.
8. 나는 언젠가 이 춤을 연습하기를 바란다.

Presentation Time

1. Do you want to _____ _____ _____ _____ in Korea?

2. Then _____ these steps.

3. First, please _____ _____ your shoes _____ you _____ _____ people's homes.

4. Next, _____ when you greet _____.

5. Also, use two hands when you _____ _____ _____ _____ _____.

6. And do not _____ _____ _____ at the table and do not _____ _____ people.

7. _____, do not _____ older people _____ their _____ _____.

1. 한국에서 즐거운 시간을 보내고 싶은가요?
2. 그러면 다음 단계를 따르세요.
3. 먼저 사람들의 집에 들어갈 때는 신발을 벗으세요.
4. 다음에 다른 사람들에게 인사할 때 절을 하세요.
5. 또한 나이가 많은 사람들에게 무언가를 줄 때는 두 손을 사용하세요.
6. 그리고 식탁에서 코를 풀지 말고 사람들을 가리키지 마세요.
7. 마지막으로 나이가 많은 사람들을 이름으로 부르지 마세요.

구석구석 지문 Test

※ 다음 우리말을 영어로 쓰시오.

Think and Write

1. 당신은 전통적인 중국 춤에 대해 아는가?
➡ _____

2. 많은 종류들이 있다.
➡ _____

3. 예를 들면, 사자춤, 부채춤, 그리고 우산 춤이 있다.
➡ _____

4. 가장 유명한 춤들 중의 하나가 사자춤이다.
➡ _____

5. 이 춤에서, 두 명의 댄서들이 사자처럼 옷을 입고 행동한다.
➡ _____

6. 사람들은 사자춤을 대개 설날과 같은 특별한 날에 춘다.
➡ _____

7. 나는 그들의 춤 동작들이 멋지다고 생각한다.
➡ _____

8. 나는 언젠가 이 춤을 연습하기를 바란다.
➡ _____

Presentation Time

1. 한국에서 즐거운 시간을 보내고 싶은가요?
➡ _____

2. 그러면 다음 단계를 따르세요.
➡ _____

3. 먼저 사람들의 집에 들어갈 때는 신발을 벗으세요.
➡ _____

4. 다음에 다른 사람들에게 인사할 때 절을 하세요.
➡ _____

5. 또한 나이가 많은 사람들에게 무언가를 줄 때는 두 손을 사용하세요.
➡ _____

6. 그리고 식탁에서 코를 풀지 말고 사람들을 가리키지 마세요.
➡ _____

7. 마지막으로 나이가 많은 사람들을 이름으로 부르지 마세요.
➡ _____

※ 다음 영어를 우리말로 쓰시오.

01 warming _____

02 waste _____

03 terrible _____

04 put _____

05 global _____

06 sea level _____

07 disappear _____

08 fan _____

09 nervous _____

10 environment _____

11 soil _____

12 enough _____

13 instead _____

14 process _____

15 interesting _____

16 pollution _____

17 lid _____

18 raise _____

19 consume _____

20 produce _____

21 bottom _____

22 fix _____

23 water _____

24 space _____

25 gardening _____

26 healthy _____

27 connect _____

28 helpful _____

29 experiment _____

30 solution _____

31 article _____

32 productive _____

33 feed _____

34 chemical _____

35 get+비교급 _____

36 in place _____

37 go up _____

38 turn off _____

39 run out _____

40 in danger _____

41 remind A of B _____

42 turn A into B _____

43 throw away _____

※ 다음 우리말을 영어로 쓰시오.

01 접시 _____

02 문제 _____

03 바닥, 맨 아래 _____

04 다큐멘터리, 기록물 _____

05 온난화 _____

06 섬 _____

07 끔찍한 _____

08 에어컨 _____

09 말하기 대회 _____

10 해결책 _____

11 오염 _____

12 정보 _____

13 (신문) 기사 _____

14 점토 _____

15 놀라운 _____

16 바느질하다 _____

17 재배하다 _____

18 먹이를 주다, 먹이다 _____

19 과정 _____

20 어디든 _____

21 화분, 그릇 _____

22 실험 _____

23 화학 물질 _____

24 전통적인 _____

25 생산적인 _____

26 매달려 있다 _____

27 해결하다 _____

28 환경 _____

29 사라지다 _____

30 먹다, 소모하다 _____

31 도움이 되는, 유용한 _____

32 정원 가꾸기, 원예 _____

33 지구의 _____

34 연결하다 _____

35 A를 B로 채우다 _____

36 올라가다, 상승하다 _____

37 위험에 처한 _____

38 A를 B로 바꾸다 _____

39 A를 B로 자르다 _____

40 A에게 B를 상기시키다 _____

41 버리다 _____

42 (전기, 가스, 수도 등을) 켜다 _____

43 ~에 관해 걱정하다 _____

※ 다음 영영풀이에 알맞은 단어를 <보기>에서 골라 쓴 후, 우리말 뜻을 쓰시오.

1 _____ : to make something or bring something into existence: _____

2 _____ : to take care of a person, or an animal or plant, until they are completely grown: _____

3 _____ : to eat or drink, especially a lot of something: _____

4 _____ : to happen, or to do something, more than once: _____

5 _____ : an empty space in an object, usually with an opening to the object's surface: _____

6 _____ : to fasten something in position so that it cannot move: _____

7 _____ : to join or be joined with something else: _____

8 _____ : to pour water on to plants or the soil that they are growing in: _____

9 _____ : a substance used in chemistry or produced by a chemical process: _____

10 _____ : producing or achieving a lot: _____

11 _____ : to give food to a person or animal: _____

12 _____ : a film or a television or radio programme that gives detailed information about a particular subject: _____

13 _____ : to cultivate or raise a plant: _____

14 _____ : material that is left over or that is unwanted after something has been made, done, used, etc.: _____

15 _____ : a flat, usually round, dish that you put food on: _____

16 _____ : a scientific test that is done in order to study what happens and to gain new knowledge: _____

보기			
produce	experiment	hole	connect
documentary	feed	productive	repeat
grow	raise	plate	chemical
consume	waste	water	fix

※ 다음 우리말과 일치하도록 빈칸에 알맞은 말을 쓰시오.

Listen & Talk 1 A

B: In my school, students _____ so much food _____ _____ _____. I'm _____ _____ _____ _____.

G: Right, that's a big problem. We _____ _____ _____ too much food on our plates.

B: You're _____. We _____.

Listen & Talk 1 B

G: Did you _____ the documentary _____ _____?

B: No, I _____. _____ was it _____?

G: It was about _____ _____. The Earth _____ _____ hotter, and sea levels are _____ _____. I'm _____ about the Earth.

B: Oh, I've _____ _____ that problem before. Some islands are _____, so people _____ _____ their homes.

G: Yes. It is _____.

B: Is there any _____ _____ _____ it?

G: We can save energy. We should _____ _____ the lights when we don't need them. We should also use fans _____ _____ air conditioners.

B: Those are great ideas. I'll _____ _____ do those things.

Listen & Talk 1 C

B: You _____ _____. What's _____?

G: I'm _____ _____ the speech contest next week. The speeches _____ _____ environmental problems and their solutions.

B: What _____ you _____ _____ talk about?

G: I want to talk about _____ _____, but I can't find _____ _____.

B: _____ _____ water problems instead? I read an article, and it said we don't have enough water. I'm really _____ _____ it. I think we have to _____ _____ about that problem.

G: But _____ _____ enough water for everyone?

B: No. In some countries, people are _____ _____ because they don't have _____ _____. Our country could have this problem _____ _____ _____ _____.

G: Oh, I didn't know that. I _____ _____ _____ that problem and its _____. Thank you _____ _____ _____!

해석

B: 우리 학교에서, 학생들이 그릇에 너무 많은 음식을 남겨. 나는 음식 낭비가 걱정이야.

G: 맞아, 큰 문제야. 우리가 접시에 너무 많은 음식을 담으면 안 돼.

B: 맞아. 우리는 그러면 안 돼.

G: 어젯밤에 다큐멘터리 봤어?

B: 아니, 못봤어. 무슨 내용이었어?

G: 지구 온난화에 대한 내용이었어. 지구가 점점 더워지면서, 해수면이 올라가고 있대. 나는 지구가 걱정돼.

B: 어, 나도 그 문제에 대해 들어 본 적 있어. 몇몇 섬들이 사라져서, 사람들이 자기 집을 잃고 있대.

G: 맞아. 끔찍해.

B: 그걸 막을 방법이 있을까?

G: 에너지를 아끼는 방법이 있지. 우리는 전등을 필요하지 않을 때 꼭 꺼야 해. 그리고 우리는 또한 에어컨보다는 선풍기를 써야 해.

B: 좋은 생각이다. 그것들을 바로 시도해 봐야겠다.

B: 너 걱정스러워 보인다. 무슨 일이야?

G: 나 다음 주에 있을 웅변대회 때문에 걱정이야. 환경 문제와 그 해결책에 관한 대회거든.

B: 너 뭐에 대해 말할 건데?

G: 토양 오염에 대해 얘기하고 싶었는데, 충분한 정보를 찾지 못했어.

B: 그러면 대신 수질 문제에 대해 이야기하는 게 어때? 나 기사를 읽었는데, 우리에게 물이 충분하지 않대. 나는 정말 그게 걱정돼. 우리 그 문제를 해결하기 위해 뭔가 해야 한다고 생각해.

G: 하지만 모든 사람한테 충분한 물이 있지 않아?

B: 아니. 몇몇 국가에서는 물이 부족해서, 사람들이 위험에 처하기도 해. 우리나라도 조만간 그런 일이 일어날 수 있어.

G: 어. 나 그건 몰랐어. 나 그러면 그 문제와 해결책에 대해 얘기할래. 조언 고마워!

Listen and Talk 2 A

G: _____ _____ this ball. Can you tell me _____ _____ use it?

M: Just play soccer _____ _____ _____, and the light will _____ _____. You can use the light _____.

G: Wow, that's _____.

Listen and Talk 2 B

B: I like your bag, Jenny. _____ did you _____ it?

G: I _____ it _____.

B: You made it _____? That's _____.

G: _____ _____ you make one? It's _____ _____.

B: Really? Can you tell me _____ _____ _____ it?

G: Sure. Find some old jeans. _____ them _____ small pieces. Then sew the _____ together.

B: That _____ _____. I'll make one _____ a birthday _____ for my sister.

Listen and Talk 2 C

G: _____ you _____ _____ Earth Hour before?

B: No, I _____. What is it?

G: It's a _____ _____ event. People _____ _____ their lights _____ _____ _____ _____.

B: _____ do they _____ that?

G: They do it to _____ people _____ our environmental problems. They believe _____ _____ small action can change the world.

B: Oh, I see. Can you tell me _____ _____ _____ it?

G: Sure. Just _____ _____ your lights from 8:30 p.m. to 9:30 p.m. on the last Saturday _____ _____.

B: That's easy. I _____ _____ the next Earth Hour.

Do It Yourself

G: You _____ _____. What's _____ _____?

B: I am _____ _____ my science homework. I need to make a short video _____ _____ the environment. But making a video is difficult.

G: Well, _____ _____ _____ this application? It's easy.

B: Can you tell me _____ _____ _____ _____ it?

G: Sure! Open the application. _____ your photos and _____ some music. Then it will make a video with your photos.

B: Wow, that _____ _____. I'll _____ it now. Thanks.

G: 이 공 좀 보세요. 어떻게 사용하는지 말해 주실래요?

M: 30분 동안 축구를 하면 전구가 켜질 거예요. 당신은 전구를 어디서든 이용할 수 있어요.

G: 와, 그거 참 재미있네요.

B: 네 가방 예쁘다, Jenny. 어디서 샀어?

G: 내가 만들었어.

B: 네가 만들었다고? 놀랍다.

G: 너도 하나 만들어 보는 게 어때? 안 어려워.

B: 그래? 어떻게 만드는지 알려 줄 수 있니?

G: 그럼. 오래된 청바지를 찾아. 그걸 작은 조각으로 잘라. 그런 다음 조각들을 함께 꿰매면 돼.

B: 쉬울 것 같아. 내 여동생 생일 선물로 하나 만들어야겠어.

G: 지구촌 전등 끄기 행사에 대해 들어 봤니?

B: 아니, 들어 본 적이 없어. 그게 뭔데?

G: 지구촌 환경 행사야. 사람들은 한 시간 동안 불을 끄지.

B: 그걸 왜 하는데?

G: 사람들에게 환경문제에 대해서 상기시키기 위해서지. 이런 작은 행동이 세상을 바꿀 수 있다고 생각하는 거야.

B: 아, 이제 알겠어. 그거 어떻게 참여하는지 말해 줄 수 있니?

G: 그럼. 그냥 3월의 마지막 토요일에 오후 8시 반부터 9시 반까지 불을 끄기만 하면 돼.

B: 쉽네. 다음 번 행사 때 참여해야겠어.

G: 너 기분이 안 좋아 보인다. 무슨 일 있니?

B: 나는 내 과학 숙제를 걱정하고 있어. 나는 환경 지키기에 대한 짧은 비디오를 만들어야 해. 그런데 영상 만드는 게 어려워.

G: 음, 이 앱을 사용해 보는 게 어때? 쉬워.

B: 어떻게 사용하는지 말해 주겠니?

G: 물론. 앱을 열어. 사진들을 추가하고 음악을 골라. 그러면 이 앱이 너의 사진들을 이용해서 영상을 만들 거야.

B: 와, 그거 쉽다. 지금 시도해 볼게. 고마워.

※ 다음 우리말에 맞도록 대화를 영어로 쓰시오.

Listen & Talk 1 A

B: _____

_____

G: _____

B: _____

B: 우리 학교에서, 학생들이 그릇에 너무 많은 음식을 남겨. 나는 음식 낭비가 걱정이야.
G: 맞아, 큰 문제야. 우리가 접시에 너무 많은 음식을 담으면 안 돼.
B: 맞아. 우리는 그러면 안 돼.

Listen & Talk 1 B

G: _____

B: _____

G: _____

_____

B: _____

_____

G: _____

B: _____

G: _____

_____

B: _____

G: 어젯밤에 다큐멘터리 봤어?
B: 아니, 못봤어. 무슨 내용이었어?
G: 지구 온난화에 대한 내용이었어. 지구가 점점 더워지면서, 해수면이 올라가고 있대. 나는 지구가 걱정돼.
B: 어, 나도 그 문제에 대해 들어 본 적 있어. 몇몇 섬들이 사라져서, 사람들이 자기 집을 잃고 있대.
G: 맞아. 끔찍해.
B: 그걸 막을 방법이 있을까?
G: 에너지를 아끼는 방법이 있지. 우리는 전등을 필요하지 않을 때 꼭 꺼야 해. 그리고 우리는 또한 에어컨보다는 선풍기를 써야 해.
B: 좋은 생각이다. 그것들을 바로 시도해 봐야겠다.

Listen & Talk 1 C

B: _____

G: _____

_____

B: _____

G: _____

B: _____

_____

G: _____

B: _____

G: _____

B: 너 걱정스러워 보인다. 무슨 일이야?
G: 나 다음 주에 있을 웅변대회 때문에 걱정이야. 환경 문제와 그 해결책에 관한 대회거든.
B: 너 뭐에 대해 말할 건데?
G: 토양 오염에 대해 얘기하고 싶었는데, 충분한 정보를 찾지 못했어.
B: 그러면 대신 수질 문제에 대해 이야기하는 게 어때? 나 기사를 읽었는데, 우리에게 물이 충분하지 않대. 나는 정말 그게 걱정돼. 우리 그 문제를 해결하기 위해 뭔가 해야 한다고 생각해.
G: 하지만 모든 사람한테 충분한 물이 있지 않아?
B: 아니, 몇몇 국가에서는 물이 부족해서, 사람들이 위험에 처하기도 해. 우리나라도 조만간 그런 일이 일어날 수 있어.
G: 어, 나 그건 몰랐어. 나 그러면 그 문제와 해결책에 대해 얘기할래. 조언 고마워!

Listen and Talk 2 A

G: _____

M: _____

_____

G: _____

Listen and Talk 2 B

B: _____

G: _____

B: _____

G: _____

B: _____

G: _____

B: _____

Listen and Talk 2 C

G: _____

B: _____

G: _____

B: _____

G: _____

B: _____

G: _____

B: _____

Do It Yourself

G: _____

B: _____

G: _____

B: _____

G: _____

B: _____

G: 이 공 좀 보세요. 어떻게 사용하는지 말해 주실래요?

M: 30분 동안 축구를 하면 전구가 켜질 거예요. 당신은 전구를 어디서든 이용할 수 있어요.

G: 와, 그거 참 재미있네요.

B: 네 가방 예쁘다, Jenny. 어디서 샀어?

G: 내가 만들었어.

B: 네가 만들었다고? 놀랍다.

G: 너도 하나 만들어 보는 게 어때? 안 어려워.

B: 그래? 어떻게 만드는지 알려 줄 수 있니?

G: 그럼. 오래된 청바지를 찾아. 그걸 작은 조각으로 잘라. 그런 다음 조각들을 함께 꿰매면 돼.

B: 쉬울 것 같아. 내 여동생 생일 선물로 하나 만들어야겠어.

G: 지구촌 전등 끄기 행사에 대해 들어 봤니?

B: 아니, 들어 본 적이 없어. 그게 뭔데?

G: 지구촌 환경 행사야. 사람들은 한 시간 동안 불을 끄지.

B: 그걸 왜 하는데?

G: 사람들에게 환경문제에 대해서 상기시키기 위해서지. 이런 작은 행동이 세상을 바꿀 수 있다고 생각하는 거야.

B: 아, 이제 알겠어. 그거 어떻게 참여하는지 말해 줄 수 있니?

G: 그럼. 그냥 3월의 마지막 토요일에 오후 8시 반부터 9시 반까지 불을 끄기만 하면 돼.

B: 쉽네. 다음 번 행사 때 참여해야겠어.

G: 너 기분이 안 좋아 보인다. 무슨 일 있니?

B: 나는 내 과학 숙제를 걱정하고 있어. 나는 환경 지키기에 대한 짧은 비디오를 만들어야 해. 그런데 영상 만드는 게 어려워.

G: 음, 이 앱을 사용해 보는 게 어때? 쉬워.

B: 어떻게 사용하는지 말해 주겠니?

G: 물론. 앱을 열어. 사진들을 추가하고 음악을 골라. 그러면 이 앱이 너의 사진들을 이용해서 영상을 만들 거야.

B: 와, 그거 쉽다. 지금 시도해 볼게. 고마워.

※ 다음 우리말과 일치하도록 빈칸에 알맞은 것을 골라 쓰시오.

1 My _____ _____ : _____ Aquaponics
   A. Project   B. Science   C. Home

2 _____ are you _____?
   A. reading   B. what

3 I'm _____ an _____ aquaponics.
   A. article   B. about   C. reading

4 It's a way of _____ plants _____.
   A. without   B. growing   C. soil

5 We can also _____ plants and _____ fish in just one _____.
   A. raise   B. grow   C. system

6 _____ that _____?
   A. possible   B. is

7 We'll _____. I'm going to _____ it _____ home for my science project.
   A. at   B. try   C. see

8 Fish, _____, and plants are the _____ _____ of aquaponics.
   A. main   B. bacteria   C. parts

9 _____ you _____ the fish, they produce _____.
   A. waste   B. feed   C. after

10 The waste is _____ _____ food for the plants _____ bacteria.
   A. turned   B. by   C. into

11 The plants _____ the water _____ _____ the food.
   A. by   B. clean   C. consuming

12 This _____ is _____ again and _____!
   A. repeated   B. process   C. again

13 _____ Aquaponics _____ Eric Jackson
   A. by   B. home

14 Questions: _____ can I _____ an aquaponics system _____ home?
   A. make   B. at   C. how

15 _____ is aquaponics _____?
   A. good   B. why

16 Period: _____ May 15 _____ August 15
   A. to   B. from

17 Materials: a pot & small stones, a fish _____, a plastic _____, a water pump, plants, some fish, a box _____, _____
   A. clay   B. tube   C. cutter   D. tank

18 Steps: I made _____ in the _____ of a _____.
   A. bottom   B. holes   C. pot

19 _____ I _____ small stones and plants _____ it.
   A. put   B. in   C. then

20 I made a big hole in the _____ of the fish tank and _____ the pot _____ the hole.
   A. put   B. in   C. lid

21 I _____ the pot _____ place _____ clay.
    A. with   B. in   C. fixed

22 I made _____ _____ in the lid and put a tube _____ it.
    A. hole   B. another   C. through

23 I _____ a water pump _____ the fish tank.
    A. in   B. put

24 I _____ the tube to _____ the pump _____ the pot.
    A. connect   B. to   C. used

25 I _____ the fish tank _____ water and _____ some fish in it.
    A. with   B. filled   C. put

26 Then I _____ _____ the pump.
    A. on   B. turned

27 Results: From this experiment, I _____ my plants and _____ fish _____ aquaponics.
    A. raised   B. with   C. grew

28 I just _____ the fish, but the plants have _____ 17 centimeters _____ three months.
    A. grown   B. in   C. fed

29 The fish _____ _____ and the water is clean _____ the _____.
    A. time   B. stay   C. all   D. healthy

30 Conclusion: Some important _____ about aquaponics were _____ from this _____.
    A. things   B. learned   C. experiment

31 First, water is _____ the plants don't need _____.
    A. because   B. watering   C. saved

32 Second, it is good _____ the environment _____ no chemicals are _____.
    A. because   B. used   C. for

33 _____, you can do aquaponics _____ because it doesn't need much _____.
    A. anywhere   B. space   C. finally

34 *I found* ... Some farmers use aquaponics to _____ vegetables and _____ fish.
    A. out   B. raise   C. produce

35 They _____ aquaponics because it is _____ than traditional _____.
    A. gardening   B. choose   C. easier   D. far

36 Also, it is a _____ more _____ way of _____ food.
    A. much   B. growing   C. productive

37 The plants grow _____ faster than plants in _____, and it _____ space.
    A. soil   B. much   C. saves

38 I hope more food is _____ in this _____ in the future _____ it is _____ for us and the environment.
    A. healthy   B. way   C. produced   D. because

21 찰흙으로 화분을 제자리에 고정하였다.

22 덮개에 또 다른 구멍을 하나 만들고 그 안에 관을 넣었다.

23 어항에 수중 펌프를 넣었다.

24 관을 이용하여 펌프를 화분에 연결하였다.

25 어항에 물을 채우고 물고기 몇 마리를 거기에 넣었다.

26 그러고 나서 펌프를 작동하였다.

27 결과: 이 실험으로 나는 아쿠아포닉스로 식물과 물고기를 키웠다.

28 나는 그저 물고기에 밥만 주었는데도 식물은 석 달 동안 17cm나 자랐다.

29 물고기는 건강을 유지하며 물은 항상 깨끗하다.

30 결론: 아쿠아포닉스에 관한 몇 가지 중요한 사항이 이 실험에서 발견되었다.

31 첫째, 식물에 물을 줄 필요가 없으므로 물이 절약된다.

32 둘째, 화학 물질이 사용되지 않으므로 아쿠아포닉스는 환경에 이롭다.

33 끝으로, 넓은 공간이 필요하지 않으므로 당신은 어디에서나 아쿠아포닉스를 쉽게 할 수 있다.

34 나는 알게 되었다... 몇몇 농부들은 채소를 생산하고 물고기를 키우는 데 아쿠아포닉스를 이용한다.

35 그들은 아쿠아포닉스가 전통 재배 방식보다 훨씬 더 쉽기 때문에 그것을 선택한다.

36 또한, 아쿠아포닉스는 식량을 재배하는 훨씬 더 생산적인 방법이다.

37 식물들이 흙에서 자라는 식물보다 훨씬 빠르게 자라고 공간도 절약한다.

38 그것은 우리와 환경에 훨씬 건강하기 때문에 나는 미래에 더 많은 식량이 이런 방식으로 생산되기를 희망한다.

※ 다음 우리말과 일치하도록 빈칸에 알맞은 말을 쓰시오.

1   My _____ _____ : Home Aquaponics

2   _____ are you _____ ?

3   I'm _____ an _____ _____ aquaponics.

4   It's a way of _____ plants _____ _____ .

5   We can also _____ plants and _____ fish in just one _____ .

6   _____ that _____ ?

7   We'll _____ . I'm going to _____ it _____ home for my science project.

8   Fish, _____ , and plants are the _____ _____ of aquaponics.

9   _____ you _____ the fish, they produce _____ .

10 The waste is _____ _____ food for the plants _____ bacteria.

11 The plants _____ the water _____ _____ the food.

12 This _____ is _____ again and _____ !

13 _____ Aquaponics _____ Eric Jackson

14 Questions: _____ can I _____ an aquaponics system _____ home?

15 _____ is aquaponics _____ ?

16 Period: _____ May 15 _____ August 15

17 Materials: a pot & small stones, a fish _____ , a plastic _____ , a water pump, plants, some fish, a box _____ , _____

18 Steps: I made _____ in the _____ of a _____ .

19 _____ I _____ small stones and plants _____ it.

20 I made a big hole in the _____ of the fish tank and _____ the pot _____ the hole.

1   나의 과학 프로젝트: 가정용 아쿠아포닉스

2   무엇을 읽고 있니?

3   아쿠아포닉스에 관한 기사를 읽고 있어.

4   흙 없이 식물을 재배할 수 있는 방법이야.

5   또 한 가지 장치만으로도 식물과 물고기를 동시에 키울 수 있어.

6   그게 가능하니?

7   곧 알게 될 거야. 내가 과학 프로젝트로 집에서 해 볼 예정이거든.

8   물고기, 박테리아, 식물이 아쿠아포닉스의 주요 부분이다.

9   물고기에게 먹이를 주면, 그것들은 배설물을 만들어 낸다.

10 이 배설물은 박테리아에 의해 식물의 먹이로 바뀐다.

11 식물은 그 먹이를 먹음으로써 물을 정화한다.

12 이러한 과정이 계속해서 반복된다!

13 가정용 아쿠아포닉스 에릭 잭슨

14 질문: 집에서 아쿠아포닉스 장치를 어떻게 만들 수 있을까?

15 아쿠아포닉스가 왜 좋은가?

16 기간: 5월 15일부터 8월 15일까지

17 재료: 화분과 작은 돌들, 어항, 플라스틱 관, 수중 펌프, 식물, 물고기, 커터칼, 찰흙

18 절차: 화분 바닥에 구멍들을 뚫었다.

19 그런 후에 화분에 작은 돌들을 넣고 식물을 심었다.

20 어항 덮개에 큰 구멍을 내고 구멍에 그 화분을 넣었다.

21 I _____ the pot _____ place _____ clay.

22 I made _____ _____ in the lid and put a tube _____ it.

23 I _____ a water pump _____ the fish tank.

24 I _____ the tube to _____ the pump _____ the pot.

25 I _____ the fish tank _____ water and _____ some fish in it.

26 Then I _____ _____ the pump.

27 Results: From this experiment, I _____ my plants and _____ fish _____ aquaponics.

28 I just _____ the fish, but the plants have _____ 17 centimeters _____ three months.

29 The fish _____ _____ and the water is clean _____ the _____.

30 Conclusion: Some important _____ about aquaponics were _____ from this _____.

31 First, water is _____ _____ the plants don't need _____.

32 Second, it is good _____ the environment _____ no chemicals are _____.

33 _____, you can do aquaponics _____ because it doesn't need much _____.

34 *I found* _____ ... Some farmers use aquaponics to _____ vegetables and _____ fish.

35 They _____ aquaponics because it is _____ _____ than traditional _____.

36 Also, it is a _____ more _____ way of _____ food.

37 The plants grow _____ faster than plants in _____, and it _____ space.

38 I hope more food is _____ in this _____ in the future _____ it is _____ for us and the environment.

21 찰흙으로 화분을 제자리에 고정하였다.
22 덮개에 또 다른 구멍을 하나 만들고 그 안에 관을 넣었다.
23 어항에 수중 펌프를 넣었다.
24 관을 이용하여 펌프를 화분에 연결하였다.
25 어항에 물을 채우고 물고기 몇 마리를 거기에 넣었다.
26 그러고 나서 펌프를 작동하였다.
27 결과: 이 실험으로 나는 아쿠아포닉스로 식물과 물고기를 키웠다.
28 나는 그저 물고기에 밥만 주었는데도 식물은 석 달 동안 17cm나 자랐다.
29 물고기는 건강을 유지하며 물은 항상 깨끗하다.
30 결론: 아쿠아포닉스에 관한 몇 가지 중요한 사항이 이 실험에서 발견되었다.
31 첫째, 식물에 물을 줄 필요가 없으므로 물이 절약된다.
32 둘째, 화학 물질이 사용되지 않으므로 아쿠아포닉스는 환경에 이롭다.
33 끝으로, 넓은 공간이 필요하지 않으므로 당신은 어디에서나 아쿠아포닉스를 쉽게 할 수 있다.
34 나는 알게 되었다... 몇몇 농부들은 채소를 생산하고 물고기를 키우는 데 아쿠아포닉스를 이용한다.
35 그들은 아쿠아포닉스가 전통 재배 방식보다 훨씬 더 쉽기 때문에 그것을 선택한다.
36 또한, 아쿠아포닉스는 식량을 재배하는 훨씬 더 생산적인 방법이다.
37 식물들이 흙에서 자라는 식물보다 훨씬 빠르게 자라고 공간도 절약한다.
38 그것은 우리와 환경에 훨씬 건강하기 때문에 나는 미래에 더 많은 식량이 이런 방식으로 생산되기를 희망한다.

※ 다음 문장을 우리말로 쓰시오.

1 My Science Project: Home Aquaponics
➡ _____

2 What are you reading?
➡ _____

3 I'm reading an article about aquaponics.
➡ _____

4 It's a way of growing plants without soil.
➡ _____

5 We can also grow plants and raise fish in just one system.
➡ _____

6 Is that possible?
➡ _____

7 We'll see. I'm going to try it at home for my science project.
➡ _____

8 Fish, bacteria, and plants are the main parts of aquaponics.
➡ _____

9 After you feed the fish, they produce waste.
➡ _____

10 The waste is turned into food for the plants by bacteria.
➡ _____

11 The plants clean the water by consuming the food.
➡ _____

12 This process is repeated again and again!
➡ _____

13 Home Aquaponics   by Eric Jackson
➡ _____

14 Questions: How can I make an aquaponics system at home?
➡ _____

15 Why is aquaponics good?
➡ _____

16 Period: From May 15 to August 15
➡ _____

17 Materials: a pot & small stones, a fish tank, a plastic tube, a water pump, plants, some fish, a box cutter, clay
➡ _____

18 Steps: I made holes in the bottom of a pot.
➡ _____

19 Then I put small stones and plants in it.
➡ _____

20 I made a big hole in the lid of the fish tank and put the pot in the hole.
➡ _____

21 I fixed the pot in place with clay.
➡ _____

22 I made another hole in the lid and put a tube through it.
➡ _____

23 I put a water pump in the fish tank.
➡ _____

24 I used the tube to connect the pump to the pot.
➡ _____

25 I filled the fish tank with water and put some fish in it.
➡ _____

26 Then I turned on the pump.
➡ _____

27 Results: From this experiment, I grew my plants and raised fish with aquaponics.
➡ _____

28 I just fed the fish, but the plants have grown 17 centimeters in three months.
➡ _____

29 The fish stay healthy and the water is clean all the time.
➡ _____

30 Conclusion: Some important things about aquaponics were learned from this experiment.
➡ _____

31 First, water is saved because the plants don't need watering.
➡ _____

32 Second, it is good for the environment because no chemicals are used.
➡ _____

33 Finally, you can do aquaponics anywhere because it doesn't need much space.
➡ _____

34 I found out... Some farmers use aquaponics to produce vegetables and raise fish.
➡ _____

35 They choose aquaponics because it is far easier than traditional gardening.
➡ _____

36 Also, it is a much more productive way of growing food.
➡ _____

37 The plants grow much faster than plants in soil, and it saves space.
➡ _____

38 I hope more food is produced in this way in the future because it is healthy for us and the environment.
➡ _____

※ 다음 괄호 안의 단어들을 우리말에 맞도록 바르게 배열하시오.

1 (Science / My / Project: / Aquaponics / Home)
➡ _____

2 (are / reading? / what / you)
➡ _____

3 (reading / I'm / article / aquaponics. / about / an)
➡ _____

4 (way / it's / of / a / growing / soil. / without / plants)
➡ _____

5 (can / we / also / plants / grow / and / fish / in / raise / system. / one / just)
➡ _____

6 (that / is / possible?)
➡ _____

7 (see. / we'll / going / I'm / try / to / at / it / home / my / for / project. / science)
➡ _____

8 (bacteria, / fish / and / are / plants / main / the / parts / aquaponics. / of)
➡ _____

9 (you / after / the / feed / fish, / they / waste. / produce)
➡ _____

10 (waste / the / turned / is / food / into / the / for / bacteria. / by / plants)
➡ _____

11 (plants / the / clean / water / the / consuming / by / food. / the)
➡ _____

12 (process / this / repeated / again! / is / again / and)
➡ _____

13 (Aquaponics / Home // Eric / by / Jackson)
➡ _____

14 (questions: can / how / make / I / aquaponics / an / home? / at / system)
➡ _____

15 (is / why / good? / aquaponics)
➡ _____

16 (period: / May / 15 / from / 15 / to / August)
➡ _____

17 (materials: / pot / a / & / stones, / small / fish / a / tank, / tube, / plastic / a / water / a / pump, / some / plants, / fish, / box / a / clay / cutter,)
➡ _____

18 (steps: / made / I / holes / the / in / bottom / pot. / a / of)
➡ _____

19 (I / then / small / put / stones / and / it. / in / plants)
➡ _____

20 (made / I / big / a / hole / the / in / lid / of / fish / the / tank / and / the / pot / put / hole. / the / in)
➡ _____

1	나의 과학 프로젝트: 가정용 아쿠아포닉스
2	무엇을 읽고 있니?
3	아쿠아포닉스에 관한 기사를 읽고 있어.
4	흙 없이 식물을 재배할 수 있는 방법이야.
5	또 한 가지 장치만으로도 식물과 물고기를 동시에 키울 수 있어.
6	그게 가능하니?
7	곧 알게 될 거야. 내가 과학 프로젝트로 집에서 해 볼 예정이거든.
8	물고기, 박테리아, 식물이 아쿠아포닉스의 주요 부분이다.
9	물고기에게 먹이를 주면, 그것들은 배설물을 만들어 낸다.
10	이 배설물은 박테리아에 의해 식물의 먹이로 바뀐다.
11	식물은 그 먹이를 먹음으로써 물을 정화한다.
12	이러한 과정이 계속해서 반복된다!
13	가정용 아쿠아포닉스 에릭 잭슨
14	질문: 집에서 아쿠아포닉스 장치를 어떻게 만들 수 있을까?
15	아쿠아포닉스가 왜 좋은가?
16	기간: 5월 15일부터 8월 15일까지
17	재료: 화분과 작은 돌들, 어항, 플라스틱 관, 수중 펌프, 식물, 물고기, 커터칼, 찰흙
18	절차: 화분 바닥에 구멍들을 뚫었다.
19	그런 후에 화분에 작은 돌들을 넣고 식물을 심었다.
20	어항 덮개에 큰 구멍을 내고 구멍에 그 화분을 넣었다.

21 (fixed / I / pot / the / place / in / clay. / with)
➡ _____

22 (another / made / I / hole / the / in / lid / and / put / through / a / it. / tube)
➡ _____

23 (put / I / water / a / pump / the / in / tank. / fish)
➡ _____

24 (used / I / tube / the / connect / to / pump / the / pot. / to / the)
➡ _____

25 (filled / I / fish / the / with / tank / water / and / put / it. / in / fish / some)
➡ _____

26 (I / then / on / turned / pump. / the)
➡ _____

27 (results: / this / from / experiment, / grew / I / plants / my / raised / and / aquaponics. / with / fish)
➡ _____

28 (just / I / fed / fish, / the / but / plants / the / grown / have / centimeters / 17 / months. / three / in)
➡ _____

29 (fish / the / stay / healthy / and / water / the / clean / is / time. / the / all)
➡ _____

30 (conclusion: / important / some / about / things / aquaponics / learned / were / from / experiment. / this)
➡ _____

31 (water / first, / saved / is / because / plants / the / watering. / need / don't)
➡ _____

32 (second, / is / good / it / for / environment / the / no / because / used. / are / chemicals)
➡ _____

33 (finally, / can / you / do / anywhere / aquaponics / because / doesn't / it / need / space. / much)
➡ _____

34 (found / I / out... // farmers / some / aquaponics / use / produce / to / and / vegetables / fish. / raise)
➡ _____

35 (choose / they / aquaponics / it / because / is / easier / far / traditional / than / gardening.)
➡ _____

36 (it / also, / is / much / a / productive / more / of / way / food. / growing)
➡ _____

37 (planrs / the / much / grow / than / faster / plants / soil, / in / and / space. / saves / it)
➡ _____

38 (hope / I / food / more / produced / is / this / in / way / the / in / future / it / because / healthy / is / us / for / environment. / the / and)
➡ _____

---

21 찰흙으로 화분을 제자리에 고정하였다.

22 덮개에 또 다른 구멍을 하나 만들고 그 안에 관을 넣었다.

23 어항에 수중 펌프를 넣었다.

24 관을 이용하여 펌프를 화분에 연결하였다.

25 어항에 물을 채우고 물고기 몇 마리를 거기에 넣었다.

26 그리고 나서 펌프를 작동하였다.

27 결과: 이 실험으로 나는 아쿠아포닉스로 식물과 물고기를 키웠다.

28 나는 그저 물고기에 밥만 주었는데도 식물은 석 달 동안 17cm나 자랐다.

29 물고기는 건강을 유지하며 물은 항상 깨끗하다.

30 결론: 아쿠아포닉스에 관한 몇 가지 중요한 사항이 이 실험에서 발견되었다.

31 첫째. 식물에 물을 줄 필요가 없으므로 물이 절약된다.

32 둘째. 화학 물질이 사용되지 않으므로 아쿠아포닉스는 환경에 이롭다.

33 끝으로. 넓은 공간이 필요하지 않으므로 당신은 어디에서나 아쿠아포닉스를 쉽게 할 수 있다.

34 나는 알게 되었다... 몇몇 농부들은 채소를 생산하고 물고기를 키우는 데 아쿠아포닉스를 이용한다.

35 그들은 아쿠아포닉스가 전통 재배 방식보다 훨씬 더 쉽기 때문에 그것을 선택한다.

36 또한. 아쿠아포닉스는 식량을 재배하는 훨씬 더 생산적인 방법이다.

37 식물들이 흙에서 자라는 식물보다 훨씬 빠르게 자라고 공간도 절약한다.

38 그것은 우리와 환경에 훨씬 건강하기 때문에 나는 미래에 더 많은 식량이 이런 방식으로 생산되기를 희망한다.

※ **다음 우리말을 영어로 쓰시오.**

1 나의 과학 프로젝트: 가정용 아쿠아포닉스

➡ _____

2 무엇을 읽고 있니?

➡ _____

3 아쿠아포닉스에 관한 기사를 읽고 있어.

➡ _____

4 흙 없이 식물을 재배할 수 있는 방법이야.

➡ _____

5 또 한 가지 장치만으로도 식물과 물고기를 동시에 키울 수 있어.

➡ _____

6 그게 가능하니?

➡ _____

7 곧 알게 될 거야. 내가 과학 프로젝트로 집에서 해 볼 예정이거든.

➡ _____

8 물고기, 박테리아, 식물이 아쿠아포닉스의 주요 부분이다.

➡ _____

9 물고기에게 먹이를 주면, 그것들은 배설물을 만들어 낸다.

➡ _____

10 이 배설물은 박테리아에 의해 식물의 먹이로 바뀐다.

➡ _____

11 식물은 그 먹이를 먹음으로써 물을 정화한다.

➡ _____

12 이러한 과정이 계속해서 반복된다!

➡ _____

13 가정용 아쿠아포닉스   에릭 잭슨

➡ _____

14 질문: 집에서 아쿠아포닉스 장치를 어떻게 만들 수 있을까?

➡ _____

15 아쿠아포닉스가 왜 좋은가?

➡ _____

16 기간: 5월 15일부터 8월 15일까지

➡ _____

17 재료: 화분과 작은 돌들, 어항, 플라스틱 관, 수중 펌프, 식물, 물고기, 커터칼, 찰흙

➡ _____

18 절차: 화분 바닥에 구멍을 뚫었다.

➡ _____

19 그런 후에 화분에 작은 돌들을 넣고 식물을 심었다.

➡ _____

20 어항 덮개에 큰 구멍을 내고 구멍에 그 화분을 넣었다.

➡ _____

21 찰흙으로 화분을 제자리에 고정하였다.

➡ _____

22 덮개에 또 다른 구멍을 하나 만들고 그 안에 관을 넣었다.

➡ _____

23 어항에 수중 펌프를 넣었다.

➡ _____

24 관을 이용하여 펌프를 화분에 연결하였다.

➡ _____

25 어항에 물을 채우고 물고기 몇 마리를 거기에 넣었다.

➡ _____

26 그러고 나서 펌프를 작동하였다.

➡ _____

27 결과: 이 실험으로 나는 아쿠아포닉스로 식물과 물고기를 키웠다.

➡ _____

28 나는 그저 물고기에 밥만 주었는데도 식물은 석 달 동안 17cm나 자랐다.

➡ _____

29 물고기는 건강을 유지하며 물은 항상 깨끗하다.

➡ _____

30 결론: 아쿠아포닉스에 관한 몇 가지 중요한 사항이 이 실험에서 발견되었다.

➡ _____

31 첫째, 식물에 물을 줄 필요가 없으므로 물이 절약된다.

➡ _____

32 둘째, 화학 물질이 사용되지 않으므로 아쿠아포닉스는 환경에 이롭다.

➡ _____

33 끝으로, 넓은 공간이 필요하지 않으므로 당신은 어디에서나 아쿠아포닉스를 쉽게 할 수 있다.

➡ _____

34 나는 알게 되었다... 몇몇 농부들은 채소를 생산하고 물고기를 키우는 데 아쿠아포닉스를 이용한다.

➡ _____

35 그들은 아쿠아포닉스가 전통 재배 방식보다 훨씬 쉽기 때문에 그것을 선택한다.

➡ _____

36 또한, 아쿠아포닉스는 식량을 재배하는 훨씬 더 생산적인 방법이다.

➡ _____

37 식물들이 흙에서 자라는 식물보다 훨씬 빠르게 자라고 공간도 절약한다.

➡ _____

38 그것은 우리와 환경에 훨씬 건강하기 때문에 나는 미래에 더 많은 식량이 이런 방식으로 생산되기를 희망한다.

➡ _____

※ 다음 우리말과 일치하도록 빈칸에 알맞은 말을 쓰시오.

After You Read

1. Window _____

2. Do you _____ _____ _____ plants in your house?

3. Then _____ window _____!

4. You can do it _____ _____ a window _____ plastic bottles.

5. _____ bottle _____ _____ the one _____, so you _____ _____ much space.

1. 창문 농경
2. 집에서 식물을 기르고 싶나요?
3. 그렇다면 창문 농경을 해 보세요!
4. 플라스틱 병으로 창문 근처 어디에서나 그것을 할 수 있습니다.
5. 각각의 병은 위에 매달려 있어서 많은 공간을 필요로 하지 않아요.

Think and Write

1. _____ Make Our School _____!

2. _____ _____ energy is _____ _____ us.

3. _____ _____ this problem, _____ _____ these things.

4. First, we should _____ _____ the lights _____ we _____ our classrooms.

5. _____, we should turn off the classroom computers _____ we are _____ _____ them.

6. _____, we should _____ the doors and windows _____ _____ _____ air conditioners.

7. _____ these things will _____ _____ to our school and the environment.

1. 우리 학교를 친환경적으로 만듭시다!
2. 우리 주변에서 많은 에너지가 낭비되고 있습니다.
3. 이 문제를 해결하기 위해, 다음과 같은 일들을 해 봅시다.
4. 먼저 우리가 교실을 나갈 때 전깃불을 꺼야 합니다.
5. 다음 우리가 교실 컴퓨터를 사용하지 않을 때 그것들을 꺼야 합니다.
6. 마지막으로 에어컨을 사용할 때 교실 문과 창문을 닫아야 합니다.
7. 이런 일들을 하는 것은 우리 학교와 환경에 도움이 될 것입니다.

Culture Link

1. This refrigerator _____ _____ electricity.

2. It _____ _____ _____ dirty water.

3. It _____ _____ _____ countries that have _____ electricity.

4. _____ you need water, just _____ this _____ _____!

5. It _____ the use of _____ _____.

6. This _____ _____ is the Warka Water Tower.

7. _____ _____ this tower, people can _____ water _____ the air. It _____ water.

1. 이 냉장고는 전력 없이 작동된다.
2. 그것은 더러운 물에 의해 동력을 공급받는다.
3. 이것은 전력이 거의 없는 나라에 유용하다.
4. 당신이 물이 필요할 때, 그냥 이 물방울을 마셔라!
5. 이것은 플라스틱 병의 사용을 줄인다.
6. 이 특별한 탑은 와카 워터 타워이다.
7. 이 탑 덕분에 사람들은 공기로부터 물을 얻을 수 있다. 이것은 물을 절약한다.

※ 다음 우리말을 영어로 쓰시오.

After You Read

1. 창문 농경
➡ _____

2. 집에서 식물을 기르고 싶나요?
➡ _____

3. 그렇다면 창문 농경을 해 보세요!
➡ _____

4. 플라스틱 병으로 창문 근처 어디에서나 그것을 할 수 있습니다.
➡ _____

5. 각각의 병은 위에 매달려 있어서 많은 공간을 필요로 하지 않아요.
➡ _____

Think and Write

1. 우리 학교를 친환경적으로 만듭시다!
➡ _____

2. 우리 주변에서 많은 에너지가 낭비되고 있습니다.
➡ _____

3. 이 문제를 해결하기 위해, 다음과 같은 일들을 해봅시다.
➡ _____

4. 먼저 우리가 교실을 나갈 때 전깃불을 꺼야 합니다.
➡ _____

5. 다음 우리가 교실 컴퓨터를 사용하지 않을 때 그것들을 꺼야 합니다.
➡ _____

6. 마지막으로 에어컨을 사용할 때 교실 문과 창문을 닫아야 합니다.
➡ _____

7. 이런 일들을 하는 것은 우리 학교와 환경에 도움이 될 것입니다.
➡ _____

Culture Link

1. 이 냉장고는 전력 없이 작동된다.
➡ _____

2. 그것은 더러운 물에 의해 동력을 공급받는다.
➡ _____

3. 이것은 전력이 거의 없는 나라에 유용하다.
➡ _____

4. 당신이 물이 필요할 때, 그냥 이 물방울을 마셔라!
➡ _____

5. 이것은 플라스틱 병의 사용을 줄인다.
➡ _____

6. 이 특별한 탑은 와카 워터 타워이다.
➡ _____

7. 이 탑 덕분에 사람들은 공기로부터 물을 얻을 수 있다. 이것은 물을 절약한다.
➡ _____

MEMO

MEMO

1학기 전과정

적중100 plus

영어 기출 문제집

영어 기출 문제집

적중100 plus
1학기 전과정

정답 및 해설

능률 | 김성곤

중 2

영어 기출 문제집

적중100

1학기

정답 및 해설

능률 | 김성곤

중 2

Express Yourself

시험대비 실력평가 p.08

01 impossible 02 ⑤　　03 ①　　04 ③
05 ②　　06 ③　　07 ②　　08 ②
09 (1) displayed　(2) hurt　(3) share　(4) understand

01　주어진 단어는 반의어 관계이다. perfect: 완벽한 imperfect: 불완전한 possible: 가능한 impossible: 불가능한
02　break: (법률·약속 등을) 어기다 / 그들은 어린 아이들을 고용함으로써 법률을 어기고 있다.
03　impossible: 불가능한 / 시끄러운 소음이 잠을 불가능하게 만들었다.
04　like: ~을 좋아하다 just like: 꼭 ~와 같이
05　incorrect: 틀린, 정확하지 않은 / 당신이 우리에게 준 정보는 사실이 아니었다.
06　③ borrow: 빌리다
07　post: 올리다, 게시하다 / 다른 사람들이 볼 수 있도록 인터넷에 컴퓨터 기록이나 메시지를 올리다
08　healthy: 건강에 좋은 / 너의 몸에 좋은
09　(1) display: (작품을) 전시하다, 보여주다 (2) hurt: 다치다, 해치다 (3) share: 공유하다 (4) understand: 이해하다

서술형 시험대비 p.09

01 (1) (r)ude　(2) public　(3) result
02 out
03 (1) interesting　(2) carefully　(3) perfect　(4) impossible
04 (1) always, (n)ervous
　　(2) probably, best
05 (1) Is it OK if I bring some friends to the party?
　　(2) Could you copy this letter and send it out?
　　(3) Their last concert was really awesome.
06 (c)omment / (e)tiquette / (r)esult
　　(1) result　(2) etiquette　(3) comments

01　(1) 반의어 관계, polite: 공손한 rude: 무례한 (2) 반의어 관계, stupid: 멍청한 smart: 똑똑한 private: 사적인 public: 공공의 (3) 동의어 관계, reason: 이유 cause: 원인 consequence: 결과 result: 결과

02　check out: 확인하다 find out: 발견하다, 찾아보다
03　(1) interesting: 흥미로운, 재미있는 (2) carefully: 신중하게, 조심스럽게 (3) perfect: 완벽한 (4) impossible: 불가능한
04　(1) always: 항상 nervous: 긴장되는, 불안해 하는 (2) probably: 아마도 best: 최고의
06　(1) result: 결과 (2) etiquette: 에티켓, 예절 (3) comment: 의견, 논평

교과서 Conversation

핵심 Check p.10~11

1 What, interested / I'm, interested
2 (1) Are you interested in animals / I'm interested in plants (2) What subject are you interested in
3 (1) Is it, if, borrow (2) I, on / afraid
4 I'm wondering if I can share your umbrella

교과서 대화문 익히기

Check(√) True or False p.12

(1) T　(2) F　(3) T　(4) T

교과서 확인학습 p.14~15

Listen & Talk 1 A
posters, What / in cooking / in photography

Listen & Talk 1 B
What, going to do / I'm going, with / Are, in / because / what are you / more interested, go to / someday

Listen & Talk 1 C
What show / what are you interested in / I'm interested in / about watching / a big fan of / don't you

Listen & Talk 1 D
What, in / I'm / interested in, social media / We, both

Listen & Talk 2 A
bring / Yes, you may / in the carrier

Listen & Talk 2 B
go / Let, see / record / may not / take / No, you may not, in front of

시험대비 기본평가 p.16

01 ④	02 ③	03 ③

01 ④ '당신은 여기서 사진을 찍어 줄 수 있습니까?'라는 질문이므로 주어진 문장과 다른 의미이다.

02 새로운 과학책을 빌려도 되느냐는 물음에 새 책은 집으로 가져갈 수 없다는 대답을 했으므로, 빈칸에는 허락 요청에 대한 거절의 대답이 나와야 한다.

03 무엇에 관심이 있는지 묻는 질문에, 축구에 관심이 있다고 대답한다. 축구장에 가는 것을 권유하자, 애완동물을 축구장에 데려갈 수 있는지 허락 여부를 묻고, 된다고 상대방이 대답을 한다. be interested in: ~에 관심[흥미]이 있다 Why don't you ~?: ~하는 게 어때?(권유)

시험대비 실력평가 p.17~18

01 ④	02 ⑤	03 ③	04 ①
05 ②		06 some pages from the new book	

07 ⑤ will → won't/will not   08 ③   09 May I feed the birds there?   10 ②   11 ①

12 ③ interest → interests   13 are interested, photography, will, presentation, tomorrow, for advice, her presentation

01 대중음악 방송을 볼 것을 권유하는 말에, 대중음악이 아닌 랩을 좋아한다는 대답을 하는 것이 적절하다.

02 (A) 이후에 언급된 음악 방송이나 남자아이가 랩을 좋아한다는 말을 볼 때, 음악에 흥미있다는 말이 어울린다. science: 과학 art: 미술, 예술 movie: 영화 music: 음악

03 ③ The Friday Pop Music Show는 랩이 아니라 pop 음악 (대중음악)과 관련이 있다.

04 책을 빌릴 수 있는지와 복사를 할 수 있는지 묻고 있으므로, 도서관에서 이루어지는 대화이다. ① library: 도서관 ② theater: 극장 ③ hospital: 병원 ④ classroom: 교실 ⑤

concert hall: 콘서트 홀, 연주회장

05 학생들이 새 책을 집에 가져갈 수 없다고 했으므로, 책을 빌려갈 수 있는지 허락을 묻는 질문에 부정의 대답이 나와야 한다.

06 them이 가리키는 것은 새로운 책의 몇 페이지를 의미한다.

07 공유하지 말라는 말에, 공유할 거라고 대답하는 것은 어색하다.

08 동물에 관심이 있는 상대방에게 가라고 권유할 수 있는 장소이자, 새에게 먹이를 줄 수 있는 장소는 동물원이다. (an art museum→ a zoo) animal: 동물 museum: 박물관

09 May I 동사원형 ~?: 제가 ~해도 될까요? feed: 먹이를 주다

10 앉아도 좋다는 승낙의 대답을 한 후 임자가 있다는 말이 이어지는 것은 어색하다.

11 주어진 문장은 무엇을 하고 있는지에 대한 대답이 될 수 있다. 또한 다음 문장의 'It is about one of my interests.'에서 It이 주어진 문장의 tomorrow's presentation을 지칭하므로 ①의 자리에 들어가야 알맞다.

12 one of 복수명사: ~ 중의 하나 interest: 관심사, 흥미

13 both: 둘 다 be interested in: ~에 관심[흥미]이 있다 photography: 사진 ask for advice: 충고를 구하다

서술형 시험대비 p.19

01 (A) What (B) what

02 Are you interested in baseball?

03 ⑤ less → more	04 bring	05 Yes,

you may.   06 (D) – (B) – (A) – (C)   07 ④ talk → will talk, ⑤ advise → advice

01 be going to 동사원형: ~할 예정이다 this weekend: 이번 주말에 What are you going to do?: 너는 무엇을 할 예정[계획]이니? be interested in: ~에 관심[흥미]이 있다 What are you interested in?: 너는 무엇에 관심이 있니?

02 be동사가 있는 의문문은 주어와 be동사의 위치를 바꾸어 만들 수 있다.

03 무엇에 관심이 있는지 묻는 질문에, 언젠가 축구 경기를 보러 가고 싶다는 말이 나왔으므로, 축구에 관심이 있다는 것을 유추할 수 있다. 그러므로 축구에 덜 관심 있다는 말보다 더 관심이 있다는 말이 어울린다.

04 어떤 것이나 사람을 지금 있는 장소나 말하는 장소로 가져오거나 데려오다 / bring: 데려오다

05 접속사 But 이후에 캐리어 안에 넣어야 한다는 내용이 나오는 것으로 보아, 버스에 데리고 탈 수는 있지만, 캐리어에 넣어야 하는 것을 알 수 있다.

06 (D) 무엇에 관심을 가지는지 묻자, (B) 음악에 관심이 있다고 대답한다. (A) 팝음악방송을 보는 것을 권유하자 (C) 팝보다 랩

을 좋아한다고 대답한다.

07 ④ 내일 말하는 것이므로 미래시제나 'be going to/be planning to+동사원형'을 사용해야 한다. ⑤ advise: 충고하다 advice: 충고

교과서 Grammar

핵심 Check p.20~21

1 (1) Taking　(2) reading
2 Make → Making
3 (1) nervous　(2) sad　(3) interesting
4 look → look like

시험대비 기본평가 p.22

01 (1) Walk → Walking[To walk]　(2) are → is
　　(3) sweetly → sweet　(4) a star → like a star
02 ③　　　03 ④　　　04 ②

01 (1) 주어가 없으므로 동명사나 to부정사가 주어가 되도록 해야 한다. (2) 동명사 주어는 단수 취급한다. (3) 감각동사는 형용사를 보어로 취한다. 부사를 쓰지 않으므로 주의해야 한다. (4) 감각동사 뒤에 보어로 명사가 올 때는 명사 앞에 like를 쓴다.
02 동명사가 문장의 주어가 되도록 해야 한다.
03 동명사 주어는 단수 취급한다.
04 감각동사는 형용사를 보어로 취한다. rough는 형용사이다.

시험대비 실력평가 p.23~25

01 ④　　　02 ⑤　　　03 (1) excited (2) like a princess (3) Growing (4) exercising　　04 ②
05 ①　　　06 ③, ④　　　07 (1) How about watching the Olympic Games on TV? (2) Her song sounds beautiful. 08 ②　　　09 Playing soccer
10 ②　　　11 ①　　　12 like　　　13 ④
14 ③　　　15 (1) playing (2) Smiling (3) writing
(4) going　　16 ⑤　　　17 ④　　　18 ①
19 (1) playing (2) Having[To have] (3) seeing[to see]
(4) swinging　　20 ③　　　21 (1) Solving math problems is interesting. (2) Lisa is good at solving difficult math problems. (3) Strawberry candy tastes sweet. (4) You look like a totally new person in that suit.

01 ④번은 과거진행형을 만드는 현재분사이고, 나머지는 모두 동명사이다.
02 감각동사는 형용사를 보어로 취한다.
03 (1) 감각동사 다음에는 형용사가 나와야 한다. (2) 감각동사 뒤에 보어로 명사가 올 때는 명사 앞에 like를 쓴다. (3) 동명사가 주어가 되도록 해야 한다. (4) 전치사의 목적어로 동명사가 적절하다. 목적어 Teakwondo가 뒤에 있으므로 exercise를 명사로 생각하면 안 된다.
04 형용사를 보어로 취할 수 있는 감각동사 looked가 적절하다.
05 ① is의 보어로 동명사 practicing이나 to practice가 적절하다. practice에 명사도 있으므로 보어로 적절하다고 생각할 수 있으나 뒤에 drawing이 목적어로 나와 있으므로 단순히 명사 보어로 생각하면 안 된다.
06 동명사 swimming을 목적어로 가질 수 있는 동사로 enjoy와 practice가 적절하다.
07 (1) 전치사의 목적어로 동명사가 적절하다. (2) 감각동사의 보어로 형용사가 적절하다.
08 감각동사 다음에 보어가 형용사로 와야 한다.
09 동명사가 문장의 주어가 되도록 해야 한다.
10 Kenneth agreed to practice playing the piano every day. ③ Erica couldn't finish doing the dishes. ④ Do you mind coming here? ⑤ Harry gave up going to the concert on account of a bad cold.
11 감각동사 다음에는 형용사가 나와야 한다.
12 감각동사 다음에 명사가 나올 때는 "감각동사+like+명사'로 쓴다.
13 stop의 목적어로 동명사가 적절하다. to부정사가 오면 '~하기 위해서 멈추다'라는 뜻이 된다.
14 감각동사 다음에 보어로 형용사가 나와야 한다.
15 (1) give up의 목적어로 동명사, (2) 동명사 또는 to부정사로 문장의 주어, (3) finish의 목적보어로 동명사, (4) 전치사의 목적어로 동명사가 적절하다.
16 ⑤ 감각동사 다음에는 형용사가 나와야 한다.
17 <보기>와 ④번은 동사의 목적어로 쓰였다. ① 주어로 쓰인 동명사, ② 보어로 쓰인 동명사, ③ 진행형을 만드는 현재분사, ⑤ 전치사의 목적어로 쓰인 동명사
18 문장의 의미에 맞는 감각동사를 선택한다.
19 (1) practice는 동명사를 목적어로 취한다. (2) 동명사나 to부정사가 주어가 되도록 해야 한다. (3) 동명사나 to부정사가 보어가 되도록 해야 한다. (4) 동명사가 전치사의 목적어가 되도록 해야 한다.
20 ③ The cake was very cold and hard, so it felt like a rock. '감각 동사+like+명사'
21 (1) 동명사 주어는 단수 취급한다. (2) 전치사의 목적어로 동명사가 적절하다. (3) 감각동사는 형용사를 보어로 취한다. (4) 감각동사 뒤에 보어로 명사가 올 때는 명사 앞에 like를 쓴다.

01 (1) doing (2) Having[To have] (3) reading (4) inviting
02 (1) Playing, fun
   (2) Being, difficult
   (3) Sleeping, happy
   (4) Not eating, healthy
   (5) Working, tired
03 (1) tasted delicious
   (2) felt tired
   (3) looked happy
   (4) smelled nice
   (5) sounded upset
04 tasted delicious
05 (1) I am interested in studying art history.
   (2) I enjoy bike riding when I have free time.
06 cooking, famous
07 looked like a good
08 (1) Learning
   (2) Swimming, is not easy.
   (3) playing
   (4) cooking
   (5) taking care of
09 (1) Grandmother's story sounded really interesting.
   (2) Judy didn't like the food. She said the food tasted very bitter.
   (3) The meat we had at the restaurant didn't taste like beef.
   (4) Watching[To watch] action movies is exciting.
   (5) Keeping[To keep] early hours is good for the health.
10 (1) nervous
   (2) beautiful
   (3) listening, Listening
   (4) eating, Eating
11 Cooking looks interesting.

01 (1) suggest의 목적어로 동명사, (2) Having 또는 To have 로 문장의 주어, (3) 전치사의 목적어로 동명사, (4) 전치사의 목적어로 동명사가 적절하다.
02 동명사가 주어가 되도록 하고 동명사의 부정은 'not+동명사'로 나타낸다. make의 목적격보어로 부사가 아닌 형용사가 쓰인다.
03 감각동사 다음에는 형용사가 와야 한다. 시제에 주의하여 작성한다.
04 smelled great, looked tasty 등 어법에 맞게 '감각동사+형용사'로 쓰면 정답.
05 전치사와 동사 enjoy의 목적어로 동명사를 써서 어법에 맞게 작성하면 정답.

06 동명사가 loves의 목적어가 되도록 해야 하고, looks의 보어로 형용사가 적절하다.
07 감각동사 뒤에 보어로 명사가 올 때는 명사 앞에 like를 써야 한다.
08 동명사가 문장의 주어, 보어, 목적어 또는 전치사의 목적어가 되도록 해야 한다.
09 (1), (2) 감각동사의 보어로 형용사가 적절하다. (3) 감각동사 뒤에 보어로 명사가 올 때는 명사 앞에 like를 쓴다. (4), (5) 주어가 없으므로 동명사나 to부정사가 주어가 되도록 해야 하며 동명사나 to부정사 주어는 단수 취급한다.
10 (1), (2) 감각동사는 형용사를 보어로 취한다. (3), (4) 동명사가 주어나 목적어가 되도록 한다. nerve(명): 신경, nervous(형): 불안해[초조해/두려워] 하는
11 동명사가 주어가 되도록 하고 감각동사의 보어로 형용사를 쓴다.

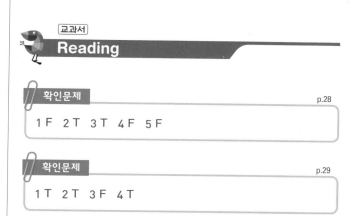

교과서 Reading

확인문제   p.28
1 F   2 T   3 T   4 F   5 F

확인문제   p.29
1 T   2 T   3 F   4 T

교과서 확인학습 A   p.30~31

01 About   02 Facts   03 Are, interested in
04 to post selfies, how much
05 Here are   06 took the world's first selfie
07 became a new word   08 took the first space selfie   09 Survey   10 Taking selfies, of daily life   11 To find out   12 from ages 14 to 16   13 Let's look at the girls, take selfies   14 90 percent of   15 Also, they use filters.   16 take selfies at school
17 some of the students' comments
18 awesome   19 Making silly faces
20 taking selfies, doing it   21 look good
22 don't look like me   23 Etiquette
24 follow etiquette for   25 Ask yourself, before   26 am I   27 appropriate places   28 Don't take selfies

29 bother   30 see this   31 Keep in mind

32 Choose carefully   33 What kinds of, leave   34 Leave, comments on

35 be rude, sounds easy, doesn't it 36 have fun with

31 Keep in mind that anyone can see your selfies.

32 Choose carefully when you post them.

33 What kinds of comments should I leave?

34 Leave nice comments on other people's selfies.

35 Don't be rude. That sounds easy, doesn't it?

36 Follow these tips and have fun with your selfies.

교과서   p.32~33

1 All About Selfies!

2 Selfie Facts

3 Are you interested in selfies?

4 You probably like to post selfies on social media, but how much do you know about selfies?

5 Here are some interesting facts.

6 Robert Cornelius took the world's first selfie in 1839.

7 Selfie became a new word in the dictionary in 2013.

8 Buzz Aldrin took the first space selfie in 1966.

9 Selfie Survey

10 Taking selfies is part of daily life for many teens, but do teens really enjoy it?

11 To find out, we did a survey.

12 We asked three questions to 300 students from ages 14 to 16.

13 Let's look at the results.

14 Surprisingly, 90 percent of the girls take selfies, but only 15 percent of the boys take selfies.

15 Also, 93 percent of these students said that they use filters.

16 The survey also showed that the students take selfies at school the most.

17 Check out some of the students' comments.

18 Lewis, 14, England Selfies are awesome.

19 Making silly faces is really fun!

20 Minwoo, 16, Korea I enjoy taking selfies, but some students spend too much time doing it.

21 Kate, 15, Denmark My pictures look good when I use filters.

22 But sometimes my selfies don't look like me.

23 Selfie Etiquette

24 You should follow etiquette for selfies.

25 Ask yourself these questions before you take, post, or look at selfies.

26 Where am I?

27 Choose appropriate places to take selfies.

28 Don't take selfies in hospitals or public restrooms.

29 It may bother other people.

30 Who can see this?

시험대비 실력평가   p.34~39

01 (A) interested   (B) are   (C) interesting   02 ④

03 ②   04 ③   05 우리는 14세부터 16세 사이의 300명의 학생들에게 세 가지 질문을 물어보았다.

06 ④   07 (1) Where am I?   (2) Who can see this?   (3) What kinds of comments should I leave?

08 ③   09 no one → anyone   10 ①, ④

11 how much do you know about selfies? 12 Buzz Aldrin   13 ④   14 ②   15 ⑤

16 she uses filters   17 (A) Where am I?   (B) them   (C) easy   18 ②, ⑤   19 ⑤

20 the results of the selfie survey   21 ④

22 ③

01 (A) 감정을 나타내는 동사는 사람을 수식할 때는 과거분사로 써야 하므로 interested가 적절하다. (B) 주어가 복수(facts)이므로 are가 적절하다. (C) 감정을 나타내는 동사는 사물을 수식할 때는 현재분사로 써야 하므로 interesting이 적절하다.

02 위 글은 셀피에 관한 몇 가지 재미있는 사실들을 소개하는 글이므로, 제목으로는 ④번 'Selfie Facts'가 적절하다.

03 ② 너는 아마 소셜 미디어에 셀피를 게시하는 것을 좋아할지도 모른다고 쓰여 있지만, '소셜 미디어에 셀피를 게시하려고 셀피를 찍는다.'고는 언급되어 있지 않다.

04 ⓐ와 ③은 동명사, 나머지는 모두 현재분사이다.

05 from ages 14 to 16: '14세부터 16세 사이'

06 ④ 학생들이 두 번째로 셀피를 많이 찍는 장소는 '집'이다.

07 뒤에 나오는 질문들을 쓰면 된다.

08 ⓑ와 ③은 형용사적 용법, ① 부사적 용법(원인), ② 부사적 용법(이유), ④ 명사적 용법, ⑤ 부사적 용법(결과)

09 셀피를 찍거나 게시하거나 보기 전에 '누구나' 너의 셀피를 볼 수 있다는 것을 명심해야 한다고 해야 하므로, no one을 anyone으로 고치는 것이 적절하다.

10 ⓐ와 ①, ④ 아마, ② 실제로, ③ 정확히, ⑤ 완전히

11 how를 보충하면 된다.

12 최초의 우주 셀피를 찍은 사람은 '버즈 올드린'이다.

13 ④ 학생들이 왜 학교에서 셀피를 찍는 것을 좋아하는지는 대답할 수 없다. ① 90 percent. ② 279 students. (300명 중에서

6 정답 및 해설

93퍼센트가 필터를 사용한다.) ③ 35 percent. ⑤ At home.

14 ②는 형용사적 용법이고 ⓐ와 나머지는 모두 부사적 용법이다. ⓐ 부사적 용법(목적), ① 부사적 용법(목적), ③ 부사적 용법(목적), ④ 부사적 용법(형용사 수식), ⑤ 부사적 용법(이유)

15 ⑤ awesome: 경탄할 만한, 어마어마한, 엄청난, ① 끔찍한, ② 어색한, ③ 재미없는, 지루한, ④ 실망스러운, '우스꽝스러운 표정을 짓는 것은 정말 재미있다!'는 말이 이어지므로, 셀피는 '굉장하다.'고 하는 것이 적절하다.

16 케이트는 '필터를 사용하기 때문에' 가끔 그녀의 셀피가 그녀처럼 보이지 않는다고 말한다.

17 (A) '내가 어디에 있는가?'는 Where am I?(혼자일 때)나 Where are we?(나를 포함하여 여럿이 물을 때)라고 해야 한다. here는 부사라서 주어 자리에 쓸 수 없다. (B) 'your selfies'를 가리키므로 them이 적절하다. (C) 감각동사 sounds 다음에 '형용사 보어'를 써야 하므로 easy가 적절하다.

18 appropriate = proper = suitable: 적절한, ① 인기 있는, ③ 흔한, ④ 매우 좋아하는

19 ⓑ on: ~에 대해서,~에 관한, ⓒ have fun with: ~와 재미있게 놀다

20 셀피 설문조사의 결과를 가리킨다.

21 ④번 다음 문장이 주어진 문장의 답에 해당하므로 ④번이 적절하다.

22 Bonny는 셀피를 가장 많이 찍는 장소를 모른다.

서술형 시험대비
p.40~41

01 interest
02 Here are some interesting facts.
03 possible → impossible
04 Choose appropriate places to take selfies.
05 it may bother other people
06 comments
07 interested
08 post
09 in 1839
10 taking selfies
11 60 또는 Sixty
12 at school

01 have의 목적어로 명사 interest를 쓰면 된다.

02 주어가 some interesting facts이므로 동사를 are로 쓰는 것이 적절하다.

03 selfie는 2013년에 사전에 새로운 단어로 실렸기 때문에, 2013년 전에는 사전에서 찾을 수 없는 단어였다.

04 appropriate: 적합한, 적절한

---

05 그것은 '다른 사람들을 신경 쓰이게 할 수 있기' 때문이다.

06 '어떤 코멘트를 남겨야 하는가?'라는 질문에 대한 답으로 다른 사람들의 셀피에 상냥한 '코멘트'를 남기라고 하는 것이 적절하다.

07 be interested in: ~에 관심[흥미]이 있다 / interesting을 변형하여 쓰면 된다.

08 post: 게시하다 / 웹사이트나 소셜 미디어를 사용하여 메시지나 사진과 같은 것을 게재하다

09 세계 최초로 Robert Cornelius가 셀피를 찍은 것은 1839년이었다.

10 '셀피 찍기'를 가리킨다.

11 300명 중에서 20%가 카페나 식당에서 셀피를 찍는다고 말했기 때문에, '60명'이 적절하다.

12 학생들은 '학교에서' 셀피를 가장 많이 찍는다.

영역별 핵심문제
p.43~47

01 ③
02 (1) sometimes, to (2) silly (3) there, public
   (4) warm, outdoors
03 (1) sound (2) spends (3) did (4) having 04 ②
05 ③   06 ④   07 going   08 ①
09 interesting → interested 10 ④
11 What are you interested in?
12 We are both interested in social media.
13 (1) inviting (2) Playing 14 ②   15 ③
16 ⑤
17 (1) Watching a movie is an adventure.
   (2) Reading this book was like having a coffee with a friend.
   (3) I want to stop talking about my personal life.
   (4) Circles feel soft because they have no angles.
   (5) My computer sounds strange.
18 (1) greatly → great (2) fish → like fish   19 ④
20 (1) to spend → spending
   (2) Break, are → Breaking[To break], is
21 ⓐ in ⓒ on 22 ②
23 (A) much (B) interesting (C) new   24 To take
25 ⓐ 90 ⓑ 15 ⓒ 93   26 ③   27 ②
28 ④   29 ⓐ Facts ⓑ Survey ⓒ Etiquette
30 ②

01 ① displayed, display: (작품을) 전시하다, 보여주다 ② Prepare, prepare: 준비하다 ③ bother, bother: 괴롭히다 ④ left, leave: 남기다 ⑤ understand, understand: 이해하다

02 (1) sometimes: 가끔 have to 동사원형: ~해야 한다 (2)

silly: 바보 같은, 어리석은 (3) there is 단수명사: ~가 있다 public: 공공의 (4) warm: 따뜻한 outdoors: 야외에서

03 (1) sound+형용사: ~하게 들리다 (2) spend 시간 -ing: ~하는 데 시간을 보내다 (3) do a survey: 조사를 하다 (4) have fun: 즐거운 시간을 보내다

04 ②는 반의어 관계이고 나머지 보기는 동의어 관계이다. ① display: 전시하다 exhibit: 전시하다 ② exciting: 신나는 boring: 지루한 ③ fact: 사실 truth: 진실 ④ hurt: 해치다 injure: 다치게 하다 ⑤ nervous: 불안한 anxious: 불안한

05 from A to B: A에서 B까지 awesome: 멋진, 굉장한 keep in mind: 명심하다 in front of: ~ 앞에서

06 ④ Of course.라고 허락하는 대답을 하고 바로 뒤에 미안하다는 말은 어울리지 않는다.

07 be going to 동사원형: ~할 것(예정)이다

08 나의 남동생이 야구를 좋아하기 때문에 내가 야구 경기를 보러 간다는 의미이므로, 이유를 나타내는 접속사 because가 어울린다.

09 be interested in: ~에 관심[흥미]이 있다 Are you interested in~?: 너는 ~에 관심이 있니?

10 ① 여자아이는 이번 주에 야구 경기를 보러 간다. ② 여자아이의 남동생은 야구를 좋아한다. ③ 여자아이는 사실 야구를 좋아하지 않는다. ④ 남자아이가 무엇에 관심을 가졌는지는 나와 있지 않다. ⑤ 여자아이는 언젠가 축구 경기를 보러 가기를 원한다.

11 be interested in: ~에 관심[흥미]이 있다 What are you interested in?: 너는 무엇에 관심이 있니?

12 both: 둘 다

13 (1) 전치사의 목적어로 동명사 (2) 주어로 동명사가 적절하다.

14 ② 감각동사는 형용사를 보어로 취한다. friendly는 'friend(명사)+ly'로 형용사이다.

15 ③번은 some birds를 수식하는 현재분사이고 나머지는 모두 동명사이다. ① 주어 ② 동사의 목적어 ④ 보어 ⑤ 전치사의 목적어

16 감각동사 다음에는 보어로 형용사가 나와야 한다. 보어로 명사가 올 때는 명사 앞에 like를 쓴다.

17 (1), (2), (3) 동명사가 주어, 동사와 전치사의 목적어가 되도록 한다. (4), (5) 감각동사의 보어로 형용사를 쓴다.

18 감각동사 다음에는 보어로 형용사가 와야 한다. 보어로 명사가 올 때는 명사 앞에 like를 쓴다.

19 ④ Stop reading that book, and go out and play.

20 (1) deny는 동명사를 목적어로 갖는다. (2) 주어가 없으므로 동명사나 to부정사가 주어가 되도록 해야 하며 동명사나 to부정사 주어는 단수 취급한다.

21 ⓐ be interested in: ~에 관심[흥미]이 있다, ⓒ post on: ~에 올리다, 게시하다

22 ⓑ와 ②는 명사적 용법(목적어), ① 형용사적 용법, ③ 부사적 용법(형용사 수식), ④ 형용사적 용법, ⑤ 부사적 용법(조건)

23 (A) 양을 나타내므로 much가 적절하다. (B) 몇 가지 '재미있는' 사실들이 있다고 해야 하므로 interesting이 적절하다. boring: 지루한, (C) 사전에 '신조어'로 등재되었다고 해야 하므로 new가 적절하다.

24 주어로 쓰인 동명사이므로 to부정사로 바꿔 쓸 수 있다.

25 ⓐ 소녀들의 '90' 퍼센트가 셀피를 찍는다. ⓑ 소년들의 '15' 퍼센트만이 셀피를 찍는다. ⓒ 학생들의 '93' 퍼센트는 필터를 사용한다고 말했다.

26 ① awesome: 경탄할 만한, 어마어마한, 엄청난, amazing: 놀랄 만한, 굉장한, ③ 민우는 셀피 찍는 것을 즐기지만 '몇몇 학생들은' 그것을 하는 데 너무 많은 시간을 보낸다고 말했다.

27 위 글은 셀피 예절에 관한 글이므로, 제목으로는 ②번 'Selfie Etiquette'가 적절하다.

28 ④ 어디에 셀피를 게시해야 하는지는 대답할 수 없다. ① 1. Choose appropriate places to take selfies. 2. Keep in mind that anyone can see your selfies. 3. Leave nice comments on other people's selfies. ② Before we take, post, or look at selfies. ③ Anyone can see them. ⑤ We should leave nice comments on other people's selfies.

29 ⓐ 셀피에 관한 '사실들', ⓑ 셀피 '설문조사' ⓒ 셀피 '예절'

30 ⓑ Do you use filters on your selfies to look good? ⓒ Where do you usually take selfies?

단원별 예상문제   p.48~51

01 (1) carefully (2) incorrect
02 (a)ppropriate / (p)ublic / (r)ude
(1) Public (2) rude (3) appropriate   **03** ③
04 ②   **05** ④   **06** (E) – (A) – (C) – (B) – (D)
07 ①   **08** ③   **09** No, you may not.
10 ②   **11** ③   **12** ④, ⑤   **13** looks lovely   **14** ②   **15** (1) Read → Reading[To read] (2) say → saying (3) sweetly → sweet (4) sound → sound like
16 (1) Robert Cornelius는 1839년에 세계 최초의 셀피를 찍었다.
(2) selfie는 2013년에 사전에 신조어로 실렸다.
(3) Buzz Aldrin은 1966년에 최초의 우주 셀피를 찍었다.
17 ②   **18** were many space selfies → was no space selfie **19** (A) etiquette (B) questions **20** ②
21 isn't that → doesn't it   **22** (1) 몇몇 학생들은 자신들의 셀피에 필터를 너무 많이 사용한다. (2) 몇몇 학생들이 똑같은 셀피를 반복해서 게시하는 것은 시간 낭비이다.   **23** ④

01 주어진 보기는 반의어의 관계이다. (1) carelessly: 부주의하게 carefully: 신중하게 (2) correct: 맞는 incorrect: 틀린

02 (1) public: 공공의 / 누구든지 사용 가능한 / 공공 도서관은 정보를 찾기 좋다. (2) rude: 무례한 / 공손하지 않거나, 사람들의 기분을 상하게 하거나, 짜증나게 하기 쉬운 방식의 말과 행동을 하는 / 나는 무례하게 굴려고 하는 것은 아니었지만, 일찍 떠나야만 했어. (3) appropriate: 적절한 / 특정한 시간, 장소, 목적에 맞거나 적합한 / 나는 청바지가 파티에 적합하다고 생각하지 않는다.

03 unexpectedly: 뜻밖에, 예상 외로 surprisingly: 놀랍게도, 의외로

04 deal with: (문제·과제 등을) 처리하다 solve: 해결하다

05 ④번은 내용을 확인하기 위해 물어보는 것이며, 나머지는 허락을 요청하기 위해 묻는 문장들이다.

06 무엇을 하고 있는지 묻는 질문에, (E) 내일 발표를 준비한다고 대답하며, 발표 내용이 자신의 관심사 중 하나라고 얘기한다. (A) 무엇에 관심을 가졌는지 질문하자 (C) 사진에 관심이 있다고 대답한다. (B) 그러자 상대방도 사진에 역시 관심이 있다고 말하자 (D) 상대방에게 내일 발표에 대해 도움을 요청한다.

07 주어진 문장은 표를 보여 달라는 말이므로, 이 다음에는 표를 보여주는 Here it is. (여기 있어요.)가 나와야 적절하다.

08 허락을 요청하는 표현에는 May I ~?, Can I ~?, Is it OK if I ~?, I'm wondering if I ~., Would it be all right if I ~?, Do you mind if I ~? 등이 있다.

09 오직 콘서트홀 앞에서만 사진을 찍을 수 있다.

10 ① 콘서트홀 입구에서 대화하고 있다. ② 밴드가 무슨 종류의 음악을 연주하는지는 알 수 없다. ③ 밴드의 사진을 찍는 것은 불가능하다. ④ 콘서트홀 앞에서만 사진 촬영이 가능하다. ⑤ 여자아이는 콘서트홀 안에서 녹음할 수 없다.

11 학생들이 새 책을 집에 못 가져가는 것이 새로운 과학책을 빌리는 것을 허락하지 않는 구체적 이유이므로 No, you may not. 다음에 나와야 적절하다.

12 ④ 모든 책이 아니라 새 책만 가져갈 수 없다. ⑤ 대화에 없는 내용이다. 과학 보고서를 위해 책이 필요하다는 내용만 언급되어 있다.

13 감각동사는 형용사를 보어로 취한다.

14 ①, ③, ⑤ give up, practice, mind 등은 동명사를 목적어로 받는다. ④ 동명사나 to부정사가 주어가 되도록 해야 한다.

15 (1) 동명사나 부정사가 주어가 되도록 해야 한다. (2) 전치사의 목적어로 동명사를 써야 한다. (3) 감각동사는 형용사를 보어로 취한다. (4) 감각동사 뒤에 보어로 명사가 올 때는 명사 앞에 like를 쓴다.

16 뒤에 이어지는 내용을 쓰면 된다.

17 take a selfie: 셀피를 찍다

18 1966년에 첫 번째 우주 셀피를 찍었다고 했기 때문에 1966년

전에는 '우주 셀피가 없었다.'고 하는 것이 적절하다.

19 셀피를 찍을 때, 따라야 하는 '예절'이 있다. 스스로에게 '여기가 어디인가?' '누가 그것을 볼 수 있는가?' '어떤 종류의 댓글을 남겨야 할까?'와 같은 '질문들'을 한 다음에 셀피를 찍거나 게시하거나 보아야 한다.

20 '누구나 당신의 셀피를 볼 수 없도록 해야 한다는 것'은 셀피 예절에 속하지 않는다.

21 문장의 동사가 일반동사이므로 'doesn't'를 쓰고 That을 'it'으로 바꾸는 것이 적절하다

22 Why? 다음의 내용을 쓰면 된다.

23 ⓐ와 ④ 낭비, ① 낭비하다(동사), ② 쓰레기, ③ 낭비하다, 막 쓰다(동사), ⑤ 쓸모가 없어진, 폐물이 된(형용사)

서술형 실전문제
p.52~53

01 ⓐ for ⓑ of ⓒ in ⓓ about

02 in photography

03 may I ask you for some advice for my presentation?

04 (1) Watch → Watching[To watch]
    (2) to do → doing
    (3) become → becoming[to become]
    (4) arrive → arriving
    (5) nicely → nice
    (6) smell → smell like

05 (1) Learning English is interesting.
    (2) Students spend too much time doing computer games.
    (3) She turned pale at hearing the news.
    (4) The fruit didn't taste like strawberries.
    (5) They felt so soft and warm.

06 playing the computer game

07 taking selfies

08 My pictures look good when I use filters.

09 (A) appropriate (B) bother (C) rude

10 To take[Taking] selfies in hospitals or public restrooms

11 enjoy yourself 또는 have a good time

01 ⓐ prepare for: ~을 준비하다 ⓑ one of 복수명사: ~ 중의 하나 ⓒ be interested in: ~에 관심[흥미]이 있다 ⓓ talk about: ~에 대해서 말하다

02 문장 맨 끝의 too가 있는 것으로 보아, 똑같이 사진에 관심을 가진 것을 알 수 있다. photography: 사진

03 May I 동사원형 ~?: 제가 ~해도 될까요? ask for advice: 충고를 구하다

04 (1) 동명사나 부정사가 주어가 되도록 해야 한다. (2) keep은 동명사를 목적어로 가지는 동사이다. (3) 동명사나 부정사가 보

9

어가 되도록 해야 한다. (4) 전치사의 목적어로 동명사가 적절하다. (5) 감각동사는 형용사를 보어로 취한다. (6) 감각동사 뒤에 보어로 명사가 올 때는 명사 앞에 like를 쓴다.

05 (1) 주어로 동명사, (2) spend+시간+동명사: ~하는 데 시간을 보내다, (3) 전치사의 목적어로 동명사, (4) 감각동사 뒤에 보어로 명사가 올 때는 명사 앞에 like를 쓴다. (5) 감각동사는 형용사를 보어로 취한다.

06 stop이 있고 컴퓨터를 끄겠다고 했으므로 동명사를 목적어로 하여 게임을 그만둘 것이다'라고 하는 것이 적절하다.

07 '셀피를 찍는 것'을 가리킨다.

08 good을 보충하면 된다.

09 (A) 셀피를 찍기에 '적합한' 장소를 선택하라고 해야 하므로 appropriate가 적절하다. appropriate: 적합한, 적절한, unsuitable: 적합하지[알맞지] 않은, (B) 공중 화장실에서 셀피를 찍는 것은 다른 사람들을 '신경 쓰이게 할 수 있다'고 해야 하므로 bother가 적절하다. bother: 신경 쓰이게 하다, 괴롭히다, encourage: 격려하다, 용기를 북돋우다, (C) 다른 사람들의 셀피에 상냥한 코멘트를 남기고 '무례하게' 굴지 마라고 해야 하므로 rude가 적절하다. polite: 예의 바른, 공손한, rude: 무례한

10 병원이나 공중 화장실에서 셀피를 찍는 것'을 가리킨다. It이 주어이므로 to부정사나 동명사를 사용하여 쓰는 것이 적절하다.

11 have fun = enjoy oneself = have a good time: 즐기다, 즐겁게 보내다

|모범답안|
01 A: What are you interested in?
   A: Why don't you go to a museum?/How[What] about going to a museum?
   B: May I take pictures[photos]
   A: No, you may not. / I'm afraid not.
02 (1) You look nervous.
   (2) She feels happy.
   (3) The soup smells sweet.
   (4) The food tasted terrible.
   (5) The news sounded good.
03 (A) language rules   (B) incorrect   (C) Finally
   (D) in mind

01 ④   02 ①   03 (1) will, able / (e)tiquette   (2) an interesting question   (3) enjoy shopping , clothes (4) lot, choose
04 (1) looked   (2) sounds   (3) agree   (4) spend
05 (A) movies   (B) Why   (C) eat snacks
06 (A) borrow   (B) copy   07 share   08 ②
09 (A) I'm interested in games and social media.
   (B) I'm interested in music and social media.
10 We are both interested in social media.
11 May I take pictures of the band?   12 in
13 ③   14 ④   15 ⑤
16 like an orange   17 (1) My pictures look beautiful when I use filters. (2) Stop playing games and be sincere.   18 posting   19 ②
20 ②   21 (A) awesome   (B) good   (C) like
22 ③   23 after → before
24 remember 25 ②

01 'awesome: 멋진, 굉장한 ① 놀라운, 멋진 ② 굉장한, 훌륭한 ③ 환상적인, 멋진 ④ 끔찍한 ⑤ 훌륭한, 좋은

02 ①은 반의어 관계이고 나머지 보기는 동의어 관계이다. ① rude: 무례한 polite: 공손한 ② finally: 마지막으로 lastly: 마지막으로 ③ bother: 괴롭히다 annoy: 귀찮게 하다 ④ comment: 의견 remark: 견해 ⑤ advice: 충고 tip: 충고

03 (1) etiquette: 에티켓, 예절 (2) interesting: 흥미로운, 재미있는 question: 질문 (3) clothes: 옷 enjoy 동사ing: ~하는 것을 즐기다 (4) a lot of: 많은 choose: 고르다

04 (1) twin: 쌍둥이 (2) sound+형용사: ~하게 들리다 (3) agree with: ~에 동의하다 (4) spend 시간 동사ing: ~하는 데 시간을 보내다

05 (A) 극장에 가는 것을 권유하고 있으므로 영화에 관심이 있는 것을 유추할 수 있다. (B) Why don't you ~?: ~하는 게 어때?(권유하기) (C) take photos of the paintings: 그림 사진을 찍다 eat snacks: 과자를 먹다 feed the birds: 새에게 먹이를 주다 record the music: 음악을 녹음하다

06 borrow: 빌리다 copy: 복사하다

07 다른 사람과 함께 무언가를 갖거나 사용하다 share: 공유하다

08 새로운 과학책을 빌려줄 수 있는지 허락을 요청하는 말에 거절했으므로, 학생들이 집에 새 책을 가져갈 수 있다는 말은 어색하다. can을 can't로 고쳐야 적절하다.

09 be interested in: ~에 관심[흥미]이 있다 social media: 소셜 미디어

10 both: 둘 다 social media: 소셜 미디어

11 May I 동사원형 ~?: 제가 ~해도 될까요? take a picture[photo] (of): (~의) 사진을 찍다

12 in: ~ 안에서 in front of: ~ 앞에서

13 ③ I'm proud of winning the prize.

14 want는 형용사를 보어로 쓰지 않는다.

15 ⑤번은 목적격 보어로 쓰인 현재분사이고 나머지는 모두 동명사이다.

16 '감각동사+like+명사'

17 (1) 감각동사는 형용사를 보어로 취한다. (2) 동명사가 Stop의 목적어로 쓰여야 한다.

18 like는 목적어로 to부정사와 동명사를 둘 다 쓸 수 있다.

19 여기에 몇 가지 재미있는 사실들이 있다고 했으므로 '셀피에 관한 몇 가지 재미있는 사실들'이 이어질 것이다.

20 학생들의 '댓글'들이 이어지고 있으므로 comments가 적절하다. ① 보고서, ③ (신문・잡지의) 글, 기사, ④ 수필, ⑤ 요약, 개요

21 (A) 셀피는 '경탄할 만하다'고 해야 하므로 awesome이 적절하다. awful: 끔찍한, 지독한, awesome: 경탄할 만한, 어마어마한, 엄청난, (B) 내 사진들은 필터를 사용할 때 '좋아' 보인다고 해야 하므로 good이 적절하다. 감각동사 look 다음에 형용사를 써야 하는데, well은 형용사일 때 '건강한'이라는 뜻이다. (C) 가끔 나의 셀피들은 나 '같이 보이지' 않는다고 해야 하므로 like가 적절하다. look like: ~인 것처럼 보이다

22 ③ 7 percent of the 'students로 고쳐야 한다.

23 네가 셀피를 찍거나 게시하거나 보기 '전에' 이런 질문들을 스스로에게 물으라고 하는 것이 적절하다.

24 keep in mind = be sure to remember: ~을 명심하다

25 ②번은 '팁, 봉사료'이고, ⓒ와 나머지는 다 '조언들'이라는 뜻이다.

Eat Right, Be Happy!

시험대비 실력평가 p.60

01 (1) traditional   (2) Vietnamese
02 (1) choice   (2) arrival   03 healthy   04 ④
05 ①   06 ①   07 ③
08 (1) more   (2) often   (3) slowly

01 주어진 보기는 명사와 형용사의 관계이다. Korea: 한국 Korean: 한국의 (1) tradition: 전통 traditional: 전통적인 (2) Vietnam: 베트남 Vietnamese: 베트남의

02 주어진 보기는 동사와 명사의 관계이다. suggest: 제안하다 suggestion: 제안 (1) choose: 고르다 choice: 선택 (2) arrive: 도착하다 arrival: 도착

03 health: 건강 healthy: 건강에 좋은

04 ① fry: 튀기다 ② recommend: 추천하다 ③ other: 다른 ④ usually: 보통, 대개 ⑤ breakfast: 아침 식사

05 ① vegetables: 야채 / 비타민 A는 간과 푸른색 야채에서 발견된다. ② meat: 고기, 육류 ③ flower: 꽃 ④ carrot: 당근 ⑤ meal: 식사

06 ① contest: 대회, 콘테스트 / 나는 내일 웅변 대회에 나가요. ② concert: 연주회, 콘서트 ③ content: 내용 ④ compete: 경쟁하다 ⑤ prize: 상

07 try + 음식: 음식을 먹어 보다, 맛을 보다 / 새로운 음식을 맛보는 것은 흥미로운 경험이다.

08 (1) more: 더 큰, 더 많은 (2) often: 종종, 자주 (3) slowly: 천천히

서술형 시험대비 p.61

01 common
02 get
03 (1) going, (c)elebrate   (2) enough money
   (3) Fresh fruit, vegetables
04 (1) common   (2) enough
05 (1) contest   (2) sweets
06 (1) side dish   (2) suggestion   (3) onion   (4) grocery
07 (1) Do you want me to cut the cake?
   (2) I've always wanted to go to Paris.

01 common: 흔한 have ~ in common: 공통으로 ~을 가지다

02 get a cold: 감기에 걸리다 get a discount: 할인받다

03 (1) be going out: 외출할 것이다 celebrate: 축하하다, 기념하다 (2) enough: 충분한 money: 돈 (3) fresh: 신선한 fruit: 과일 vegetables: 야채

04 (1) high: 높은 low: 낮은 (반의어 관계) rare: 희귀한, 드문 common: 흔한 (2) awesome: 엄청난 wonderful: 훌륭한 (동의어 관계) sufficient: 충분한 enough: 충분한

05 (1) contest: 대회, 콘테스트 / 둘 또는 그 이상의 사람이나 그룹이 서로 겨루는 경쟁이나 상황 (2) sweets: 단 음식, 단것 / 설탕이나 초콜릿으로 만들어진 작은 조각의 단 음식

06 (1) side dish: 반찬 (2) suggestion: 제안 (3) onion: 양파 (4) grocery: 식료품

07 (1) cut: 자르다 (2) always: 항상

[교과서]
Conversation

핵심 Check   p.62~63

1 You'd better, before / I'll
2 (B) → (D) → (A) → (C)
3 you recommend / There
4 What sport do you recommend?
  I strongly recommend
5 What book do you recommend?
  I'd like to recommend this book.

교과서 대화문 익히기

Check(√) True or False   p.64

(1) F   (2) F   (3) T   (4) T

교과서 확인학습   p.66~67

Listen & Talk 1 A

I think I eat, sweets these days / good for, health. You'd bette, instead

Listen & Talk 1 B

look / often feel tired / usually eat / You'd better eat, gives you energy / any other suggestions / should also exercise

Listen & Talk 1 C

contest, going to / What, put in them / You'd better, in, about / I'm not going to / we should, healthy / I should

Listen and Talk 2 A

It's, first time, What, recommend / I recommend

Listen and Talk 2 B

What are you doing / searching for / When / too expensive / don't you check, went / Sounds, What do, recommend / recommend the noodle soup / think we should

Listen and Talk C

Are you ready / What do you recommend / recommend, sandwich, the most popular / recommend something else / about / don't you, with, get, discount

Do It Yourself A

What's / one / What do you recommend / fried / sounds delicious / health, better, don't you try / will

시험대비 기본평가   p.68

01 ⑤   02 ②   03 ④
04 (C) → (B) → (A)

01 상대방에게 매일 아침을 먹으라고 충고하는 표현으로 매일 아침을 먹으라고 권유하는 문장인 Why don't you eat breakfast every day?로 바꿔 쓸 수 있다.

02 단것을 너무 많이 먹는다는 상대에게 과일을 대신 먹으라는 충고를 할 수 있다. fruit: 과일 instead: 대신에

03 처음 와서 어떻게 주문할지 모르는 상황에서 추천을 요청하고 있다. 이에 대한 대답으로 피자와 샐러드를 추천해 준다. recommend: 추천하다

04 have a cold: 감기에 걸리다 recommend: 추천하다 You'd better 동사원형 ~: 너는 ~하는 편이 좋겠다 green tea: 녹차

시험대비 실력평가   p.69~70

01 ④   02 ②   03 ⑤
04 exercising every day   05 ③   06 ①
07 ①   08 vegetable(s)   09 ④
10 you had better drink milk   11 ④
12 ③   13 ③   14 ④

01 남자아이가 아침 식사를 안 한다는 말에, 아침 식사를 하는 게 좋겠다고 얘기하는 것이 어울리므로 ④가 적절하다.

02 ① 행복한 ② 피곤한 ③ 화난 ④ 흥미로운 ⑤ 신난 / 다음 문장에서 잠을 잘 못 잤느냐고 질문하는 것으로 보아, 피곤해 보인다고 말하는 것이 어울린다.

03 ① 그래서 ② ~ 때문에 ③ 그리고 ④ ~ 때문에, ~한 이후로 ⑤ 하지만 / 잠을 잘 잤다는 내용과 나는 아침에 자주 피곤하다는 것을 연결하기 위해서는 But(하지만)이 어울린다.

04 (C)의 that은 앞 문장의 매일 운동하는 것을 가리킨다. exercise: 운동하다 every day: 매일

05 남자아이의 대답인 '나는 샌드위치를 만들 것이다.'로 미래의 계획에 대해 이야기하고 있으므로 be going to 동사원형을 이용한 질문을 할 수 있다. be going to 동사원형: ~할 것이다. ~할 예정이다

06 put A in B: A를 B 안에 넣다

07 ⓐ, ⓑ, ⓒ는 샌드위치 ⓓ, ⓔ는 양파와 당근을 가리킨다.

08 vegetable: 야채 / 예를 들어 양배추, 당근 또는 완두콩 같은 날 것으로 먹거나 요리해 먹는 식물

09 ④ 집에 일찍 가서 쉬라고 충고해 주는 말에 너는 괜찮을 거라는 말은 어색하다. ① You'd better+동사원형 ~: ~하는 게 좋겠다 go to bed early: 일찍 잠자리에 들다 ② I think you should ~: 나는 네가 ~해야 한다고 생각한다. ③ What kind of ~: 무슨 종류의 ~ ④ Why don't you ~?: 네가 ~하는 건 어때? ⑤ recommendation: 추천

10 You'd better + 동사원형 ~: ~하는 게 좋겠다 drink: 마시다

11 한 번도 Chang's 식당을 가 본 적이 없는데 음식과 가격이 좋았다고 말하는 것은 어색하다.

12 right now: 바로 지금 ① (형) 정확한 ② (명) 권리 ③ (부) 바로 ④ (형) 올바른, 옳은 ⑤ (명) 오른쪽

13 Why don't you ~?(~하는 게 어때?)는 충고하는 표현이다.

14 ④ Chang's 식당에 대한 위치는 언급되어 있지 않다.

01 (C) → (B) → (A) → (D)
02 (B) → (C) → (A)
03 ③ Yes, I do → No, I don't.
04 suggestions
05 you should also exercise every day
06 (A) What   (B) When   (C) Why
07 for
08 ⓒ Bella's Restaurant ⓓ to Chang's Restaurant

02 무엇을 만들지 묻는 질문에 (B) 샌드위치를 만들 것이라고 대답한다. (C) 이어서, 샌드위치 안에 무엇을 넣을지 묻는 질문

(A) 닭고기, 치즈, 달걀을 넣을 거라고 대답한다.

03 여자아이가 아침 식사를 하는 편이 좋겠다고 충고하고 있으므로, 남자아이는 아침식사를 하지 않는 것을 알 수 있다.

04 suggestion: 제안

05 should + 동사원형: ~해야 한다 also: 또한 exercise: 운동하다 every day: 매일

06 (A) 지금 무엇을 하는지 질문하고 있다. (B) 다음 주 금요일이 대답이므로, 시간의 정보에 관해서 묻고 있다. (C) Why don't you ~?: ~하는 건 어때?

07 search for: ~을 찾다 for: ~를 위해

08 ⓒ는 Bella 식당을 의미하고, ⓓ는 Chang 식당을 의미한다.

1 (1) who[that]   (2) which[that]
2 (1) always   (2) often   (3) never

01 ①
02 (1) who → which[that]   (2) which → who[that]
   (3) helps sometimes → sometimes helps
   (4) always will → will always
03 ⑤
04 (1) a man who has a dream
   (2) often go for a walk

01 선행사가 the person으로 사람이며 came의 주어 역할을 할 수 있는 주격 관계대명사 who나 that이 적절하다.

02 (1) 선행사가 사물이므로 who를 which나 that으로 고쳐야 한다. (2) 선행사가 사람이므로 which를 who나 that으로 고쳐야 한다. (3) 빈도부사는 일반동사 앞에 위치한다. (4) 빈도부사는 조동사나 be동사 뒤에 위치한다.

03 좋아하지 않는다고 했으므로 seldom이 적절하다. seldom: 거의 ~ 않다

04 (1) 선행사가 사람이므로 who를 쓴다. (2) 빈도부사는 일반동사 앞에 위치한다.

01 ④   02 ③   03 ①   04 ②

05 (1) rarely goes   (2) is often   (3) who   (4) which

    (5) that   06 ⑤

07 My mom always gets up early in the morning.

08 ④

09 How often do you help him after school

10 (1) If you hurry up, you can always go to school on time.

    (2) Parents often make great sacrifices for their children.

    (3) This is hardly the place to talk about the problem.

11 ③   12 (1) that   (2) who is

13 (1) Americans usually fly the nest

    (2) It is always so hard to

    (3) I will never do anything

14 (1) A baguette is a type of bread which is popular in France.

    (2) I met the woman who came from England.

    (3) I have a dog that has brown hair.

    (4) There is a house whose windows are broken.

    (5) I like the book that Mom bought for me.

15 ②   16 ⑤   17 ①   18 ③

19 ④

20 (1) Are you the person who dropped this?

    (2) We have to break the bad habits which can cause serious problems.

    (3) She always uses my phone without asking.

01 선행사가 사물이므로 which나 that이 적절하다.

02 ③ 빈도부사는 일반동사 앞에, 조동사 뒤에 위치한다.

03 모두 주격이나 목적격으로 사용된 관계대명사 that이 들어갈 수 있지만 ①번은 소유격 관계대명사 whose가 들어가야 한다.

04 빈도부사는 조동사나 be동사 다음에 위치한다.

05 (1), (2) 빈도부사는 일반동사 앞에, be동사나 조동사 뒤에 위치한다. (3), (4), (5) 선행사가 사람이면 who나 that을 쓰고 선행사가 사물이나 동물이면 which나 that을 쓴다.

06 관계대명사의 선행사가 사람이면 who, whom이나 that을 쓰고, 사물이면 which나 that을 쓴다.

07 빈도부사는 일반동사 앞에 위치한다.

08 선행사가 사람이므로 who나 that을 이용하고 주격이므로 관계대명사 뒤에 주어로 쓰인 she는 쓰지 말아야 한다.

09 가끔 도와준다고 했으므로 often을 이용하면 얼마나 자주 돕는지 물어야 한다.

10 빈도부사는 일반동사 앞, 조동사나 be동사 뒤에 위치한다.

11 ③번은 접속사이지만 나머지는 모두 관계대명사이다.

12 목적격 관계대명사와 '주격 관계대명사+be동사'는 생략할 수 있다.

13 빈도부사는 일반동사 앞에, 조동사나 be동사 다음에 위치한다.

14 관계대명사는 공통으로 쓰이는 (대)명사와 접속사의 역할을 한다. 선행사인 (대)명사가 주어이면 주격, 목적어이면 목적격, 소유격이면 소유격 관계대명사를 쓴다.

15 빈도부사는 일반동사 앞에, 조동사나 be동사 다음에 위치한다. 조동사 used to의 경우, 보통 빈도부사가 그 앞에 위치한다.

16 선행사가 사물이므로 which나 that을 쓰고, 관계대명사는 접속사와 대명사 역할을 하므로 주어나 목적어로 쓰인 it이 없어야 한다.

17 책 읽는 것을 좋아한다고 했으므로 ①번이 어울린다.

18 선행사가 사람이면 who나 that을 쓰고 선행사가 사물이나 동물이면 which나 that을 쓴다.

19 frequent는 형용사이며, 빈도를 나타내는 부사는 frequently이다.

20 (1), (2) 선행사가 사람이면 who나 that을 쓰고 선행사가 사물이나 동물이면 which나 that을 쓴다. (3) 빈도부사는 일반동사 앞에 위치한다.

01 (1) The girl is eating rice noodle soup.

    (2) It is made in Korea.

    (3) Emily bought a new computer.

    (4) They were dancing.

02 (1) Amy never studied math last week.

    (2) Don often studied math last week.

    (3) Ann sometimes studied math last week.

03 (1) The girl who is wearing a red skirt is my daughter.

    (2) Jenny has a brother who plays the violin well.

    (3) A cheetah is an animal that can run fast.

    (4) Bill always gets up late on Sundays.

    (5) Cindy is often busy at the end of the month.

04 (1) reading / who[that] is reading   (2) sleeping / which[that] is sleeping

05 is never late / always sends text messages / usually uses the Internet

06 (1) whom[who]   (2) that   (3) with whom   (4) I spent my vacation with

07 I can hardly wait to see you.

08 has two sons who became doctors

09 (1) On a hot day, sunlight is usually enough to melt chocolate.

    (2) He always wears very clean clothes.

(3) I can never find a parking space downtown.

10 which[that] mean long life

11 (1) It is a TV show which[that] is always popular.

(2) The painting shows a couple who[that] are dancing.

(3) I took the train that had a restaurant.

(4) I am never late for school.

01 주격 관계대명사는 선행사가 사람이면 who나 that, 사물이나 동물이면 which나 that을 쓰고 관계대명사절에서 주어 역할을 하며 다음에 동사가 나온다.

02 빈도부사(frequency adverb)를 사용하여 답한다.

03 빈도부사는 일반동사 앞에, 조동사나 be동사 다음에 위치한다.

04 '주격 관계대명사+be동사'는 생략 가능하다.

05 빈도부사는 조동사나 be동사 다음에, 일반동사 앞에 위치한다.

06 선행사가 사람이므로 whom[who]이나 that을 쓴다. 관계대명사가 전치사의 목적격일 경우 전치사를 관계대명사 앞으로 옮길 수 있으나 관계대명사 that은 전치사 다음에 쓸 수 없다. 목적격 관계대명사는 생략 가능하다.

07 빈도부사는 조동사 다음에 위치한다. hard: 열심히, 몹시 hardly: 거의 ~ 않는

08 선행사가 사람이고 주어로 쓰여야 하므로 주격 관계대명사 who를 써서 문장을 완성한다.

09 빈도부사는 일반동사 앞에, 조동사나 be동사 다음에 위치한다.

10 선행사가 사물이므로 which나 that을 쓴다..

11 (1), (2), (3) 선행사가 사람이면 who나 that이 적절하고 선행사가 사물이면 which나 that이 적절하다. (4) 빈도부사는 be동사 다음에 위치한다.

Reading

확인문제 p.80

1 F 2 T 3 F 4 T

확인문제 p.80

1 T 2 F 3 T 4 F

확인문제 p.81

1 T 2 F 3 T 4 F

확인문제 p.81

1 T 2 F 3 F 4 T 5 F 6 T

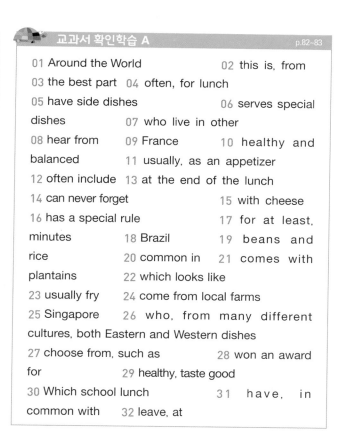

교과서 확인학습 A p.82~83

01 Around the World   02 this is, from

03 the best part 04 often, for lunch

05 have side dishes   06 serves special dishes   07 who live in other

08 hear from 09 France 10 healthy and balanced 11 usually, as an appetizer

12 often include 13 at the end of the lunch

14 can never forget 15 with cheese

16 has a special rule 17 for at least, minutes 18 Brazil 19 beans and rice 20 common in 21 comes with plantains 22 which looks like

23 usually fry 24 come from local farms

25 Singapore 26 who, from many different cultures, both Eastern and Western dishes

27 choose from, such as 28 won an award for 29 healthy, taste good

30 Which school lunch 31 have, in common with 32 leave, at

교과서 확인학습 B p.84~85

1 School Lunches Around the World

2 Hello, this is food reporter Minjun from Korea.

3 For many students, lunch is the best part of the school day.

4 In Korea, we often eat rice and soup for lunch.

5 We also have side dishes, such as *Bulgogi* or *Gimchi*.

6 Sometimes our school serves special dishes, such as pizza, *Bibimbap*, or pasta.

7 What do students who live in other countries eat for lunch?

8 Let's hear from our food reporters!

9 Belle, France

10 Our school serves healthy and balanced meals.

11 We usually eat a salad as an appetizer.

12 Main dishes often include meat or fish.

13 We also eat fresh fruit at the end of the lunch.

14 Oh, I can never forget about baguettes!

15 They're great with cheese.

16 Our school also has a special rule.

17 We must stay at the lunch table for at least 30 minutes.

18 Bruno, Brazil

19 Usually, we have beans and rice for lunch.

20 Meat and vegetables are common in our side dishes.

21 My favorite lunch comes with plantains.

22 A plantain is a fruit which looks like a banana.

23 We usually fry plantains.

24 Our school lunches are fresh because the vegetables and fruit come from local farms.

25 Nicole, Singapore

26 People who live in Singapore come from many different cultures, so we have both Eastern and Western dishes at lunch.

27 Students can choose from many dishes, such as curry, noodle soup, or pasta, each day.

28 My school won an award for healthy school food last year.

29 Our lunches are always healthy, and they taste good, too!

30 Which school lunch do you want to try?

31 Does it have anything in common with your school lunch?

32 Please leave your comments at www. chopchoplunch.com.

시험대비 실력평가 p.86~91

01 ②, ④ 02 ② 03 ⑤ 04 ①
05 ⑤ 06 They usually have beans and rice.
07 ④ 08 학생들은 적어도 30분간 점심 식탁에
반드시 머물러야 한다. 09 ④
10 1. 점심에 동양식과 서양식을 모두 먹는다.
   2. 점심이 항상 건강에 좋고 맛 또한 좋다.
11 like 12 ④ 13 ③ 14 ①, ④
15 (A) balanced (B) include (C) at least
16 baguettes 17 ②
18 (A) beans and rice (B) meat and vegetables
19 (A) a banana (B) fry 20 ②, ⑤
21 여러분이 먹어 보고 싶은 학교 급식
22 in common 23 ④ 24 that
25 The girl who is wearing glasses is eating rice noodle soup. 26 happily → happy
27 A: 한국, 이유: 김치를 아주 좋아하기 때문에.
   B: 프랑스, 이유: 바게트와 치즈를 좋아하고, 적어도 30분간 점심 식탁에 머물러야 하는 것이 재미있기 때문에.
   C: 싱가포르, 이유: 급식으로 동양식과 서양식을 모두 선택하는 것이 재미있게 들리기 때문에.
28 ②

01 선행사가 사람(students)이고 주어 자리이므로, 주격 관계대명사 who나 that이 적절하다.

02 위 글은 한국의 학교 급식에 대해 소개하는 글이므로, 제목으로는 ② '한국의 학교 급식'이 가장 적절하다.

03 '가끔' 제공해 준다.

04 ⓐ come with: ~와 함께 나오다, ⓒ come from: ~에서 나오다[비롯되다/생산되다]

05 ⓑ와 ⑤ '~와 같이', 나머지는 모두 '좋아하다'

06 그들은 보통 '콩과 밥'을 먹는다.

07 주어진 문장의 They에 주목한다. ④번 앞 문장의 baguettes를 받고 있으므로 ④번이 적절하다.

08 뒤에 이어지는 내용을 쓰면 된다.

09 싱가포르에 사는 사람들은 매우 다양한 '문화권'에서 오기 때문에, 점심에 동양식과 서양식을 모두 먹는다. ① 의견, ② 목적, ③ 관심사, ④ 문화, ⑤ 믿음

10 1. 싱가포르에 사는 사람들은 매우 다양한 문화권에서 오기 때문에, 점심에 동양식과 서양식을 모두 먹는다. 2. 니콜의 학교는 작년에 건강한 학교 음식 상을 받았다.

11 such as = like: ~와 같은

12 (C)에서 한국에서는 점심으로 자주 밥과 국을 먹는다고 한 다음 (A)에서 also를 사용하여 반찬과 특식을 소개하므로 (C) 다음에 (A)가 이어지고 그 다음에 (B)에서 다른 나라에 사는 학생들은 점심으로 무엇을 먹는지에 대해 음식 취재 기자들에게서 들어보겠다고 하는 것이 적절하므로 (A) 다음에 (B)가 와야 한다. 그러므로 (C)-(A)-(B)의 순서가 적절하다.

13 ⓐ와 ③ 요리, ①과 ⑤ 설거지감[그릇들], ② (요리를 접시에) 담아 주다, ④ 접시들

14 ② 특식, ③ 주요리, ⑤ 특식

15 (A) '균형 잡힌' 식사라고 해야 하므로 balanced가 적절하다. (B) 고기나 생선을 '포함한다'고 해야 하므로 include가 적절하다. exclude: 제외[배제]하다, (C) '적어도' 30분간이라고 해야 하므로 at least가 적절하다. at least: 적어도, at last: 마침내, 드디어

16 '바게트'를 가리킨다.

17 ②는 의문형용사이고, ⓐ와 나머지는 모두 관계대명사이다.

18 (A) 주요리: 콩과 밥, (B) 흔한 곁들임 음식: 고기와 채소

19 플랜테인은 '바나나'처럼 생긴 과일이다. 브라질에서는 보통 플랜테인을 '튀긴다.'

20 ⓐ와 ①, ③, ④는 명사적 용법, ② 형용사적 용법, ⑤ 부사적 용법(목적)

21 앞 문장에서 물어보고 있는 내용을 가리킨다.

22 have something in common with somebody: (특징 등을) 공통적으로 지니다

23 ⓓ have something in common with somebody: (특징 등을) 공통적으로 지니다, ⓔ 전화번호나 이메일 주소를 알려 줄 때

at을 사용한다.

24 ⓐ 주격 관계대명사 which나 that을 쓸 수 있다. ⓑ 주격 관계대명사 who나 that을 쓸 수 있다.

25 'is'를 보충하면 된다.

26 감각동사 look의 보어로 형용사를 쓰는 것이 적절하다.

27 본문을 참조할 것.

28 ⓑ와 ②는 동명사이고, 나머지는 모두 현재분사이다.

서술형 시험대비 p.90~91

01 rice and soup
02 such as 또는 like
03 lives → live
04 dessert
05 during → for
06 must stay at the lunch table for at least 30 minutes
07 (A) like (B) fry (C) local
08 (A) meat, (B) vegetables
09 fried potatoes → plantains
10 people who live in Singapore come from many different cultures
11 good
12 prize
13 Review
14 high → low
15 (A) fresh (B) delicious

01 한국에서는 점심으로 자주 '밥과 국'을 먹는다.

02 such as = like: ~와 같은

03 선행사가 복수(students)이므로, 'live'로 고쳐야 한다.

04 디저트: 식사 끝에 먹는 과일이나 푸딩과 같은 달콤한 것

05 뒤에 숫자가 나오므로 for로 고치는 것이 적절하다. during+기간을 나타내는 명사

06 학생들이 적어도 30분간 점심 식탁에 반드시 머물러야 하는 것이 벨의 학교의 특별한 규칙이다.

07 (A) 바나나'처럼' 생겼다고 해야 하므로 like가 적절하다. look like: ~인 것처럼 보이다, look at: ~을 보다, (B) '튀긴다'라고 해야 하므로 fry가 적절하다. fry: 튀기다, fly: 날다, (C) 채소와 과일이 '현지의' 농장에서 오기 때문에 신선하다고 해야 하므로 local이 적절하다. local: 현지의, global: 세계적인

08 곁들임 음식에 '고기와 채소'가 흔하다고 했다.

09 브루노가 가장 좋아하는 점심에는 '플랜테인'이 나온다.

10 '싱가포르에 사는 사람들은 매우 다양한 문화권에서 오기' 때문에, 점심에 동양식과 서양식을 모두 먹는다.

11 니콜의 학교 급식은 건강에 '좋고' 맛 또한 '좋다'.

12 award = prize: 상

13 위 글은 '음식점 방문 후기'이다. review (책·연극·영화 등에 대한) 논평[비평], 감상문

14 가격이 '싸기' 때문에 추천한다고 해야 하므로, high를 low로 고쳐야 한다. price가 비싸거나 싼 것을 표현할 때는 보통 high나 low를 사용한다.

15 정말 '신선하고' '맛있는' 음식 때문에, 글쓴이는 Antonio's Restaurant를 추천한다.

영역별 핵심문제 p.97~101

01 ② 02 ④ 03 ③ 04 ④
05 ①
06 you'd better drink milk / for your advice
07 It's my first time here / I recommend the pizza
08 ① much → many ② eating → eat 09 ④
10 Do you usually eat breakfast?
11 (B) eat (C) gives 12 ③ 13 ④
14 (A) to (B) about (C) with 15 ④
16 ②, ⑤ 17 ③ 18 ④ 19 ①
20 (1) which(또는 that) sells noodles
   (2) which(또는 that) sells sushi
   (3) which(또는 that) sells pizza
21 (1) are always (2) rarely knew (3) should always
22 ⑤
23 (1) I am looking for the girl who left her cell phone on the bus.
   (2) An elephant is an animal which has a long nose.
   (3) The box which has many books is very heavy.
   (4) Dad always drives his car very carefully.
   (5) You should never leave a baby alone.
24 ⑤ 25 ④ 26 ② 27 ②
28 ④ 29 ② 30 ③ 31 ①, ④
32 ② 33 Our lunches

01 ② sweets: 단 음식, 단것

02 traditional: 전통적인

03 ① choice: 선택, 종류 ② culture: 문화 ③ health: 건강 ④ contest: 대회 ⑤ appetizer: 전채, 식욕을 돋우는 것

04 주어진 대화의 have는 '먹다'의 의미이다. ① have to 동사원형: ~해야 한다 ②, ⑤ 가지다 ③ 당하다 ④ 먹다

05 come from: ~에서 나오다, ~ 출신이다 come with: ~와 함께 나오다, ~이 딸려 있다

06 had better+동사원형: ~하는 게 좋겠다 thank you for ~: ~에 대해 감사하다 advice: 충고

07 first: 처음의 recommend: 추천하다.

08 ① snack은 셀 수 있는 명사로 many의 수식을 받는다.

17

② had better+동사원형: ~하는 게 좋겠다

09 아침을 먹으라는 조언을 한 이유를 듣고 또 다른 조언이 있는지 질문하고 있다.

10 빈도부사는 일반동사의 앞에, be동사나 조동사의 뒤에 위치한다.

11 (B) had better+동사원형: ~하는 게 좋겠다 (C) Breakfast는 3인칭 단수이고 일반적인 사실을 말하므로, 현재형을 써야 하며 동사에 's'를 붙인다.

12 should: ~해야 한다

13 the more popular → the most popular

14 (A) be ready to 동사원형: ~할 준비가 되다 (B) How about ~?: ~은 어때? (C) with: ~와 함께

15 ④ 닭고기 샌드위치가 가장 인기 있는 샌드위치이다.

16 주어진 문장과 ②, ⑤번의 who는 주격 관계대명사이다. ①, ③번은 목적격 관계대명사, ④번은 의문대명사

17 ③ 빈도부사는 조동사 다음에 위치한다.

18 ④ 선행사가 사물이므로 which나 that을 써야 한다.

19 빈도부사는 조동사나 be동사 뒤에, 일반동사 앞에 위치한다.

20 선행사가 restaurant로 사물이므로 which나 that을 쓴다.

21 빈도부사는 일반동사 앞에, 조동사나 be동사 뒤에 위치한다.

22 빈도부사는 일반동사 앞에, 조동사나 be동사 뒤에 위치한다.

23 (1), (2), (3) 선행사가 사람이면 who를 쓰고 선행사가 사물이나 동물이면 which를 쓴다. (4), (5) 빈도부사는 일반동사 앞에, 조동사 다음에 위치한다.

24 주어진 문장은 ⑤번 다음 문장에서 들어보려고 하는 내용에 해당하므로 ⑤번이 적절하다.

25 ⓐ food reporter Minjun from Korea: 한국에서 온 음식 취재 기자 민준, hear from: ~로부터 듣다, ⓑ For many students: 많은 학생들에게, for lunch: 점심으로

26 왜 많은 학생들에게 점심시간이 학교 일과 중 가장 좋은 부분인지는 대답할 수 없다. ① From Korea. ③ Rice and soup. ④ *Bulgogi* or *Gimchi*. ⑤ Pizza, *Bibimbap*, or pasta.

27 ⓐ와 ② [역할·자격·기능·성질 따위를 나타내어] ~으로서(의), ① ~와 같이, ~하는 대로, ③ ~이므로, ~이기 때문에, ④ [보통 as ~ as로 형용사·부사 앞에서] ~와 같은 정도로, ⑤ ~일 때

28 벨의 학교에서 '카레'를 먹는다는 말은 없다.

29 주어진 글에서 주요리에 관해 말했고 이어서 (B)에서 곁들임 음식에 대해 계속 말하고 있으므로 (B)가 제일 먼저 오고, (A)에서 (B)의 마지막에 나오는 플랜테인을 설명하고 있으므로 (B) 다음에 (A)가 이어지고, (C)에서는 앞에서 말한 음식들이 신선한 이유를 설명하고 있으므로 (A) 다음에 (C)가 와야 한다. 그러므로 (B)-(A)-(C)의 순서가 적절하다.

30 ③ 플랜테인은 바나나처럼 생겼고 보통 튀긴다고 했을 뿐이다.

31 선행사가 사물(a fruit)이고 주어 자리이므로, 주격 관계대명사 that이나 which가 적절하다.

32 ⓒ 'each+단수 명사'이므로 → each day, ⓔ 긍정문에서

'역시'는 'too'로 써야 한다. 부정문에서 '역시'라는 뜻일 때는 'either'를 사용한다.

33 '우리의 점심'을 가리킨다.

단원별 예상문제
p.98~101

01 That's good for your health. → That's not good for your health.

02 You'd better eat fruit instead.

03 up　　04 at　　05 ④　　06 ④

07 (1) (f)resh　(2) (d)ifferent　(3) (c)ommon

(4) (i)nclude　　08 ②　　09 ③

10 ⑤　　11 ③　　12 ④　　13 ①, ④

14 ⑤

15 (1) I want to buy a vest which has many pockets.

(2) I met Eva who was listening to music on the bus.

(3) She has a parrot which can speak 100 words.

(4) Math problems are always difficult for me.

16 (1) Dad usually goes to work by bike.

(2) Dorothy is always busy every day.

(3) I can never forget about baguettes.

17 (A) this　(B) What　(C) eat　　　　18 ③

19 (A) lunch　(B) such as　20 ⑤

21 appetizer　22 ③　　23 ⑤

24 the vegetables and fruit come from local farms

25 which → who 또는 that　26 ⓑ Eastern, ⓒ Western

27 ④

01 be good for: ~에 좋다 health: 건강

02 had better + 동사원형: ~하는 게 좋겠다 fruit: 과일 instead: 대신에

03 get up: 일어나다 heat ~ up: ~을 덥히다

04 at least: 적어도, 최소한 at the end of ~: ~의 끝에

05 파엘라(쌀, 닭고기, 생선, 채소를 넣은 스페인 요리)

06 public transportation: 공공 운송[교통] 기관

07 주어진 보기는 반의어의 관계이다. Eastern: 동양의 Western: 서양의 (1) rotten: 상한, 부패한 fresh: 신선한 (2) same: 같은 different: 다른 (3) rare: 희귀한, 드문 common: 흔한 (4) exclude: 배제하다 include: 포함하다

08 엄마의 생일이 다가오는데 돈이 없어서 직접 선물을 만들라고 추천하는 것이 어울리므로, enough를 no로 바꿔야 적절하다.

09 점심 먹고 대개 복통이 있다는 말에, 천천히 먹으라는 충고를 할 수 있다.

10 여자아이가 샌드위치에 채소(양파와 당근)를 넣으라고 충고하고, 그 의견을 받아들이는 것이 마지막 문장(You're right.)이므로, 그 뒤에 주어진 문장이 나와야 적절하다 go shopping: 쇼핑하러 가다 grocery: 식료품

11 여기서 them은 샌드위치이며, 질문은 샌드위치에 무엇을 넣는지 질문하고 있으므로 put in them이 적절하다. put A in B: A를 B에 넣다

12 ④ 양파와 당근을 첨가하지 않을 것이라는 말 뒤에 그 야채를 좋아한다는 말이 나오는 것은 어색하다. I don't like those vegetables.로 바꿔야 적절하다.

13 선행사가 사람이고 주격이므로 who나 that을 써야 한다.

14 빈도부사는 일반동사 앞에, 조동사나 be동사 다음에 위치한다.

15 (1)~(3) 선행사가 사람이면 who를, 사물이나 동물이면 which를 쓴다. (4) 빈도부사는 일반동사 앞에, 조동사나 be동사 다음에 위치한다.

16 빈도부사는 일반동사 앞에, 조동사나 be동사 다음에 위치한다.

17 (A) 자신을 소개할 때 this is가 적절하다. (B) eat의 목적어를 써야 하므로 What이 적절하다. (C) 조동사 do 다음에 본동사 eat이 적절하다.

18 ⓐ와 ⓔ은 관계대명사이고, 나머지는 모두 의문대명사이다.

19 민준이는 주요리, 반찬 그리고 특식과 '같은' 한국의 학교 '점심'에 대해 소개한다.

20 (C)에서 식전 음식에 대해 설명하고 있으므로 제일 먼저 오고 (B)에서 후식에 대한 설명이 이어지므로 (C) 다음에 (B)가 이어지고 (A)의 They가 (B)의 마지막에 나오는 바게트를 가리키므로 (B) 다음에 (A)가 와야 한다. 그러므로 (C)-(B)-(A)의 순서가 적절하다.

21 appetizer: 식전 음식, 적은 양의 음식으로 된 식사의 첫 번째 코스

22 'ⓑ with cheese: 치즈와 함께 먹으면, ⓒ for+숫자: ~ 동안

23 왜 사람들이 대개 플랜테인을 튀기는지는 알 수 없다. ① Beans and rice. ② Meat and vegetables. ③ With plantains. ④ A fruit which looks like a banana.

24 '채소와 과일이 현지 농장에서 오기 때문에' 브루노의 학교 점심이 신선하다.

25 선행사가 사람(People)이고 주어 자리이므로, which를 주격 관계대명사 who나 that으로 고쳐야 한다.

26 각각 형용사로 고치면 된다.

27 ④ '작년에' 수상했다.

🦉 서술형 실전문제
p.102~103

01 ① No, I didn't. → Yes, I did.

02 breakfast

03 often feels tired, the boy should, also exercise every day

04 (1) I think Minhee is a girl who[that] is always kind.
   (2) Teresa who[that] is singing on the stage has a beautiful voice.

(3) Cloe lives in a house which[that] has a nice swimming pool.

(4) I like the dog which[that] belongs to Kelly.

(5) There were a man and his horse that were crossing the river.

05 (1) The man who[that] works at this restaurant is serving food.

(2) These are the poems which[that] were written by Robert Frost.

(3) The girl who[that] wears a white dress is very pretty.

06 Lunch

07 We also have side dishes, such as *Bulgogi* or *Gimchi*. 또는 We have side dishes, such as *Bulgogi* or *Gimchi*, too.

08 another → other

09 (A) special rule   (B) for at least 30 minutes

10 (A) a salad   (B) meat or fish   (C) fresh fruit

11 with cheese

01 But이 있으므로, 잠을 잘 잤음에도 피곤하다는 의미가 들어가야 어울리므로, 'Yes, I did.'로 고치는 게 적절하다.

02 아침에 먹는 식사 / breakfast: 아침식사

03 often: 종종, 자주 tired: 피곤한 should 동사원형: ~해야 한다 exercise: 운동하다 every day: 매일

04 (1), (2) 선행사가 사람이므로 관계대명사 who나 that을 써야 한다. (3), (4) 선행사가 사물이나 동물이므로 관계대명사 which나 that을 써야 한다. (5) 선행사가 '사람+동물'이므로 관계대명사 that을 써야 한다.

05 (1) 선행사가 사람이므로 that이나 who가 적절하다. (2) 선행사가 사물이므로 that이나 which를 쓴다. 또한 관계대명사절에서 그 수는 선행사에 일치시키므로 poems에 맞추어 were가 되어야 한다. (3) who를 목적격 whom 대신 쓸 수 있지만 whom을 who 대신 쓰지는 않는다.

06 많은 학생들에게 '점심시간'이 학교 일과 중 가장 좋은 부분이다.

07 also를 동사 앞에 또는 too를 문장 끝에 보충하면 된다.

08 '다른 나라들'에서 사는 학생들이라고 해야 하므로 other countries라고 하는 것이 적절하다. another+단수 명사

09 벨의 학교의 '특별한 규칙'은 학생들이 '적어도 30분간' 점심 식탁에 있어야 한다는 것이다.

10 식전 음식: 샐러드, 주요리: 고기나 생선, 후식: 신선한 과일

11 바게트는 '치즈와 함께 먹으면' 맛이 아주 좋다.

|모범답안|

01 B: You had better write her a letter.
   B: I think you also should give a little present to your friend with words of apology.

02 (1) a smart phone which my dad bought for me
  (2) a computer which is very nice
  (3) some pictures which were taken when I visited my grandmother's
  (4) some comic books which are very interesting

03 (A) Spanish   (B) Mixed paella
  (C) fresh, delicious (D) low

01 in   02 for

03 (l)ocal / (r)ecommend / (m)ixed
  (1) mixed (2) local (3) recommend

04 (1) check (2) such (3) take (4) tasted

05 (1) I get often colds these days. → I often get colds these days.
  (2) a lot → a lot of/lots of/much
  (3) washed → wash

06 (1) Which food do you recommend?
  (2) Do you have any recommendations?

07 (A) What are you doing right now?
  (B) When is the party?
  (C) Why don't you check out Chang's Restaurant?
  (D) What do you recommend there?

08 ⑤   09 I think we should go there.

10 ②   11 ⑤   12 order

13 Could you recommend something else?

14 ④   15 ⑤   16 ③   17 ②, ④

18 (1) Mom usually gets up at 7 in the morning.
  (2) Abigail is always kind and frequently smiles.
  (3) Richard seldom went swimming in the river.

19 (1) who → which[that]
  (2) which he → who[that]
  (3) helps never → never helps   20 ③

21 ④   22 ②   23 ②

24 because of → because   25 fry

26 curry, noodle soup, or pasta   27 ①

01 live in: ~에서 살다 put A in B: A를 B에 넣다

02 for+기간: ~ 동안 for a long time: 오랫동안 be good for: ~에 좋다 thanks for ~: ~에 대해 감사하다

03 (1) mixed: 섞인, 복합된 / 식초가 섞인 와인이 좋았다. (2) local: 현지의, 지역의 / 우리는 지역 시장을 방문했고, 예쁜 귀걸이를 보았다. (3) recommend: 추천하다 / 그 여자를 위해 무엇을 추천합니까?

04 (1) check out: 확인하다, 조사하다 (2) such as: ~와 같은 (3) take care of: ~을 돌보다 (4) taste+형용사: ~한 맛이 나다

05 (1) 빈도부사는 일반동사의 앞에, be동사와 조동사의 뒤에 위치한다. (2) a lot of: 많은 (3) drink와 wash는 and로 연결된 병렬구조이다.

06 추천하는 표현으로 What do you recommend?, Which 명사 do you recommend?, Do you have any recommendations? 등이 있다.

07 (A) be동사의 현재형+동사ing: ~하고 있다 What are you doing right now?: 너 지금 뭐 하고 있니? (B) when: 언제 (C) check out: 확인하다, 조사하다 (D) recommend: 추천하다

08 The food and prices가 주어로 복수형이기 때문에 was를 were로 바꾸어야 한다.

09 I think 주어 should 동사원형: 나는 ~가 …해야 한다고 생각한다.

10 추천을 요청하는 말에, 닭고기 샌드위치가 가장 인기 있다고 대답했다. ② 뒤의 문장 It이 the chicken sandwich를 받는 대명사이다.

11 ① 병원 ② 학교 ③ 집 ④ 빵집 ⑤ 식당

12 order: 주문하다

13 Could you recommend something else? = What else do you recommend?: 다른 제안해 줄 것 있니? -thing으로 끝나는 말(something, anything, nothing 등)은 보통의 다른 명사들과 달리 형용사가 뒤에서 수식한다.

14 get a discount: 할인받다

15 선행사가 사물일 경우 주격 관계대명사는 that이나 which를 쓴다.

16 ③ 빈도부사는 일반동사 앞에, be동사나 조동사 다음에 위치한다.

17 ①, ③, ⑤는 접속사로 쓰인 that이고, ②와 ④는 관계대명사이다.

18 빈도부사는 일반동사 앞에, be동사나 조동사 다음에 위치한다.

19 (1) 선행사가 사물이므로 who를 which나 that으로 고쳐야 한다. (2) 선행사가 사람이므로 which를 who나 that으로 고쳐야 하며 관계대명사가 접속사와 대명사의 역할을 하므로 주어로 쓰인 he를 삭제해야 한다. (3) 빈도부사는 일반동사 앞에 위치한다.

20 위 글은 한국의 급식에 대해 소개하는 글인데, '전 세계에 많은

맛있는 반찬들이 있다'는 ③번 문장은 전체 글의 흐름에서 벗어
난다.

21 특식을 '제공한다'고 해야 하므로 'serves'가 적절하다.
serve: (음식을) 제공하다, (음식을 상에) 차려 주다

22 다른 나라에서 사는 학생들은 점심으로 무엇을 먹는지 음식 취
재 기자들에게서 들어보겠다고 했기 때문에, 뒤에 올 내용으로
는 ②번이 적절하다.

23 주어진 문장의 plantains에 주목한다. ②번 다음 문장에서 플랜
테인에 대한 설명을 하고 있으므로 ②번이 적절하다.

24 because of 뒤에는 '주어+동사'가 올 수 없고, because 뒤에
'주어+동사'가 올 수 있다.

25 플랜테인을 보통 '튀긴다'고 했다.

26 카레, 국수, 혹은 파스타가 ⓐ에 해당한다.

27 ⓑ choose from: ~로부터 선택하다, ⓒ an award for: ~에
대한 상

Lesson
3

Understand the World

시험대비 실력평가   p.112

01 ⑤   02 ①   03 ②   04 ③
05 ①
06 (1) scary   (2) international   (3) traditional
07 (1) Tony got lost in the darkness.
   (2) The girls are having a pillow fight.   08 ④

01 last: 계속되다, 지속되다

02 greet: 맞이하다, 환영하다 welcome: 환영하다

03 represent: 나타내다, 상징하다 wreath: 화환, 화관

04 ③ try -ing: (시험삼아) ~해 보다 pray: 기도하다 ease: 편안
하게 하다 ④ meditation: 명상

05 lock: 자물쇠; 잠그다

06 (1) scary: 무서운, 두려운, 겁나는/그녀는 내게 무서운 이야기
들을 해 주었다. (2) international: 국제적인, 세계적인/수출
법규가 국제 통상에서 중요한 요인이 되었다. (3) traditional:
전통의, 전통적인/그녀는 한국 전통 의상을 입고 있다.

07 (1) darkness: 어둠, 암흑 (2) pillow: 베개

08 toward: ~ 쪽으로

서술형 시험대비   p.113

01 (1) (r)ude   (2) (t)ry   (3) (e)vil   (4) (v)ictory
02 (1) experience   (2) mean   (3) arrive   (4) celebrate
03 (1) face   (2) separation, able
04 colored
05 (1) at   (2) of
06 (1) She greeted us with a kind smile.
   (2) The meeting lasted three hours.
   (3) I put the coin in her palm.
   (4) A red flag represents danger.

01 보기는 동의어 관계이다. good: 좋은 nice: 좋은 (1) impolite:
버릇없는, 무례한 rude: 무례한 (2) attempt: 시도하다 try: 한
번 해 보다 (3) wicked: 못된, 사악한 evil: 사악한, 악마의 (4)
success: 성공, 성과 victory: 승리, 성공

02 (1) experience: 경험하다/호기심을 지키는 것은 내가 지속적

21

으로 새로운 것을 배우는 즐거움을 경험하도록 할 것이다. (2) mean: 의미하다/그것이 내가 게으르다는 것을 의미하는 것은 아니다. (3) arrive: 도착하다/다음 기차는 언제 도착하나요? (4) celebrate: 축하하다/그들은 크리스마스와 새해를 같이 축하한다.

03 (1) face: ~을 향하다 (2) separation: 분리, 이별 be able to 동사원형: ~할 수 있다

04 color: ~에 색칠하다 colored: 채색된, 색깔이 있는

05 (1) stay at: ~에서 머무르다 point at: ~을 가리키다 (2) be afraid of: ~을 두려워하다 remind A of B: A에게 B를 생각나게 하다

06 (1) greet: 맞이하다, 환영하다 (2) last: 계속되다, 지속되다 (3) palm: 손바닥 (4) represent: 나타내다, 상징하다

교과서
Conversation

p.114~115
핵심 Check

1 (C) → (A) → (B)　2 explain what, means

3 I'd like to know what that means.
　It means you should think carefully

4 Have you watched / have, Have

5 (C) → (A) → (D) → (B)

6 Have you had *gimchi* before?

교과서 대화문 익히기

Check(√) True or False
p.116

(1) T　(2) T　(3) F　(4) T

교과서 확인학습
p.118~119

Listen & Talk 1 A
Have you, been / haven't, Have / have, last year, was / sounds, to go, someday

Listen & Talk 1 B
to, Festival, many different traditional games / looks, Which, should / Have you ever / No, I haven't / from / How / on, throw, at / sounds fun

Listen & Talk 1 C
There is, in, this / a traditional Indian festival, colored powder, each / sounds exciting. Have you ever been / told me / When / on, on / like, Should / clothes, the colored powder, clothes / for

Listen and Talk 2 A
gave me, What does that mean in Korea / means

Listen and Talk 2 B
this, isn't it / about buying, one / something bad / What does, mean in China / means separation, separation / about

Listen and Talk 2 C
What a, Are / took / look at, rude / who is making, palm is facing toward / meaning in / What does that mean / victory or peace

Do It Yourself
brings / to / means / Have you ever been to / I haven't, What does / means

시험대비 기본평가
p.120

01 ①　　02 ②　　03 ③　　04 ④
05 ①

01 경험 유무를 물을 때 "Have you (ever) 과거분사 ~?"로 말한다.

02 mean: 의미하다 in Korea: 한국에서

03 'Have you 과거분사 ~?'는 경험을 묻는 표현이다.

04 (C) 고로드키 게임을 해 봤는지 묻자, (A) 안 해봤다고 대답하고 무엇인지 질문한다. (B) 상대방은 고로드키 게임이 러시아 전통 게임이라고 설명해 준다.

05 'have been to 장소'는 '~에 가 본 경험이 있다'의 의미이고, 'have gone to 장소'는 '~에 갔다(그래서 지금 없다)'는 의미이므로 gone을 been으로 바꿔야 적절하다.

시험대비 실력평가
p.121~122

01 ③　　02 ②　　03 ②　　04 What does an umbrella mean in China?　　05 ②
06 ②, ④　　07 (A) What is that?　(B) Have you ever been to a Holi festival?　(C) When is the festival?　(D) Should I bring anything?　　08 ④　　09 ③
10 exciting　　11 ①　　12 a traditional game from, play, putting five sticks, throwing a bat

01 (A) give+me(간접목적어)+Yeot(직접목적어): 나에게 엿을 주다 (B) What does that mean (in Korea)?: (한국에서는) 이게 어떤 의미니? mean: 의미하다

02 브라질에 가 본 경험을 묻는 질문에, (B) 없다고 대답하며 상대 방의 경험을 묻고 (A) 작년에 갔었는데 삼바 축제가 있었다고 답하자 (C) 삼바 축제에 흥미를 가지며 가고 싶다고 말한다.

03 'What about you?'는 상대방의 생각이나 의견을 묻는 표현이 다. 여자아이는 상대방의 질문에 답하면서 상대방은 무엇을 살 지 'What about you?'로 물어보고 있다.

04 What does ~ mean?: ~이 어떤 의미니?

05 ⓓ bad something → something bad, -thing으로 끝나는 부정대명사(something, anything, nothing 등)는 형용사가 뒤에서 수식한다. ⓔ sounds → sound, 주어가 the words로 복수 명사이므로 동사에 s를 붙이지 않는다.

06 ① 여자아이는 책을 Ling의 선물로 살 것이다. ② 중국에서 책의 의미는 대화에서 나와 있지 않다. ③ 이번 주 수요일이 Ling 의 생일이다. ④ 초콜릿을 사러 갈 장소는 나와 있지 않다. ⑤ 중국인에게 우산은 이별을 의미하므로, 좋은 선물이 아니다.

07 (A) 다음에 Holi festival에 대해 설명하고 있다. (B) 다음에 'No, I haven't.'라고 답하고 있다. (C) 다음에 언제인지 답하고 있다. (D) 다음에 하얀 옷을 입어야 한다고 답하고 있다.

08 ④ 색깔이 있는 옷이 아니라 하얀 옷을 입어야 한다.

09 상대방의 경험에 대해 물어볼 때는, 현재완료 시제를 사용하여 'Have you 과거분사 ~?'라고 묻는다. 경험을 묻는 말에 'Yes, I have.'나 'No, I haven't.'로 대답할 수 있다.

10 exciting: 흥미로운

11 ⓑ~ⓔ는 gorodki를 가리키지만 ⓐ는 여러 가지 전통적인 게임을 하는 것을 가리킨다.

12 traditional: 전통적인 from: (출처·기원) … 출신의[에서 온] the way to 동사원형: ~하는 방법 throw: ~을 던지다 at: (방향) ~으로

서술형 시험대비 p.123

01 His palm is facing toward himself.
02 meaning
03 ③ which → who
04 showing your palm and making a V sign
05 What
06 getting her hair cut on a Tuesday
07 It means bad luck.
08 Have you ever been to Brazil?

01 palm: 손바닥 face: ~을 향하다 toward: ~쪽으로

02 mean: 의미하다 meaning: 의미

03 사람(The boy)이 선행사이므로 주격 관계대명사 who를 사용해야 한다. The boy who is making the V sign: V사인을 하고 있는 소년

04 (C)가 가리키는 것은 여자아이가 말한 손바닥을 보여 주면서 V 사인을 만드는 것을 의미한다..

05 What do you see in this picture?: 이 그림에서 무엇이 보이니? What does that mean?: 이게 어떤 의미니?

06 get+목적어+목적격보어(p.p): 목적어가 ~되도록 시키다 on+ 요일: ~요일에

07 mean: 의미하다 bad luck: 불운

08 Have you ever been to 장소?: ~에 가 본 적 있니? Brazil: 브라질

교과서
Grammar

핵심 Check p.124~125

1 (1) have gone   (2) have, visited   (3) Have, read
2 (1) so busy that   (2) so big that

시험대비 기본평가 p.126

01 (1) visit → visited   (2) has finished → finished
(3) Do you have → Have you   (4) what → that
(5) very → so   (6) for → since   (7) have → has
02 ③   **03** ①

01 (1) 현재완료는 'have[has]+과거분사'의 형태이다. (2) 현재완료는 과거를 나타내는 어구와 함께 쓸 수 없다. (3) 현재완료의 의문문은 have 동사를 주어 앞으로 보낸다. (4), (5) 'so+형용사[부사]+that+주어+동사'의 형태로 '매우 …해서 ~하다'는 의미를 나타낸다. (6) 현재완료에서 'since+시간 명사', 'for+기간 명사'를 쓴다. (7) 주어가 3인칭 단수이므로 has를 써야 한다.

02 ③ Joel has worked for 6 hours straight.

03 so ... that ~: 너무 …해서 ~하다

시험대비 실력평가 p.131~133

01 ④	02 ①	03 ⑤	04 ③

05 (1) visited   (2) has   (3) gone   (4) before   (5) hasn't
06 ①   07 ⑤   08 (1) so   (2) that

23

(3) such　(4) couldn't　　09 ④　　　　10 ②

11 ②

12 (1) Julia got too angry to speak.

(2) Sean is rich enough to buy the expensive car.

(3) The panda is too cute for me to take my eyes off him.

(4) The house was nice enough for Melanie to want to live there.

13 ④　　　　14 ④

15 (1) Suyeon has just arrived at Busan Station. 또는 Suyeon arrived at Busan Station an hour ago.

(2) Ron and his sisters have gone to England.

(3) Grace was too fat to wear the beautiful dress. Grace was so fat that she couldn't wear the beautiful dress.

(4) The drama was so boring that I turned off the TV.

(5) He has lived in Busan since 2010.

16 ⓐ visited ⓑ been

17 (1) for → since　(2) gone → been　(3) too → so

(4) poor enough → so poor　(5) has lost → lost

18 ②

01 현재완료 의문문은 'Have+주어+과거분사~?'이다. 'have gone to ~'는 '~에 가버리고 없다'는 뜻이므로 1인칭 주어를 쓸 수 없다.

02 '…해서 ~하다'의 의미인 'so ... that ~' 구문이다.

03 현재완료형의 질문에 대한 답은 have[has] 동사를 이용해 답한다.

04 so ... that ~은 '너무[매우] ~해서 …하다'의 의미로 원인과 결과를 나타낸다.

05 (1) 현재완료는 'have[has]+과거분사'의 형태이다. (2) 주어가 3인칭 단수이므로 has가 적절하다. (3) have[has] gone to는 '~에 가고 없다'는 결과를 나타낸다. (4) ago는 단독으로 쓸 수 없다. (5) 현재완료의 부정형은 'have[has] not+과거분사'이다.

06 ① Dad's explanation was so clear that we could understand it easily.

07 현재완료의 부정은 have 다음에 not이나 never를 붙인다.

08 (1), (2) '매우 …해서 ~하다'의 의미인 'so ... that ~' 구문이다. (3) 'so ... that' 구문에서 that 앞에 형용사나 부사 대신 명사가 오면 so 대신 such를 쓴다. (4) so+형용사/부사+that+주어+couldn't+동사원형: 너무 ~하여 …할 수 없었다

09 현재완료에서 'since+시간 명사', 'for+기간 명사'

10 'so ... that ~'은 so 뒤의 형용사나 부사가 원인을 나타내며, 접속사 that 뒤에는 그에 따른 결과를 나타낸다.

11 ②번은 경험 용법으로 쓰였고 나머지는 다 완료 용법으로 쓰였

다.

12 (1) so ... that 주어 can't ~ = too ... to ~ (2) so ... that 주어 can ~ = = ... enough to ~ (3), (4) 'so ... that ~' 구문에서 주어가 서로 다를 경우 'too ... to ~'나 '... enough to ~'로 바꿔 쓸 때 'for+목적격'으로 주어를 나타낸다.

13 현재완료의 결과적 용법(…해서 (그 결과) 지금 ~하다)을 이용하여 과거에 러시아로 가서 아직도 그곳에 머무르고 있다는 현재의 결과를 나타내도록 한다.

14 so ... that ~: 너무 …해서 ~하다

15 (1) 현재완료는 과거를 나타내는 어구와 함께 쓸 수 없다. (2) have[has] been to는 '~에 가 본적이 있다'는 경험을 나타내고, have[has] gone to는 '~에 가고 없다'는 결과를 나타내므로 have gone to로 고쳐야 한다. (3), (4) 'so ... that ~'이나 'too ... to ~'로 나타내는 것이 적절하다. (5) 현재완료에서 'since+시간 명사', 'for+기간 명사'

16 ⓐ last week이라는 과거를 나타내는 부사구가 있으므로 과거형으로 써야 한다. ⓑ 'have gone to'는 결과를 나타내는 말로 1인칭을 주어로 쓸 수 없다. 여기서 there는 to Vietnam을 대신하고 있다.

17 (1) 현재완료에서 'since+시간 명사', 'for+기간 명사' (2) have[has] been to는 '~에 가 본 적이 있다'는 경험을 나타내고, have[has] gone to는 '~에 가고 없다'는 결과를 나타낸다. (3), (4) so ... that ~: 너무 …해서 ~하다 (5) 현재완료는 과거를 나타내는 어구와 함께 쓸 수 없다.

18 too ... to ~ = so ... that 주어 can't ~, ... enough to ~ = so ... that 주어 can

서술형 시험대비

p.130~131

01 (1) Laura has lived in Chicago since 1998.

(2) Dan has lost his cell phone.

02 (1) Kate is so young that she can't drive a car.

(2) Stefanie is so wise that she can give advice to her friends.

03 (1) James has played soccer since he was a child.

(2) It rains so heavily that we can't go outside.

(3) Charlie has studied Korean for six months.

04 (1) Mr. Brown has lived in New York since 2015.

(2) We have been to Sydney.

(3) Elle didn't take a walk yesterday.

(4) My long padding coat is warm enough for me to endure the winter.

(5) Lylian was so afraid that she couldn't open her eyes.

05 (1) Mike was too sick to go to work yesterday.

(2) The *samgyetang* was so hot that Amy could not eat it.

(3) His essay was nice enough for his teacher to be satisfied.

(4) Tom ran so fast that he could catch the last bus.

06 (1) His neighbor's party was so noisy that he couldn't sleep at all.

(2) Rose has not arrived at the library yet.

(3) The man was so kind that he helped me right away.

(4) I have been to Paris once.

(5) Andrew has left his smartphone in the train.

07 (1) Bella has never(not) driven a car before.

(2) Bella has visited Angkor Wat before.

(3) Bella has never[not] tasted Vietnamese food before.

(4) Bella has practiced yoga before.

08 (1) The flowers are so beautiful that many people come to see them.

(2) The house was so expensive that we decided not to buy it.

(3) This dish is so spicy that I need to drink a lot of milk.

(4) The movie was so sad that I cried a lot.

(5) You are so smart that you always get A's.

09 has gone

01 (1) 1998년에 살기 시작해서 지금도 살고 있는 것이므로 현재완료의 '계속'을 이용한다. (2) cell phone을 잃어버려서 지금 없는 것이므로 현재완료의 '결과'를 이용한다.

02 too ... to ~ = so ... that 주어 can't ~, ... enough to ~ = so ... that 주어 can

03 (1), (3) 현재완료의 계속적 용법을 이용한다. (2) so ... that 주어 can't ~: 너무 …해서 ~할 수 없다

04 (1) 현재완료에서 'since+시간 명사', 'for+기간 명사' (2) have gone to는 3인칭만 주어가 될 수 있다. (3) 현재완료는 과거를 나타내는 부사와 함께 쓸 수 없다. (4) enough 는 형용사 다음에 와서 '... enough to ~'의 형식으로 쓰인다. (5) so ... that 주어 can't ~ = too ... to ~: 너무 …해서 ~할 수 없다

05 too ... to ~ = so ... that 주어 can't ~, ... enough to부정사 = so ... that 주어 can ~ / 이때 to부정사 앞에 for 목적격으로 쓰인 것은 to부정사의 의미상의 주어로 that 이하의 절로 바꿀 때는 주격으로 바꿔야 하며, to부정사로 썼을 때 생략된 동사의 목적어는 써 주어야 한다.

06 (1), (3) so+형용사[부사]+that+주어+동사: 매우 …해서 ~하

다 (2) 현재완료의 '완료' 용법 (4) 현재완료의 '경험' 용법 (5) 현재완료의 '결과' 용법

07 현재완료의 '경험' 용법을 이용한다.

08 'so+형용사[부사]+that+주어+동사'의 형태로 '매우 …해서 ~하다'라는 의미이다. so 뒤의 형용사나 부사는 원인을 나타내며, 접속사 that 뒤에 나오는 내용은 그에 따른 결과를 나타낸다.

09 현재완료의 '결과' 용법을 이용한다.

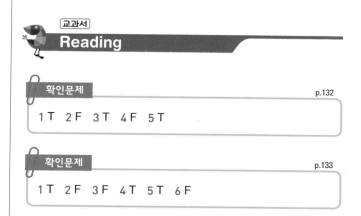

Reading

교과서

확인문제   p.132

1 T   2 F   3 T   4 F   5 T

확인문제   p.133

1 T   2 F   3 F   4 T   5 T   6 F

교과서 확인학습 A   p.134~135

01 Traditional   02 from a sister school
03 stay at, for a week   04 him the guest room   05 stay here   06 is full of
07 Look at   08 these things   09 They're
10 on my pillow, scary   11 Not really, symbols of   12 surprising, remind, of
13 shows   14 meet, greet each other
15 Have you ever seen
16 haven't, so, that   17 For a long time, good guards   18 close their eyes   19 interesting   20 watch over, That's why, like   21 understand   22 walk around
23 that piece of paper   24 Do you mean
25 a rooster   26 crow   27 a new day
28 go away, crows   29 I've never heard   30 Actually, afraid
31 for me   32 draw a big rooster
33 Put, above, protect   34 will
35 so much that   36 traditional Korean symbols
37 a lot of them   38 with my family

1 Traditional Korean Symbols

2 Peter is visiting Korea to meet a friend, Mina, from a sister school.

3 Peter is going to stay at her grandfather's house for a week.

4 When he arrives, Mina shows him the guest room.

5 Peter, you will stay here.

6 This guest room is full of traditional Korean things.

7 Look at this pillow.

8 What are these things?

9 They're bats.

10 Bats on my pillow? That's scary!

11 Not really. In Korea, bats are symbols of luck and a long life.

12 That's surprising. In many Western countries, bats remind people of darkness and scary things.

13 Mina shows Peter her grandfather's room.

14 Peter and Mina's grandfather meet and greet each other.

15 Hi, Peter! Have you ever seen this kind of lock before?

16 No, I haven't. It's so old that I can't really tell, but is it a fish?

17 Yes. For a long time, Koreans have thought that fish are good guards.

18 Fish don't close their eyes, even when they sleep.

19 That's interesting.

20 We think fish can watch over valuable things. That's why this lock looks like a fish.

21 Now I understand.

22 They go outside and walk around the garden.

23 What is on that piece of paper? It looks scary.

24 Do you mean this painting of a rooster?

25 Oh, is it a rooster?

26 Yes, it is. Roosters crow every morning.

27 Their crowing means that a new day is beginning.

28 For many years, Koreans have believed evil spirits go away when a rooster crows.

29 Really? I've never heard that before.

30 Actually, I'm afraid of darkness and evil spirits.

31 Could you draw a rooster for me, Mina?

32 Sure. I'll draw a big rooster for you!

33 Put the drawing above your door. Then it will protect you.

34 Yes, I will.

35 I'm enjoying this trip so much that I want to stay

longer.

36 I love all the traditional Korean symbols in this house.

37 Now I understand a lot of them.

38 I want to visit Korea again with my family.

01 내 베개 위에 박쥐가 있는 것

02 한국에서는 박쥐가 행운과 장수의 상징이기 때문이다.

03 ②   04 ④   05 ③, ⑤

06 No, I haven't.   07 sister school   08 ⑤

09 ④   10 ③   11 lock

12 That's why this lock looks like a fish.

13 looks like → looks   14 ③   15 ⑤

16 (A) As   (B) so   17 ④   18 ⑤

19 (1) at any time → on special days, such as New Year's Day

  (2) three → two

20 (A) During   (B) a lot   (C) interesting

21 ②   22 (A) beginning   (B) protect   (C) will

23 ②, ⑤   24 (A) afraid   (B) go away

01 that은 지시대명사로 앞 문장의 내용을 받는다.

02 바로 뒤에 그 이유를 설명하고 있다.

03 ② 피터는 '일주일'간 미나네 할아버지 댁에 머무를 것이다.

04 ④ watch over: ~을 보살피다[보호하다/지켜보다], ~을 지키다, ① ~에게 (~을) 둘러보도록 안내하다[구경시켜 주다], ② ~을 기다리다, ③ ~을 조사하다, ⑤ ~을 기대하다, 즐거운 마음으로 기다리다

05 ⓐ와 ③과 ⑤는 경험 용법, ① 결과 용법, ② 계속 용법, ④ 완료 용법

06 현재완료로 물었기 때문에 No, I haven't.로 답하는 것이 적절하다.

07 sister school: 자매학교, 재정적으로, 역사적으로 혹은 사회적으로 다른 학교에 연결되어 있는 학교

08 베개에 박쥐 디자인이 있다는 것에 대해 Peter가 '무섭다'고 하니까 미나는 한국에서 박쥐는 행운과 장수의 상징이라고 말하고 있으므로 빈칸에는 동의하지 않는 말이 들어가야 한다. 그러므로 ⑤번의 '사실은 그렇지 않아.'가 적절하다. 나머지는 다 동의를 나타낼 때 쓰는 말이다. ② Why not?: (동의를 나타내어) 왜 아니겠어?

09 베개에 박쥐가 있는 것에 '무서워'하다가 한국에서 박쥐는 행운과 장수의 상징이라는 말에 '놀라워'했다. disappointed: 실망한, scared: 무서워하는, ashamed: 부끄러운, ⑤ depressed: 우울한

10 ⓐ와 ③은 '종류(명사)', 나머지는 다 '친절한(형용사)'

11 미나의 할아버지가 Peter에게 보여주신 '자물쇠'를 가리킨다.

12 'why'를 보충하면 된다.

13 look + 형용사, look like + 명사: ~처럼 보이다

14 위 글은 수탉 그림의 의미를 설명하는 글이므로, 제목으로는 ③번 '수탉 그림이 무엇을 의미하는가?'가 적절하다.

15 ⑤ 할아버지가 피터에게 그 그림을 그의 문 아래가 아닌 문 위에 걸어 놓으라고 한 이유는 대답할 수 없다. ① Peter, Mina's grandfather, and Mina. ② No, he doesn't. ③ It means that a new day is beginning. ④ A big rooster.

16 문장 앞에 As를 쓰거나 문장 중간에 so를 써서 고치는 것이 적절하다. For는 부가적인 이유를 나타낼 때 쓸 수 있으므로 (A)에 들어가기에는 적절하지 않다.

17 ④ '피터가 전통적인 한국의 상징물들에 대해 계속 공부하고 싶어 한다'는 내용은 본문에 없다.

18 앞의 내용의 예가 나오고 있으므로 For example이 가장 적절하다. ① 그러나, ② 다시 말해, ③ 그러므로, ④ 게다가

19 (1) 사람들은 사자춤을 '설날과 같은 특별한 날에' 춘다. (2) '두 명'의 댄서들이 사자처럼 옷을 입고 행동한다.

20 (A) 'during+특정 기간을 나타내는 명사', 'for+숫자가 붙은 기간'이므로 During이 적절하다. (B) 뒤에 명사가 없으므로 a lot이 적절하다. a lot of+명사 (C) 감정을 나타내는 말은 사람을 수식할 때는 보통 과거분사로, 사물을 수식할 때는 보통 현재분사로 쓰기 때문에 interesting이 적절하다.

21 ② 여행 기간은 알 수 없다. ① 한국, ③ 미나와 미나의 할아버지, ④ 전통적인 한국의 상징물들, ⑤ 재미있었다.

22 (A) 수탉이 매일 아침 운다고 했으므로, 수탉의 울음은 새로운 날이 '시작하는(beginning)' 것을 의미한다고 하는 것이 적절하다. (B) 그것이 너를 '지켜줄' 거라고 해야 하므로 protect가 적절하다. prevent: 막다[예방/방지하다], (C) '네, 그럴게요.'라고 해야 하므로 will이 적절하다.

23 Actually = In fact = As a matter of fact: 사실, ① 그 결과, ③ 무엇보다도, 특히, ④ 다시 말해서

24 피터는 어둠과 악령들을 '무서워하고,' 수탉 그림 덕분에 그것들이 '물러가기를' 원하기 때문이다.

🦉 **서술형 시험대비** p.142~143

01 Mina shows the guest room to him.

02 luck and a long life

03 happiness and pleasant → darkness and scary

04 greet to → greet

05 Have you ever seen this kind of lock before?

06 fish don't close their eyes, even when they sleep

07 a fish

---

08 The painting of a rooster.

09 (1) 새로운 날이 시작하는 것을 의미한다.
   (2) 수탉이 울 때 악령이 물러간다.

10 I've never heard that before.

11 is filled with

12 ⑤번, → surprising

13 (A) luck   (B) a long life   (C) negative

---

01 show는 to를 사용하여 3형식으로 고친다.

02 한국에서 박쥐는 '행운과 장수'를 상징한다.

03 서구의 많은 나라들에서, 박쥐는 사람들에게 '어둠과 무서운 것들'을 상기시켜 준다.

04 greet: ~에게 인사하다(타동사)

05 'before'를 보충하면 된다.

06 물고기는 잘 때도 눈을 감지 않기 때문이다.

07 미나의 할아버지가 피터에게 보여주는 자물쇠는 '물고기'처럼 생겼다.

08 피터가 가리키고 있는 종이 위에는 '수탉 그림'이 있다.

09 수탉의 울음은 '새로운 날이 시작하는 것을 의미'하고, 여러 해 동안, 한국 사람들은 '수탉이 울 때 악령이 물러간다.'고 믿어 왔다.

10 5단어로 영작하기 위하여 I have를 I've로 축약하면 된다.

11 be full of = be filled with: ~로 가득 차 있다

12 피터는 서구의 많은 나라들에서 박쥐는 사람들에게 어둠과 무서운 것들을 상기시켜 준다고 말하고 있기 때문에, 한국에서 박쥐가 행운과 장수의 상징이라는 미나의 말에 대한 응답으로는 'reasonable'이 아니라 'surprising'과 같이 '놀랍다'는 뜻의 단어로 고치는 것이 적절하다. reasonable: 타당한, 사리에 맞는, 합리적인

13 한국에서 박쥐는 사람들에게 '행운'과 '장수'와 같은 긍정적인 것들을 상기시켜 준다. 반면에, 서구의 많은 나라들에서, 박쥐는 어둠과 무서운 것들과 같은 '부정적인' 것들의 상징이다.

🦉 **영역별 핵심문제** p.145~149

01 ③   02 ①, ④, ⑤   03 (c)row   04 (p)alm

05 ③ have been → went, 또는 last year → before

06 ②   07 ④   08 ①   09 means

10 Have you ever been to a Spanish festival before?

11 ④   12 (A) to   (B) from   (C) on   (C) at

13 traditional 14 ③, ④   15 ③   16 ①

17 ⑤   18 so, that

19 (1) has, been   (2) has gone

20 ②

21 (1) The car was so fast that the police couldn't catch it.

(2) The concert was so good that many people went to see it again.

22 (1) Lin has spent all the money for shopping.
(2) Jeremy has played the piano for six years.

23 ①, ⑤   24 (A) traditional (B) scary (C) remind

25 ④   26 Fish don't close their eyes, even when they sleep.   27 ⑤   28 ①

29 ③   30 ②   31 ②

32 it → them

---

01 ③ try는 '한번 해 보다'의 뜻으로 여기서는 '한번 먹어 보다'의 의미로 사용되었다.

02 face: ~을 향하다 ① 손바닥은 천장을 향해 있어야 됩니다. ④ 스캔할 사진 면이 위를 향하도록 해야 합니다. ⑤ 정원은 남쪽을 향해 있습니다. ②, ③ face: 얼굴 wrinkle: 주름

03 crow: 까마귀; (닭이) 울다/까마귀 날자 배 떨어진다./ 그들은 해가 뜨는 매일 아침 같은 시간에 웁니다.

04 palm: 손바닥; 야자나무 / 그가 손바닥으로 그녀의 턱을 괴었다. / 그들은 야자나무에 쉽게 올라갈 수 있다.

05 완료 시제를 사용할 때는 ~ ago, yesterday, when 등과 같이 명백한 과거를 나타내는 말과 함께 사용하지 않는다.

06 ⓒ와 ⓕ를 제외한 나머지 보기는 대화의 내용과 일치한다.

07 ④ have been to: ~에 가 본 적이 있다.

08 'What brings you here today?'가 어떤 일로 여기 왔는지 질문을 하는 것이므로, 주어진 문장이 이에 대한 대답이 될 수 있다.

09 mean: 의미하다

10 Have you ever been to~?: ~에 가 본 적 있니? Spanish: 스페인의 festival: 축제

11 ④ 무대에 큰 글씨 gracias가 있다.

12 (A) welcome to ~: ~에 오신 걸 환영합니다 (B) from: (출처·기원) ~ 출신의[에서 온] (C) on: ~ 위에 on the ground: 바닥에 (D) throw: ~을 던지다 at: (방향) ~으로

13 traditional: 전통적인

14 <보기>의 문장과 ③, ④번은 현재완료의 '경험'이다. ① 계속 ② 완료 ⑤ 결과

15 'so ... that ~'은 '너무[매우] ~해서 …하다'의 의미로 원인과 결과를 나타낸다.

16 현재완료는 특정한 과거를 나타내는 when과 함께 쓸 수 없다. When did you visit London?으로 써야 한다.

17 'so ... that ~'은 '너무[매우] ~해서 …하다'의 의미로 원인과 결과를 나타낸다.

18 so ... that ~: 너무[매우] ~해서 …하다

19 have[has] been to는 '~에 가 본 적이 있다'는 경험을, have[has] gone to는 '~에 가고 없다'는 결과를 나타낸다.

20 ② Nicole was so tired that she couldn't go shopping.

21 'so ... that ~'은 '너무[매우] ~해서 …하다'의 의미로 원인과 결과를 나타낸다.

22 현재완료의 '결과' 용법과 '계속' 용법을 이용한다.

23 ⓐ와 ①, ⑤ 부사적 용법, ②, ③ 명사적 용법, ④ 형용사적 용법

24 (A) 이 손님방은 한국의 '전통' 물건들로 가득 차 있다고 해야 하므로 traditional이 적절하다. modern: 현대의, (B) 뒷부분에 서구의 많은 나라들에서 박쥐는 사람들에게 어둠과 무서운 것들을 상기시켜 준다는 말이 나오기 때문에, 베개에 박쥐 디자인이 있다는 것에 대해 피터는 '겁난다'고 해야 하므로 scary가 적절하다. terrific 아주 좋은, 멋진, 훌륭한, (C) 어둠과 무서운 것들을 '상기시켜 준다'고 해야 하므로 remind가 적절하다. remain: 계속[여전히] ~이다

25 so ~ that ...: 너무 ~해서 …하다

26 물고기는 잘 때도 눈을 감지 않는다는 것을 가리킨다.

27 이 글은 자물쇠가 물고기처럼 생긴 이유를 설명하는 글이므로, 주제로는 ⑤ '자물쇠가 물고기처럼 생긴 이유'가 가장 적절하다.

28 수탉의 울음은 새로운 날이 시작하는 것을 의미한다고 했기 때문에, 수탉이 울 때 '악령이 물러간다.'고 믿어왔다고 하는 것이 적절하다.

29 ⓑ be afraid of: ~을 두려워하다, ⓒ draw A for B: B를 위해 A를 그려 주다

30 피터는 '저 종이에는 무엇이 그려져 있는 거죠?' '오, 그게 수탉이에요?'라고 물어보고 있으므로, 종이 위에 수탉 그림이 있는 것을 모르고 있었다.

31 ⓐ, ②, ⑤ 명사적 용법, ① 형용사적 용법(It은 비인칭주어), ③ 부사적 용법(목적), ④ 형용사적 용법

32 이 집의 모든 전통적인 한국의 상징물들을 가리키므로 'them'이 적절하다.

단원별 예상문제   p.150~153

01 (C) → (B) → (A) → (D)   02 (D) → (F) → (A) → (B) → (E) → (C)   03 (A) haven't (B) Have (C) have

04 ④   05 ④   06 Chinese

07 separation   08 about

09 (b)ow, (c)row, (l)ast, (1) lasted (2) crows (3) bow

10 (A) listened (B) Spanish

11 It means good luck for 12 months   12 ①, ⑤

13 (1) He is so fat that there is hardly any shirt that fits him.
(2) His voice was so small that I couldn't hear him talk.
(3) Jenny has waited for Sunny for an hour.

14 ①

15 (1) It has rained for a week.

    (2) Elvis has gone to Wien.

16 ④   **17** of

18 This guest room is full of traditional Korean things.

19 (A) haven't   (B) are   (C) why

20 그것은 너무 오래되어서 사실 알아볼 수가 없어요.

21 ④   **22** sheet   **23** the drawing above your door   **24** ③

25 he is enjoying this trip so much

26 visiting → to visit

01 Holi Festival이 있다는 말에 (C)에서 Holi가 무엇인지 질문하고 (B)에서 대답한다. (A)에서 축제에 흥미를 보이며, Holi Festival에 가 본 경험을 묻고 (D)에서 대답한다.

02 주어진 글의 무례하다는 말에, (D) 누가 무례한지 묻고 (F) 남자애가 하는 행동을 설명하며 언급하고 (A) 무엇이 잘못 되었는지 묻자 (B) 손바닥이 자기 쪽을 향하는 것은 나쁜 뜻을 가지고 있고, 손바닥을 보여 주면서 브이 사인을 만드는 것은 괜찮다고 대답한다. (E) 마지막으로, 손바닥을 보여주면서 브이 사인을 만드는 것의 의미를 묻고 (C) 대답한다.

03 상대방의 경험에 대해 물어볼 때는, 현재완료 시제를 사용하여 'Have you 과거분사 ~?'라고 묻는다. 경험을 묻는 말에 긍정으로 대답할 경우에는 'Yes, I have.', 부정으로 대답할 때는 'No, I haven't.'로 대답한다. (B)의 Have you? 다음에는 'ever been to Brazil'이 생략되어 있다.

04 (D) 작년에 있었다는 내용이므로 과거형을 사용해야 한다. 또한 a big samba festival이 단수명사이므로 was가 적절하다. (E) sound+형용사: ~하게 들리다 sound like + 명사: ~하게 들리다 (F) hope+to 동사: ~하기를 희망하다

05 It이 가리키는 것이 an umbrella이므로, What does an umbrella mean in China?(중국에서 우산이 뭘 의미하는데?)의 대답으로 나와야 적절하다.

06 Chinese: 중국의; 중국어

07 separation: 분리, 이별

08 hear about: ~에 대해서 듣다 / 넌 꽃박람회에 대해 들어 본 적이 있니? think about: ~에 대해 생각[고려]하다 / 나는 그녀에게 우산을 사주려고 생각하고 있어. talk about: ~에 대해 말하다 / 사람들은 여가 시간에 관해서 말하기를 좋아한다.

09 (1) last: 계속되다, 지속되다 / 그 회의는 어제 세 시간 동안 계속되었다. (2) crow: (닭이) 울다 / 수탉은 약 한 시간에 한 번씩 운다. (3) bow: (인사를 위해) 머리를 숙이다, 절하다 / 나는 항상 선생님께 고개 숙여 인사한다.

10 Have you 과거분사 ~?: ~해 본 경험이 있니? Spanish: 스페인의

11 mean: 의미하다 good luck: 행운 for+기간: ~ 동안

12 ② Mary has lived here for 10 years. ③ Have you ever been to Malaysia? ④ Scarlet moved to Los Angeles 5 years ago.

13 (1), (2) 'so ... that ~' 구문과 (3) 현재완료의 '계속' 용법을 이용한다.

14 'so ... that ~' 구문은 맞지만 현재완료가 아니라 과거시제이므로 ate이 알맞다.

15 (1) 현재완료의 '계속', (2) '결과' 용법을 이용한다.

16 ④ 한국에서 박쥐는 행운과 장수의 '상징'이라고 하는 것이 적절하다. ① (논의 등의) 주제[대상/화제], 과목 ② 전통, ③ 의견, ⑤ 문화

17 remind A of B: A에게 B를 상기시켜 주다, A에게 B가 생각나게 하다

18 'of'를 보충하면 된다.

19 (A) 현재완료로 물었기 때문에 대답에도 haven't가 적절하다. (B) fish는 단수와 복수의 형태가 같은데 물고기 한 마리는 a fish라고 하므로, fish 다음에는 are가 적절하다. (C) That's why = For that reason으로 why 다음에는 앞의 내용의 결과에 해당하는 말이 나온다. because 다음에는 이유를 나타내는 말이 나온다.

20 so ~ that 주어 can't ... : 너무나 ~해서 …할 수 없다

21 ④ 물고기는 잘 때도 눈을 감지 않는다.

22 종이는 'piece'나 'sheet'를 사용하여 셀 수 있다.

23 '문 위에 붙여 놓은 그림'을 가리킨다.

24 ③ 이 글은 '한국인들이 문 위에 수탉 그림을 걸어놓은 이유'를 설명하는 글이다.

25 '이번 여행이 매우 즐거워서' 더 오래 머무르고 싶어 한다.

26 want는 목적어로 to부정사를 써야 한다.

서술형 실전문제

p.154~155

01 (A) to buy   (B) buying

02 ① that's a good → that's not a good

03 umbrella

04 (1) Charlie has studied Korean for six months.

    (2) I have lost my umbrella.

05 (1) My uncle has worked for the company since 2007.

    (2) I have never seen such a beautiful bridge.

    (3) The mountain is so high that I can't walk to the top.

    (4) My parents are so wise that I usually follow their advice.

06 (1) The dogs are so cute that I can't take my eyes off them.

(2) The weather was so nice that they went on a picnic.

07 (A) for　(B) him　(C) surprising

08 In Korea, bats are symbols of luck and a long life.

09 행운과 장수의 상징이다. / 사람들에게 어둠과 무서운 것들을 상기시켜 준다.

10 Do you mean this painting of a rooster?

11 the sun is setting → a new day is beginning

12 For many years, Koreans have believed evil spirits go away when a rooster crows.

01 (A) be going to 동사원형: ~할 것이다, ~할 예정이다 (B) 전치사 다음에는 명사나 동명사가 나올 수 있다.

02 우산이 중국에서 나쁜 것을 뜻한다고 말했기 때문에, 우산이 중국 사람들에게 좋은 선물이라고 말하는 것은 어색하므로 not을 붙여서 부정문으로 바꿔야 적절하다.

03 one은 앞에 이미 언급했거나 상대방이 알고 있는 사물을 가리킬 때 명사의 반복을 피하기 위해 사용하는데, 여기서는 umbrella를 가리킨다.

04 (1) 현재완료의 '계속', (2) '결과' 용법을 이용한다.

05 (1) 현재완료의 '계속' (2) 현재완료의 '경험' (3), (4) so ... that ~: 너무[매우] ~해서 …하다

06 'so+형용사[부사]+that+주어+동사'의 형태로 '매우 …해서 ~하다'라는 의미이다.

07 (A) 'for+숫자가 붙은 기간', 'during+특정 기간을 나타내는 명사'이므로 for가 적절하다. (B) 4형식 문장이므로 간접목적어로 him을 쓰는 것이 적절하다. show는 3형식으로 고칠 때 to를 사용한다. (C) 감정을 나타내는 말은 사람을 수식할 때는 보통 과거분사로, 사물을 수식할 때는 보통 현재분사로 쓰기 때문에 surprising이 적절하다.

08 한국에서 박쥐가 행운과 장수의 상징이라는 것을 가리킨다.

09 한국에서 박쥐는 행운과 장수의 상징이지만, 서구의 많은 나라들에서, 박쥐는 사람들에게 어둠과 무서운 것들을 상기시켜 준다.

10 'of'를 보충하면 된다.

11 수탉이 매일 아침 우는 울음은 '새로운 날이 시작하는 것'을 의미한다.

12 '오랫동안 한국인들은 수탉이 울 때 악령이 물러간다고 믿어 왔다.'는 것을 가리킨다.

창의사고력 서술형 문제　p.156

|모범답안|

01 A: been to Spain
　B: I haven't.
　A: visited Spain
　A: a traditional Spanish, throw tomatoes at each other
　B: When is the festival?

02 (A) traditional　(B) is　(C) like　(D) special
　(E) to practice

단원별 모의고사　p.157~160

01 ④　　02 ④　　03 (1) palm　(2) face

04 ③　　05 What does that mean?

06 (1) Do you? → Have you?
　(2) Yes, I do. → Yes, I have.

07 (A) Which　(B) What　(C) How

08 Have you ever played gorodki?

09 ⑤ Putting → Put　10 ②　11 ③

12 a traditional Indian festival, Busan, throw colored powder and water at each other, white clothes, look more beautiful

13 ⑤

14 (1) The soup smelled too bad for me to have.
　(2) Einstein was clever enough to understand the theory.

15 (1) When did you go there?
　(2) I have studied English for 5 years.
　(3) I was so busy that I couldn't help her. 또는 I was too busy to help her.
　(4) The bunjee jump was so scary that we screamed a lot.

16 (1) for　(2) since

17 Phillip has lived in China for such a long time that he can speak Chinese very well.

18 ②

19 bats remind people of darkness and scary things

20 ④　　21 guards　　22 ④

23 (A) don't close (B) watch over　　24 ④

25 If 또는 When

01 접속사 But 앞에서 잘못된 이유를 이야기하고 손바닥을 보여 주면서 브이 사인을 만드는 것이 괜찮다고 말하는 것이 적절하다.

02 ⓐ What a nice picture! ⓑ Which boy? ⓒ The boy who is making the V sign. ⓓ His palm is facing toward himself.

03 (1) palm: 손바닥 (2) face: ~을 향하다

04 ③ in Spanish: 스페인어로

05 mean: 의미하다

06 브라질에 다녀온 경험에 대해 계속 이야기하고 있으므로 do동사가 아니라 have를 이용해서 질문과 대답을 해야 한다.

07 (A) 많은 다른 전통적인 게임들 중에서 하나를 선택하는 것이므로 Which가 어울린다. (B) 고로드키 게임이 무엇인지 질문하고 있다. (C) 게임을 하는 방법에 대해 설명하고 있으므로, 게임을 어떻게 하는지 질문해야 한다.

08 상대방의 경험에 대해 물어볼 때는, 현재완료 시제를 사용하여 'Have you ever 과거분사 ~?'라고 묻는다.

09 게임 방법을 명령문으로 설명하고 있다.

10 주어진 문장은 Holi festival이 무엇인지에 대한 대답이므로 ②가 어울린다.

11 ⓒ '가본 적이 있어 하지만 인도 친구가 그것에 대해 내게 많이 이야기해 줬어.'는 어색하므로, 'No, I haven't.'가 어울린다.

12 traditional: 전통적인 Indian: 인도의 festival: 축제 be held: 개최되다 in+장소: ~에서 throw: ~을 던지다 at: (방향) ~으로 colored: 채색된, 색깔이 있는 clothes: 옷, 의복

13 <보기>와 ⑤번은 경험 용법 ①, ③ 완료 용법 ② 계속 용법 ④ 결과 용법

14 (1) so ... that 주어 can't ~ = too ... (의미상의 주어: for+목적격) to ~ (2) so ... that 주어 can ~ = ... enough to ~

15 (1) 현재완료는 과거의 특정 시점을 나타내는 when과는 함께 쓰이지 않는다. (2) 현재완료에서 'since+시간 명사', 'for+기간 명사' (3) so ... that 주어 can't ~ = too ... to ~ (4) 'so+형용사[부사]+that+주어+동사'의 형태로 '매우 …해서 ~하다' 'so that ~'은 '~하도록'의 의미로 쓰인다.

16 현재완료에서 'since+시간 명사', 'for+ 기간 명사'

17 'so+형용사[부사]+that+주어+동사' 구문에서 that 앞에 형용사나 부사 대신 명사가 오면 so 대신 such를 쓴다.

18 '내 베개 위에 박쥐가? 그거 겁나는데!'라고 했기 때문에 ②번의 'grateful'은 알맞지 않다. grateful: 고마워하는, 감사하는, 나머지는 다 '무서워[두려워]하는', '겁이 난'이라는 뜻이다.

19 remind A of B: A에게 B를 상기시켜 주다, A에게 B가 생각나게 하다

20 이 글은 '전통적인 한국의 상징물들 중 박쥐의 의미를 소개'하기 위한 글이다.

21 guard: 경비[감시/수비] 요원, 파수꾼, 어떤 것이나 사람을 지키는 사람들

22 ⓑ와 ④는 '~처럼', '~와 비슷한', 나머지는 다 '좋아하다'는 뜻이다.

23 물고기는 잘 때도 눈을 '감지 않기' 때문에, 사람들은 물고기가 귀중품을 '지킬 수' 있다고 생각한다. 그런 이유로 이 자물쇠가 물고기처럼 생겼다.

24 ⓐ와 ②번은 계속 용법, ① 결과 용법, ③ 완료 용법, ④ 경험용법, ⑤ 완료 용법

25 '그러면'은 '그 그림을 네 문 위에 걸어놓으면[놓을 때]'이라는 뜻이다.

Go Green Together

끄다 (3) get+비교급: 점점 ~해지다 / be동사와 결합되어 현재진행형(be+동사원형-ing)이 되어야 한다.

05 (1) 완전히 자랄 때까지 사람이나 동물 또는 식물을 돌보다 (2) 더 이상 보는 것이 불가능해지다

시험대비 실력평가 p.164

01 (c)onsume 02 ② 03 ① 04 ③
05 ④ 06 how to use 07 ⑤ 08 ③

01 둘은 동의어 관계이다. 초조한 – 먹다, 먹어 치우다

02 remind A of B: A에게 B를 상기시키다

03 Why don't you+동사원형은 ~? '~하는 게 어때?'라고 권유하는 말이다.

04 한 번 이상 일어나거나 어떤 것을 하다

05 움직이지 못하도록 무언가를 자리에 고정시키다

06 how(의문사) to+동사원형: '~하는 방법'

07 cut A into B: A를 B로 자르다, put A on B: A를 B에 놓다[두다]

08 '식물을 재배하다'는 grow가 일반적이고, raise를 사용하기도 한다. '물고기나 가축을 기르다'는 주로 raise를 사용하고, rear를 사용할 수 있다.

서술형 시험대비 p.165

01 (1) consuming (2) article (3) productive (4) turned
02 (1) feed (2) solutions (3) connect (4) bottom
03 (1) worried about (2) turn off (3) getting hotter
04 (1) (g)lobal warming (2) (t)hrow away
    (3) in (d)anger (4) (h)ang
05 (1) raise (2) disappear

01 (1) 식물은 먹이를 먹음으로써 물을 정화한다. 전치사 by 뒤에 동명사가 와야 한다. (2) 아쿠아포닉스에 관한 기사를 읽고 있어. (3) 아쿠아포닉스는 식량을 재배하는 훨씬 더 생산적인 방식이다. 명사 way를 수식하는 형용사 형태가 적절하다. (4) 이 배설물은 박테리아에 의해 식물의 먹이로 바뀐다. 주어인 waste가 음식으로 바뀌는 수동의 의미이므로 수동태로 'be+과거분사' 형태가 적절하다.

02 (1) 물고기에게 먹이를 주면, 그것들은 배설물을 만들어 낸다. (2) 그 연설은 환경문제와 그 해결책에 관한 것이다. (3) 나는 관을 이용하여 펌프를 화분에 연결하였다. (4) 나는 화분 바닥에 구멍을 뚫었다.

03 (1) be worried about ~: ~에 관해 걱정하다 (2) turn off: ~을

교과서 Conversation

핵심 Check p.166~167

1 ②
2 worried about wasting
3 ④
4 ⑤
5 how to draw

교과서 대화문 익히기

Check(√) True or False p.168

(1) T (2) F (3) F (4) T

교과서 확인학습 p.170~171

Listen & Talk 1 A
leave, on, worried about wasting / put, on / shouldn't

Listen & Talk 1 B
What, about / was about, getting hotter, going up, worried / about, before, disappearing, losing / terrible / to stop / turn off, them, instead of / try to

Listen & Talk 1 C
nervous / worried, about, solutions / talk about / enough information / instead, said, have to / isn't / in danger because, near / talk about, for, advice

Listen and Talk 2 A
how to use / turn, on / anywhere / interesting.

Listen and Talk 2 B
get / myself / amazing / Why don't you / how to make / Cut, into, sew, together / easy

Listen and Talk 2 C
Have, heard of / turn off, for / to remind, of, such / how to join / turn off, from, to, on, in

Do It Yourself
look upset / am worried about, saving, making / how about using / to use / Add / sounds easy

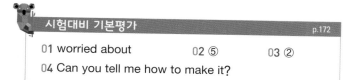

01 worried about   02 ⑤   03 ②
04 Can you tell me how to make it?

01 'be worried about ~'은 '~에 관해 걱정하다'라는 뜻이다.

02 남자의 대답이 '단지 30분 동안 축구를 하면 전구가 켜질 것이다.'라고 방법을 말해 주고 있기 때문에 빈칸에는 방법을 물어보는 말이 오는 것이 자연스럽다.

03 상대방에게 권유나 제안하는 표현으로 Why don't you+동사원형 ~? = How[What] about+-ing ~? = What do you say to+ -ing ~?를 사용한다. 동사원형 make가 있기 때문에 Why don't you가 적절하다.

04 조동사 can으로 시작하는 의문문으로, '~에게 …을 말하다'는 'tell+간접목적어(~에게)+직접목적어(…을/를)' 어순을 취한다. 직접목적어 자리에 '의문사+to부정사' 형태로 '어떻게 ~하는지'를 쓴다.

01 ③   02 how I should use it   03 ①, ④
04 ⑤   05 a bag   06 ①   07 ②
08 ③   09 ⑤   10 turn off   11 to
remind, of   12 ④

01 '무슨 일이니?'라는 질문에 대한 답으로 글의 내용상 숙제를 하는 것에 대해 걱정하는 내용이 자연스럽다.

02 '의문사+to부정사'는 '의문사+주어+should+동사원형'으로 바꾸어 쓸 수 있다.

03 재귀대명사의 강조 용법으로 재귀대명사는 강조하는 말 뒤나 문장의 끝에 온다.

04 소녀가 가방을 만드는 방법에 대해 말하고 있으므로 how to 부정사가 적절하다.

05 one은 앞에 나온 명사를 가리키는 부정대명사로 a bag을 가리킨다.

06 '그것은 무엇에 관한 것이었니?' '그것은 지구 온난화에 관한 것이었어.' '~에 관한'은 about이다.

07 B의 첫 대화에서 학생들이 음식을 너무 많이 남긴다고 했기 때문에 B는 음식을 낭비하는 것에 대해 걱정하고 있다는 것을 알 수 있다.

08 We shouldn't는 We shouldn't put too much food on our plates.의 의미이므로 먹을 수 있는 만큼 음식을 식판에 담자는 의도다.

09 ⑤번의 A는 초콜릿 하루 생산량을 물었는데 B는 로봇이 초콜릿을 생산한다고 말하는 것은 어색하다.

10 버튼을 누름으로써 기계, TV, 엔진이나 전등이 작동하는 것을

멈추도록 하다

11 '~하기 위해'는 부정사를 이용하여 나타낸다. '~에게 …을 상기시키다'는 remind A of B 형태를 사용한다.

12 ④ Earth Hour 행사는 3월 마지막 토요일에 1시간 동안 불을 끔으로써 참여 가능하다고 했다.

01 Can you tell me how to make it?
02 (1) how to make   (2) old   (3) Cut, into   (4) Sew
03 I'm worried about the Earth.
04 getting hotter, going up, disappearing / Turn off, don't need, use, instead of
05 We shouldn't put too much food on our plates.

01 'how to+동사원형': '~하는 방법, 어떻게 ~하는지'

02 가방을 만드는 방법은 소녀의 마지막 말에 언급되어 있다.

03 be worried about: ~에 관해 걱정하다

05 We shouldn't.는 음식을 식판에 너무 많이 담아서는 안 된다는 의미다.

교과서
Grammar

1 (1) was found   (2) to   (3) with
2 (1) far   (2) even   (3) much

01 ⑤   02 ②   03 (1) was broken
(2) was written   (3) much[far, still]   (4) far[much, still]
04 (1) very → much, still, even, far, a lot 중의 하나
(2) cleans → is cleaned

01 동사를 'be+pp'로 바꾸고 수동태 문장의 주어 자리에는 능동태 문장의 목적어가 오고, by 다음에는 능동태 문장의 주어를 목적격으로 쓴다.

02 very는 원급의 형용사[부사]를 수식하며, 비교급은 수식하지 않는다.

03 (1) 수동태는 'be+pp'의 형태이다. (2) 책 이름은 단수로 취급한다. (3), (4) 비교급을 강조할 때는 비교급 앞에 much, still,

even, far, a lot 등의 부사(구)를 쓰므로 much, still, far 중의 하나를 쓰면 정답이다.

04 (1) 비교급을 강조할 때는 비교급 앞에 much, still, even, far, a lot 등의 부사를 쓴다. (2) 방이 청소되는 것이므로 수동태가 적절하다.

시험대비 실력평가 p.179~181

01 ⑤　　02 ③　　03 ④　　04 ②
05 ①　　06 (1) to (2) for (3) of　　07 ③
08 ④　　09 ③　　10 ⑤　　11 ②
12 ⑤　　13 ②
14 (1) *Sunflower* was painted by Van Gogh.
　 (2) The pictures were not taken by Mel.
　 (3) The building was made of stone.
　 (4) Health is far more important than money.
　 (5) The computer I wanted to buy was a lot cheaper than the old one.　　15 bigger
16 is cleaned / are made / faster / more important
17 ⑤　　18 ④　　19 (1) was happened → happened (2) invented → was invented (3) many → much

01 *The Kiss*가 그려진 것이므로 수동태가 적절하다.

02 very는 원급의 형용사[부사]를 수식하며, 비교급은 수식하지 않는다.

03 ④ send는 간접목적어 앞에 to를 붙여야 한다. for me → to me

04 4형식의 직접목적어를 주어로 하는 수동태에서 buy는 간접목적어 앞에 for를 쓰는 동사이다.

05 비교급을 강조할 때는 비교급 앞에 much, still, even, far, a lot 등의 부사를 쓴다.

06 직접목적어를 주어로 한 수동태에서 간접목적어 앞에 (1) show는 전치사 to를, (2) make는 전치사 for를, (3) ask는 전치사 of를 쓴다.

07 ③번은 명사를 수식하고 있지만 나머지는 비교급을 강조하고 있다.

08 비교급을 강조할 때는 비교급 앞에 much, still, even, far, a lot 등의 부사를 쓰며, 첫 문장은 의미상 much가 적절하다.

09 <보기>와 ③ (비교급을 강조하여) 한층, 훨씬 ① …조차(도) ② 짝수의 ④ (수량·득점 따위가) 같은, 동일한 ⑤ (표면·판자 따위가) 평평한

10 ⑤ 목적격보어가 원형부정사인 경우, 수동태 문장에서는 to부정사로 바뀐다. Dan was made to finish the work by next Monday by them.

11 be satisfied with: ~에 만족하다 be filled with: ~로 가득 차다

12 throw away는 구동사로 하나의 단어처럼 취급하여 be thrown away로 나타낸다. away나 by를 빠뜨리지 않도록 주의한다.

13 조동사가 있는 문장의 수동태는 '조동사+be+p.p.' 형식을 갖는다.

14 (1), (2) *Sunflower*가 그려지고, 사진들이 찍히지 않은 것이므로 수동태가 적절하다. (3) be made of: ~로 만들어지다(물리적 변화) (4), (5) far와 a lot으로 비교급을 강조한다.

15 much로 수식받으면서 than이 뒤에 나오므로 비교급이 적절하다.

16 교실이 청소되어지고 차가 만들어지는 것이므로 수동태가 적절하다. even과 a lot으로 수식받고 있고 than이 이어지고 있으므로 비교급이 적절하다.

17 choose는 직접목적어를 주어로 한 수동태에서는 간접목적어 앞에 for를 쓴다.

18 시제가 saw로 과거형이므로 was seen으로 쓰고, 목적격보어 flying은 그대로 쓴다. (원형부정사일 경우에는 to부정사로 써야 한다.)

19 (1) happen은 자동사이므로 수동태로 쓰이지 않는다. (2) 냉장고가 발명된 것이므로 수동태가 적절하다. (3) 비교급 강조는 many가 아니라 much로 한다.

서술형 시험대비 p.182~183

01 (1) Our scientists discovered solutions to this problem.
　 (2) I will sing this song.
　 (3) The cookies were made for her by Dan.
　 (4) Something must be done to help him by us.
　 (5) By whom was the telephone invented in 1876?
02 (1) Cars are far more expensive than bicycles.
　 (2) It was still more beautiful than I had imagined.
　 (3) Manchester United is hoping to do even better this year.
　 (4) It'll be a lot cheaper than buying a new jacket.
　 (5) Jane is much cleverer than her twin brother.
03 (1) When we waste paper, so many trees are destroyed. 또는 When we waste paper, we destroy so many trees.
　 (2) How much chocolate is produced in a day?
　 (3) Wine is made from grapes.
　 (4) Matt was seen to dance on the stage by his friends.
　 (5) *Bibimbap* will be cooked for Mariel by Minjun tomorrow.
　 (6) Robert will read a storybook to his little brother. 또는 A storybook will be read to his

little brother by Robert.

04 nicer

05 (1) This dress was designed by my friend.

   (2) *Charlie* and the *Chocolate Factory* was not
written by William Shakespeare.

   (3) The interview was carried out in both Korean
and English.

   (4) These items were asked of each respondent.

   (5) A long letter was written (to) her by him.

   (6) Annabel was satisfied with her life in Seoul.

06 (1) many, (2) too, (3) ever, (4) very, (5) lots를 much,
still, even, far, a lot 등으로 바꾸면 정답.

07 (1) This tower is a lot higher than that (one).

   (2) My brother jumps even higher than I.

   (3) She is much more active than her brother.

   (4) Brenda is far kinder than before.

   (5) Democracy is still better than communism.

08 (1) I was taught math by Amanda last year.,
Math was taught (to) me by Amanda last year.

   (2) A chocolate cake was chosen for us by
Teresa.

   (3) A question was asked of me by Ann.

09 Sumi runs much faster than Yuri.

01 (2) 미래시제의 수동태는 'will be+과거분사'이다. (3) make
는 직접목적어를 주어로 하는 수동태만 가능하다. (4) 조동사가
있는 문장의 수동태는 '조동사+be+p.p.' 형식을 갖는다. (5) 의
문사 who가 whom으로 바뀌는 것에 주의한다.

02 비교급을 강조할 때는 비교급 앞에 much, still, even, far, a
lot 등의 부사(구)를 쓰므로 much, still, even, far, a lot 등을
비교급 앞에 쓰면 된다.

03 (1) tree를 주어로 하면 수동태가, we를 주어로 하면 능동태가 적
절하다. (2) 초콜릿이 무엇을 생산하는 것이 아니므로 진행형이
아닌 수동태 'be+과거분사' (3) be made of: ~로 만들어지다(물
리적 변화), be made from: ~로 만들어지다(화학적 변화) (4)
목적격보어가 원형부정사인 경우 수동태 문장에서는 to부정사로
바뀐다. (5) cook은 직접목적어를 주어로 한 수동태에서는 간접
목적어 앞에 for를 쓴다. (6) read는 직접목적어를 주어로 하는
수동태만 가능하다.

04 much로 수식을 받으며 뒤에 than이 있으므로 비교급이 적절하다.

05 (1) 수동태는 '주어+be동사+과거분사+by+행위자'의 형식이
다. (2) 수동태의 부정은 'be+not+과거분사'이다. (3) carry
out을 하나의 단위처럼 생각해서 'be carried out'으로 써야 한
다. (4) ask는 직접목적어를 주어로 한 수동태에서는 간접목적
어 앞에 전치사 of를 써야 한다. (5) write는 직접목적어를 주
어로 하는 수동태만 가능하다. (6) be satisfied with: ~에 만

족하다

06 비교급 앞에 much, still, even, far, a lot 등의 부사로 비교급
을 강조한다.

07 비교급 앞에 much, still, even, far, a lot 등의 부사(구)로 비
교급을 강조한다.

08 직접목적어를 주어로 한 수동태에서 간접목적어 앞에 (1) teach
는 전치사 to를, (2) choose는 for를, (3) ask는 of를 쓴다.

09 비교급 앞에 much를 써서 비교급을 강조한다.

교과서
Reading

확인문제	p.184

1 T 2 F 3 T 4 F

확인문제	p.185

1 T 2 F 3 T

확인문제	p.185

1 T 2 F 3 F

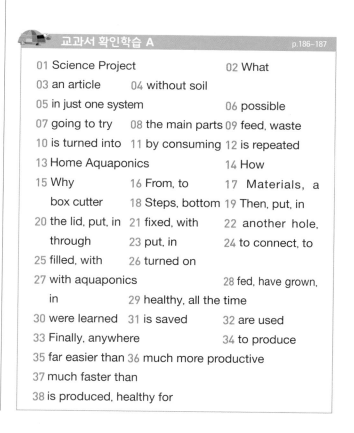

교과서 확인학습 A   p.186~187

01 Science Project   02 What

03 an article   04 without soil

05 in just one system   06 possible

07 going to try   08 the main parts   09 feed, waste

10 is turned into   11 by consuming   12 is repeated

13 Home Aquaponics   14 How

15 Why   16 From, to   17 Materials, a
box cutter   18 Steps, bottom   19 Then, put, in

20 the lid, put, in   21 fixed, with   22 another hole,
through   23 put, in   24 to connect, to

25 filled, with   26 turned on

27 with aquaponics   28 fed, have grown,
in   29 healthy, all the time

30 were learned   31 is saved   32 are used

33 Finally, anywhere   34 to produce

35 far easier than   36 much more productive

37 much faster than

38 is produced, healthy for

1 My Science Project: Home Aquaponics

2 What are you reading?

3 I'm reading an article about aquaponics.

4 It's a way of growing plants without soil.

5 We can also grow plants and raise fish in just one system.

6 Is that possible?

7 We'll see. I'm going to try it at home for my science project.

8 Fish, bacteria, and plants are the main parts of aquaponics.

9 After you feed the fish, they produce waste.

10 The waste is turned into food for the plants by bacteria.

11 The plants clean the water by consuming the food.

12 This process is repeated again and again!

13 Home Aquaponics / by Eric Jackson

14 Questions: How can I make an aquaponics system at home?

15 Why is aquaponics good?

16 Period: From May 15 to August 15

17 Materials: a pot & small stones, a fish tank, a plastic tube, a water pump, plants, some fish, a box cutter, clay

18 Steps: I made holes in the bottom of a pot.

19 Then I put small stones and plants in it.

20 I made a big hole in the lid of the fish tank and put the pot in the hole.

21 I fixed the pot in place with clay.

22 I made another hole in the lid and put a tube through it.

23 I put a water pump in the fish tank.

24 I used the tube to connect the pump to the pot.

25 I filled the fish tank with water and put some fish in it.

26 Then I turned on the pump.

27 Results: From this experiment, I grew my plants and raised fish with aquaponics.

28 I just fed the fish, but the plants have grown 17 centimeters in three months.

29 The fish stay healthy and the water is clean all the time.

30 Conclusion: Some important things about aquaponics were learned from this experiment.

31 First, water is saved because the plants don't need watering.

32 Second, it is good for the environment because no chemicals are used.

33 Finally, you can do aquaponics anywhere because it doesn't need much space.

34 I found out... Some farmers use aquaponics to produce vegetables and raise fish.

35 They choose aquaponics because it is far easier than traditional gardening.

36 Also, it is a much more productive way of growing food.

37 The plants grow much faster than plants in soil, and it saves space.

38 I hope more food is produced in this way in the future because it is healthy for us and the environment.

01 ⓐ ②, ③ ⓑ ①, ④, ⑤   02 aquaponics

03 ③   04 (A) bacteria (B) into (C) consuming

05 (A) fish (B) bacteria (C) plants   06 ③

07 ④   08 ⓐ hole, ⓑ tube   09 ⑤

10 ③   11 ⑤   12 ②   13 ③

14 ①   15 ②   16 ②, ⑤

17 ⓐ Questions ⓑ Period ⓒ Materials ⓓ Steps

18 ⑤   19 ②   20 ④   21 ①

22 ⓐ Lots of energy is wasted around us. ⓑ the classroom computers   23 To do   24 ⑤

01 ⓐ: 현재분사, ⓒ: 동명사

02 '아쿠아포닉스(수경 식물과 수중 생물을 기르는 것을 합친 시스템)'를 가리킨다.

03 ③ '아쿠아포닉스는 '한 가지' 장치만으로도 식물과 물고기를 동시에 키울 수 있다.

04 (A) bacteria가 복수이고 단수는 bacterium이다. (B) '먹이로 바뀐다'고 해야 하므로 into가 적절하다. be turned into: ~로 바뀌다, (C) 그 먹이를 '먹음으로써'라고 해야 하므로 consuming이 적절하다. consume: 먹다, 소모하다, save: 절약하다, 저축하다

05 아쿠아포닉스의 주요 부분은 '물고기', '박테리아', '식물'이다.

06 ③ '비교적', ⓐ와 나머지는 다 '몇 번이고', '되풀이해서'라는 뜻이다.

07 ④ 위 글은 '실험 보고서'이다. ① 요약, 개요, ② (특히 기계 등을 사면 따라 나오는) 설명서. ③ (책·연극·영화 등에 대한) 논평[비평], 감상문, 전기, ⑤ 독후감

08 덮개에 또 다른 '구멍'을 하나 만들고 그 안에 '관'을 넣었다.

09 ⑤ 가정용 아쿠아포닉스 시스템에 어떤 식물이 적합한지는 대답할 수 없다. ① He used a pot & small stones, a fish tank, a plastic tube, a water pump, plants, some fish, a box cutter, and clay. ② Small stones and plants. ③ With clay. ④ He used a tube.

10 ③ 아쿠아포닉스 시스템에서는 물고기가 먹이를 먹고 만들어 낸 배설물을 박테리아가 식물의 먹이로 바꿔준다. 그러므로 그저 '물고기에 밥만 주었는데도' 식물은 석 달 동안 17cm나 자랐다고 하는 것이 적절하다.

11 ⓑ와 ⑤ 마지막으로(순서), ①과 ④ 게다가, ② 그러므로, ③ 처음에는

12 ② 위 글은 '아쿠아포닉스의 많은 장점'에 관한 글이다.

13 주어진 문장의 Also에 주목한다. ③번 앞 문장의 내용에 덧붙여서 설명을 하고 있으므로 ③번이 적절하다.

14 ⓐ와 ②는 부사적 용법(목적), ①과 ⑤ 명사적 용법, ③과 ④ 형용사적 용법

15 ②는 원급을 강조하는 말이고, ⓐ와 나머지는 다 '훨씬, 한층'이라는 뜻으로 비교급을 강조하는 말이다.

16 '꽃삽'과 '물뿌리개'는 준비물에 속하지 않는다.

17 ⓐ 질문, ⓑ 기간, ⓒ 재료, ⓓ 절차

18 (C)의 the pot가 주어진 글의 a pot을 가리키므로 제일 먼저 오고 (B)의 another hole은 (C)의 a big hole에 이어 또 다른 구멍을 만든 것이므로 (C) 다음에 (B)가 이어지고 마지막으로 어항에 물을 채우고 물고기를 넣고 펌프를 작동해야 하므로 마지막에 (A)가 와야 한다. 그러므로 (C)-(B)-(A)의 순서가 적절하다.

19 ② 이 글은 아쿠아포닉스에 관해 소개하는 글이므로, 제목으로는 ② '아쿠아포닉스는 무엇인가?'가 적절하다.

20 ④ 아쿠아포닉스는 한 가지 장치만으로도 식물과 물고기를 동시에 키울 수 있다는 말이 이어지고 있기 때문에 물고기를 기르기 위한 물은 있어야 되므로, 식물을 '흙 없이' 재배할 수 있는 방법이라고 하는 것이 적절하다. aqua: 물, 수분

21 ⓑ와 ① (가축을) 사육하다, (작물을) 재배하다, ② 인상하다, ③ 모금하다, ④ (안건, 문제 등을) 제기[언급]하다, ⑤ 들어 올리다

22 ⓐ 우리 주변에서 많은 에너지가 낭비되고 있는 것을 가리킨다. ⓑ 교실 컴퓨터들

23 동명사 주어를 to부정사로 바꿔 쓸 수 있다.

24 ⑤ 에어컨을 사용할 때는 교실 문과 창문을 '닫아야' 한다.

서술형 시험대비
p.194~195

01 article
02 (A) one (B) without
03 feed
04 consuming
05 (A) waste (B) Bacteria (C) plants
06 in the bottom of a pot

07 ⓐ a pot ⓑ another hole (in the lid) ⓒ the fish tank
08 pot → fish tank, fish tank → pot
09 I just fed the fish, but the plants have grown 17 centimeters in three months.
10 (1) 식물에 물을 줄 필요가 없으므로 물이 절약된다.
    (2) 화학 물질이 사용되지 않으므로 환경에 이롭다.
    (3) 넓은 공간이 필요하지 않으므로 당신은 어디에서나 아쿠아포닉스를 쉽게 할 수 있다.
11 three
12 bottom
13 I used the tube to connect the pump to the pot.

01 article: (신문·잡지의) 글, 기사
02 아쿠아포닉스로 우리는 흙 '없이' '한 가지' 장치만으로도 식물과 물고기를 동시에 키울 수 있다.
03 food의 동사형인 'feed'를 쓰는 것이 적절하다.
04 전치사 뒤에 '동명사'로 쓰는 것이 적절하다.
05 1. 물고기가 먹이를 먹고 '배설물'을 만들어 낸다. 2. '박테리아'가 그 배설물을 식물의 먹이로 바꾼다. 3. '식물'이 그 먹이를 먹고 물을 정화한다.
06 '화분 바닥에' 구멍을 뚫었다.
07 ⓐ 화분, ⓑ 또 다른 구멍, ⓒ 어항을 가리킨다.
08 '어항'에 수중 펌프를 넣고 관을 이용하여 펌프를 '화분'에 연결하였다.
09 'in'을 보충하면 된다.
10 결론에서 말하고 있는 내용을 쓰면 된다.
11 5월 15일부터 8월 15일까지 실험을 했으므로 '약 3달' 한 것이다.
12 화분 '바닥'에 구멍을 뚫었다.
13 connect A to B: A를 B에 연결하다

영역별 핵심문제
p.197~201

01 near   02 ⑤   03 ③   04 ①
05 ②   06 ③   07 I am[I'm] worried about my science homework.   08 ⑤
09 3월 마지막 주 토요일 오후 8시 30분부터 9시30분까지 한 시간 동안 불을 끄는 것   10 ③   11 ④
12 getting hotter, going up   13 ②   14 ②
15 ④   16 ③
17 (1) I heard 17 trees are used to make one ton of paper.
   (2) A car accident happened a few days ago in front of the school.
   (3) A beautiful dress is being made for her daughter by Angie.
   (4) The tree was planted by her grandfather right after he bought the house.

(5) Yesterday Don was seen to cross the road by Bella.

(6) The expensive car will be bought by someone for whom money grows on trees.

18 ⑤

19 (1) Days are much shorter in winter than in summer.

(2) Ann is far more humorous than comedians.

(3) Soccer is even more popular than baseball in Korea.　　**20** ⑤

21 Bacteria turn the waste into food for the plants.

22 is repeated　　**23** ②, ④　　**24** ③

25 ①　　**26** ⑤　　**27** ⓐ easier ⓑ more productive ⓒ faster ⓓ more

28 aquaponics　　**29** ③

01 반의어 관계이다. 낭비하다 : 절약하다 – 먼 : 가까운

02 ⓐ는 의문사+to부정사 ⓑ는 전구가 켜진다는 turn on이 자연스럽다.

03 어떤 것을 만들거나 존재하게 하다

04 식물이 자라고 있는 토양이나 식물에 물을 붓다

05 fill A with B: A를 B로 채우다, run out: (시간이) 다 되다

06 ③ feed는 타동사로 '먹이를 주다'는 뜻이다. '~을 먹다'는 feed on을 사용한다.

08 어플리케이션을 사용하는 방법을 알려달라는 Ben의 말에 (C) 긍정의 답을 하고, 어플리케이션을 열라는 말이 온다. (B) 사진을 추가하고 음악을 선택하면 (A) 그것(어플리케이션)이 비디오를 만들 것이라는 말이 온다.

10 소녀가 Earth Hour에 참여하는 방법을 말해 주고 있으므로 ③이 적절하다.

11 Earth Hour에 참여하는 사람들은 그들의 행동이 세상을 바꿀 수 있다고 믿는다는 내용이다. exchange는 교환하다의 뜻이므로 change로 고쳐야 한다.

12 '점점 ~해지다'는 'get+비교급'을 사용한다. 상승하고 있다는 go up을 사용하여 현재진행형 형태로 쓴다.

13 에어컨 대신에 선풍기를 사용해야 한다는 의미로 instead of가 적절하다.

14 ① The cat was much bigger than yours. ③ The car in the show room was far more expensive than I thought. ④ My brother wasn't made to wash the car by my dad. ⑤ The waste is[was] turned into food for the plants by bacteria.

15 비교급을 강조할 때는 비교급 앞에 much, still, even, far, a lot 등의 부사(구)를 쓴다.

16 첫 문장은 뒤에 than이 나오므로 비교급과 강조하는 표현이 있는 far nicer, 두 번째 문장은 by로 보아 수동태로 쓰인 were made가 적절하다.

17 (1) 나무들이 사용되는 것이므로 수동태 (2) happen은 자동사

이므로 수동태로 쓰이지 않는다. (3) 직접목적어를 주어로 한 수동태에서 make는 간접목적어 앞에 for를 쓴다. (4) 과거 시제이므로 was가 되어야 하고 나무를 심은 주체를 by로 나타내야 한다. (5) 목적격보어가 원형부정사인 경우, 수동태 문장에서는 to부정사로 바뀐다. (6) 조동사가 있는 문장의 수동태는 '조동사+be+p.p.' 형식을 갖는다.

18 be satisfied with: ~에 만족하다. 나머지는 전치사 by를 쓴다.

19 비교급을 강조할 때는 비교급 앞에 much, still, even, far, a lot 등의 부사(구)를 쓴다.

20 ⓐ와 ⑤ 배설물, 폐기물, ① 낭비하다, ② 낭비, ③ '기회 따위'를 놓치다, ④ 이용[활용]되고 있지 않은(형용사)

21 bacteria를 주어로 하여 고치면 된다.

22 과정이 계속해서 '반복된다.'라고 해야 하므로, 수동태로 쓰는 것이 적절하다.

23 ⓐ와 ①, ③, ⑤는 부사적 용법, ② 명사적 용법, ④ 형용사적 용법

24 ③ 어항 '덮개'에 큰 구멍을 내고 구멍에 화분을 넣었다.

25 ⓐ in: (시간의 경과를 나타내어) ~ 후에, ⓑ be good for: ~에 좋다, be good at: ~을 잘하다

26 ⑤ 아쿠아포닉스를 하기 위해 무엇이 필요한지는 대답할 수 없다. ① Yes. ② The water is clean all the time. ③ Because the plants don't need watering. ④ Because no chemicals are used.

27 ⓐ~ⓒ는 규칙 변화를 하는 형용사들이다. productive는 앞에 more를 붙이면 된다. ⓓ는 불규칙 변화를 하는 형용사이다.

28 '아쿠아포닉스'를 가리킨다.

29 ③ 화학 물질의 사용을 줄여준다는 내용은 언급되어 있지 않다.

단원별 예상문제　　p.202~205

01 connect　　**02** ③　　**03** fixed, place / watering

04 (A) feed (B) plants (C) process　　**05** ②

06 ⑤　　**07** She wanted to talk about soil pollution.　　**08** ③　　**09** ④　　**10** ①

11 ④　　**12** ①　　**13** ③

14 (1) much[even/far/still/a lot] faster

(2) much[even/far/still/a lot] cheaper

15 (1) will be seen by Sandra tonight

(2) was invented by John Logie Baird in 1925

16 (1) The laptop is much more useful than the computer.

(2) She looks even younger than her little sister.

17 the fish　　**18** waste　　**19** ③

20 I made holes in the bottom of a pot

21 (A) fixed (B) through (C) on　　**22** ⑤

23 ③　　**24** is saved

25 because Eric watered the plants → though Eric just fed the fish 또는 though Eric didn't water the plants

01 유의어 관계이다. 선택하다 = 연결하다

02 물체의 빈 공간, 대개 물체의 표면에 있는 틈(구멍)

03 (A) fix(고정시키다)의 과거형을 쓰고, '제자리에'는 in place
를 쓴다. (B) 동사 need 뒤에 동명사를 사용하여 수동의 의미를
나타낸다.

04 아쿠아포닉스 시스템 작동 원리를 설명하는 글이다. 물고기에게
(A)먹이를 주면(feed) 물고기가 노폐물을 배설하고 그 노폐물을
박테리아가 (B)식물(plants)을 위한 먹이로 바꾸어 준다. (C)그
과정(process)이 반복된다는 내용이다. produce는 명사로 '농
산물'이란 의미고, 동사(생산하다)는 주어가 될 수 없다.

05 지구가 점점 뜨거워지고 있고, 해수면이 상승하고 있다는 말 뒤
에 지구가 걱정이 된다는 말이 자연스럽다.

06 위 대화는 지구 온난화로 인한 문제점에 관한 것이고, 빈칸 (B)
뒤에 사람들이 그들의 집을 잃어버리고 있다는 내용이 나오는 것
으로 보아 일부 섬들이 사라지고 있다는 것이 가장 자연스럽다.

07 처음에 여자아이는 토양 오염에 관해 말하기를 원했다. 질문의
시제가 과거이므로 동사도 과거형으로 답을 한다.

08 토양오염에 관한 충분한 정보를 찾지 못했다는 말에 새로운 대
안을 제시하는 말이기 때문에 (A)에는 '대신에'라는 instead가
오는 것이 적절하고, (B)는 사람들이 위험에 처해 있는 원인을
나타내는 문장이 뒤에 오기 때문에 because가 적절하다.

09 소녀는 소년이 말한 물 부족에 관해서 잘 알지 못했다.

10 ⓐ 소년은 음식을 낭비하는 것에 관해 걱정하기 때문에 식판에
음식을 너무 많이 남긴다(leave)는 말이 자연스럽고, ⓑ 식판에
너무 많은 음식을 담아서(put)는 안 된다는 말이 적절하다.

11 ④ The children이 보살펴지는 대상이므로 수동태로 써야 적
절하다.

12 비교급을 강조할 때는 비교급 앞에 much, still, even, far, a
lot 등의 부사(구)를 쓴다.

13 ③ Old people are taken good care of by them at
home. take care of를 한 단어처럼 취급해야 한다.

14 비교급을 강조할 때는 비교급 앞에 much, still, even, far, a
lot 등의 부사(구)를 쓴다.

15 능동태의 목적어가 주어 자리에 있으므로 수동태로 쓴다.

16 비교급을 강조할 때는 비교급 앞에 much, still, even, far, a
lot 등의 부사(구)를 쓴다.

17 '물고기'를 가리킨다.

18 '배설물'이 물고기에 의해 만들어진 뒤에, 박테리아가 그것을 식
물의 먹이로 바꾼다.

19 이 배설물은 '박테리아'에 의해 식물의 먹이로 바뀐다.

20 Then = 화분 바닥에 구멍을 뚫은 후에

21 (A) 찰흙으로 '고정하였다'고 해야 하므로 fixed가 적절하다.
fix: 고정시키다, 수리하다, repair: 수리하다, (B) 그 '안에' 관
을 넣었다고 해야 하므로 through가 적절하다. threw는 동사
throw의 과거형이다. (C) 펌프를 '작동하였다'고 해야 하므로
on이 적절하다. turn off: ~을 끄다

22 fill A with B: B로 A를 채우다

23 ② healthy, ③ were, ④ watering

24 물이 '절약된다'고 해야 하므로 수동태로 써야 한다.

25 에릭이 '그저 물고기에게 밥만 주었는데도' 식물은 석 달 동안
17cm나 자랐다.

01 a flower pot / how to make /, the bottom, fill, with

02 (A) water pollution (B) use less soap

03 (A) global warming (B) turn off the lights

04 (1) What was done by him last weekend?
(2) These paintings were painted by Van Gogh.
(3) That watch was given (to) me by my father
years ago. 또는 I was given that watch by my
father years ago.

05 (1) He is much[far, even, still] taller than his son.
(2) Sue uses far[much, even] more water than Nick.

06 How

07 to connect the pump to the pot

08 After

09 I learned some important things about aquaponics
from this experiment.

10 to be watered

11 (1) save water
(2) use chemicals
(3) much space

01 플라스틱 컵으로 화분을 만든 그림이다. B의 빈칸에는 'how
to+동사원형'을 사용하여 그것을 만드는 법을 말해 줄 수 있니?
라는 질문을, 마지막 A의 대답에는 'fill A with B' 형태를 사용
한다.

02 (A)는 수질 오염에 대해 걱정하고 있다는 말이 적절하고 (B)에
는 그에 대한 해결책으로 비누를 덜 사용해야 한다는 말이 자연
스럽다.

03 (A)는 지구가 점점 더워지고 있다고 했으므로 지구 온난화에 관
한 대화라는 것을 알 수 있다. (B)는 지구 온난화에 대한 해결책
으로 전등이 필요 없을 때는 꺼야 한다는 말이 자연스러우므로
turn off the lights가 적절하다.

04 (1) 의문문의 수동태는 능동태의 의문문을 평서문으로 바꾼 후
이것을 수동태로 고치고, 다시 의문문으로 바꾸면 쉽다. (3) 4형
식 문장의 수동태는 간접목적어와 직접목적어를 주어로 하는 수
동태가 가능하며 직접목적어를 주어로 한 수동태에서 give 동사
는 간접목적어 앞에 전치사 to를 쓴다.

05 than으로 이어지고 있으므로 비교급이 나와야 하며 비교급을 강
조할 때는 비교급 앞에 much, still, even, far, a lot 등의 부사
(구)를 쓴다.

06 위 글은 집에서 아쿠아포닉스 장치를 '어떻게' 만들 수 있을까?에
관한 글이다.

07 펌프를 화분에 연결하기 위하여

08 Then(그러고 나서): 어항에 물을 채우고 물고기 몇 마리를 거기에 넣고 나서

09 실험자인 'I'를 주어로 해서 능동태로 고치는 것이 적절하다.

10 need 뒤에 동명사가 쓰이면 수동의 의미(to be p.p.)를 나타낸다.

11 (1) 식물에 물을 줄 필요가 없으므로 물을 절약할 수 있다.
　　(2) 화학 물질을 사용하지 않으므로 아쿠아포닉스는 환경에 이롭다.
　　(3) 넓은 공간이 필요하지 않으므로 어디에서나 아쿠아포닉스를 쉽게 할 수 있다.

창의사고력 서술형 문제　　　　　　p.208

|모범답안|

01 (1) A: I'm worried about my friend. She uses her smartphone too often. Can you tell me how to solve this problem?
　　　B: I think she should find a new hobby.
　　(2) A: I'm worried about my cat. He is missing. Can you tell me how to solve this problem?
　　　B: I think you should put up posters to find him.

02 (A) is wasted (B) turn off (C) using (D) close
　　(E) helpful

단원별 모의고사　　　　　　p.209~212

01 ⑤　　　02 disappear　03 ①　　　04 ⑤

05 ④　　　06 Cut them into small pieces.

07 Can you tell me how to join it?　　　08 ②

09 ①　　　10 people are in danger because they don't have enough water.　　　11 ④

12 ③　　　13 ④　　　14 The stone is much heavier than the feather.

15 (1) Paper is made from wood.
　　(2) The chicken soup was cooked for Olivia by her mother.
　　(3) A man appeared on the stage slowly.
　　(4) I didn't know you were interested in Latin dance.
　　(5) Some birds were heard to sing on the tree.

16 (A) without (B) raise (C) see

17 We can also grow plants and raise fish in just one system.　　　18 ④

19 I fixed the pot in place with clay.

20 ⓐ plants ⓑ fish　　　21 ③　　　22 ④

23 soil → aquaponics system, aquaponics system → soil

01 ⑤번의 remind(상기시키다): 해야 하는 일을 기억하도록 하다는 의미로 forget을 remember로 바꾸어야 한다. ① 올바른

위치에 있는, ② 많은 것을 생산하거나 성취[달성]하는, ③ 어떤 것을 많이 먹거나 마시다 ④ 어떤 것을 다시 사용하다

02 반의어 관계이다. 끄다 : 켜다 = 나타나다 : 사라지다

03 냄비, 상자 또는 용기 등의 열려 있는 부분에 대한 덮개

04 (A) 지구를 위한 시간이 다 되어가고 있다. (B) 지구가 위험에 처해 있다는 것을 기억해라.

05 ④는 가방을 만드는 것(to make a bag)을 가리키고, 나머지는 모두 Jenny가 만든 가방을 가리킨다.

06 '~ 해 줄 수 있니?'의 의미로 Can you tell me ~?를 쓴다. '~하는 방법'은 'how to+동사원형'을 이용한다.

08 Jenny가 웅변 대회에서 토양오염에 관해 말하는 이유는 언급되어 있지 않다.

09 ⓐ는 an article을 가리키고, 나머지는 물 부족을 가리킨다.

10 '위험에 처해 있다'는 be in danger이다. because는 접속사로 뒤에 '주어+동사'가 와야 한다.

11 ④ 일반 사람이 주어인 능동태를 수동태로 바꿀 때 'by+일반 사람'은 생략 가능하다.

12 much와 far는 비교급을 강조하는 부사로 ③은 원급임에 유의한다. 나머지는 모구 빈칸 뒤에 비교급이 나오고 있다.

13 ④번은 과거 동사로 쓰였고 나머지는 과거분사로 수동태를 만들고 있다.

14 비교급을 강조할 때는 비교급 앞에 much, still, even, far, a lot 등의 부사(구)를 쓴다.

15 (1) be made of: ~로 만들어지다(물리적 변화) be made from: ~로 만들어지다(화학적 변화) (2) cook은 간접목적어를 주어로 수동태를 만들 수 없으며 수동태로 바뀔 때 간접목적어 앞에 for를 쓴다. (3) appear는 자동사이므로 수동태로 쓰이지 않는다. (4) be interested in: ~에 흥미가 있다 (5) 목적격보어가 원형부정사인 경우, 수동태 문장에서는 to부정사로 바뀐다.

16 (A) 제니퍼가 그게 가능하냐고 물어보고 있기 때문에 흙 '없이' 식물을 재배할 수 있는 방법이라고 해야 하므로 without이 적절하다. (B) 식물과 물고기를 동시에 '키울 수' 있다고 해야 하므로 raise가 적절하다. rise: 오르다, 올라가다, raise: 키우다[기르다], (C) '곧 알게 될 거야.'라고 해야 하므로 see가 적절하다. We'll see.: 곧 알게 되겠지. I'll show it.: 그것을 보여주겠다. show: ~을 보여 주다[증명하다]

17 '한 가지 장치만으로도 식물과 물고기를 동시에 키울 수 있다'는 것을 가리킨다.

18 ④는 to를 써야 한다. connect A to B: A를 B에 연결하다, 나머지는 모두 in을 쓰는 것이 적절하다.

19 'place'를 보충하면 된다.

20 에릭은 아쿠아포닉스로 '식물'과 '물고기'를 키웠다.

21 ③ 식물에 물을 줄 필요가 없으므로 물이 절약된다.

22 비교급을 강조할 때는 비교급 앞에 much, still, ever, far, a lot 등을 쓸 수 있다.

23 '아쿠아포닉스 시스템'의 식물들이 '흙에서 자라는' 식물보다 훨씬 빠르게 자란다.

교과서 파헤치기

Lesson
1

01 개인의, 사적인	02 신중하게, 조심스럽게	
03 적절한	04 의견, 논평	
05 가져오다, 데려오다		06 사전
07 멋진, 굉장한	08 필터, 여과기	09 이해하다
10 마지막으로, 마침내		11 불가능한
12 공유하다	13 빌리다	
14 신나는, 흥미진진한		15 다치다, 해치다
16 부분	17 바보 같은, 어리석은	
18 에티켓, 예절	19 괴롭히다	20 화장실
21 공공의	22 과목	23 해결하다
24 틀린, 정확하지 않은		
25 흥미로운, 재미있는		26 보고서
27 십대	28 놀랍게도	29 환경
30 조리법	31 준비하다	
32 야외에서, 옥외에서		33 가끔
34 긴장되는, 불안해 하는		35 A에서 B로
36 명심하다	37 법을 어기다	
38 ~하는 데 시간을 보내다		
39 즐거운 시간을 보내다		40 ~ 앞에
41 꼭 ~와 같이	42 확인하다	
43 발견하다, 찾아보다		

01 break	02 carrier	03 photography
04 post	05 copy	06 fact
07 poster	08 topic	09 prepare
10 healthy	11 perfect	12 display
13 leave	14 nervous	15 outdoors
16 environment	17 choose	18 sometimes
19 probably	20 surprisingly	21 result
22 selfie	23 recipe	24 rude
25 clothes	26 survey	27 appropriate
28 borrow	29 impossible	30 bother
31 understand	32 dictionary	33 restroom

34 look at	35 be interested in	
36 break the law	37 first of all	38 keep in mind
39 agree with	40 in front of	41 check out
42 find out	43 around the world	

1 healthy, 건강에 좋은   2 public, 공공의
3 share, 공유하다   4 appropriate, 적절한   5 solve, 해결하다
6 comment, 의견, 논평   7 fact, 사실   8 recipe, 조리법
9 etiquette, 에티켓. 예절   10 prepare, 준비하다
11 photography, 사진술   12 rude, 무례한
13 post, 올리다, 게시하다   14 result, 결과
15 bring, 가져오다, 데려오다   16 borrow, 빌리다

Listen & Talk 1 A

Look at. interested in / in cooking. What about / interested in

Listen & Talk 1 B

are going to / going to do, with / Are. interested in / going, because / what, interested / most interested, want to go, someday

Listen & Talk 1 C

What, looking at / listings. should , watch, interested in / I'm interested / about watching / a big fan of, listen to / why don't

Listen & Talk 1 D

What. interested in / in, What about / interested in, social media / We both

Listen & Talk 2 A

bring, on / may, should put

Listen & Talk 2 B

Can, go / Let, see / Here, May, record / No, may not / take pictures of / may not, take, in front of, enjoy

Listen & Talk 2 C

Excuse / What. for / May, borrow, you may not, can't take, home / may, copy / Yes, you may / don't share / won't

Let's communicate 1

are, in / I'm interested in / Why don't / Sounds, May, record / may, may not

Do It Yourself A

are, doing / preparing, presentation, one of / sounds fun, are, interested in / interested in, talk about / interested in, too / may, ask

Listen & Talk 1 A

G: Look at these club posters. What are you interested in?

B: I'm interested in cooking. What about you?

G: I'm interested in photography.

Listen & Talk 1 B

B: What are you going to do this weekend?

G: I'm going to go to a baseball game with my brother.

B: Are you interested in baseball?

G: Not really. I'm going to the baseball game because my brother likes baseball.

B: You're so nice! Then what are you interested in?

G: I'm more interested in soccer. I want to go to a soccer game someday.

Listen & Talk 1 C

G: What are you looking at?

B: I'm looking at TV program listings. What show should I watch?

G: Well, what are you interested in?

B: I'm interested in music.

G: Then how about watching the Friday Pop Music Show?

B: I'm actually not a big fan of pop music. I like to listen to rap music.

G: Then why don't you watch Hit the Beat?

B: Good idea.

Listen & Talk 1 D

A: What are you interested in?

B: I'm interested in games and social media. What about you?

A: I'm interested in music and social media.

B: We are both interested in social media.

Listen & Talk 2 A

B: May I bring my dog on the bus?

W: Yes, you may. But you should put your dog in the carrier.

Listen & Talk 2 B

G: Hi. Can I go in now?

M: Sure. Let me see your ticket, please.

G: Here it is. May I record the music in the concert hall?

M: No, you may not.

G: Okay. May I take pictures of the band?

M: No, you may not. You can only take pictures in front of the concert hall. Please enjoy the concert.

G: Oh, okay. Thank you.

Listen & Talk 2 C

B: Excuse me.

W: Hello. What can I do for you?

B: May I borrow this new science book?

W: No, you may not. Students can't take new books home.

B: Then may I copy some pages from the book? I need them for my science report.

W: Yes, you may. But please don't share them online.

B: Okay, I won't. Thank you!

Let's communicate 1

A: What are you interested in?

B: I'm interested in music.

A: Why don't you go to a concert hall this weekend?

B: Sounds good. May I record the music there?

A: Yes, you may. / No, you may not.

Do It Yourself A

M: Hey, Yumi. What are you doing?

G: Hello, Mr. King. I'm preparing for tomorrow's presentation. It is about one of my interests.

M: That sounds fun! What are you interested in?

G: I'm interested in photography. I will talk about it tomorrow.

M: Oh, I'm interested in photography, too.

G: Really? Then may I ask you for some advice for my presentation?

M: Sure.

01 All About　　　　02 Selfie Facts

03 Are, interested in

04 probably, post, much　　　　05 Here, facts

06 took, first, in　07 became, word, dictionary

08 took space selfie　　　　09 Selfie Survey

10 Taking, daily, enjoy　　　　11 To, out, survey

12 questions, ages, to　　　　13 Let's, at

14 Surprisingly, percent, only

15 Also, that, filters

16 survey, showed, take

17 Check out, comments

18 England, awesome　　　　19 silly, really

20 taking, spend, doing

21 look good, use

22 sometimes, look like

23 Selfie Etiquette

24 etiquette, selfies

25 yourself, before, post   26 Where am

27 appropriate, selfies

28 Don't, hospitals, restrooms   29 bother other

30 Who, this   31 Keep, anyone, see

32 Choose, when, post

33 kinds, comments, leave

34 Leave, comments, other

35 Don't, sounds, doesn't   36 Follow, tips, fun

---

01 About   02 Facts   03 interested in

04 like to post, how much, about   05 Here are, facts

06 took, first selfie

07 became, in the dictionary

08 took, first space   09 Survey

10 Taking selfies, daily life, but

11 To find out, survey

12 asked, from ages, to   13 Let's look at

14 Surprisingly, take selfies, 15 percent of the boys

15 that, use filters

16 survey, showed, take selfies

17 Check out, comments

18 Selfies, awesome   19 Making, faces

20 enjoy taking selfies, spend, doing

21 look good, use filters

22 sometimes, don't look like   23 Etiquette

24 should follow etiquette

25 Ask yorself, take, post, look at   26 Where am

27 appropriate, to take selfies

28 Don't take, public restrooms   29 bother other

30 can see   31 Keep in mind

32 Choose, when, post

33 What kinds of, leave

34 Leave, other people's selfies

35 be rude, doesn't it

36 Follow, have fun

---

6 로버트 코닐리어스가 1839년에 전 세계 최초의 셀피를 찍었다.

7 selfie는 2013년에 사전에 신조어로 등재되었다.

8 버즈 올드린이 1966년에 최초의 우주 셀피를 찍었다.

9 셀피 설문 조사

10 셀피 찍기는 많은 십대들에게 일상생활의 한 부분인데, 십대들은 정말로 그것을 즐기고 있는가?

11 알아보기 위해 우리는 설문 조사를 했다.

12 우리는 14세에서 16세 사이의 학생 300명에게 세 가지를 질문했다.

13 그 결과를 보자.

14 놀랍게도, 소녀들의 90퍼센트가 셀피를 찍지만, 소년들의 15퍼센트만이 셀피를 찍는다.

15 또한 이 학생들의 93퍼센트는 필터를 사용한다고 대답했다.

16 설문은 또한 학생들이 학교에서 가장 많이 셀피를 찍는다는 것을 보여 주었다.

17 학생들의 의견 몇 가지를 확인해 보라.

18 루이스, 14세, 영국: 셀피는 굉장하다.

19 우스꽝스러운 표정을 짓는 것은 정말로 재미있다!

20 민우, 16세, 한국: 나는 셀피 찍는 것을 즐기지만 몇몇 학생들은 그것을 하는 데 너무 많은 시간을 쓴다.

21 케이트, 15세, 덴마크: 내 사진은 필터를 사용할 때 멋져 보인다.

22 하지만 가끔 나의 셀피가 나처럼 보이지 않는다.

23 셀피 예절

24 당신은 셀피 예절을 따라야 한다.

25 셀피를 찍고, 게시하거나 보기 전에 스스로 이 질문들을 물어보라.

26 내가 어디에 있는가?

27 셀피를 찍기에 적합한 장소를 선택하라.

28 병원이나 공중화장실에서 셀피를 찍지 마라.

29 그것은 다른 사람들을 신경 쓰이게 할 수 있다.

30 누가 이것을 볼 수 있는가?

31 누구나 당신의 셀피를 볼 수 있다는 것을 명심하라.

32 그것들을 게시할 때 신중하게 골라라.

33 어떤 코멘트를 남겨야 하는가?

34 다른 사람들의 셀피에 상냥한 코멘트를 남겨라.

35 무례하게 굴지 마라. 쉬운 것처럼 들린다. 그렇지 않은가?

36 이러한 조언들을 따라서 당신의 셀피와 즐거운 시간을 보내라.

---

1 셀피에 대한 모든 것!

2 셀피에 관련된 사실들

3 당신은 셀피에 관심이 있는가?

4 당신은 아마 소셜 미디어에 셀피를 게시하기를 좋아할지도 모르지만, 셀피에 대해 얼마나 많이 알고 있는가?

5 여기 몇 가지 재미있는 사실들이 있다.

---

1 All About Selfies!

2 Selfie Facts

3 Are you interested in selfies?

4 You probably like to post selfies on social media, but how much do you know about selfies?

5 Here are some interesting facts.

6 Robert Cornelius took the world's first selfie in 1839.

7 *Selfie* became a new word in the dictionary in 2013.

8 Buzz Aldrin took the first space selfie in 1966.

9 Selfie Survey

10 Taking selfies is part of daily life for many teens, but do teens really enjoy it?

11 To find out, we did a survey.

12 We asked three questions to 300 students from ages 14 to 16.

13 Let's look at the results.

14 Surprisingly, 90 percent of the girls take selfies, but only 15 percent of the boys take selfies.

15 Also, 93 percent of these students said that they use filters.

16 The survey also showed that the students take selfies at school the most.

17 Check out some of the students' comments.

18 Lewis, 14, England Selfies are awesome.

19 Making silly faces is really fun!v

20 Minwoo, 16, Korea I enjoy taking selfies, but some students spend too much time doing it.

21 Kate, 15, Denmark My pictures look good when I use filters.

22 But sometimes my selfies don't look like me.

23 Selfie Etiquette

24 You should follow etiquette for selfies.

25 Ask yourself these questions before you take, post, or look at selfies.

26 Where am I?

27 Choose appropriate places to take selfies.

28 Don't take selfies in hospitals or public restrooms.

29 It may bother other people.

30 Who can see this?

31 Keep in mind that anyone can see your selfies.

32 Choose carefully when you post them.

33 What kinds of comments should I leave?

34 Leave nice comments on other people's selfies.

35 Don't be rude. That sounds easy, doesn't it?

36 Follow these tips and have fun with your selfies.

Project Link

1. is interested in
2. made
3. recorded, posted

4. can, at

Think and Write

1. Be, user
2. When, should follow, rules
3. can enjoy, more
4. First, should, because, may
5. Also, post, true
6. may, incorrect
7. Fianlly, should not leave
8. can, others'
9. Keep, in mind
10. will be

Culture Link

1. from, interested, environment
2. created, superhero, posted
3. also, just like

Project Link

1. Our group is interested in dance.
2. We made a dance.
3. We recorded a dance video and posted it online.
4. You can see it at www.yutu.com.

Think and Write

1. Be a Great Internet User!
2. When we use the internet, we should follow some rules.
3. Then we can enjoy the internet more.
4. First of all, we should follow language rules because people may not understand us.
5. Also, we should post only true information.
6. People may believe our incorrect information.
7. Finally, we should not leave rude comments.
8. We can hurt others' feelings.
9. Keep these rules in mind.
10. Then you will be a great internet user!

Culture Link

1. A student from the United States is interested in the environment.
2. He created a cartoon superhero, *GoGreenMan*, and posted it online.
3. He also helps the environment just like his character, *GoGreenMan*.

단어 TEST Step 1   p.21

01 흔한	02 야채	03 고기, 육류
04 더 큰, 더 많은	05 영국의	06 떨어뜨리다
07 그 밖의, 다른	08 섞인, 복합된	09 신선한
10 천천히	11 달콤한, 단	12 다른
13 전통적인	14 단 음식, 단것	15 ~로서
16 튀기다	17 먹다	18 부분
19 선택, 종류	20 대회, 콘테스트	21 당근
22 포함하다	23 인도의	24 대신에
25 항상	26 서양의	
27 (양 정도가) 더 적은		28 현지의, 지역의
29 종종, 자주	30 보통, 대개	31 양파
32 규칙	33 반찬	
34 축하하다, 기념하다		35 적어도, 최소한
36 ~할 준비가 되다	37 확인하다, 조사하다	
38 ~와 함께 나오다, ~이 딸려 있다		39 오랫동안
40 ~하는 것이 좋다[낫다]		
41 공통으로 ~을 가지다		42 ~을 덮히다
43 ~와 같은		

단어 TEST Step 2   p.22

01 grocery	02 special	03 breakfast
04 Eastern	05 add	06 exercise
07 culture	08 bean	09 tired
10 serve	11 fried	12 curry
13 delicious	14 Spanish	15 appetizer
16 healthy	17 turkey	18 suggestion
19 balanced	20 sometimes	21 health
22 fruit	23 order	24 noodle
25 recommend	26 Vietnamese	27 also
28 main dish	29 enough	30 especially
31 traditional	32 mixed	33 instead
34 common	35 at the end of ~	
36 both A and B	37 get a discount	38 put A in B
39 stay at	40 take care of	41 these days
42 throw away	43 win an award	

단어 TEST Step 3   p.23

1 fried, 튀겨진   2 tired, 피곤한   3 breakfast, 아침 식사
4 appetizer, 식전 음식   5 common, 흔한

6 mixed, 섞인, 복합된   7 order, 주문하다
8 grocery, 식료품   9 sweets, 단 음식, 단것
10 local, 현지의   11 suggestion, 제안
12 vegetable, 야채   13 contest, 대회. 콘테스트
14 serve, 음식물을 제공하다   15 recommend, 추천하다
16 noodle, 국수

대화문 TEST Step 1   p.24~25

Listen & Talk 1 A
think, eat, these days / not good for, You'd better eat

Listen & Talk 1 B
look, tired, Didn't, sleep / often feel tired / especially / usually eat / don't / You'd better eat, gives, energy / didn't, have, other suggestions / should also exercise, will, help / will

Listen & Talk 1 C
cooking contest, are, going to / going to make / want to put / Chicken, eggs / better put, in, How about / not going to, don't like / idea, should make healthy / right, should go, buy

Listen & Talk 2 A
first time, What, recommend / recommend

Listen & Talk 2 B
What, right now / searching for, for / When / want to go, but, too expensive / Why don't, check out, once, prices, good / Sounds, recommend / noodle soup / think, should go

Listen & Talk 2 C
Are, ready to / first time, do, recommend / recommend, most popular item / don't like, Could, recommend something else, How about / love, have / Why don't, order / get a, discount / have, too

Do It Yourself A
What's for / have, choices which one / some noodles, recommend / fried nooldes, sounds delicious, have, What about / don't, not hungry / But for, you'd better, Why don't, try / right

대화문 TEST Step 2   p.26~27

Listen & Talk 1 A
G: I think I eat too many sweets these days.
B: That's not good for your health. You'd better eat fruit instead.

G: You look very tired today. Didn't you sleep well?

B: Yes, I did. But I often feel tired these days, especially in the morning.

G: Do you usually eat breakfast?

B: No, I don't.

G: You'd better eat breakfast. Breakfast gives you energy.

B: I didn't know that. Do you have any other suggestions?

G: Well, you should also exercise every day. That will help you.

B: Okay. I will.

G: Justin, our school cooking contest is tomorrow. What are you going to make?

B: I'm going to make sandwiches.

G: What do you want to put in them?

B: Chicken, cheese, and eggs.

G: You'd better put vegetables in your sandwiches. How about onions and carrots?

B: No, I'm not going to add them. I don't like those vegetables.

G: That's not a good idea. Mr. Kim said we should make healthy food for the contest.

B: You're right. I should go grocery shopping and buy onions and carrots.

G: It's my first time here. What do you recommend?

M: I recommend the pizza and salad.

B: Good morning, Jiwoo. What are you doing right now?

G: I'm searching for a restaurant for my class party.

B: Wow! When is the party?

G: It's next Friday. We want to go to Bella's Restaurant, but it is too expensive.

B: Why don't you check out Chang's Restaurant? I went there once. The food and prices were good.

G: Sounds great. What do you recommend there?

B: I recommend the noodle soup.

G: I think we should go there. Thank you.

W: Hello. Are you ready to order?

B: It's my first time here. What do you recommend?

W: I recommend the chicken sandwich. It is the most popular item at our restaurant.

B: Well, I don't like chicken very much. Could you recommend something else?

W: How about the turkey sandwich?

B: Oh, I love turkey. I'll have that.

W: Why don't you order a drink with the sandwich? You can get a 500-won discount.

B: That's great. Then I'll have an orange juice, too.

G: What's for lunch today?

B: We have four choices. Which one do you want?

G: Well, I want some noodles. What do you recommend?

B: I recommend the fried noodles.

G: That sounds delicious. I will have that. What about you?

B: I don't know. I'm not hungry.

G: But for your health, you'd better have some food. Why don't you try some tomato soup?

B: All right. I will.

본문 TEST Step 1   p.28~29

01 Around, World	02 this is, from
03 many, best part	04 In, often, for
05 side dishes, as	
06 Sometimes, serves, such	
07 What, who, other	08 Let's, from
09 Belle, France 10 serves, balanced meals	
11 usually, as, appetizer	
12 Main, include, fish	13 fresh, at, end
14 can never 15 great with	16 Our, also, rule
17 stay at, for, least	18 Bruno, Brazil
19 Usually, beans	
20 Meat, common, side	
21 favorite, comes with	
22 plantain, which, like	23 usually fry
24 fresh because, come, local	
25 Nicole, Singapore	
26 different, have, Eastern, Western	
27 choose from, such as	
28 award, healthy, last	
29 healthy, tast, too	
30 Which, want, try	
31 have, in common	32 leave, at

01 Around, World

02 this is, reporter, from

03 For, the best part of

04 often eat, for lunch

05 side dishes, as

06 serves, dishes, such as

07 students who live, other countries

08 Let's hear from   09 France

10 healthy, balanced meals   11 usually eat, as

12 often include, fish

13 also eat, at the end of

14 can never forget   15 great with

16 also has, special rule

17 must stay at, at least   18 Brazil

19 have beans, rice

20 common in, side dishes

21 favorite, comes with   22 fruit, look like

23 usually fry

24 fresh because, come from local farms

25 Singapore

26 who live in, come from, both, and

27 can choose from, such as, each day

28 won an award, last year

29 always healthy, taste good,

30 Which, want to try

31 have, in common with

32 leave yours comments

1 세계 각국의 학교 급식

2 안녕하세요, 저는 한국에서 온 음식 취재 기자 민준입니다.

3 많은 학생들에게 점심시간은 학교 일과 중 가장 좋은 부분입니다.

4 한국에서는 점심으로 자주 밥과 국을 먹습니다.

5 우리는 불고기나 김치 같은 반찬도 먹습니다.

6 때때로 우리 학교는 피자, 비빔밥 또는 파스타 같은 특식을 제공합니다.

7 다른 나라에서 사는 학생들은 점심으로 무엇을 먹을까요?

8 우리 음식 취재 기자들에게서 들어보겠습니다!

9 벨, 프랑스

10 우리 학교는 건강하고 균형 잡힌 식사를 제공합니다.

11 우리는 보통 식전 음식으로 샐러드를 먹습니다.

12 주요리는 보통 고기나 생선을 포함합니다.

13 우리는 점심의 끝에 신선한 과일도 먹습니다.

14 오, 절대 바게트를 빠뜨릴 수는 없죠!

15 바게트는 치즈와 잘 어울립니다.

16 우리 학교에서 또한 특별한 규칙이 있습니다.

17 우리는 적어도 30분간 점심 식탁에서 반드시 머물러야 합니다.

18 브루노, 브라질

19 보통, 우리는 점심으로 콩과 밥을 먹습니다.

20 우리는 곁들임 음식에는 고기와 채소가 흔히 나옵니다.

21 내가 가장 좋아하는 점심에는 플랜테인이 나옵니다.

22 플랜테인은 바나나처럼 생긴 과일입니다.

23 우리는 보통 플랜테인을 튀깁니다.

24 채소와 과일이 현지 농장에서 오기 때문에 우리 학교 급식은 신선합니다.

25 니콜, 싱가포르

26 싱가포르에 사는 사람들은 매우 다양한 문화권에서 오기 때문에, 우리는 점심에 동양식과 서양식을 모두 먹습니다.

27 학생들은 매일 카레, 국수 또는 파스타와 같이 많은 요리 중에서 선택할 수 있습니다

28 우리 학교는 작년에 건강한 학교 음식 상을 받았습니다.

29 우리의 점심은 항상 건강에 좋고, 맛 또한 좋습니다!

30 여러분은 어떤 학교 급식을 먹어 보고 싶나요?

31 그것이 여러분의 학교 급식과 공통되는 것이 있습니까?

32 여러분의 의견을 www.chopchoplunch.com에 남겨 주세요.

1 School Lunches Around the World

2 Hello, this is food reporter Minjun from Korea.

3 For many students, lunch is the best part of the school day.

4 In Korea, we often eat rice and soup for lunch.

5 We also have side dishes, such as Bulgogi or Gimchi.

6 Sometimes our school serves special dishes, such as pizza, Bibimbap, or pasta.

7 What do students who live in other countries eat for lunch?

8 Let's hear from our food reporters!

9 Belle, France

10 Our school serves healthy and balanced meals.

11 We usually eat a salad as an appetizer.

12 Main dishes often include meat or fish.

13 We also eat fresh fruit at the end of the lunch.

14 Oh, I can never forget about baguettes!

15 They're great with cheese.

16 Our school also has a special rule.

17 We must stay at the lunch table for at least 30 minutes.

18 Bruno, Brazil

19 Usually, we have beans and rice for lunch.

20 Meat and vegetables are common in our side dishes.

21 My favorite lunch comes with plantains.

22 A plantain is a fruit which looks like a banana.

23 We usually fry plantains

24 Our school lunches are fresh because the vegetables and fruit come from local farms.

25 Nicole, Singapore

26 People who live in Singapore come from many different cultures, so we have both Eastern and Western dishes at lunch.

27 Students can choose from many dishes, such as curry, noodle soup, or pasta, each day.

28 My school won an award for healthy school food last year.

29 Our lunches are always healthy, and they taste good, too!

30 Which school lunch do you want to try?

31 Does it have anything in common with your school lunch?

32 Please leave your comments at www. chopchoplunch.com.

구석구석지문 TEST Step 1 p.38

Think and Write

1. Review, Favorite
2. My, restaurant
3. Spanish
4. near
5. most popular dish
6. All, is, delicious, low
7. recommend

Culture Link

1. In, on
2. to break, to live
3. curry from
4. a lot of
5. dish, dinner
6. traditional Vietnamese
7. at weddings
8. Eating, means, have a happy life

9. eat turkey to celebrate

10. give thanks for

구석구석지문 TEST Step 2 p.39

Think and Write

1. Review of My Favorite Restaurant
2. My favorite restaurant is Antonio's Restaurant.
3. It is a Spanish restaurant.
4. It is near my home.
5. Mixed paella is the most popular dish at this restaurant.
6. All of the food is really fresh and delicious, and the prices are low.
7. I recommend this restaurant!

Culture Link

1. In China, people eat noodles on their birthday.
2. Chinese people don't want to break the noodles to live a long life.
3. Doro wat is a chicken curry from Ethiopia.
4. There are a lot of vegetables in it.
5. People eat this dish for New Year's dinner.
6. Bánh xu xê is a traditional Vietnamese cake.
7. People eat this cake at weddings.
8. Eating the cake means the husbands and wife will have a happy life together.
9. In the United States, people eat turkey to celebrate Thanksgiving.
10. They give thanks for the food and their health.

단어 TEST Step 1 p.40

01 무례한	02 계속되다, 지속되다	
03 중국의; 중국어	04 달력	05 사악한, 악마의
06 자물쇠; 잠그다	07 ~을 향하다	08 채색된, 색깔이 있는
09 보름달	10 한번 해 보다	
11 (인사를 위해) 머리를 숙이다, 절하다		12 분리, 이별
13 나타내다, 상징하다		14 보초, 경비병
15 국제적인, 세계적인		16 작년에
17 베트남의; 베트남어		18 손님
19 맞이하다, 환영하다		20 손바닥; 야자나무
21 영혼, 정신	22 자매 학교	
23 무서운, 두려운, 겁나는		24 흔들다, 흔들리다
25 보호하다	26 상징(물), 기호	
27 값비싼, 귀중한, 가치 있는		28 행운
29 (닭이) 울다; 까마귀		30 베개
31 생각나게 하다, 상기시키다		32 전통의, 전통적인
33 평화, 화해	34 어둠, 암흑	
35 ~에 대해 이야기하다		36 코를 풀다
37 ~을 주시하다, 지키다		38 (옷 등을) 벗다
39 ~을 두려워하다	40 ~에 가 본 적이 있다	
41 ~으로 가득 차다	42 사라지다, 떠나가다	
43 A에게 B를 생각나게 하다		

단어 TEST Step 2 p.41

01 beach	02 powder	03 clothes
04 crow	05 experience	06 festival
07 bat	08 umbrella	09 gift shop
10 darkness	11 pillow	12 Indian
13 lock	14 half moon	15 arrive
16 musical	17 luck	18 traditional
19 pay	20 mean	21 peace
22 rooster	23 remind	24 tell
25 victory	26 toward	27 spirit
28 palm	29 represent	30 rude
31 protect	32 colored	33 evil
34 shake	35 go away	36 take off
37 remind A of B	38 point at	39 talk about
40 be full of	41 listen to	42 watch over
43 be afraid of		

단어 TEST Step 3 p.42

1 rooster, 수탉 2 darkness, 어둠, 암흑
3 evil, 사악한, 악마의 4 pillow, 베개
5 greet, 맞이하다, 환영하다 6 face, ~을 향하다
7 represent, 나타내다, 상징하다 8 crow, (닭이) 울다
9 victory, 승리, 성공 10 valuable, 값비싼, 귀중한, 가치 있는
11 palm, 손바닥 12 protect, 보호하다
13 remind, 생각나게 하다, 상기시키다
14 scary, 무서운, 두려운, 겁나는
15 bow, (인사를 위해) 머리를 숙이다, 절하다
16 symbol, 상징(물), 기호

대화문 TEST Step 1 p.43~44

Listen & Talk 1 A

Have, been to / haven't, Have / have, last, was / sounds, to go, someday

Listen & Talk 1 B

Welcome to, different traditional / looks exciting, Which, should / Let's, Have, played / haven't / traditional, from / How, play / Put, on, throw, at / sounds fun, try

Listen & Talk 1 C

is, this year / festival, What / traditional Indian, throw, at each other / sounds exciting, Have, been to / haven't, told, a lot / When / on, full moon, on March 21 / Should, bring / should wear, colored, look, beautiful / Thank you for

Listen & Talk 2 A

gave, as, What, mean / means, on a test

Listen & Talk 2 B

this, isn't it / going to buy, for, about / thinking about, cute one / good gift for, something bad / does, mean / mean separation, in Chinese / how about / idea

Listen & Talk 2 C

What a nice / took, a lot of / look at, rude / Which / is making, facing toward / wrong with / bad meaning, showing, making / does mean / means peace

Do It Yourself A

brings / to see, Spanish / too, did, say / means, Look at, moves / they / Have, been to, before / haven't, on, What, mean / means

대화문 TEST Step 2 p.45~46

Listen & Talk 1 A

G: Have you ever been to Brazil?

B: No, I haven't. Have you?

G: Yes, I have. I went there last year. There was a big samba festival.

B: That sounds interesting. I hope to go there someday.

Listen & Talk 1 B

W: Welcome to the International Games Festival. You can play many different traditional games here.

B: Wow! It looks exciting! Which game should I play first?

W: Let's see. Have you ever played gorodki?

B: No, I haven't. What is it?

W: It's a traditional game from Russia.

B: How do I play it?

W: Put five sticks on the ground. Then throw a bat at them.

B: That sounds fun. I'll try that first.

Listen & Talk 1 C

B: There is a Holi festival in Busan this year.

G: A Holi festival? What is that?

B: It's a traditional Indian festival. People throw colored powder and water at each other.

G: That sounds exciting. Have you everbeen to a Holi festival?

B: No, I haven't. But my Indian friend told me a lot about it.

G: When is the festival?

B: It's on the last full moon of the Hindu calendar. This year, it's on March 21.

G: I'd like to go. Should I bring anything?

B: No, but you should wear white clothes. Then the colored powder on your clothes will look more beautiful.

G: Okay. Thank you for the information.

Listen & Talk 2 A

G: Jinwoo, my Korean friend, gave me Yeot as a gift. What does that mean in Korea?

B: It means good luck on a test.

Listen & Talk 2 B

B: Ling's birthday is this Wednesday, isn't it?

G: Yes. I'm going to buy a book for her. What about you?

B: Well, I'm thinking about buying her an umbrella. I found a cute one in a gift shop.

G: Oh, that's not a good gift for Chinese people. It means something bad.

B: Really? What does an umbrella mean in China?

G: It means separation. The words for separation and

umbrella sound the same in Chinese.

B: I see. Then how about chocolate?

G: That's a good idea.

Listen & Talk 2 C

G: What a nice picture! Are these your friends?

B: Yes. We took this picture at the beach. We had a lot of fun.

G: Oh, look at that boy. That's really rude.

B: Which boy?

G: The boy who is making the V sign. His palm is facing toward himself.

B: What's wrong with that?

G: It has a bad meaning in England. But showing your palm and making a V sign is okay.

B: What does that mean?

G: It means victory or peace.

Do It Yourself A

G: Hello, Santiago! What brings you here today?

B: Bienvenido, Cathy. I came to see the Spanish festival.

G: Me, too. But what did you just say?

B: Bienvenido! It means "welcome" in Spanish. Look at those dancers. Their dance moves are so great.

G: Yes, they are.

B: Have you ever been to a Spanish festival before?

G: No, I haven't. Santiago, can you see the big letters on the stage? What does that mean?

B: Oh, gracias. That means "thank you."

본문 TEST Step 1   p.47~48

01 Traditional, Symbols

02 visiting, to, from   03 stay at, for

04 arrives, shows guest   05 stay here

06 guest, full, traditional   07 at, pillow

08 are, things   09 They're bats

10 on, pillow, scary

11 symbols, luck, life

12 surprising, remind, darkness

13 shows, her grandfather's

14 meet, greet, other

15 Have, seen, kind

16 haven't, so, that

17 For, thought, guards

18 close, even, sleep

19 That's interesting   20 over, why, like

21 Now understand

22 outside, walk around

23 on, piece, scary

24 mean, painting   25 it, rooster

26 crow every   27 crowing, that, beginning

28 evil, away, crows

29 never heard, before

30 Actually, afraid, spirits   31 draw, for

32 draw, rooster   33 Put, above, protect

34 Yes, will   35 so, that, longer

36 all, traditional, in

37 understand, lot   38 want, visit, with

본문 TEST Step 2   p.49~50

01 Traditional, Symbols

02 visiting, to meet, from

03 going to stay at, for

04 When, arrives, guest room   05 will stay here

06 is full of traditional   07 Look at

08 three things   09 bats

10 Bats on, pillow, scary

11 symbols of luck, long life

12 Western countries, remind, of darkness, scary

13 shows, grandfather's room

14 meet, greet each other

15 Have, seen, kind of look

16 haven't, so, that, can't

17 For a long time, have thought

18 don't close, when, sleep   19 interesting

20 watch over, why, looks like

21 Now understand

22 go outside, walk around

23 on the piece, looks scary

24 mean, rooster   25 is it

26 crow every morning

27 means, beginning

28 have believed, go away when, crows

29 never heard, before

30 Actually, afraid of, evil spirits

31 Could, draw, for   32 draw, for

33 Put, above, will protect   34 will

35 so, that, to stay longer

36 traditional Korean symbols   37 a lot of

38 want to visit, with

본문 TEST Step 3   p.51~52

1 전통적인 한국의 상징물

2 피터는 자매 학교 친구인 미나를 만나기 위해 한국을 방문 중이다.

3 피터는 일주일간 미나네 할아버지 댁에 머무를 것이다.

4 그가 도착하자, 미나가 그에게 손님방을 보여준다.

5 피터, 넌 여기에 머무르게 될 거야.

6 이 손님방은 한국의 전통 물건들로 가득 차 있어.

7 이 베개를 봐.

8 이것들은 뭐야?

9 그건 박쥐들이야.

10 내 베개 위에 박쥐? 그거 겁나는데!

11 그렇지 않아. 한국에서는 박쥐가 행운과 장수의 상징이거든.

12 그거 놀라운 일인데. 서구의 많은 나라들에서 박쥐는 사람들에게 어둠과 무서운 것들을 상기시키거든.

13 미나는 피터에게 할아버지의 방을 보여준다.

14 피터와 미나의 할아버지가 만나서 서로 인사한다.

15 안녕, 피터! 너는 이런 종류의 자물쇠를 전에 본 적 있니?

16 아니요, 본 적 없어요. 그 자물쇠는 너무 오래되어서 사실 알아볼 수가 없는데, 그건 물고기인가요?

17 맞아. 오랜 세월 동안, 한국인들은 물고기가 훌륭한 파수꾼이라고 생각해 왔단다.

18 물고기는 잘 때도 눈을 감지 않거든.

19 그거 재미있군요.

20 우리는 물고기가 귀중품을 지킬 수 있다고 생각해. 그것이 이 자물쇠가 물고기 모양으로 생긴 이유란다.

21 이제 이해가 되는군요.

22 그들은 밖에 나가서 정원을 걷는다.

23 저 종이에는 무엇이 그려져 있는 거죠? 무서워 보여요

24 이 수탉 그림을 말하는 거니?

25 오, 그게 수탉이에요?

26 응, 그렇단다. 수탉은 매일 아침 울지.

27 수탉의 울음은 새로운 날이 시작하는 것을 의미해.

28 오랫동안 한국인들은 수탉이 울 때 악령이 물러간다고 믿어 왔단다.

29 우리의 점심은 항상 건강에 좋고, 맛 또한 좋습니다!

30 정말요? 전 그런 말을 들어본 적이 없어요.

31 미나야, 날 위해 수탉을 그려 줄 수 있니?

32 물론이지. 내가 널 위해 커다란 수탉을 그려줄게!

33 그 그림을 네 문 위에 걸어 놓으렴. 그러면 그게 널 지켜 줄 거야.

34 네, 그럴게요.

35 난 이번 여행이 매우 즐거워서 더 오래 머무르고 싶다.

36 난 이 집의 모든 전통적인 한국의 상징물들이 아주 마음에 든다.

37 나는 이제 그것들을 많이 알게 되었다.

38 난 우리 가족과 함께 한국을 다시 방문하고 싶다.

1 Traditional Korean Symbols

2 Peter is visiting Korea to meet a friend, Mina, from a sister school.

3 Peter is going to stay at her grandfather's house for a week.

4 When he arrives, Mina shows him the guest room.

5 Peter, you will stay here.

6 This guest room is full of traditional Korean things.

7 Look at this pillow.

8 What are these things?

9 They're bats.

10 Bats on my pillow? That's scary!

11 Not really. In Korea, bats are symbols of luck and a long life.

12 That's surprising. In many Western countries, bats remind people of darkness and scary things.

13 Mina shows Peter her grandfather's room.

14 Peter and Mina's grandfather meet and greet each other.

15 Hi, Peter! Have you ever seen this kind of lock before?

16 No, I haven't. It's so old that I can't really tell, but is it a fish?

17 Yes. For a long time, Koreans have thought that fish are good guards.

18 Fish don't close their eyes, even when they sleep.

19 That's interesting.

20 We think fish can watch over valuable things. That's why this lock looks like a fish.

21 Now I understand.

22 They go outside and walk around the garden.

23 What is on that piece of paper? It looks scary.

24 Do you mean this painting of a rooster?

25 Oh, is it a rooster?

26 Yes, it is. Roosters crow every morning.

27 Their crowing means that a new day is beginning.

28 For many years, Koreans have believed evil spirits go away when a rooster crows.

29 Really? I've never heard that before.

30 Actually, I'm afraid of darkness and evil spirits.

31 Could you draw a rooster for me, Mina?

32 Sure. I'll draw a big rooster for you!

33 Put the drawing above your door. Then it will protect you.

34 Yes, I will.

35 I'm enjoying this trip so much that I want to stay longer.

36 I love all the traditional Korean symbols in this house.

37 Now I understand a lot of them.

38 I want to visit Korea again with my family.

Think and Write

1. traditional Chinese dances

2. There are

3. For example, are, fan

4. One of, dances is

5. dress, act like

6. usually, on, such as

7. dance moves, great

8. to practice, someday

Presentation Time

1. have a good time

2. follow

3. take off, when, go into

4. bow, others

5. give something to older people

6. blow your nose, point at

7. Lastly, call, by, first names

Think and Write

1. Do you know about traditional Chinese dances?

2. There are many kinds.

3. For example, there are a lion dance, a fan dance, and an umbrella dance.

4. One of the most famous dances is the lion dance.

5. In this dance, two dancers dress and act like lions.

6. They usually dance on special days, such as New Year's Day.

7. I think their dance moves are great.

8. I hope to practice this dance someday.

Presentation Time

1. Do you want to have a good time in Korea?

2. Then follow these steps.

3. First, please take off your shoes when you go into people's homes.

4. Next, bow when you greet others.

5. Also, use two hands when you give something to older people.

6. And do not blow your nose at the table and do not point at people.

7. Lastly, do not call older people by their first names.

Lesson 4

11 feed, 먹이를 주다　12 documentary, 다큐멘터리
13 grow, 재배하다　14 waste, 쓰레기, 폐기물
15 plate, 접시　16 experiment, 실험

01 온난화	02 낭비하다; 쓰레기, 폐기물	
03 끔찍한	04 두다, 놓다	05 지구의
06 해수면	07 사라지다	08 선풍기, 부채
09 초조한, 긴장된	10 환경	11 토양, 흙
12 충분한; 충분히	13 대신에	14 과정
15 흥미로운	16 오염	17 뚜껑
18 기르다, 키우다	19 섭취하다, 먹다, 소모하다	
20 생산하다, 만들다	21 바닥, 맨 아래	22 고정하다
23 물을 주다	24 공간	25 정원 가꾸기, 원예
26 건강한, 건강에 좋은		27 연결하다
28 도움이 되는, 유용한		29 실험
30 해결책	31 (신문) 기사	32 생산적인
33 먹이를 주다, 먹이다		34 화학 물질
35 점점 ~해지다	36 제자리에	37 올라가다, 상승하다
38 (전기, 가스, 수도 등을) 끄다		39 (시간이) 다 되다
40 위험에 처한	41 A에게 B를 상기시키다	
42 A를 B로 바꾸다	43 버리다	

01 plate	02 problem	03 bottom
04 documentary	05 warming	06 island
07 terrible	08 air conditioner	09 speech contest
10 solution	11 pollution	12 information
13 article	14 clay	15 amazing
16 sew	17 grow	18 feed
19 process	20 anywhere	21 pot
22 experiment	23 chemical	24 traditional
25 productive	26 hang	27 solve
28 environment	29 disappear	30 consume
31 helpful	32 gardening	33 global
34 connect	35 fill A with B	36 go up
37 in danger	38 turn A into B	39 cut A into B
40 remind A of B	41 throw away	42 turn on
43 be worried about		

1 produce, 생산하다　2 raise, 기르다, 키우다
3 consume, 먹다　4 repeat, 반복하다　5 hole, 구멍
6 fix, 고정시키다　7 connect, 연결하다　8 water, 물을 주다
9 chemical, 화학 물질　10 productive, 생산적인

Listen and Talk 1 A

leave, on their plates, worried about wasting food / should not put / right, shouldn't

Listen and Talk 1 B

watch, last night / didn't, What, about / global warming, is getting, going up, worried / heard about, disappearing, are losing / terrible / way to stop / turn off, instead of / try to

Listen and Talk 1 C

look nervous, wrong / worried about, are about / are, going to / soil pollution, enough information / What about, worried about, to do something / isn't there / in danger, enough water, in the near future / will talk about, solutions, for your advice

Listen and Talk 2 A

Look at, how to / for thirty minutes, turn on, anywhere / interesting

Listen and Talk 2 B

Where, get / made, myself / yourself, amazing / Why don't, not difficult / how to make / Cut, into, pieces / sounds easy, as, present

Listen and Talk 2 C

Have, heard of / haven't / global environmental, turn off, for an hour / Why, do / remind, of / such a / how to join / turn off, in March / will join

Do It Yourself

look upset, going on / worried about, about saving / how about using / how to use / Add, choose / sounds easy, try

Listen and Talk 1 A

B: In my school, students leave so much food on their plates. I'm worried about wasting food.
G: Right, that's a big problem. We should not put too much food on our plates.
B: You're right. We shouldn't.

Listen and Talk 1 B

G: Did you watch the documentary last night?

B: No, I didn't. What was it about?

G: It was about global warming. The Earth is getting hotter, and sea levels are going up. I'm worried about the Earth.

B: Oh, I've heard about that problem before. Some islands are disappearing, so people are losing their homes.

G: Yes. It is terrible.

B: Is there any way to stop it?

G: We can save energy. We should turn off the lights when we don't need them. We should also use fans instead of air conditioners.

B: Those are great ideas. I'll try to do those things.

Listen and Talk 1 C

B: You look nervous. What's wrong?

G: I'm worried about the speech contest next week. The speeches are about environmental problems and their solutions.

B: What are you going to talk about?

G: I want to talk about soil pollution, but I can't find enough information.

B: What about water problems instead? I read an article, and it said we don't have enough water. I'm really worried about it. I think we have to do something about that problem.

G: But isn't there enough water for everyone?

B: No. In some countries, people are in danger because they don't have enough water. Our country could have this problem in the near future.

G: Oh, I didn't know that. I will talk about that problem and its solutions. Thank you for your advice!

Listen and Talk 2 A

G: Look at this ball. Can you tell me how to use it?

M: Just play soccer for thirty minutes, and the light will turn on. You can use the light anywhere.

G: Wow, that's interesting.

Listen and Talk 2 B

B: I like your bag, Jenny. Where did you get it?

G: I made it myself.

B: You made it yourself? That's amazing.

G: Why don't you make one? It's not difficult.

B: Really? Can you tell me how to make it?

G: Sure. Find some old jeans. Cut them into small pieces. Then sew the pieces together.

B: That sounds easy. I'll make one as a birthday present for my sister.

Listen and Talk 2 C

G: Have you heard of Earth Hour before?

B: No, I haven't. What is it?

G: It's a global environmental event. People turn off their lights for an hour.

B: Why do they do that?

G: They do it to remind people of our environmental problems. They believe such a small action can change the world.

B: Oh, I see. Can you tell me how to join it?

G: Sure. Just turn off your lights from 8:30 p.m. to 9:30 p.m. on the last Saturday in March.

B: That's easy. I will join the next Earth Hour.

Do It Yourself

G: You look upset. What's going on?

B: I am worried about my science homework. I need to make a short video about saving the environment. But making a video is difficult.

G: Well, how about using this application? It's easy.

B: Can you tell me how to use it?

G: Sure! Open the application. Add your photos and choose some music. Then it will make a video with your photos.

B: Wow, that sounds easy. I'll try it now. Thanks.

본문 TEST Step 1   p.66~67

01 Science Project, Home   02 What, reading
03 reading, article about
04 growing, without soil
05 grow, raise, system   06 Is, possible
07 see, try, at   08 bacteria, main parts
09 After, feed, waste   10 turned into, by
11 clean, by consuming
12 process, repeated, again   13 Home, by
14 How, make, at 15 Why, good   16 From, to
17 tank, tube, cutter, clay
18 holes, bottom, pot   19 Then, put, in
20 lid, put, in   21 fixed, in, with
22 another, hole, through   23 put, in
24 used, connect, to   25 filled, with, put
26 turned on   27 grew, raised, with
28 fed, grown, in 29 stay healthy, all, time
30 things, learned, experiment
31 saved because, watering
32 for, because, used
33 Finally, anywhere, space
34 out, produce, raise
35 choose, far easier, gardening
36 much, productive, growing
37 much, soil, saves
38 produced, way, because, healthy

p.68~69

01 Science Project
02 What, reading
03 reading, article about
04 growing, without soil
05 grow, raise, system
06 Is, possible
07 see, try, at
08 bacteria, main parts
09 After, feed, waste
10 turned into, by
11 clean, by consuming
12 process, repeated, again
13 Home, by
14 How, make, at
15 Why, good
16 From, to
17 tank, tube, cutter, clay
18 holes, bottom, pot
19 Then, put, in
20 lid, put, in
21 fixed, in, with
22 another hole, through
23 put, in
24 used, connect, to
25 filled, with, put
26 turned on
27 grew, raised, with
28 fed, grown, in
29 stay healthy, all time
30 things, learned, experiment
31 saved because, watering
32 for, because, used
33 Finally, anywhere, space
34 out, produce, raise
35 choose, far easier, gardening
36 much, productive, growing
37 much, soil, saves
38 produced, way, because, healthy

 p.70~71

1 나의 과학 프로젝트: 가정용 아쿠아포닉스
2 무엇을 읽고 있니?
3 아쿠아포닉스에 관한 기사를 읽고 있어.
4 흙 없이 식물을 재배할 수 있는 방법이야.
5 또 한 가지 장치만으로도 식물과 물고기를 동시에 키울 수 있어.
6 그게 가능하니?
7 곧 알게 될 거야. 내가 과학 프로젝트로 집에서 해 볼 예정이거든.
8 물고기, 박테리아, 식물이 아쿠아포닉스의 주요 부분이다.
9 물고기에게 먹이를 주면, 그것들은 배설물을 만들어 낸다.
10 이 배설물은 박테리아에 의해 식물의 먹이로 바뀐다.
11 식물은 그 먹이를 먹음으로써 물을 정화한다.
12 이러한 과정이 계속해서 반복된다!
13 가정용 아쿠아포닉스   에릭 잭슨
14 질문: 집에서 아쿠아포닉스 장치를 어떻게 만들 수 있을까?
15 아쿠아포닉스가 왜 좋은가?
16 기간: 5월 15일부터 8월 15일까지
17 재료: 화분과 작은 돌들, 어항, 플라스틱 관, 수중 펌프, 식물, 물고기, 커터칼, 찰흙
18 절차: 화분 바닥에 구멍들을 뚫었다.
19 그런 후에 화분에 작은 돌들을 넣고 식물을 심었다.
20 어항 덮개에 큰 구멍을 내고 구멍에 그 화분을 넣었다.
21 찰흙으로 화분을 제자리에 고정하였다.
22 덮개에 또 다른 구멍을 하나 만들고 그 안에 관을 넣었다.
23 어항에 수중 펌프를 넣었다.

24 관을 이용하여 펌프를 화분에 연결하였다.
25 어항에 물을 채우고 물고기 몇 마리를 거기에 넣었다.
26 그러고 나서 펌프를 작동하였다.
27 결과: 이 실험으로 나는 아쿠아포닉스로 식물과 물고기를 키웠다.
28 나는 그저 물고기에 밥만 주었는데도 식물은 석 달 동안 17cm나 자랐다.
29 물고기는 건강을 유지하며 물은 항상 깨끗하다.
30 결론: 아쿠아포닉스에 관한 몇 가지 중요한 사항이 이 실험에서 발견되었다.
31 첫째, 식물에 물을 줄 필요가 없으므로 물이 절약된다.
32 둘째, 화학 물질이 사용되지 않으므로 아쿠아포닉스는 환경에 이롭다.
33 끝으로, 넓은 공간이 필요하지 않으므로 당신은 어디에서나 아쿠아포닉스를 쉽게 할 수 있다.
34 나는 알게 되었다...몇몇 농부들은 채소를 생산하고 물고기를 키우는 데 아쿠아포닉스를 이용한다.
35 그들은 아쿠아포닉스가 전통 재배 방식보다 훨씬 더 쉽기 때문에 그것을 선택한다.
36 또한, 아쿠아포닉스는 식량을 재배하는 훨씬 더 생산적인 방법이다.
37 식물들이 흙에서 자라는 식물보다 훨씬 빠르게 자라고 공간도 절약한다.
38 그것은 우리와 환경에 훨씬 건강하기 때문에 나는 미래에 더 많은 식량이 이런 방식으로 생산되기를 희망한다.

 p.72~75

1 My Science Project: Home Aquaponics
2 What are you reading?
3 I'm reading an article about aquaponics.
4 It's a way of growing plants without soil.
5 We can also grow plants and raise fish in just one system.
6 Is that possible?
7 We'll see. I'm going to try it at home for my science project.
8 Fish, bacteria, and plants are the main parts of aquaponics.
9 After you feed the fish, they produce waste.
10 The waste is turned into food for the plants by bacteria.
11 The plants clean the water by consuming the food.
12 This process is repeated again and again!
13 Home Aquaponics   by Eric Jackson
14 Questions: How can I make an aquaponics system at home?
15 Why is aquaponics good?
16 Period: From May 15 to August 15
17 Materials: a pot & small stones, a fish tank, a plastic tube, a water pump, plants, some fish, a box cutter, clay
18 Steps: I made holes in the bottom of a pot.

19 Then I put small stones and plants in it.

20 I made a big hole in the lid of the fish tank and put the pot in the hole.

21 I fixed the pot in place with clay.

22 I made another hole in the lid and put a tube through it.

23 I put a water pump in the fish tank.

24 I used the tube to connect the pump to the pot.

25 I filled the fish tank with water and put some fish in it.

26 Then I turned on the pump.

27 Results: From this experiment, I grew my plants and raised fish with aquaponics.

28 I just fed the fish, but the plants have grown 17 centimeters in three months.

29 The fish stay healthy and the water is clean all the time.

30 Conclusion: Some important things about aquaponics were learned from this experiment.

31 First, water is saved because the plants don't need watering.

32 Second, it is good for the environment because no chemicals are used.

33 Finally, you can do aquaponics anywhere because it doesn't need much space.

34 I found out... Some farmers use aquaponics to produce vegetables and raise fish.

35 They choose aquaponics because it is far easier than traditional gardening.

36 Also, it is a much more productive way of growing food.

37 The plants grow much faster than plants in soil, and it saves space.

38 I hope more food is produced in this way in the future because it is healthy for us and the environment.

구석구석지문 TEST Step 1   p.76

After You Read
1. Farming
2. want to grow
3. try, farming
4. anywhere near, with
5. Each, hangs from, above, don't need

Think and Write
1. Let's, Green
2. Lots of, wasted around
3. To solve, let's do
4. turn off, when, leave
5. Next, when, not using
6. Lastly, close, when we use
7. Doing, be helpful

Culture Link
1. works without
2. is powered by
3. is useful for, little
4. When, have, water drop
5. reduces, plastic bottles
6. special tower
7. Thanks to, get, from, saves

구석구석지문 TEST Step 2   p.77

After You Read
1. Window Farming
2. Do you want to grow plants in your house?
3. Then try window farming!
4. You can do it anywhere near a window with plastic bottles.
5. Each bottle hangs from the one above, so you don't need much space.

Think and Write
1. Let's Make Our School Green!
2. Lots of energy is wasted around us.
3. To solve this problem, let's do these things.
4. First, we should trun off the lights when we leave our classrooms.
5. Next, we should turn off the classroom computers when we are not using them.
6. Lastly, we should close the doors and windows when we use air conditioners.
7. Doing these things will be helpful to our school and the environment.

Culture Link
1. This refrigerator works without electricity.
2. It is powered by dirty water.
3. It is useful for countries that have little electricity.
4. When you need water, just have this water drop!
5. It reduces the use of plastic bottles.
6. This special tower is the Warka Water Tower.
7. Thanks to this tower, people can get water from the air. It saves water.

적중100 plus

1학기 전과정

영어 기출 문제집

정답 및 해설

능률 | 김성곤

적중 **100** + 특별부록

Plan B

우리학교
최신기출

능률 · 김성곤 교과서를 배우는

학교 시험문제 분석 · 모음 · 해설집

전국단위 학교 시험문제 수집 및 분석
출제 빈도가 높은 문제 위주로 선별
문제 풀이에 필요한 상세한 해설

중2-1
영어

능률 · 김성곤

2학년 영어 1학기 중간고사(1과) 1회

반 이 름		점수	

문항수 : 선택형(24문항) 서술형(5문항)   20 . . .

◎ 선택형 문항의 답안은 컴퓨터용 수정 싸인펜을 사용하여 OMR 답안지에 바르게 표기하시오.
◎ 서술형 문제는 답을 답안지에 반드시 검정 볼펜으로 쓰시오.
◎ 총 29문항 100점 만점입니다. 문항별 배점은 각 문항에 표시되어 있습니다.

[경북 ○○중]

1. 다음 주어진 단어와 영영풀이의 뜻과 일치하지 <u>않는</u> 것은? (3점)

① photography: a person who takes photographs
② result: something that happens at the end of an event
③ comment: to give your opinion about something
④ appropriate: being good for a special situation
⑤ public: relating to all the people in a country or community

[서울 서초구 ○○중]

2. 다음 짝지어진 단어의 의미상 관계가 <u>다른</u> 하나는? (3점)

① polite : rude
② wide : narrow
③ private : public
④ suggestion : comment
⑤ same : different

[서울 강동구 ○○중]

3. 다음 〈보기〉의 영영풀이에 해당되는 단어는? (3점)

> **보기**
> a set of rules for proper social behavior

① etiquette   ② rule
③ comment   ④ tip
⑤ appropriate

[서울 강동구 ○○중]

4. 다음 중 문맥이나 어법이 자연스러운 것은? (4점)

① Joe called his friend, and who lives in Canada.
② Look at the girl which is eating rice noodle soup.
③ Mom is interested in cooking, so I'll buy her a cookbook who likes it.
④ We're going to Bella's Restaurant which food and prices are good.
⑤ They are searching for a restaurant that is good for their class party this Friday.

[전북 ○○중]

5. 다음 대화의 밑줄 친 부분의 의도로 적절한 것은? (3점)

> A: Hi. <u>Can I go in now?</u>
> B: Sure. Let me see your ticket.

① 불평하기
② 거절하기
③ 허가 요청하기
④ 확실성 정도 파악하기
⑤ 기대하기

6. 다음 중 대화가 가장 <u>어색한</u> 것은? (2점)

① A: What are you interested in?
  B: I'm interested in playing computer games.

② A: May I have some coffee here?
  B: Yes, you may.

③ A: May I feed the dogs there?
  B: No, I may not.

④ A: Why don't you go to a public library this
    Saturday?
  B: Sounds good.

⑤ A: What are you going to do tomorrow?
  B: I'm going to go to a baseball game with
    my brother.

7. 위 대화가 자연스럽게 이어지도록 빈칸 (A)~(D)에 문장 @~@를 가장 알맞은 순서로 배열한 것은? (4점)

① ⓑ-ⓐ-ⓓ-ⓒ

② ⓑ-ⓐ-ⓒ-ⓓ

③ ⓒ-ⓓ-ⓑ-ⓐ

④ ⓒ-ⓐ-ⓑ-ⓓ

⑤ ⓐ-ⓑ-ⓒ-ⓓ

8. 위 대화가 이루어지는 장소로 가장 알맞은 것은?
(3점)

① 미술관   ② 박물관

③ 밴드 연습실   ④ 음악실

⑤ 음악 공연장

[7-8] 다음 대화를 읽고 물음에 답하시오.

> Girl: Hi. Can I go in now?
> Man: (A)_____
> Girl: (B)_____
> Man: (C)_____
> Girl: (D)_____
> Man: No, you may not. You can only take
>   pictures in front of the concert hall. Please
>   enjoy the concert.
> Girl: Oh, okay. Thank you.

> ⓐ Okay. May I take pictures of the band?
> ⓑ No, you may not.
> ⓒ Sure. Let me see your ticket, please.
> ⓓ Here it is. May I record the music in the
>   concert hall?

9. 다음 밑줄 친 우리말을 아래의 〈조건〉에 맞게 주어진 단어를 사용하여 영어로 쓰시오. (5점)

> A new school year started, and I wanted to make new friends. I'm good at playing the guitar, so I joined the music club. I met Chris there. Nowadays, (A)<u>그에게 메시지를 보내는 것은 재미있다.</u> Also, (B)<u>서로에게 노래를 추천해주는 것은 나를 행복하게 만든다.</u>

조건
1. (A)와 (B) 모두 동명사 주어를 반드시 사용할 것
2. 주어진 단어들을 반드시 사용하되, 필요할 경우 어형을 바꿀 것

(A) _____

  (fun, send, to, messages 사용)

(B) _____

  (to each other, recommend, make 사용)

10. 다음 중 문법적으로 옳은 문장의 개수는? (3점)

a. I enjoy listen to music.
b. Your friend looks friendly.
c. Posting rude comments are not good.
d. She visited the store which sells jackets.
e. I'm interested in take selfies at home.
f. Look at the dog who is playing with a ball.

① 1개   ② 2개   ③ 3개
④ 4개   ⑤ 5개

12. 다음 괄호 안의 단어를 활용하고, to 부정사 또는 동명사를 사용하여 주어진 우리말을 영어로 쓰시오. (필요시 단어 추가 가능) (6점)

(1) 아이들을 데리고 와야 하는 것 잊지 마!
    (forget / pick up the children)
(2) 우리는 해변으로 가기로 결정했다.
    (decide / go to the beach)
(3) 그 소음 그만 내요!
    (stop / make that noise)

(1)_____

_____

(2)_____

_____

(3)_____

_____

11. 다음 밑줄 친 ⓐ~ⓒ의 알맞은 형태로 짝지어진 것은? (4점)

A: Selfies are awesome. ⓐMake silly faces is really fun!
B: I enjoy ⓑtake selfies, but some students spend too much time ⓒdo it.

	ⓐ	ⓑ	ⓒ
①	To make	taking	to do
②	Making	to take	doing
③	Making	to take	to do
④	To make	to take	doing
⑤	Making	taking	doing

13. 다음 중 밑줄 친 부분의 용법이 나머지 넷과 다른 하나는? (3점)

① My hobby is listening to music.
② Buying things online can save your time.
③ Reading novels is good for writing.
④ She is studying math for the exam.
⑤ Playing soccer with his friends is his hobby.

[14-15] 다음 대화를 읽고 물음에 답하시오.

[Dialogue 1]

Tom: What are you going to do this weekend?

Amy: I'm going to go to a baseball game with my brother.

Tom: Are you interested in baseball?

Amy: Not really. I'm going to the baseball game because my brother likes baseball.

Tom: You're so nice! Then (A)_____

_____

Amy: I'm more interested in soccer. I want to go to a soccer game someday.

[Dialogue 2]

Jane: What are you looking at?

Eric : I'm looking at TV program listings. What show should I watch?

Jane: Well, (A)_____

Eric : I'm interested in music.

Jane: Then how about watching the *Pop Music Show*?

Eric : I'm not a big fan of pop music. I like to listen to rap music.

Jane: Then why don't you watch *Hit the Beat*?

Eric: Good idea.

14. 위 대화의 빈칸 (A)에 공통으로 들어갈 말은? (3점)

① may I join you?

② what are you interested in?

③ let me see the schedule, please.

④ Can I borrow your books about it?

⑤ we are both interested in sports and music.

15. Which are TRUE according to the dialogues? Choose two. (3점)

① Tom and Amy will go to a soccer game together.

② Tom already knew that Amy's favorite sport is soccer.

③ Amy is going to watch a baseball game this weekend.

④ Eric decided to watch *Hit the Beat* after Jane's suggestion.

⑤ Jane tells Eric to watch the *Pop Music Show* because she herself likes pop music.

[16-18] 다음 글을 읽고 물음에 답하시오.

Do you think your selfies are boring? Then these special tips will help you take better selfies. First, you should just be yourself. If you try too hard, others will notice. Smiling can help you look more welcoming and cheerful. Second, try different angles to find your best angle. For girls, taking pictures from above makes them look cuter. For guys, taking pictures from below makes them look cooler. Third, filters are amazing. They make ordinary pictures look more dramatic! Lastly, _____. Common ones like the V-sign are too boring. Be creative and use other poses to show your personality. Make your selfies fun, so you can have lasting memories.

16. 위 글의 빈칸에 들어갈 말로 가장 적절한 것은?
(3점)

① smile a lot

② copy others' gestures

③ create your own poses

④ follow the trend of selfies

⑤ use the most common poses

17. 위 글을 읽고 다음 질문에 대한 답을 완전한 영어 문장으로 쓰시오.
(5점)

> (1) Q: How can smiling help you?
> A: _____
>
> (2) Q: Why does the writer suggest using filters?
> A: It is because _____.

(1)_____

(2)_____

18. Which is NOT true according to the passage?
(3점)

① Filters make ordinary pictures look more dramatic.

② Taking pictures from above makes everyone look cuter.

③ There are some tips that will help you take better selfies.

④ When you smile, you look more welcoming and cheerful.

⑤ Using your own poses makes your selfies less boring.

[19~20] 다음 글을 읽고 물음에 답하시오.

> (A) Are you interested in selfies? (B) You probably like to post selfies on social media, (C) but how much do you know about selfies? (D)
>
> 1. Robert Cornelius took the world's first selfie in 1839.
> 2. *Selfie* became a new word in the dictionary in 2013.
> 3. Buzz Aldrin took the first space selfie in 1966. (E)

19. 위 글의 제목으로 가장 알맞은 것은?
(4점)

① Selfie Facts

② Selfie Rules

③ Selfie Clubs

④ Selfie Survey

⑤ Selfie Etiquette

20. 다음 (A)~(E) 중 주어진 문장이 들어갈 위치로 가장 적절한 곳은?
(3점)

> Here are some interesting facts.

① (A)   ② (B)   ③ (C)

④ (D)   ⑤ (E)

[21-24] 다음 글을 읽고 물음에 답하시오.

> You should follow etiquette for selfies. Ask ㉠_____ these questions before you take, post, or look at selfies.
>
> 1. (A)_____
> Choose appropriate places to take selfies. Don't take selfies in hospitals or public restrooms.
>
> 2. Who can see this?
> Keep in mind ⓐthat anyone can see your selfies.
> Choose carefully when you post them.
>
> 3. What kind of comments should I leave?
> Leave nice comments on other people's selfies. Don't be rude.
>
> That sounds easy, ㉡_____ _____?
> Follow these tips and have fun with your selfies!

22. 위 글의 빈칸 (A)에 가장 알맞은 말은? (3점)

① Where am I?
② Who is taking this?
③ When can I post it?
④ How can you take it?
⑤ Where do you post this?

23. 위 글의 ㉠, ㉡에 들어갈 적절한 단어를 쓰시오. (5점)

(1) ㉠: _____ (너 자신)
(2) ㉡: _____ _____ (그렇지 않니)

21. 위 글을 읽고 답할 수 없는 질문은? (4점)

① Where shouldn't we take selfies?
② Where is the best places to take selfies?
③ How many etiquettes are there for selfies?
④ What should we do before posting our selfies?
⑤ What kind of comments should we leave on other people's selfies?

24. 위 글의 밑줄 친 ⓐthat과 쓰임이 같은 것은? (3점)

① We don't need that much time.
② Is that your new English teacher?
③ I don't think you are taller than that girl.
④ Did he say that he left nice comments?
⑤ It's a lotion that is popular among teenagers.

[25-27] 다음 글을 읽고 물음에 답하시오.

Are you interested in selfies? You ⓐprobably like to post selfies on social media, but ⓑhow much do you know about selfies? Here are some ⓒinteresting facts.

1. Robert Cornelius took the world's first selfie in 1839.
2. *Selfie* became a new word in the ⓓdictionary in 2013.
3. Buzz Aldrin took the first ⓔspace selfie in 1966.

25. 위 글의 문맥상, ⓐ~ⓔ의 의미가 바르게 연결되지 않은 것은? (2점)

① probably : 확실히
② how much : 얼마나 많이
③ interesting : 흥미로운
④ dictionary : 사전
⑤ space : 우주

27. 위 글에서 〈보기〉의 질문에 대한 답을 포함하는 문장을 찾아 그대로 쓰시오. (3점)

> **보기**
> Who took the world's first selfie?

답: _____

[28-29] 다음 글을 읽고 물음에 답하시오.

- Lewis, 14, England
  Selfies are awesome. Making silly faces ⓐare really fun!
- Minwoo, 16, Korea
  I enjoy ⓑtaking selfies, but some students spend too much time ⓒdoing it.
- Kate, 15, Denmark
  My pictures look ⓓgood when I use filters. But sometimes my selfies don't ⓔlook like me.

28. 위 글의 밑줄 친 ⓐ~ⓔ 중 어법상 가장 어색한 것은? (3점)

① ⓐ   ② ⓑ   ③ ⓒ
④ ⓓ   ⑤ ⓔ

26. 위 글의 내용과 일치하지 않는 것은? (3점)

① 세계 최초의 셀피를 찍은 사람은 Robert Cornelius 다.
② selfie라는 신조어는 2013년에 사전에 등재되었다.
③ Buzz Aldrin은 selfie라는 신조어를 만들었다.
④ Buzz Aldrin은 우주에서 셀피를 찍었다.
⑤ Buzz Aldrin은 1966년에 셀피를 찍었다.

29. 위 글의 주제로 가장 알맞은 것은? (4점)

① Why do teens like taking selfies?
② The most popular students' selfies
③ Why is taking selfies fun?
④ The review about the teen's selfies
⑤ The students' comments about taking selfies

2학년 영어 1학기 중간고사(1과) 2회

반		점수	
이름			

문항수 : 선택형(19문항) 서술형(11문항)   20 . . .

◎ 선택형 문항의 답안은 컴퓨터용 수정 싸인펜을 사용하여 OMR 답안지에 바르게 표기하시오.
◎ 서술형 문제는 답을 답안지에 반드시 검정 볼펜으로 쓰시오.
◎ 총 30문항 100점 만점입니다. 문항별 배점은 각 문항에 표시되어 있습니다.

[전북 ○○중]

1. 다음의 영영풀이에 해당하는 단어는?　(3점)

correct for a particular time, situation, or purpose

① serious　　　　② appropriate
③ comfortable　　④ convenient
⑤ comprehensive

[서울 서초구 ○○중]

2. 다음 빈칸에 들어갈 말로 어울리는 것은?　(4점)

- I have an ___①___ in travel.
- You need to have a more ___②___ diet.
- She accepted her mother's ___③___.
- I ___④___ the book from the library.
- They___⑤___ inappropriate comments.

① interested　　② served
③ advise　　　　④ lent
⑤ left

[서울 종로구 ○○중]

3. 〈보기〉의 (A), (B)에 공통으로 들어갈 한 단어를 쓰시오.　(3점)

> 보기
> - It is very interesting to (A)_____ pictures in the garden.
> - I usually (B)_____ a walk after school.

→ _____

[서울 성북구 ○○중]

4. 다음 짝지어진 대화 중 흐름이 가장 자연스럽지 않은 것은?　(3점)

① A: Can I go in now?
　 B: Sure. Let me see your ticket, please.
② A: Hello. What can I do for you?
　 B: Can I borrow this new science book?
③ A: Are you ready to order?
　 B: It's my first time here. What do you recommend?
④ A: Look at these club posters. What are you interested in?
　 B: Yes, I am. I'm interested in photography.
⑤ A: I often feel tired these days, especially in the morning.
　 B: I think you should eat breakfast. Breakfast gives you energy.

[서울 강동구 ○○중]

5. 다음 〈보기〉에서 어법상 올바른 문장을 모두 고른 것은?　(3점)

> 보기
> a. I hope seeing you soon.
> b. I don't mind starting right away.
> c. We don't like swimming in the sea.
> d. They finished to clean the classroom.
> e. When did you begin learning French?

① a, b　　　　② a, c, d
③ b, c, e　　　④ b, d, e
⑤ c, e

6. 다음 〈보기〉에서 어법상 <u>어색한</u> 한 단어를 바르게 변형시켜 문장을 다시 쓰시오. (3점)

보기

This steak smells deliciously.

답: _____.

[7-8] 다음 대화를 읽고 물음에 답하시오.

A: Excuse me.
B: Hi, Eric! ⓐ<u>How may I help you?</u>
A: May I borrow this new science book?
B: ⓑ<u>I am sorry, but you can't.</u> Students can't take new books home.
A: ⓒ<u>Then may I copy some pages from the book?</u> I need them for my science report.
B: Yes, you may. ⓓ<u>But please don't share them online.</u>
A: ⓔ<u>Okay, I will.</u> Thank you!

7. 위 대화의 밑줄 친 ⓐ~ⓔ 중 가장 <u>어색한</u> 것은?(3점)
① ⓐ   ② ⓑ   ③ ⓒ
④ ⓓ   ⑤ ⓔ

8. 아래의 빈칸 (A), (B)를 채워 위 대화를 요약하시오. (3점)

Eric can't (A)_____ the new science book, but he can (B)_____ some pages from the book.

9. 다음 〈보기〉와 같은 뜻이 되는 문장은? (3점)

보기

누구나 당신의 셀피를 볼 수 있다는 것을 명심하라.

① Kept in mind that anyone can see your selfies.
② Keep in mind that anyone can see your selfies.
③ Keeps in mind that anyone can see your selfies.
④ Keeping in mind that anyone can see your selfies.
⑤ To keep in mind that anyone can see your selfies.

10. 다음 글의 밑줄 친 우리말을 아래의 〈조건〉에 맞게 주어진 단어를 사용하여 영어로 쓰시오. (5점)

I'm at the festival with my brother.
(A) <u>꽃들이 아름답게 보인다.</u>
The music sounds great.
(B) <u>모든 음식이 맛있는 냄새가 난다.</u>
I feel very happy.

조건

• 감각동사를 반드시 활용할 것

(A) _____
   (the flowers 사용)
(B) _____
   (tasty 사용)

11. 다음 주어진 문장의 어법상 <u>어색한</u> 부분을 찾아 올바른 문장으로 고쳐서 다시 쓰시오. (4점)

(1) The singer's voice sounded friend.
→ _____

(2) The girl looks happily.
→ _____

[12~14] 다음 글을 읽고 물음에 답하시오.

Do you think your selfies are boring? Then these special tips will help you take better selfies. First, you should just be yourself and pose naturally. If you try too (A)<u>hard</u>, others will notice. Smiling can help you look more welcoming and cheerful. Second, try different angles to find your best angle. For girls, taking pictures from above makes them look cuter. For guys, taking pictures from below makes them look cooler. Third, filters are (B)_____. They make ordinary pictures look more dramatic! Lastly, create your own poses. Common ones like the V-sign are too boring. Be creative and use other poses to show your personality. Make your selfies fun, so you can have lasting memories.

12. 위 글의 빈칸에 들어갈 말로 가장 적절한 것은? (2점)

① amazing   ② awful

③ boring   ④ excited

⑤ nervous

13. 위 글의 밑줄 친 (A)hard와 뜻이 가장 유사한 것은? (3점)

① The hill is <u>hard</u> to climb.

② The chairs felt <u>hard</u> and uncomfortable.

③ It is <u>hard</u> to believe that she's only nine.

④ Work <u>hard</u> and play hard, that's my motto.

⑤ It hasn't rained in a long time, and the ground is <u>hard</u>.

14. 위 글의 내용과 일치하지 <u>않는</u> 것은? (3점)

① 자연스런 포즈로 사진을 찍는 것이 좋다.

② 셀카를 잘 찍기 위한 특별한 비법이 있다.

③ 사진을 찍을 때 웃는 것은 활기찬 느낌을 준다.

④ 창의적인 포즈로 자신의 개성을 드러낼 수 있다.

⑤ 여학생들은 아래 각도의 사진이 더 귀여워 보인다.

15. 다음 대화의 빈칸에 들어갈 알맞은 표현은? (3점)

Boy: Excuse me.
Girl: Hello. What can I do for you?
Boy: May I borrow this new science book?
Girl: _____ Students can't take new books home.
Boy: Then may I copy some pages from the book? I need them for my science report.
Girl: Of course. But please don't share them online.
Boy: Okay, I won't. Thank you!

① Yes, you may.

② No problem.

③ Sure, you can.

④ No, you may not.

⑤ I'm sorry, but you can.

[16–20] 다음 글을 읽고 물음에 답하시오.

#Selfie Survey

(A)[Take / Taking] selfies is part of daily life for many teens, but do teens really enjoy it? (B)[Finding out / To find out], we did a survey. We asked three questions to 300 students from ages 14 to 16. Let's look at the results.

Q1. Do you take selfies?

Q2. Do you use filters on your selfies to look good?

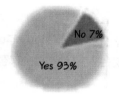

Q3. Where do you usually take selfies?

Surprisingly, 90 percent of the girls take selfies, but only 15 percent of the boys take selfies. Also, 93 percent of these students said (가)that they use filters. The survey also showed that the students take selfies at school the most. Check out some of the students' comments.

Lewis, 14, England: Selfies are awesome. Making silly faces is really fun!

Minwoo, 16, Korea: I enjoy (C)[to take / taking] selfies, but some students spend too much time do it.

Kate, 15, Denmark: My pictures look good when I use filters. But sometimes my selfies don't look like me.

16. 위 글의 밑줄 친 (가)that의 쓰임과 <u>다른</u> 것은?(3점)

① I don't think <u>that</u> it will rain.

② I didn't know <u>that</u> my friend would give me a gift.

③ I bought a jacket <u>that</u> has many pockets.

④ Can you believe <u>that</u> he is a scientist?

⑤ She said <u>that</u> he would come to the party.

17. Which one is NOT true according to the passage? (3점)

① Not many boys take selfies.

② A lot of teens use filters on their selfies.

③ The survey asked three questions.

④ Seven percent of the students don't use filters on their selfies.

⑤ The students take selfies at home the most.

18. 위 글의 괄호 (A)~(C) 안에 알맞은 말끼리 바르게 짝 지어진 것은? (4점)

① Take — To find out — taking

② Take — Finding out — to take

③ Taking — Finding out — taking

④ Taking— To find out — taking

⑤ Taking— To find out — to take

19. 위 글에서 어법상 <u>어색한</u> 부분을 찾아 바르게 고치시오. (4점)

답: _____ → _____

20. 위 글의 설문조사 그래프를 보고 그 결과를 요약한 글이다. 빈칸 (A)~(F)에 알맞은 말을 쓰시오. (6점)

Surprisingly, 90 percent of the (A)_____ take selfies, but 85 percent of the boys (B)_____ (C)_____ selfies.

Also, 93 percent of these students said that they use (D)_____.

The survey also showed that the students take selfies (E)_____ (F)_____ the most.

(A) _____

(B) _____

(C) _____

(D) _____

(E) _____

(F) _____

[21-23] 다음 글을 읽고 물음에 답하시오.

Check out some of the students' comments.

Lewis, 14, England
  Selfies are awesome. Making silly faces is really fun!

Minwoo, 16, Korea
  (A)나는 셀피 찍는 것을 즐긴다, but, (B)<u>some students spend too much time doing it</u>.

Katie, 15, Denmark
  I always use filters when I take selfies. But sometimes (가)<u>나의 셀피가 나처럼 보이지 않는다</u>.

21. 위 글의 밑줄 친 (가)의 의미가 되도록 〈보기〉에 주어진 단어를 알맞게 재배열한 것은? (4점)

보기
don't / me / look / my selfies / like

① my selfies don't look me like
② don't look like my selfies me
③ my selfies don't me look like
④ my selfies don't look like me
⑤ look like me my selfies don't

22. 위 글의 (A)의 우리말 문장을 주어진 단어들을 이용하여 영어 문장으로 쓰시오. (3점)

enjoy / take

→ _____

23. 위 글의 밑줄 친 (B)의 뜻을 우리말로 쓰시오. (4점)

→ _____

_____

25. 위 글의 내용과 일치하지 않는 것은? (3점)

① 세계 최초의 selfie는 space selfie이다.

② Robert Cornelius가 최초로 selfie를 찍었다.

③ 최초의 selfie 촬영은 1839년에 이루어졌다.

④ Buzz Aldrin는 최초로 space selfie를 찍었다.

⑤ selfie라는 단어는 2013년에 사전에 등재되었다.

[24-25] 다음 글을 읽고 물음에 답하시오.

Are you interested in selfies? You probably like to post selfies on social media, but how much do you know about selfies? Here are some interesting _____.

1. Robert Cornelius took the world's first selfie in 1839.
2. *Selfie* became a new word in the dictionary in 2013.
3. Buzz Aldrin took the first space selfie in 1966.

24. 위 글의 내용상 빈칸에 들어갈 가장 적절한 단어는?

(3점)

① surveys ② facts

③ manners ④ people

⑤ pictures

[26-30] 다음 글을 읽고 물음에 답하시오.

You should ⓐfollow etiquette for selfies. Ask yourself these questions before you take, post, or look at selfies.

1. (A)_____ am I?

Choose ⓑappropriate places to take selfies. Don't take selfies in hospitals or public restrooms. It (가)may ⓒhelp other people.

2. (B)_____ can see this?

Keep in mind that anyone can see your selfies. Choose carefully when you post them.

3. (C)_____ kinds of comments should I ⓓleave?

Write nice comments on other people's selfies. Don't be ⓔrude.

(나)[doesn't / easy / it / sound / that]?
Follow these tips and have fun with your selfies!

26. 위 글의 밑줄 친 부분 중 문맥상 낱말의 쓰임이 적절하지 않은 것은? (3점)

① ⓐ follow
② ⓑ appropriate
③ ⓒ help
④ ⓓ leave
⑤ ⓔ rude

29. 위 글의 내용과 일치하지 않는 것은? (3점)

① 셀카에 관한 몇 가지 예절이 있다.
② 셀카를 찍기 전에 내가 어디에 있는지 고려해야 한다.
③ 셀카를 게시하면 누구나 그것을 볼 수 있다.
④ 셀카를 게시할 때에는 신중해야 한다.
⑤ 다른 사람의 셀카에 대해 부정적이더라도 솔직한 코멘트를 해야 한다.

27. 위 글의 밑줄 친 (A), (B), (C)에 각각 들어갈 w로 시작하는 단어를 쓰시오. (3점)

(A): _____
(B): _____
(C): _____

28. 위 글의 (가)may와 같은 용법으로 쓰인 것은?(3점)

① Tom bought a new car. He <u>may</u> be rich.
② Students <u>may</u> not copy the new book.
③ <u>May</u> I take pictures of the band?
④ You <u>may</u> go home if you want.
⑤ Her birthday is on <u>May</u> 4th.

30. 위 글의 흐름을 고려하여 (나)에서 주어진 단어들을 올바르게 배열하여 문장을 완성하시오. (단, 단어의 형태를 바꿀 수 있음) (3점)

doesn't / easy / it / sound / that

답 : _____ _____ _____, _____ _____?

◎ 선택형 문항의 답안은 컴퓨터용 수정 싸인펜을 사용하여 OMR 답안지에 바르게 표기하시오.
◎ 서술형 문제는 답을 답안지에 반드시 검정 볼펜으로 쓰시오.
◎ 총 30문항 100점 만점입니다. 문항별 배점은 각 문항에 표시되어 있습니다.

[전북 ○○중]

1. 다음 중 단어의 관계가 적절하지 <u>않은</u> 것은? (2점)

① eat – eaten

② find – found

③ think – thought

④ see – saw

⑤ bring – brought

[충북 ○○중]

2. 다음 중 단어의 영영풀이로 옳지 <u>않은</u> 것은? (3점)

① serve: to give food to people

② price: how much something costs

③ share: to use something with another person

④ appetizer: a small dish served after the main dish

⑤ exercise: to work out to make someone's body stronger

[충남 ○○중]

3. 주어진 우리말에 맞게 <보기>에서 단어를 고른 후 바르게 배열하여 문장을 완성하시오. (3점)

보기

better / you / should / eat / had / fruit / would

A: I think I eat too many candies these days.
B: 너는 과일을 먹는 게 더 좋겠어.

답: _____

[서울 성북구 ○○중]

4. 다음 중 어법상 옳은 문장은? (3점)

① The book which is on the sofa is mine.

② There are some kids that is playing soccer.

③ The woman who passed by were wearing a hat.

④ He wants to meet somebody which can help him.

⑤ Look at the person which is dancing on the street.

[울산시 ○○중]

5. 다음 관계대명사와 괄호 안의 어구를 활용하여 직업이나 물건을 설명하는 문장을 쓰시오. (필요시 단어 추가 가능) (5점)

(1) A thief _____.
    (person / steal things from people)

(2) A microwave _____.
    (thing / heat up the cold food)

(1)_____
_____

(2)_____
_____

[경북 ○○중]

Woman: Hello. Are you ready to order?

Boy: It's my first time here. What do you recommend?

Woman: I recommend the chicken sandwich. It is the most popular item at our restaurant.

Boy: Well, I don't like chicken very much. Could you recommend something else?

Woman: How about the turkey sandwich?

Boy: Oh, I love turkey. I'll have that.

Woman: Why don't you order a drink with the sandwich? You can get a 500-won discount.

Boy: (A)_____ Then I'll have an orange juice, too.

7. 위 대화의 빈칸 (A)에 들어갈 대답으로 가장 적절한 것은? (3점)

① I don't want to order it.

② That sounds good.

③ What do you recommend?

④ That's great but I don't like it.

⑤ I don't like a drink.

[서울 성북구 ○○중]

8. 다음 달력은 Sally가 방과 후에 도서관에 가는 날을 표시한 것이다. 달력을 보고 Sally의 일정을 설명한 것으로 가장 적절한 것은? (3점)

Aprill 2021

MON	TUE	WED	THU	FRI
1	2	3	4	5
8	9	10	11	12
15	16	17	18	19
22	23	24	25	26
29	30			

① Sally goes to the library once after school.

② Sally never goes to the library after school.

③ Sally sometimes goes to the library after school.

④ Sally usually goes to the library after school.

⑤ Sally always goes to the library after school.

[경북 ○○중]

6. 위 대화에서 남자 아이가 주문한 음식과 그 이유로 알맞게 짝지어진 것은? (3점)

① 치킨 샌드위치 - 치킨을 좋아하기 때문에

② 치킨 샌드위치 - 레스토랑에서 추천한 음식이라서

③ 오렌지 주스 - 600원을 할인해 주기 때문에

④ 칠면조 샌드위치 - 칠면조를 좋아하기 때문에

⑤ 칠면조 샌드위치 - 레스토랑에서 가장 유명한 음식이라서

9. 다음 〈보기〉에서 어법상 적절한 것만을 골라 바르게 묶은 것은? (4점)

a. The picture on the wall looks great.
b. Tom takes usually a walk after dinner.
c. Drinking too many soft drinks is not healthy.
d. Nara is wearing a hat who is too big for her.

① a, b   ② a, c
③ b, c   ④ b, d
⑤ c, d

10. 위 대화의 빈칸에 들어갈 질문으로 알맞은 것은? (3점)

① Why don't you go there?
② Who's going with you?
③ Where is the party?
④ When is the party?
⑤ What are you going to do there?

11. Which one is true according to the dialog? (4점)

① Jiwoo will go to Bella's Restaurant.
② The price of Chang's Restaurant was good.
③ The party won't be held.
④ Jiwoo doesn't want to search for a restaurant.
⑤ Jiwoo recommends the noodle soup.

[10–12] 다음 대화를 읽고 물음에 답하시오.

Mike: Good morning, Jiwoo. What are you doing right now?
Jiwoo: I'm searching for a restaurant for my class party.
Mike: Wow! _____
Jiwoo: It's next Friday. We want to go to Bella's Restaurant, but it is too expensive.
Mike: Why don't you check out Chang's Restaurant? I went there once. The food and prices were good.
Jiwoo: Sounds great. What do you recommend there?
Mike: I recommend the noodle soup.
Jiwoo: (A)[we / go / think / I / should / there]. Thank you.

12. 위 대화의 괄호 (A) 안에 있는 단어들을 문맥에 맞게 배열하여 문장을 완성하시오. (3점)

[we / go / think / I / should / there]

→ _____

13. 다음 대화를 읽고 답할 수 <u>없는</u> 것은? (3점)

Yuna: Justine, our school cooking contest is tomorrow. What are you going to make?

Justin: I'm going to make sandwiches.

Yuna: What do you want to put in them?

Justin: Chicken, cheese, and eggs.

Yuna: You'd better put vegetables in your sandwiches. How about onions and carrots?

Justin: No, I'm not going to add them. I don't like those vegetables.

Yuna: That's not a good idea. Mr. Kim said we should make healthy food for the contest.

Justin: You're right. I should go grocery shopping and buy onions and carrots.

① When is the cooking contest?

② What is Justin going to make?

③ What vegetables does Justin like?

④ Why does Yuna suggest putting vegetables?

⑤ What is Justin going to do after the conversation?

14. 다음 (A)~(D)를 자연스러운 대화가 되도록 알맞게 배열한 것은? (3점)

(A) Are you interested in baseball?

(B) I'm going to go to a baseball game with my brother.

(C) Not really. I'm going to go to the baseball game because my brother likes baseball.

(D) What are you going to do this weekend?

① (A)-(B)-(C)-(D)

② (B)-(C)-(A)-(D)

③ (C)-(A)-(D)-(B)

④ (D)-(C)-(A)-(B)

⑤ (D)-(B)-(A)-(C)

15. 다음 글을 읽고 〈보기〉의 부사들 중 하나를 선택하여 주어진 질문에 완전한 문장으로 답하시오. (3점)

These days, Dana is very busy. She goes to the library to study for the mid-term exam every day. And she takes yoga lessons five times a week for her health. So she has no time to walk her dog.

┌─ 보기 ─────────────────
often, sometimes, never
└────────────────────────

Q: How often does Dana do yoga?

A: _____

I: You look very tired today. Didn't you sleep well?

J: Yes, I did. I always sleep very well. But I often feel tired these days, especially in the morning.

I: Do you usually eat breakfast?

J: No, I never eat breakfast.

I: Why don't you eat breakfast? Breakfast gives you energy.

J: I didn't know that. Do you have any other suggestions?

I: Well, you should also exercise every day. That will help you.

J: Okay. I sometimes take a walk, but I'll do it more.

* I: Inho, J: Jiwoo

[경기 ○○중]

16. What are two things that Inho recommends? (4점)

조건
• 질문에 대한 답 2가지를 위 글에서 찾아 우리말로 작성할 것

(A)_____

(B)_____

[경기 ○○중]

17. Does Jiwoo eat breakfast? (4점)

조건
• 주어, 동사가 있는 완전한 영어 문장으로 답할 것
• 내용에 맞는 적절한 빈도부사를 이용하여 답할 것

→_____

Everyone tries to eat the right food, but junk food is everywhere. Is junk food good for your health? The answer is no. Cakes and cookies have too much sugar. Ice cream is also full of sugar. Potato chips are fried and have lots of fat and salt. Junk food tastes good, but it is bad for your health. (A)_____, the following foods are good for you. First, carrots can keep your eyes healthy. Also, garlic helps prevent colds. (B)_____, fish is good for your brain. The *mineral *zinc in fish can improve your thinking and memory.

So next time when you're in the school cafeteria, remember the good things about the right foods. Don't forget that each meal is important.

*mineral 무기물, *zinc 아연

[경기 ○○중]

18. 위 글의 빈칸 (A), (B)에 들어갈 말로 가장 적절한 것은? (4점)

	(A)	(B)
①	However	In addition
②	For example	So
③	Thus	For instance
④	In other words	Lastly
⑤	On the other hand	Therefore

19. 위 글의 내용과 일치하는 것은? (3점)

① 정크 푸드는 맛도 좋고 몸에도 좋다.

② 감자 칩에 가장 많은 소금이 들어 있다.

③ 마늘은 몸을 따뜻하게 해주는 음식이다.

④ 케이크와 쿠키에는 많은 지방이 들어 있다.

⑤ 생선은 사고력과 기억력 향상에 도움이 된다.

[20-28] 다음 글을 읽고 물음에 답하시오.

Hello, this is food reporter Minjun from Korea. For many students, lunch is the best part of the school day. In Korea, we often eat rice and soup for lunch. We also have side dishes, such as *Bulgogi* or *Gimchi*. Sometimes we have special dishes, such as pizza, *Bibimbap*, or pasta. What do students (가)_____ live in other countries eat for lunch? Let's hear (A)<u>from</u> our food reporters!

<Belle, France>

Our school ⓐ<u>serves</u> healthy and balanced meals. We usually eat a salad (B)<u>as</u> an appetizer. Main dishes often ⓑ<u>include</u> meat or fish. We also eat fresh fruit at the end of the lunch. Oh, I can never forget (C)<u>about</u> baguettes! They're great with cheese. Our school also has a special rule. We must stay at the lunch table for at least 30 minutes.

<Bruno, Brazil>

Usually, we have beans and rice for lunch. Meat and vegetables are common in our side dishes. My favorite lunch comes with plantains. A plantain is _____. We usually fry plantains. Our school lunches are fresh because the vegetables and fruit come from local farms.

<Nicole, Singapore>

People (가)_____ live in Singapore come from many different cultures, so we have both Eastern (D)<u>or</u> Western dishes at lunch. Students can choose from many dishes, such as curry, noodle soup, or pasta, each day. My school ⓒ<u>won</u> an award for healthy school food last year. Our lunches are always healthy, and they ⓓ<u>sound good</u>, too!

Which school lunch do you want to ⓔ<u>try</u>? Does it have anything (E)<u>in</u> common with your school lunch? Please write your comments at www.chopchoplunch.com.

20. 위 글의 (가)에 공통으로 들어갈 말로 가장 적절한 것은? (3점)

① who   ② where

③ which   ④ how

⑤ when

21. 위 글의 내용상 밑줄 친 단어의 쓰임이 자연스럽지 않은 것은? (3점)

① ⓐ serves　　② ⓑ include

③ ⓒ won　　④ ⓓ sound

⑤ ⓔ try

22. 위 글의 (A)∼(E) 중 어법상 알맞지 않은 것은? (3점)

① (A)　　② (B)　　③ (C)

④ (D)　　⑤ (E)

23. 위 글의 빈칸에 〈보기〉의 우리말 해석과 일치하도록 주어진 단어를 그대로 이용하거나 변형하고 다른 단어를 추가하여 문장을 완성하시오. (4점)

보기

plantain은 바나나처럼 보이는 과일이다.

답: A plantain is _____.

　　(a banana, a fruit, like, look)

24. 위 글의 내용과 일치하는 것은? (4점)

① Pizza and pasta are common for school lunch in Korea.

② Belle eats salad before she has meat or fish.

③ Bruno only has beans for lunch at school.

④ Bruno can have fresh food from different countries at school.

⑤ Nicole usually has traditional food at school.

25. 위 글의 내용과 일치하지 않는 것은? (4점)

① Minjun: 많은 학생들에게 점심시간은 학교에서 가장 신나는 순간이지.

② Belle: 나는 치즈를 곁들인 바게트를 정말 좋아해.

③ Belle: 우리 학교는 학생들이 정해진 시간 동안 점심을 먹도록 하고 있어.

④ Bruno: 나는 plantain이 나오는 점심을 좋아하지.

⑤ Nicole: 우리 학교는 매일 다른 식단을 선택해서 제공해 주고 있어.

26. 위 글의 제목으로 가장 적절한 것은? (3점)

① Healthy Food and Life

② Living in Other Countries

③ School Life in Other Countries

④ Favorite Food at School Lunch

⑤ School Lunches Around the World

27. 다음 학생들의 대답과 어울리는 ⓐ의 질문은? (3점)

Q. ⓐ_____
Student 1. I always eat breakfast.
Student 2. I never drink coke.
Student 3. I sometimes eat slowly.
Student 4. I eat enough fruit and vegetables.
Student 5. I never eat sweets.

① Do you have any plans?

② When do you eat noodles?

③ What are your eating habits?

④ What are you doing right now?

⑤ How much will you pay for this?

28. 위 글의 내용과 일치하도록 대화의 빈칸에 들어갈 알맞은 말로 짝지어진 것은? (3점)

> A: Which country's school lunch do you want to have?
> B: I want to have a school lunch from (A)_____. They learn to stay at the lunch table for at least half an hour. That's an interesting rule.
> C: I'm interested in a school lunch from (B)_____. It will be fun to look at many different dishes such as curry, noodle soup, or pasta at lunch. How about you?
> A: I think school lunches from (C)_____ are the best. I love rice and soup with *Bulgogi* so much!

	(A)	(B)	(C)
①	France	Singapore	Korea
②	France	Singapore	Brazil
③	France	Brazil	Korea
④	Brazil	Korea	Singapore
⑤	Brazil	Singapore	Korea

[29-30] 다음 글을 읽고 물음에 답하시오.

> **You Are What You Eat**
> Everyone tries to eat the right food, but junk food is everywhere. Is junk food good for your health? The answer is no. Cakes and cookies have too much sugar. Ice cream is full of sugar, ⓐtoo. Potato chips are fried and have lots of fat and salt. Junk food tastes good. ⓑIn addition, it is bad for your health.
> ⓒOn the other hand, the following foods are good for you. First, carrots can keep your eyes healthy. Also, garlic helps prevent colds. ⓓBesides, fish is good for your brain. The mineral zinc in fish can improve your thinking and memory.
> ⓔTherefore, remember the good things about the right foods next time when you're in the school cafeteria. Don't forget that each meal is important.

29. 위 글의 밑줄 친 ⓐ~ⓔ 중 글의 흐름상 어색한 것은? (4점)

① ⓐ   ② ⓑ   ③ ⓒ

④ ⓓ   ⑤ ⓔ

30. 위 글을 읽고 알 수 없는 것은? (3점)

① the effect of mineral zinc in fish

② the food that is good for eye health

③ the things that potato chips have in them

④ the right meals that the school cafeteria serves

⑤ the reason junk food is not good for our health

문항수 : 선택형(20문항) 서술형(10문항)　20 . . .

◎ 선택형 문항의 답안은 컴퓨터용 수정 싸인펜을 사용하여 OMR 답안지에 바르게 표기하시오.
◎ 서술형 문제는 답을 답안지에 반드시 검정 볼펜으로 쓰시오.
◎ 총 30문항 100점 만점입니다. 문항별 배점은 각 문항에 표시되어 있습니다.

[경북 ○○중]

1. 다음 〈보기〉의 짝지어진 단어와 같이 반대말의 관계가 <u>아닌</u> 것은? (3점)

┌ 보기 ─────────────
　　　　healthy - unhealthy
└──────────────────

① like - dislike
② balanced - unbalanced
③ famous - infamous
④ popular - unpopular
⑤ possible - impossible

[충남 ○○중]

2. 주어진 문장이 〈보기〉와 같은 과정을 거칠 때 밑줄 친 부분에 들어갈 문장을 4단어로 쓰시오. (3점)

┌ 보기 ─────────────
The dog which is playing outside is cute.
　　　↓
The dog is cute.
It is playing outside.
└──────────────────

The man who lives next door is an artist.
　　　↓
The man is an artist.

답: ＿＿＿＿ ＿＿＿＿ ＿＿＿＿ ＿＿＿＿

[3-4] 다음 대화를 읽고 물음에 답하시오.

┌──────────────────────┐
G: Our school cooking contest is tomorrow. What are you going to make?
B: I'm going to make sandwiches.
G: What do you want to put in them?
B: Chicken, cheese, and eggs.
G: ⓐ너는 야채를 포함하는 샌드위치를 만드는 것이 좋겠어. How about onions and carrots?
B: No, I'm not going to add them. I don't like those vegetables.
G: That's not a good idea. Mr. Kim said we should make healthy food for the contest.
B: You're right. I should go grocery shopping and buy onions and carrots.
　　　　　　　　　　* G: girl, B: boy
└──────────────────────┘

[경기 ○○중]

3. Why does the girl recommend putting vegetables in the sandwich? (4점)

→ It is because ＿＿＿＿＿＿＿＿＿＿＿＿.

[경기 ○○중]

4. 위 대화의 ⓐ와 같은 뜻이 되도록 〈조건〉에 맞게 완전한 영어 문장으로 쓰시오. (4점)

┌ 조건 ───────────────
• 관계대명사를 반드시 사용할 것
• better를 포함시킬 것
└──────────────────

→＿＿＿＿＿＿＿＿＿＿＿＿＿＿

5. 다음 중 어법상 옳지 <u>않은</u> 것은? (3점)

① Do you know the man standing over there?

② The toys which are on the table is made in Japan.

③ The movie I saw with Jane yesterday was very exciting.

④ This is the picture which was taken more than ten years ago.

⑤ The boy who lives next door is my cousin.

7. 위 대화의 밑줄 친 우리말 (A)를 아래 괄호 속 단어를 활용하여 영어로 쓰시오. (3점)

[better / breakfast / you / had / eat]

→ _____

[6–7] 다음 대화를 읽고 물음에 답하시오.

G: You look very tired today. Didn't you sleep well?

B: Yes, I did. But I often feel tired these days, especially in the morning.

G: Do you usually eat breakfast?

B: No, I don't.

G: (A)너는 아침을 먹는 것이 좋아. Breakfast gives you energy.

B: I didn't know that. Do you have any other suggestions?

G: Well, you should also exercise every day. That will help you.

B: Okay. I will.

* G: girl   B: Boy

6. 위 대화의 내용과 일치하지 <u>않는</u> 것은? (3점)

① 소년은 피곤해 보였다.

② 소년은 잠을 잘 자지 못했다.

③ 소년은 아침을 안 먹는다.

④ 소년은 매일 운동을 할 것이다.

⑤ 소년은 소녀의 제안을 받아들였다.

8. 다음 대화의 빈칸에 들어갈 말을 <보기>에서 찾아 순서대로 바르게 연결한 것은? (4점)

A: What's for lunch today?

B: We have four choices. Which menu do you want?

A: (A)_____ What do you recommend?

B: (B)_____

A: That sounds delicious. I will have that. What about you?

B: I don't know. I'm not hungry.

A: (C)_____ Why don't you try some tomato soup?

B: All right. I will.

보기
ⓐ I want to go there.

ⓑ I'd like to eat some sandwiches.

ⓒ I recommend the chicken sandwiches.

ⓓ I don't want to have any kinds of food now.

ⓔ But for your health, you should have some food.

① ⓐ-ⓒ-ⓓ ② ⓑ-ⓒ-ⓔ

③ ⓑ-ⓓ-ⓔ ④ ⓓ-ⓔ-ⓐ

⑤ ⓓ-ⓐ-ⓑ

[9~10] 다음 대화를 읽고 물음에 답하시오.

B: Good morning, Jiwoo. What are you doing right now?
G: I'm searching for a restaurant for my class party.
B: Wow! When is the party?
G: It's next Friday. We want to go to Bella's Restaurant, but it is too expensive.
B: How about checking out Chang's Restaurant? I went there once. The food and prices were good.
G: Sounds great.
　(A)_____.
B: I recommend the noodle soup.
G: I think we should go there. Thank you.

10. 위 대화의 내용과 일치하는 것은? (3점)

① 여자는 생일파티를 할 식당을 찾고 있다.
② 여자는 파티를 다음 주 토요일에 할 계획이다.
③ 남자는 음식과 가격 면에서 Chang의 식당을 추천했다.
④ 남자는 Bella의 식당에 가고 싶어 하지만 그곳은 너무 비싸다고 생각한다.
⑤ 여자는 파티를 위해 Bella의 식당에 갈 것이다.

9. 위 대화를 읽고, (A)에 들어갈 말로 가장 적절한 것은? (3점)

① What are you interested in?
② What do you recommend there?
③ Which restaurant do you recommend?
④ Could you recommend something else?
⑤ How about recommending another restaurant?

11. 다음 〈보기〉의 문장들 중 의미가 연결되는 문장을 2개씩 골라 주어진 관계대명사를 사용하여 각각 합쳐 쓰시오. (5점)

보기
- He is a chef.
- The dictionary is very old.
- He studied cooking in Italy.
- It is always on the teacher's table.

(A) _____
　(who 사용)

(B) _____
　(which 사용)

[12–14] 다음 글을 읽고 물음에 답하시오.

Hello, this is food reporter Minjun from Korea. For many students, (A) lunch is the best part of the school day. In Korea, (B) we often eat rice and soup for lunch. We also have side dishes, (가)_____ *Bulgogi* or *Gimchi*. (C) Sometimes our school serves special dishes, (가)_____ pizza, *Bibimbap*, or pasta. (D) Let's hear from our food reporters! (E)

[경기 ○○중]

12. 다음 글의 밑줄 친 부분 (가)에 공통으로 들어갈 말은? (3점)

① alike
② with
③ for
④ like
⑤ through

[서울 강동구 ○○중]

13. 위 글 (A)~(E) 중 주어진 문장이 들어갈 위치로 알맞은 곳은? (3점)

What do students who live in other countries eat for lunch?

① (A)
② (B)
③ (C)
④ (D)
⑤ (E)

[서울 강동구 ○○중]

14. 위 글 다음으로 이어질 내용으로 가장 알맞은 것은? (2점)

① 한국의 식사 문화
② 학생들이 좋아하는 음식
③ 다른 나라 학생들의 점심식사
④ 각 나라 학생들의 조리법
⑤ 다른 나라의 요리 경연대회

[15–18] 다음 글을 읽고 물음에 답하시오.

< Bruno, Brazil >
Usually, we have beans and rice for lunch. Meat and vegetables are common in our side dishes. My favorite lunch comes (A)_____ plantains. ⓐ플렌테인은 바나나와 같이 보이는 과일이다. We usually fry (가)them. Our school lunches are fresh because the vegetables and fruit come (B)_____ local farms.

< Nicole, Singapore >
ⓑSingapore에서 살고 있는 사람들은 많은 다른 문화권 출신이다, so we have both Eastern and Western dishes at lunch. Students can choose from many dishes, such as curry, noodle soup, or pasta, each day. My school won an award for healthy school food last year. Our lunches are always healthy, and they taste good, too!
Which school lunch do you want to try? Does it have anything (C)_____ common with (나)yours? Please leave your comments at www.chopchoplunch.com.

[경기 ○○중]

15. 위 글에서 (가)와 (나)가 가리키는 것을 알맞게 짝지은 것은? (3점)

	(가)	(나)
①	plantains	your school rule
②	plantains	your school lunch
③	bananas	your school rule
④	bananas	your school lunch
⑤	vegetables	your school student

16. 위 글의 내용과 일치하는 것은? (3점)

① Nicole prefers Eastern food to Western food.

② Plantains are usually fried for lunch in Brazil.

③ Bruno eats meat and vegetables as main dishes.

④ In Singapore, all the students have the same meal.

⑤ There is an award for healthy school food in Brazil.

18. 위 글의 우리말 문장을 영어 문장으로 주어진 단어들을 활용하여 〈조건〉에 맞게 완성하시오. (5점)

> 조건
> 1. 한 문장으로 쓸 것
> 2. 관계대명사를 반드시 사용할 것
> 3. 필요시 단어를 추가하거나 변형할 것

(1) 플랜테인은 바나나와 같이 보이는 과일이다.
  (a plantain, look, a fruit)

(2) Singapore에서 살고 있는 사람들은 많은 다른 문화권 출신이다.
  (live / come / cultures / different)

(1)_____

(2)_____

17. 위 글의 빈칸 (A)~(C)에 순서대로 들어갈 말로 적절한 것은? (3점)

	(A)	(B)	(C)
①	with	from	in
②	off	from	on
③	with	across	on
④	off	up	within
⑤	from	with	in

[19~20] 다음 글을 읽고 물음에 답하시오.

(가)싱가폴에 사는 사람들은 다양한 문화 출신이다. So we have both Eastern (**A**)[or / and] Western dishes at lunch. Students can choose from many dishes, such as curry, noodle soup, or pasta, each day. My school (**B**)[wins / won] an award for healthy school food last year. Our lunches (**C**)[always are / are always] healthy, and they taste good, too!

19. 위 글의 (A)~(C)에 들어갈 말로 알맞은 것은? (3점)

	(A)	(B)	(C)
①	or	wins	always are
②	or	won	are always
③	and	won	always are
④	and	won	are always
⑤	and	wins	always are

21. 위 대화가 자연스럽게 이어지도록 〈보기〉 문장이 들어갈 곳은? (3점)

How about onions and carrots?

① (A)　　② (B)　　③ (C)

④ (D)　　⑤ (E)

22. 위 대화에서 G의 마지막 말에 대한 B의 대답으로 가장 적절한 것은? (3점)

① Yes. Mr. Kim loves sandwiches, too.

② Oh, I don't care. I will buy vegetables.

③ Right, meat and fish are good for health.

④ OK, I'd better put vegetables in my sandwiches.

⑤ I already knew that Mr. Kim likes French fries the most.

20. 위 글의 밑줄 친 (가)의 우리말을 〈보기〉의 주어진 9단어만을 모두 사용하여 영어 한 문장으로 쓰시오. (4점)

보기

different, who, come, in, cultures, from, people, Singapore, live

→ _____

[21-22] 다음 대화를 읽고 물음에 답하시오.

G: Justin, our school cooking contest is tomorrow. What are you going to make?
B: I'm going to make sandwiches. (A)
G: What do you want to put in them? (B)
B: Chicken, cheese, and eggs. (C)
G: You'd better put vegetables in your sandwiches. (D)
B: No, I'm not going to add them. I don't like those vegetables. (E)
G: That's not a good idea. Mr. Kim said we should make healthy food for the contest.
B: _____

[23-25] 다음 글을 읽고 물음에 답하시오.

Belle, France

(A) They're great with cheese. Our school also has a special rule. We must stay at the lunch table for at least 30 minutes.

(B) Our school serves healthy and balanced meals. First, we eat a salad as an appetizer.

(C) Main dishes often include meat or fish. We also eat fresh fruit at the end of the lunch. Oh, I can never forget about baguettes!

23. 위 글의 (A), (B), (C)를 내용에 맞게 순서대로 나열한 것은? (2점)

① (A)−(B)−(C)
② (A)−(C)−(B)
③ (B)−(A)−(C)
④ (B)−(C)−(A)
⑤ (C)−(A)−(B)

26. 다음 (A)와 (B)를 관계대명사를 이용하여 한 문장으로 만드시오. (4점)

조건
관계대명사는 반드시 사용하되 **that**은 사용하지 말 것

(A) The dolls are my sister's.
(B) They are on the table.

→ _____

_____

24. 위 글을 쓴 목적으로 가장 적절한 것은? (3점)

① to ask the tour schedule of France
② to explain the school lunch of France
③ to order food in a restaurant of France
④ to advertise a local restaurant of France
⑤ to discuss the bad points about school lunch of France

[27–29] 다음 글을 읽고 물음에 답하시오.

Hello, this is food ⓐ<u>reporter</u> Minjun from Korea. For many students, lunch is the best part of the school day. In Korea, we often eat rice and soup for lunch. We also have side dishes, such as *Bulgogi* or *Gimchi*. Sometimes our school ⓑ<u>serves</u> special dishes, (가)_____ pizza, *Bibimbap*, or pasta. What do students from other countries eat for lunch? Let's hear from our food reporters!

< Belle, France >

Our school serves healthy and ⓒ<u>balanced</u> meals. We usually eat a salad as an ⓓ<u>appetizer</u>. Main dishes often include meat or fish. We also eat fresh fruit at the end of the lunch. Oh, I can never forget about baguettes! They're great with cheese. Our school also has a special ⓔ<u>rule</u>. We must stay at the lunch table for at least 30 minutes.

25. 다음 질문에 대한 답을 〈조건〉에 맞게 쓰시오. (3점)

조건
(1) 본문에서 찾아 영어로 쓸 것
(2) 단어의 형태를 변형하지 말고 그대로 쓸 것

Q: What is the special rule at Belle's school?

→ They _____.

27. 위 글의 문맥상 밑줄 친 ⓐ~ⓔ에 대한 설명으로 어색한 것은? (3점)

① ⓐ: a person who tells about important things that have happened

② ⓑ: to give food to people

③ ⓒ: having all parts in equal or good amounts

④ ⓓ: a small dish served after the main dish

⑤ ⓔ: a statement that says what someone can or can't do

29. 위 글의 (가)에 들어갈 말로 옳은 것은? (4점)

① with   ② on

③ for   ④ such as

⑤ alike

30. 다음 우리말과 일치하도록 주어진 단어를 이용하여 영작하시오. (반드시 관계대명사를 사용하고 필요 시 단어 추가 및 어형을 변화시켜 문장을 완성할 것. that은 사용하지 말 것.) (5점)

(1) 옆집에 사는 남자는 화가이다.

(the man, next door, an artist)

→ _____

_____

(2) 그들은 아름다운 정원을 가진 집에 산다.

(live, a house, have, a beautiful garden)

→ _____

_____

28. 위 글을 읽고 대답할 수 없는 질문은? (3점)

① What rule does Belle have to follow?

② What do Korean students eat for lunch?

③ What does Belle think is great with cheese?

④ What food do French students eat as an appetizer?

⑤ How many side dishes are there in Korean lunch?

2학년 영어 1학기 기말고사(3과) 1회

반		점수
이름		

문항수 : 선택형(28문항) 서술형(2문항)   20 .   .   .

◎ 선택형 문항의 답안은 컴퓨터용 수정 싸인펜을 사용하여 OMR 답안지에 바르게 표기하시오.
◎ 서술형 문제는 답을 답안지에 반드시 검정 볼펜으로 쓰시오.
◎ 총 30문항 100점 만점입니다. 문항별 배점은 각 문항에 표시되어 있습니다.

[경기 ○○중]

1. 다음 영영풀이에 해당하는 단어를 고르면? (3점)

> very important, useful and helpful

① evil   ② colored   ③ valuable
④ separated   ⑤ traditional

[서울 관악구 ○○중]

2. 다음 빈칸에 공통으로 들어갈 것은? (3점)

> A: What does dreaming of pigs _____ in Korea?
> B: It _____s good luck.

> A: What does an umbrella _____ in China?
> B: It _____s separation. The words for separation and umbrella sound the same in Chinese.

① mean   ② greet   ③ crow
④ play   ⑤ protect

[서울 노원구 ○○중]

3. 다음 대화의 빈칸 (A)에 알맞은 것은? (3점)

> A: What does eating Tteokguk on New Year's Day mean in Korea?
> B: (A)_____

① It means separation.
② It means rain the next day.
③ It means good luck on a test.
④ It means becoming a year older.
⑤ It means welcome home in Korea.

[서울 강동구 ○○중]

4. 다음 중 짝지어진 대화가 가장 자연스러운 것은? (정답 2개) (3점)

① A: What brings you here today?
   B: I bring my pet here every day.
② A: I'm worried about wasting food.
   B: We should not eat too much.
③ A: Does Sumi still play the piano?
   B: Yes, she has played the piano for 10 years.
④ A: How long have you lived in Seoul?
   B: I lived in Seoul for three years.
⑤ A: What does gracias mean in Spanish?
   B: That means "Thank you."

[대전 ○○중]

5. 다음을 자연스러운 대화가 되도록 배열한 것은? (4점)

> (A) No, I haven't. Have you?
> (B) Have you ever been to Brazil?
> (C) That sounds interesting. I hope to go there someday.
> (D) Yes, I have. I went there last year. There was a big samba festival.

① (B)-(A)-(C)-(D)
② (B)-(A)-(D)-(C)
③ (B)-(D)-(A)-(C)
④ (C)-(B)-(D)-(A)
⑤ (D)-(C)-(B)-(A)

[6–7] 다음 대화를 읽고 물음에 답하시오.

A: Hello, Santiago! What brings you here today?
B: *Bienvenido*, Cathy. (A)
A: Me, too. But what did you just say?
B: *Bienvenido*. It means "welcome" in Spanish. (B) Look at those dancers. Their dance moves are so great. (C)
A: Yes, they are. (D)
B: <u>너는 전에 스페인 축제에 가 본 적 있니?</u>
A: No, I haven't. Santiago, can you see the big letters on the stage? What does that mean? (E)
B: Oh, *gracias*. That means "thank you."

[대구 ○○중]

6. 위 대화의 (A)~(E) 중 주어진 문장이 들어갈 알맞은 곳은?   (4점)

I came to see the Spanish festival.

① (A) ② (B) ③ (C) ④ (D) ⑤ (E)

[대구 ○○중]

7. 위 대화의 밑줄 친 우리말을 〈보기〉의 단어들을 배열하여 영어로 쓰시오.   (3점)

ever / have / to / before / you / a Spanish festival / been

정답 : _____

[서울 강동구 ○○중]

8. 다음 대화의 빈칸에 들어갈 말로 가장 자연스러운 것은?   (4점)

A: _____
B: No, I haven't. Have you?
A: Yes, I have. I went there last year. There was a big samba festival.

① Did you go to Brazil?
② Have you gone to Brazil?
③ Have you been to Brazil?
④ Did you see a samba festival?
⑤ Have you seen a samba festival?

[9–10] 다음 대화를 읽고 물음에 답하시오.

(A) What's wrong with that?
(B) Which boy?
(C) What does that mean?
(D) It has a bad meaning in England. But showing your palm and making a V sign is okay.
(E) The boy who is making the V sign. His palm is ⓐ<u>facing</u> toward himself.
(F) It means victory or peace.

[서울 노원구 ○○중]

9. 다음 주어진 문장에 이어질 대화의 순서로 가장 알맞은 것은?   (4점)

Is this the picture you took with your friends at the beach? Oh, look at that boy. That's really rude.

① (A)–(E)–(B)–(C)–(D)–(F)
② (A)–(D)–(B)–(E)–(C)–(F)
③ (B)–(E)–(A)–(D)–(C)–(F)
④ (B)–(E)–(C)–(F)–(A)–(D)
⑤ (C)–(D)–(B)–(E)–(A)–(F)

10. 위 대화의 ⓐfacing과 문맥상 의미가 같은 것은?

(3점)

① Most of the rooms face the beach.

② It's not always easy to face the truth.

③ He tried to make a funny face for his son.

④ The company is facing a serious financial crisis.

⑤ We saw many new faces on the first day of classes.

12. 다음 〈보기〉와 같이 괄호 안의 단어를 활용하여 문장을 완성하고 우리말로 해석하시오. (6점)

> 보기
> It has rained for five days. (rain)
> → 해석: 5일 동안 비가 왔다.

(1) I _____ _____ to England before. (be)

→ 해석: _____

(2) She _____ _____ her English book. (lose)

→ 해석: _____

11. 다음 주어진 문장이 들어가기에 가장 알맞은 곳은?

(3점)

> One of the most famous dances is the lion dance.

> Do you know about traditional Chinese dances? (A) There are many kinds. (B) For example, there is a lion dance, a fan dance, and an umbrella dance. (C) In this dance, two dancers dress and act like lions. They usually dance on special days, such as New Year's Day. (D) I think their dance moves are great. (E) I hope to practice this dance someday.

① (A)　　② (B)　　③ (C)

④ (D)　　⑤ (E)

[13-14] 다음 대화를 읽고 물음에 답하시오.

> A: Welcome ⓐ_____ the International Games Festival. You can play many different traditional games here.
> B: Wow! It looks exciting! (A)
> A: Let's see. (B) Have you ever played *gorodki*?
> B: No, I haven't. (C) What is it?
> A: It's a traditional game from Russia. (D)
> B: How do I play it? (E)
> A: Put five sticks ⓑ_____ the ground. Then throw a bat at them.
> B: That sounds fun. I'll try that first.

13. 위 대화의 (A)~(E) 중 다음 문장이 들어갈 곳으로 가장 알맞은 곳은? (3점)

> Which game should I play first?

① (A)　　② (B)　　③ (C)

④ (D)　　⑤ (E)

14. 위 대화의 빈칸 ⓐ, ⓑ에 들어갈 단어가 순서대로 짝지어진 것은? (2점)

① at – to
② at – toward
③ to – to
④ to – in
⑤ to – on

15. 다음 대화의 내용과 일치하는 것은? (3점)

BOY: There is a Holi festival in Busan this year.
GIRL: A Holi festival? What is that?
BOY: It's a traditional Indian festival. People throw colored powder and water at each other.
GIRL: That sounds exciting. Have you ever been to a Holi festival?
BOY: No, I haven't. But my Indian friend told me a lot about it.
GIRL: When is the festival?
BOY: It's on the last full moon of the Hindu calendar. This year, it's on March 21.
GIRL: I'd like to go. Should I bring anything?
BOY: No, but you should wear white clothes. Then the colored powder on your clothes will look more beautiful.
GIRL: Okay. Thank you for the information.

① Holi is a traditional festival in Busan.
② Only Indian people use the Hindu calendar.
③ The girl will go to the Holi festival in Busan with the boy.
④ Wearing white clothes is recommended at the Holi festival.
⑤ The date of Holi festival is always March 21 every year.

[16–20] 다음 글을 읽고 물음에 답하시오.

Peter is visiting Korea to meet a friend, Mina, from a sister school. Peter is going to stay at her grandfather's house for a week. When he arrives, Mina shows him the guest room.

Mina: Peter, you will stay here. This guest room is full of traditional Korean things. Look at this pillow.
Peter: What are these things? (A)
Mina: (B) They're bats.
Peter: Bats on my pillow? That's scary!
Mina: (C) In Korea, bats are _____ of luck and a long life.
Peter: (D) That's surprising. In many Western countries, (가)박쥐들은 사람들에게 어둠과 무서운 것들을 상기시켜. (E)

16. 위 글의 흐름으로 보아 주어진 문장이 들어가기에 가장 적절한 곳은? (3점)

Not really.

① (A)
② (B)
③ (C)
④ (D)
⑤ (E)

17. 위 글의 빈칸에 들어갈 말의 뜻으로 가장 적절한 것은? (3점)

① 상징
② 부분
③ 결핍
④ 중요함
⑤ 보호

18. 위 글의 내용상 빈칸 (A)와 (B)에 가장 알맞은 것은?
(3점)

> Bats have (A)_____ meanings in Korea. They remind Korean people of luck and a long life. On the other hand, in many Western countries, bats have (B)_____ meanings such as darkness and scary things.

	(A)	(B)
①	different	secret
②	pleasant	negative
③	multiple	deeper
④	similar	hidden
⑤	symbolic	positive

19. 위 글의 내용과 일치하지 않는 것은?　　　(3점)

① Mina는 Peter의 자매 학교 친구이다.

② Peter는 Mina의 할아버지 댁에 머무를 것이다.

③ Mina는 Peter에게 그가 머물 손님방을 보여주고 있다.

④ 손님방은 전통적인 한국의 물건들로 가득 차 있다.

⑤ 서구의 많은 나라들에서 박쥐는 행운을 상기시킨다.

20. 위 글의 우리말 (가)를 〈보기〉의 단어들을 배열하여 영어로 옮겨 쓰시오.　　　(5점)

보기

people / scary things / remind / darkness / of / bats / and

정답 : _____

> B: Ling's birthday is this Wednesday, ⓐ<u>isn't it</u>?
> G: Yes. I'm going to buy a book for her. What about you?
> B: Well, ⓑ<u>I'm thinking about buying her an umbrella</u>. I found a cute one in a gift shop.
> G: Oh, that's not a good gift for Chinese people. It means something bad.
> B: Really? ⓒ<u>What do an umbrella mean in China</u>?
> G: It means separation. ⓓ<u>The words for *separation* and *umbrella* sound the same in Chinese</u>.
> B: I see. Then ⓔ<u>how about chocolate</u>?
> G: That's a good idea.
>
> *B: Boy, G: Girl

21. 위 대화의 ⓐ~ⓔ 중 어법상 옳지 않은 것은? (3점)

① ⓐ　　　　② ⓑ　　　　③ ⓒ

④ ⓓ　　　　⑤ ⓔ

22. 위 대화의 내용과 일치하는 것은?　　　(4점)

① 중국인들에게 우산 선물은 좋은 의미이다.

② 중국어로 우산과 이별은 발음이 동일하다.

③ 소녀는 선물가게에서 귀여운 우산을 발견했다.

④ 소년은 Ling의 생일 선물로 책을 구입할 것이다.

⑤ 소녀는 중국에서 우산 선물이 어떤 의미를 가지는 지 알지 못했다.

[23~26] 다음 대화를 읽고 물음에 답하시오.

Peter: What is on that piece of paper? It looks scary. (A)

Grandfather: Do you mean this painting of a rooster?

Peter: Oh, is it a rooster? (B)

Grandfather: Yes, it is. Roosters crow every morning. Their crowing means that a new day is beginning. (C) For many years, Koreans have believed evil spirits go away when a rooster crows.

Mina: Really? I've never heard ⓐthat before.

Peter: Actually, I'm afraid of the darkness and evil spirits. (D)

Mina: Sure. I'll draw a big rooster for you!

Grandfather: Put the drawing above your door. (E) Then it will protect you.

Peter: Yes, I will.

23. 위 대화의 (A)~(E) 중 주어진 문장이 들어가기에 가장 적절한 곳은? (4점)

Could you draw a rooster for me?

① (A)　　② (B)　　③ (C)

④ (D)　　⑤ (E)

24. 위 대화의 밑줄 친 ⓐthat이 가리키는 의미로 가장 알맞은 것은? (2점)

① The painting of a rooster looks scary.

② Mina will draw a big rooster for Peter.

③ Evil spirits go away when a rooster crows.

④ Peter is afraid of darkness and evil spirits.

⑤ You should put the drawing above the door.

25. 위 대화의 내용과 일치하지 않는 것은? (3점)

① A rooster is on that piece of paper.

② Peter is afraid of evil spirits.

③ Roosters' crowing means a new day is beginning.

④ Grandfather will draw a big rooster for Peter.

⑤ Peter will put the drawing above his door.

26. 위 대화의 대화가 끝난 후 피터와 미나가 할 일은? (정답 2개) (3점)

① 미나는 피터에게 큰 수탉을 그려줄 것이다.

② 피터는 미나에게 큰 수탉을 그려줄 것이다.

③ 피터는 그의 문 위에 큰 수탉 그림을 붙일 것이다.

④ 피터는 그의 문 아래에 큰 수탉 그림을 붙일 것이다.

⑤ 미나는 피터의 문 위에 큰 수탉 그림을 붙여줄 것이다.

[서울 성북구 ○○중]

Mina shows Peter her grandfather's room. Peter and Mina's grandfather meet and greet each other.

Grandfather: Hi, Peter! (A)<u>Have</u> you ever <u>seen</u> this kind of lock before?
Peter: No. It's so old that I can't really tell, but is it a fish?
Grandfather: Yes. For a long time, Koreans have thought that fish are good guards. Fish don't close their eyes, even when they sleep.
Peter: That's interesting.
Grandfather: We think fish can (B)<u>watch over</u> valuable things. That's ⓐ _____ this lock looks like a fish.
Peter: Now I understand.

28. 위 글의 (B) 대신에 쓸 수 있는 표현은? (정답 2개)

(3점)

① save   ② take

③ protect   ④ guard

⑤ find out

[충북 ○○중]

29. 위 글의 빈칸 ⓐ에 들어갈 말로 가장 적절한 것은?

(3점)

① how   ② why

③ what   ④ when

⑤ where

[서울 성북구 ○○중]

[충북 ○○중]

27. 위 글의 (A)와 현재완료 용법이 같은 것은? (3점)

① She <u>has gone</u> to Paris.

② I <u>have</u> never <u>been</u> to Paris.

③ The doctor <u>has</u> not <u>arrived</u> yet.

④ You <u>have studied</u> English for five years.

⑤ The plane <u>has</u> just <u>arrived</u> at the airport.

30. 위 글을 읽고 답할 수 <u>없는</u> 질문은?   (4점)

① 물고기는 잠을 잘 때 눈을 감나요?

② 자물쇠는 무엇과 비슷하게 생겼나요?

③ 미나는 피터에게 누구의 방을 보여주나요?

④ 물고기는 피터에게 무엇이 생각나게 하나요?

⑤ 왜 한국 사람들은 물고기가 좋은 경비원이라고 생각했나요?

◎ 선택형 문항의 답안은 컴퓨터용 수정 싸인펜을 사용하여 OMR 답안지에 바르게 표기하시오.
◎ 서술형 문제는 답을 답안지에 반드시 검정 볼펜으로 쓰시오.
◎ 총 30문항 100점 만점입니다. 문항별 배점은 각 문항에 표시되어 있습니다.

[서울 강동구 ○○중]

1. 다음 빈칸에 공통으로 들어갈 말은? (3점)

・He _____ed his school at the concert.
・A red flag _____s danger.

① represent ② join ③ remind
④ protect ⑤ consume

[경기 ○○중]

2. 다음 〈보기〉의 문장을 조건에 맞게 영작할 때 (A)에 오는 단어는? (3점)

> **보기**
> 나는 전에 베트남 음식을 먹어본 적이 없습니다.
> → I _____ _____ _____ (A)_____
> _____ _____.
> (조건: 현재완료시제, never 사용)

① have ② tried ③ food
④ Vietnamese ⑤ before

[강원 ○○중]

3. 다음 빈칸에 들어갈 말로 가장 알맞은 것은? (3점)

Girl: Jisoo, my Korean friend gave me *Yeot* as a gift. What does that mean in Korea?
Boy: Oh, *Yeot* is a Korean traditional candy. It means _____.

① it will rain tomorrow
② good luck on a test
③ you will lose your money
④ victory or peace
⑤ you will earn money

[서울 노원구 ○○중]

4. 다음 글의 내용상 빈칸 (A)∼(E)에 들어갈 표현이 알맞은 것은? (4점)

Do you want to have a good time in Korea? Then follow these tips. First, please (A)_____ your shoes when you go into people's homes. Next, (B)_____ when you greet others. Also, do not (C)_____ your nose at the table and do not call older people by (D)_____. Lastly, use two hands when you give something to (E)_____.

① (A) - put on
② (B) - point at people
③ (C) - touch
④ (D) - their first names
⑤ (E) - younger people

[대구 ○○중]

5. 다음 중 짝지어진 대화가 가장 어색한 것은? (3점)

① A: Can you tell me how to join Earth Hour event?
   B: That's easy. I will join the next Earth Hour.
② A: Should I bring anything?
   B: No, but you should wear white clothes.
③ A: When is the festival?
   B: It's on the last full moon of the Hindu calendar.
④ A: What does eating *Miyeokguk* mean on a test day in Korea?
   B: It means failing a test.
⑤ A: How should we play *gorodki*?
   B: We should put five sticks on the ground and throw a bat at them.

A: There is a Holi festival in Busan this year.
B: A Hoil festival? What is that?
A: ⓐIt's a traditional Indian festival. ⓑPeople throw colored powder and water at each other.
B: When is the festival?
A: ⓒIt's on the last full moon of the Hindu calendar. ⓓPut five sticks on the ground. This year, it's on March 21.
B: I'd like to go. Should I bring anything?
A: No, but you should wear white clothes. Then the colored powder on your clothes will look more beautiful.
B: Okay. ⓔThank you for the information.

7. 위 대화의 밑줄 친 ⓐ~ⓔ 중 글의 흐름에 맞지 <u>않은</u> 것은? (3점)

① ⓐ   ② ⓑ   ③ ⓒ
④ ⓓ   ⑤ ⓔ

8. 위 대화에서 Holi Festival에 대한 설명으로 옳은 것은? (3점)

① 인도의 전통 축제이다.
② 사람들은 하얀 가루와 물을 서로 던진다.
③ 축제는 힌두력의 마지막 반달이 뜨는 날이다.
④ 축제는 매년 3월 21에 열린다.
⑤ 하얀 가루가 잘 보이도록 검은 옷을 가져가는 것이 좋다.

6. 위 내용을 요약한 다음 글의 빈칸 (A)~(D) 안에 들어갈 알맞은 말로 짝지어진 것은? (4점)

Welcome to the Holi Festival in Busan!
March 21, 2019
A Traditional (A)_____ Festival
· Throw colored powder and (B)_____.
· Celebrate the last (C)_____ of the Hindu calendar.
· Wear (D)_____ clothes.

	(A)	(B)	(C)	(D)
①	Indian	water	full moon	white
②	Indian	water	half moon	white
③	Korean	water	full moon	white
④	Indian	water	full moon	colored
⑤	Hindu	water	half moon	colored

9. 다음 글의 밑줄 친 우리말을 영어로 바르게 옮긴 것은? (3점)

Peter's Diary   May 28
<u>나는 이 여행을 너무 즐기는 중이라서 더 오래 머물고 싶다</u>. I love all the traditional Korean symbols in this house. Now I understand a lot of them. I want to visit Korea again with my family.

① I'm enjoying this trip so much than I want to stay long.
② I'm enjoying this trip so much that I want to stay longer.
③ I enjoy this trip so that I want to stay long.
④ I enjoy this trip so much that I want to stay long.
⑤ I'm enjoying this trip much that I will stay longer.

10. 다음 대화 중 〈보기〉의 문장이 들어갈 위치로 가장 적절한 것은? (3점)

보기

Which game should I play first?

W: Welcome to the International Games Festival. You can play many different traditional games here. (A)
B: Wow! It looks exciting! (B)
W: Let's see. Have you ever played *gorodki*?
B: No, I haven't. What is it? (C)
W: It's a traditional game from Russia. (D)
B: (E) How do I play it?
W: Put five sticks on the ground. Then throw a bat at them.
B: That sounds fun. I'll try that first.

① (A)   ② (B)   ③ (C)
④ (D)   ⑤ (E)

11. 다음 밑줄 친 (가)~(마) 중 어법상 옳지 않은 것은 모두 몇 개인가? (4점)

An (가)Amazing Traditional China Dance

Do you know about traditional Chinese dances? There are many kinds. For example, there is a lion dance, a fan dance, and an umbrella dance. One of the most famous dances (나)is the lion dance. In this dance, two dancers dress and (다)act lions. They usually dance on special days, (라)such as New Year's Day. I think their dance moves are great. I hope (마)practicing this dance someday.

① 1개   ② 2개   ③ 3개
④ 4개   ⑤ 5개

[12~14] 다음 대화를 읽고 물음에 답하시오.

보검: Ling's birthday is this Wednesday, isn't it?
민영: Yes. I'm going to buy a book for her. What about you?
보검: I am thinking about buying an umbrella (A)_____ her. I found a cute one in a gift shop.
민영: Oh, that's not a good gift for Chinese people. It means something bad.
보검: Really? What does an umbrella mean in China?
민영: It means separation. The words (B)_____ 'separation' and 'umbrella' sound the same in Chinese.
보검: I see. Then how about chocolate?
민영: That's a good idea.

12. 위 대화의 내용과 일치하지 <u>않는</u> 것은? (3점)

① Ling은 중국 사람이다.
② 민영이는 Ling의 생일 선물로 책을 사려고 한다.
③ 보검이는 선물가게에서 우산을 구입했다.
④ 우산은 중국인들에게 안 좋은 선물로 여겨진다.
⑤ 우산과 이별이라는 단어는 중국어로 발음이 동일하다.

13. 위 대화의 빈칸 (A)와 (B)에 공통으로 알맞은 말은? (2점)

① of   ② for   ③ as
④ to   ⑤ with

14. Which canNOT be answered? (3점)

① What are they talking about?

② When is Ling's birthday party?

③ Who is going to buy chocolate for Ling?

④ Which word sounds the same as separation in Chinese?

⑤ Why do Chinese people think an umbrella isn't a good present?

15. 위 글의 문맥상 (가), (나)에 공통으로 들어갈 말로 알맞은 것은? (3점)

① a crow ② a garden

③ a rooster ④ a hen

⑤ evil spirits

16. 위 글의 빈칸 (A)에 들어갈 표현으로 어법상 가장 적절한 것은? (2점)

① hear ② hears

③ hearing ④ to hear

⑤ heard

[15-20] 다음 글을 읽고 물음에 답하시오.

> They go outside and walk around the garden.
>
> P: What is on that piece of paper? It looks scary.
> G: (a)Do you mean this painting of a rooster?
> P: Oh, is it a rooster?
> G: Yes, it is. Roosters crow every morning. Their crowing means that a new day is beginning. For many years, Koreans have believed evil spirits go away when a rooster crows.
> M: Really? I've never (A)_____ that before.
> P: Actually, I'm afraid of a darkness and evil spirits. Could you draw (가)_____ for me, Mina?
> M: Sure, I'll draw (나)_____ for you!
> G: Put the drawing above your door. Then it will protect you.
> P: Yes, I will.
>   *P: Peter, M: Mina, G: Mina's grandfather

17. 위 글에서 미나의 할아버지가 피터에게 시킨 일로 적절한 것은? (3점)

① 수탉 그림을 보호하기

② 큰 수탉 그림을 그리기

③ 장롱 밑에 수탉 그림을 두기

④ 문 위에 수탉 그림을 붙이기

⑤ 미나에게 수탉 그림을 선물하기

18. 위 글의 내용과 일치하지 않는 것은? (4점)

① Peter는 그림의 수탉이 무서워 보였다.

② 수탉의 울음은 새 날의 시작을 의미한다.

③ 한국인은 수탉이 악령을 쫓는다고 믿는다.

④ Mina는 수탉 그림을 그릴 것이다.

⑤ Peter는 문 아래 그림을 붙일 것이다.

19. 위 글의 밑줄 친 (a)의 의도로 가장 적절한 것은?
(3점)

① 피터가 무엇에 대하여 말하고 있는지 확인하려고
② 수탉 그림이 그려져 있는 장소를 알아내기 위해서
③ 피터 생각에도 그림이 수탉을 닮았는지 알고 싶어서
④ 수탉 그림에 대한 피터의 관심을 이끌어내기 위해서
⑤ 수탉 그림에 대한 자신의 비슷한 의견을 공유하려고

20. 위 글을 읽고 질문과 답이 잘못 쓰인 것을 고르면?
(4점)

① How does the rooster painting look to Peter when he first sees it?
→ It looks scary to him.

② What have Koreans believed for many years about when a rooster crows?
→ They have believed evil spirits go away when a rooster crows.

③ What does Peter ask Mina to do?
→ He asks her to put the drawing of a rooster above his door.

④ Why does Mina's grandfather tell Peter put the drawing above his door?
→ It's because the drawing will protect him from evil spirits.

⑤ What did Peter learn about Korea?
→ He learned about traditional Korean symbols and their meanings.

[21-25] 다음 글을 읽고 물음에 답하시오.

Mina ⓐshowing Peter her grandfather's room. Peter and Mina's grandfather meet and greet each other.

Mina: Hi, Peter! ⓑHave you ever seen this kind of lock before?
Peter: No, I ⓒhave. It's so old (A)_____ I can't really tell, but is it a fish?
Mina: Yes. For a long time, Koreans ⓓhas thought (B)_____ fish are good guards. Fish don't close their eyes, even when they sleep.
Peter: That's interesting.
Mina: We think fish can watch over valuable things. That's ⓔwhich this lock looks like a fish.
Peter: Now I understand.

21. 위 글의 빈칸 (A), (B)에 공통으로 들어갈 표현으로 가장 적절한 것은?
(3점)

① so
② if
③ how
④ that
⑤ which

22. 위 글의 밑줄 친 ⓐ~ⓔ 중 어법상 옳은 것은? (4점)

① ⓐ
② ⓑ
③ ⓒ
④ ⓓ
⑤ ⓔ

23. 위 글의 내용과 일치하는 것은? (4점)

① 열쇠는 물고기를 닮았다.

② 물고기는 눈을 감고 잔다.

③ 미나는 피터에게 자신의 방을 보여준다.

④ 피터는 미나가 보여주는 자물쇠를 본 적이 있다.

⑤ 한국인들은 물고기가 좋은 파수꾼이라고 생각해 왔다.

24. 위 글을 읽고 답할 수 있는 질문을 2개 고른 것은? (4점)

① Who made a fish-shaped lock first?

② Where does Peter meet Mina's grandfather?

③ What does Peter ask Mina's grandfather to do?

④ Why do Korean people think fish are good guards?

⑤ What comes to mind when you think of valuable things?

25. 위 글의 밑줄 친 ⓑHave ... seen과 현재완료의 쓰임이 같은 것은? (3점)

① I have just had lunch.

② The concert has already started.

③ I have heard of his news once recently.

④ Tom and his brothers have gone to Italy.

⑤ The girls have learned Spanish for three years.

[26-29] 다음 글을 읽고 물음에 답하시오.

Peter is visiting Korea to meet a friend, Mina, from a sister school. Peter is going to stay at her grandfather's house for a week. When he arrives, Mina shows him the guest room.

Mina: Peter, you will stay here. This guest room is full of traditional Korean things. Look at this pillow.

Peter: What are these things?

Mina: They're bats.

Peter: Bats on my pillow? That's scary!

Mina: Not really. In Korea, bats are symbols of luck and a long life.

Peter: That's surprising. In many Western countries, (a)박쥐가 사람들에게 어둠과 무서운 것들을 상기시켜.

26. 위 글의 내용과 일치하도록 다음 빈칸에 알맞은 단어를 쓰시오. (각각의 빈칸에 1단어)　　　(5점)

> Korean people and Western people think of bats differently. To Korean people, bats mean (a)_____ and (b)_____ _____. On the other hand, Western people think of bats as (c)_____ and (d)_____ _____.

27. 위 글의 내용으로 보아 한국에서 박쥐가 상징하는 것은? (정답 2개)　　　(3점)

① 행운　　　　② 친구
③ 부귀　　　　④ 명예
⑤ 장수

28. 위 글의 밑줄 친 부분 (a)와 같은 뜻이 되는 문장은?　　　(4점)

① Bats people darkness and scary things remind of.
② Bats remind people darkness and scary things.
③ Bats remind of people darkness and scary things.
④ Bats remind people of darkness and scary things.
⑤ Bats remind darkness and scary things of people.

29. 위 글의 내용과 일치하지 <u>않는</u> 것은?　　　(3점)

① Peter will stay at Mina's grandfather's house.
② The guest room has many traditional things.
③ Mina shows a pillow to Peter.
④ Both Peter and Mina are scared of bats.
⑤ Bats mean different things in Korea and Western countries.

30. 다음 (A)~(D)에 들어갈 말로 알맞게 짝지은 것은?　　　(4점)

> Do you know about traditional Chinese dances? There are many (A)[kind / kinds]. For example, there is a lion dance, a fan dance, and an umbrella dances. One of the most famous (B)[dance / dances] is the lion dance. In this dance, two dancers (C)[dresses and acts / dress and act] like lions. They usually dance on special days, such as New Year's Day. I think their dance moves (D)[is / are] great. I hope to practice this dance someday.

	(A)	(B)	(C)	(D)
①	kinds	dance	dresses and acts	is
②	kind	dance	dress and act	is
③	kinds	dances	dress and act	are
④	kind	dances	dresses and acts	are
⑤	kinds	dances	dress and act	is

◎ 선택형 문항의 답안은 컴퓨터용 수정 싸인펜을 사용하여 OMR 답안지에 바르게 표기하시오.
◎ 서술형 문제는 답을 답안지에 반드시 검정 볼펜으로 쓰시오.
◎ 총 30문항 100점 만점입니다. 문항별 배점은 각 문항에 표시되어 있습니다.

[서울 서초구 ○○중]

1. 다음 주어진 의미에 해당하는 단어가 들어갈 수 <u>없는</u> 것은? (4점)

ⓐ to use something again
ⓑ to take something into the body
ⓒ tiny living things that often cause illness
ⓓ useless materials that are thrown away
ⓔ powder, liquid, or gas that is used to do things such as kill bugs or clean
ⓕ dirty and dangerous materials that go into air or water

① Take the can and open the _____.
② Wash the can and _____ it.
③ The car will _____ a lot of fuel.
④ The air _____ is getting worse.
⑤ Some _____ can cause diseases.

[서울 강동구 ○○중]

2. 다음 단어와 뜻이 <u>어색하게</u> 연결된 것은? (2점)

① lid - 뚜껑
② material - 재료
③ pollution - 감소
④ conclusion - 결론
⑤ experiment - 실험

[서울 강동구 ○○중]

3. 다음 우리말과 같은 뜻이 되도록 괄호 안의 말을 이용하여 영작하시오. (4점)

그녀는 코미디언들보다 훨씬 더 웃긴다.
(humorous / much / comedians)

→ _____

[경기 ○○중]

4. 다음 대화의 밑줄 친 ⓐ~ⓔ 중, 표현이 적절한 것만을 짝지은 것은? (4점)

A: What does this picture mean?
B: It means we ⓐ<u>are wasted</u> paper. Paper ⓑ<u>is made</u> from wood.
A: I heard 17 trees ⓒ<u>are used to</u> make one ton of paper.
B: Yes. When we ⓓ<u>are thrown away</u> paper, so many trees ⓔ<u>are destroying</u>.

① ⓐ, ⓓ
② ⓑ, ⓒ
③ ⓐ, ⓓ, ⓔ
④ ⓑ, ⓒ, ⓔ
⑤ ⓑ, ⓒ, ⓓ, ⓔ

[5-8] 다음 대화를 읽고 물음에 답하시오.

Sue: How pretty! I like your bag. Where did you get ⓐ<u>it</u>?
Ann: I made ⓑ<u>it</u> myself.
Sue: You made it (A)_____? ⓒ<u>It</u> looks unique.
Ann: Why don't you make one? ⓓ<u>It's</u> not difficult.
Sue: Really? Can you tell me how to make ⓔ<u>it</u>?
Ann: Sure. Find some old jeans. Cut them into small pieces. Then sew the pieces together.
Sue: That sounds easy. I'll make one as a birthday present for my sister.

[서울 관악구 ○○중]

5. 위 대화의 흐름상 빈칸 (A)에 알맞은 것은? (3점)

① myself
② himself
③ herself
④ yourself
⑤ ourselves

6. 위 대화의 내용에 이어질 내용의 빈칸에 알맞은 것을 차례대로 연결한 것은? (2점)

> First, find some _____ jeans.
> Then _____ the jeans into small pieces.
> Finally _____ the pieces together.

① old - cut - sew

② cut - sew - old

③ sew - cut - old

④ old - sew - cut

⑤ cut - old - sew

7. 위 대화의 밑줄 친 ⓐ~ⓔ 중 가리키는 것이 다른 하나는? (3점)

① ⓐ   ② ⓑ   ③ ⓒ

④ ⓓ   ⑤ ⓔ

8. 위 대화의 내용과 일치하도록 다음 질문에 대해 수동태 문장으로 답하시오. (5점)

> What will Sue use to make a bag for her sister?

정답 : _____

_____

9. 다음 대화를 읽고, 'Earth Hour'에 대한 설명으로 옳지 않은 것은? (3점)

> G: Have you heard of *Earth Hour* before?
> B: No, I haven't. What is it?
> G: It's a global environmental event. People turn off their lights for an hour.
> B: Why do they do that?
> G: They do it to remind people of our environmental problems. They believe such a small action can change the world.
> B: Oh, I see. Can you tell me how to join it?
> G: Sure. Just turn off your lights from 8:30 p.m. to 9:30 p.m. next Saturday.
> B: That's easy. I will join *Earth Hour* next week.

① 지구 환경을 위한 행사이다.

② 사람들은 1시간 동안 불을 끈다.

③ 사람들에게 환경문제들을 상기시키기 위한 것이다.

④ 행사에 참여하는 사람들은 작은 실천이 세상을 바꿀 수 있다고 믿는다.

⑤ 지난 주 토요일에 열렸다.

10. 다음 대화의 흐름상, 어색한 것은? (3점)

> Jennifer: What are you reading?
> Eric: I'm reading a ⓐpaper about aquaponics. It's a way of growing plants without ⓑsoil. We can also grow plants and ⓒrise fish in just one system.
> Jennifer: Is that ⓓpossible?
> Eric: We'll ⓔsee. I'm going to try it at home for my science project.

① ⓐ   ② ⓑ   ③ ⓒ

④ ⓓ   ⑤ ⓔ

11. 다음 대화의 내용과 일치하지 <u>않는</u> 것은? (4점)

Bora: You look nervous. What's wrong?

Nari: I'm worried about the speech contest next week. The speeches are about environmental problems and their solutions.

Bora: What are you going to talk about?

Nari: I want to talk about soil pollution, but I can't find enough information.

Bora: What about water problems instead? I read an article, and it said we don't have enough water. I'm really worried about it. I think we have to do something about that problem.

Nari: But isn't there enough water for everyone?

Bora: No. In some countries, people are in danger because they don't have enough water. Our country could have this problem in the near future.

Nari: Oh, I didn't know that. I will talk about that problem and its solutions. Thank you for your advice!

① Nari is worried about the speech contest.

② Nari is going to talk about water problems.

③ Nari thought that there is enough water for everyone.

④ Nari didn't know that our country could have water problems in the near future.

⑤ Nari has read an article about water problems before.

[12-13] 다음 대화를 읽고 물음에 답하시오.

A: Did you watch the documentary last night?

B: No, I didn't. What was it about?

A: It was about global warming. The Earth is getting hotter, and sea levels are going up. I'm worried about the Earth.

B: Oh, I've heard about that problem before. Some islands are disappearing, so people are losing their homes.

A: Yes. It is terrible.

B: Is there any <u>way</u> to stop it?

A: We can save energy. We should turn off the lights when we don't need them. We should also use fans instead of air conditioners.

B: Those are great ideas. I'll try to do those things right away.

12. 위 대화의 주제로 가장 적절한 것은? (3점)

① ways to save water

② what makes the Earth dirty

③ how to stop the global warming

④ the importance of turning off the lights

⑤ what to recycle for the environment

13. 위 대화의 밑줄 친 way를 대신할 수 있는 단어로 가장 적절한 것은? (3점)

① solution   ② subject

③ truth   ④ place

⑤ news

[14-17] 다음 글을 읽고 물음에 답하시오.

> Fish, bacteria, and plants ⓐare the main parts of aquaponics. After you ⓑfeed the fish, they ⓒproduce waste. (A)_____. The plants clean the water by (B)consume the food. This process is ⓓrepeat ⓔagain and again!

16. 위 글의 밑줄 친 ⓐ~ⓔ 중 어법상 옳지 않은 것은? (3점)

① ⓐ   ② ⓑ   ③ ⓒ

④ ⓓ   ⑤ ⓔ

14. 위 글의 제목으로 가장 적절한 것은? (3점)

① The Process of Aquaponics

② Aquaponics for My Science Project

③ How to Raise Fish at Home

④ Some Problems in Aquaculture

⑤ From Food to Waste

17. 위 글의 밑줄 친 (B)를 문맥에 맞게 알맞은 형태로 바꾸시오. (3점)

정답 : _____

[18-20] 다음 글을 읽고 물음에 답하시오.

> From this science project, I grew my plants and ⓐraised fish with aquaponics. I just fed the fish, but the plants ⓑhave grown 17 centimeters in three months. The fish ⓒ stay healthy and the water is clean all the time.
>
> Some important things about aquaponics were learned from this experiment. First, aquaponics save water because the plants don't need ⓓwatering. Second, it is good for the environment because no chemicals ⓔ used. Finally, you can do aquaponics anywhere because (A)_____.

15. 위 글의 빈칸 (A)에 들어갈 문장으로 가장 알맞은 것은? (4점)

① The bacteria make more energy.

② The fish can live without food forever.

③ The fish waste can be food for bacteria.

④ The fish produce the air by moving in the water.

⑤ The waste is turned into food for the plants by bacteria.

18. 위 글의 ⓐ~ⓔ 중 어법상 어색한 것은? (3점)

① ⓐ   ② ⓑ   ③ ⓒ

④ ⓓ   ⑤ ⓔ

19. 위 글의 흐름상 빈칸 (A)에 들어갈 알맞은 것은?
(3점)

① a lot of space is not needed
② there is not much space for it
③ they can save much more space
④ it helps plants grow faster
⑤ it works well enough without electricity

[21~22] 다음 글을 읽고 물음에 답하시오.

<Results>

From this experiment, I grew my plants and raised fish with aquaponics. I just fed the fish, but the plants have grown 17 centimeters in three months. The fish stay healthy and the water is clean all the time.

<Conclusion>

Some important things about aquaponics (**A**)[learned / were learned] from this experiment. First, water is saved because the plants don't need (**B**)[to water / watering]. Second, it is good for the environment because no chemicals are (**C**)[used / using]. Finally, you can do aquaponics anywhere because it doesn't need much space.

20. 위 글에 나온 아쿠아포닉스 시스템에 대한 내용과 일치하지 <u>않는</u> 것은?
(4점)

① 그저 물고기에 먹이만 주었는데도 식물은 석 달 동안 17cm나 자랐다.
② 물고기는 건강을 유지하며 물은 항상 깨끗하다.
③ 식물에 물을 줄 필요가 없으므로 물이 절약된다.
④ 화학 물질이 사용되지만 아쿠아포닉스는 환경에 이롭다.
⑤ 아쿠아포닉스는 넓은 공간을 필요로 하지 않는다.

21. 위 글의 Aquaponics에 대해 제대로 이해한 사람은?
(4점)

① 슬기: I just need to water the plants to use aquaponics.
② 웬디: I can save my money because I don't need to feed the fish.
③ 조이: With aquaponics, we can grow plants and raise fish at the same time.
④ 아이린: Water is wasted because we have to use a lot of water to raise fish.
⑤ 예리: Aquaponics is good for the environment because it needs only small amounts of chemicals.

22. 위 글의 빈칸 (A)~(C)에 들어갈 말이 바르게 짝지어진 것은? (4점)

	(A)	(B)	(C)
①	were learned	watering	used
②	learned	watering	used
③	were learned	to water	using
④	learned	to water	used
⑤	were learned	watering	using

24. 위 글의 Home Aquaponics system을 만드는 재료가 아닌 것은? (3점)

① clay ② a pot

③ a hole ④ plants

⑤ stones

[23-25] 다음 글을 읽고 물음에 답하시오.

Home Aquaponics - Eric Jackson

I made holes in the bottom of a pot. Then I put small stones and plants in it.

(A) I made another hole in the lid and put a tube through it.
(B) I put a water pump in the fish tank and connected it to the tube.
(C) I fixed the pot in place with clay.
(D) I made a big hole in the lid of a fish tank and put the pot in it.

I filled the fish tank with water and put some fish in it.

---

23. 위 글의 (A)~(D)를 Aquaponics를 만드는 과정으로 알맞게 배열한 것은? (4점)

① (A)-(C)-(D)-(B)

② (B)-(A)-(C)-(D)

③ (C)-(D)-(B)-(A)

④ (D)-(C)-(A)-(B)

⑤ (A)-(B)-(C)-(D)

25. Which is NOT correct about the steps of making Aquaponics? (3점)

① 화분 바닥에 구멍을 뚫었다.

② 어항 바닥에 구멍을 뚫어 관을 두었다.

③ 찰흙으로 화분을 제자리에 고정하였다.

④ 어항 덮개에 큰 구멍을 내고 구멍에 그 화분을 넣었다.

⑤ 덮개에 또 다른 구멍을 하나 만들고 그 안에 관을 넣었다.

[26-30] 다음 글을 읽고 물음에 답하시오.

I found out that some farmers use ⓐ aquaponics to produce vegetables and raise fish. ⓑThey choose aquaponics because ⓒit is (A)_____ easier than traditional gardening. Also, ⓓit is a much more productive way of growing food. The plants grow (A)_____ faster than plants in soil, and it (B)공간을 절약한다. I hope more food is produced in this way in the future because ⓔit is healthy for us and the environment.

26. 위 글의 밑줄 친 ⓐ~ⓔ 중 가리키는 대상이 <u>다른</u> 것은? (2점)

① ⓐ   ② ⓑ   ③ ⓒ

④ ⓓ   ⑤ ⓔ

27. 위 글의 빈칸 (A)에 공통으로 들어갈 수 있는 단어를 〈보기〉에서 있는 대로 고른 것은? (3점)

> **보기**
> ⓐ even / ⓑ very / ⓒ far / ⓓ lots of / ⓔ still

① ⓐ, ⓑ, ⓒ

② ⓐ, ⓒ, ⓔ

③ ⓐ, ⓓ, ⓔ

④ ⓑ, ⓒ, ⓓ

⑤ ⓑ, ⓒ, ⓔ

28. 위 글의 밑줄 친 (B)를 문맥에 맞게 영어로 바꾸어 쓰시오. (3점)

정답 : _____ _____

29. 위 글의 주제로 가장 적절한 것은? (4점)

① 아쿠아포닉스의 문제점들

② 전통적인 재배 방식의 활용법

③ 물고기를 기르는 다양한 방법들

④ 아쿠아포닉스의 다양한 장점들

⑤ 아쿠아포닉스 장치를 만드는 유용한 조언

30. 위 글의 내용과 일치하지 <u>않는</u> 것은? (4점)

① 몇몇 농부들은 채소를 생산하고 물고기를 키우는 데 아쿠아포닉스를 이용한다.

② 농부들은 아쿠아포닉스가 최신 재배 방식보다 훨씬 쉽기 때문에 그것을 선택한다.

③ 아쿠아포닉스는 식량을 재배하는 더 생산적인 방법이다.

④ 식물들이 흙에서 자라는 식물보다 훨씬 빠르게 자란다.

⑤ 아쿠아포닉스는 우리와 환경에 건강한 방식이다.

◎ 선택형 문항의 답안은 컴퓨터용 수정 싸인펜을 사용하여 OMR 답안지에 바르게 표기하시오.
◎ 서술형 문제는 답을 답안지에 반드시 검정 볼펜으로 쓰시오.
◎ 총 29문항 100점 만점입니다. 문항별 배점은 각 문항에 표시되어 있습니다.

[서울 강동구 ○○중]

1. 다음 중 단어의 영영풀이가 어색한 것은?   (3점)

① reuse: to use something again

② valuable: very important or expensive

③ bow: to lower your head or bend your body

④ pollution: dirty and dangerous materials that go into air or water

⑤ connect: to put something firmly in place so that it doesn't move

[인천 ○○중]

2. 대화의 빈칸에 들어갈 말로 가장 적절한 것은? (3점)

Brian: In my school, students leave so much food on their plates. I'm worried about _____.

Sera: Right, that's a big problem. We should not put too much food on our plates.

① soil pollution

② wasting food

③ wasting water

④ using more energy

⑤ the amount of plastic waste

[인천 ○○중]

3. 다음 중 어법상 어색한 것은?   (3점)

① The sea is polluted by people's trash.

② Yusin is even more handsome than Jihun.

③ The refrigerator is powered by dirty water.

④ The telephone was invented by Alexander Bell in 1876.

⑤ The movie *Jurassic Park* made by Steven Spielburg in 1993.

[경기 ○○중]

4. 다음 제시된 문장의 수동태 표현이 옳은 것은? (4점)

① Robots make our chocolate.

→ Our chocolate was made by robots.

② Van Gogh painted *Sunflower*.

→ *Sunflower* is painted by Van Gogh.

③ Our scientists discovered solutions to this problem.

→ This problem was discovered solutions by our scientists.

④ The Wright brothers invented the airplane in 1903.

→ The airplane was invented the Wright brothers in 1903.

⑤ Many kids and adults read the book *Harry Potter*.

→ The book *Harry Potter* is read by many kids and adults.

A: I watched the documentary about ⓐ_____ last night. The Earth is getting hotter, and sea levels are going up.

B: Some islands are disappearing, so people are losing their homes.

A: Yes. It is terrible.

B: Is there any way to stop it?

A: We can save energy. We should turn off the lights when we don't need them. We should use fans instead of air conditioners.

B: Those are great ideas. I'll try to do ⓑunderline those things right away.

[서울 관악구 ㅇㅇ중]

5. 위 대화의 빈칸 ⓐ에 알맞은 것은? (3점)

① food waste

② plastic waste

③ good weather

④ global warming

⑤ healthy condition

[서울 관악구 ㅇㅇ중]

6. 위 대화의 ⓑthose things가 가리키는 것을 대화 중에서 찾은 것은? (4점)

① Earth is getting hotter.

② Sea levels are going up.

③ We are losing our homes.

④ Some islands are disappearing in the near future.

⑤ People should use fans instead of air conditioners.

[서울 종로구 ㅇㅇ중]

7. 다음 대화를 읽고, 화자들이 걱정하는 것은? (3점)

① food waste ② global warming

③ plastic waste ④ soil pollution

⑤ water waste

[서울 관악구 ㅇㅇ중]

8. 다음 중 단어의 쓰임이 자연스럽지 않은 것은? (4점)

A: What are you ⓐreading?

B: I'm reading an article about aquaponics. It's a way of ⓑgrowing plants without soil. We can also grow plants and ⓒrise fish in just one system.

A: Is that possible?

B: We'll ⓓsee. I'm going to ⓔtry it at home for my science project.

① ⓐ ② ⓑ ③ ⓒ

④ ⓓ ⑤ ⓔ

[서울 관악구 ㅇㅇ중]

9. 다음 중 일상생활에서 발생할 수 있는 문제와 해결책이 바른 것은? (3점)

① Problem: It is a big trash problem.

Solution: You should go to bed early.

② Problem: She uses her smart phone too often.

Solution: She should make a shopping list.

③ Problem: He always buys too many things.

Solution: He should clean up the park together.

④ Problem: I can't sleep well at night.

Solution: You should find a new hobby.

⑤ Problem: My cat is missing.

Solution: You should put up posters to find it.

[10~12] 다음 대화를 읽고 물음에 답하시오.

A: You look nervous. What's wrong?

B: (A)_____ The speeches are about environmental problems and their solutions.

A: What are you going to talk about?

B: I want to talk about soil pollution, but I can't find enough information.

A: What about water problems instead? I read an article, and it said (B)_____ _____. I'm really worried about it. I think we have to do something about that problem.

B: But isn't there enough water for everyone?

A: No. In some countries, people are in danger because they don't have enough water. Our country could have this problem in the near future.

B: Oh, I didn't know that. I will talk about that problem and its solutions. Thank you for your advice!

*A: Boy, B: Girl

11. 위 대화의 빈칸 (B)에 들어갈 말로 가장 적절한 것은?

(3점)

① we can solve them together

② we don't have enough water

③ drinking water makes you healthier

④ water is very important in daily life

⑤ not many people are interested in the environment

10. 위 대화의 빈칸 (A)에 들어갈 말로 적절한 것은?

(3점)

① I'm worried about the Earth.

② I'm worried about the speech contest tomorrow.

③ Why don't we talk about environmental problems?

④ Can you tell me how to solve environmental problems?

⑤ What topic do I have to talk about in the speech contest?

12. 위 대화의 내용과 일치하지 않는 것은? (3점)

① 소녀는 내일 있을 스피치 대회를 걱정하고 있다.

② 스피치 대회의 주제는 환경 문제와 그 해결책에 대한 것이다.

③ 소녀는 토양 오염에 대해 충분한 정보를 찾지 못하고 있다.

④ 소년이 읽었던 기사는 물 오염에 관한 것이다.

⑤ 소녀는 스피치 대회에서 물 문제와 그 해결책에 대해 말할 것이다.

13. 다음 어법상 옳은 문장만을 〈보기〉에서 있는 대로 고른 것은? (4점)

보기

(A) Lisa dances very harder than Sue.

(B) This song, Chandelier, was sung by Sia Furler.

(C) Seventeen trees used to make one ton of paper.

(D) Thomas Edison was invented the light bulb in 1879.

(E) Tony's essay was a lot more impressive than Amy's.

(F) Solutions to the problem was discovered by scientists.

(G) The artwork *Sunflowers* was painted by Van Gogh.

① (A), (C)　　　　② (B), (D)

③ (B), (E), (G)　　④ (A), (C), (D), (F)

⑤ (B), (E), (F), (G)

[14–17] 다음 대화를 읽고 물음에 답하시오.

A: Jackson, have you heard of *Earth Hour* before?

B: No, I haven't. What is it, Emma?

A: It's a global environmental event. People turn off their lights (a)<u>for</u> an hour.

B: Why do they do that?

A: They do it to make people think about our environmental problems. They believe such a small action can change the world.

B: Oh, I see. (A)<u>그 행사에 어떻게 참여하는지 알려줄 수 있니?</u>

A: Sure. Just turn off your lights from 8:30 p.m. to 9:30 p.m. on the last Saturday in March.

B: That's easy. I will join the next *Earth Hour*.

14. 위 대화의 내용과 일치하지 <u>않는</u> 것은? (3점)

① *Earth Hour* is an international event.

② Jackson hasn't heard of *Earth Hour* before.

③ *Earth Hour* event is on the last Sunday in March.

④ People can join *Earth Hour* by turning off their lights for an hour in the evening.

⑤ The purpose of *Earth Hour* is to make people think about our environmental problems.

15. 위 대화의 밑줄 친 (A)의 우리말과 의미가 같은 문장을 아래의 〈조건〉을 참고하여 영어로 쓰시오. (5점)

조건

• join, tell을 반드시 사용할 것

• 9단어의 의문문으로 쓸 것

정답 : _____

16. 위 대화를 읽고 *Earth Hour*에 대해 알 수 <u>없는</u> 것은? (3점)

① 시작 시간

② 지속 시간

③ 행사 주최자

④ 참여 방법

⑤ 행사 목적

17. 위 대화의 (a)for와 〈보기〉 (A)~(G)의 밑줄 친 부분이 같은 의미로 쓰인 문장의 개수는? (3점)

19. 다음 대화의 빈칸 (A)에 들어갈 말로 가장 적절한 것은? (3점)

보기

(A) I'll not be here <u>for</u> a few days.

(B) How much did you pay <u>for</u> the birthday present?

(C) Is this train <u>for</u> Mt. Dobong?

(D) <u>For</u> a month, I have to work at a high school.

(E) It's a book <u>for</u> children.

(F) She has stood there <u>for</u> two hours.

(G) I'm free <u>for</u> the whole day.

① 1개   ② 2개   ③ 3개

④ 4개   ⑤ 5개

B: I like your bag. Where did you get it?

G: I made it myself.

B: You made it yourself? That's amazing!

G: Why don't you make one? It's not difficult.

B: Really? (A)_____

G: Sure. First, find some old jeans. Second, cut them into small pieces. Then sew the pieces together.

B: That sounds easy. I'll make one as a birthday gift for my sister.

① Have you ever bought old jeans before?

② Can you give me directions to the closest store?

③ Can you pass me the scissors?

④ Can you tell me how to make it?

⑤ I'm worried about making mistakes.

18. 다음 문제점의 해결 방법으로 어울리는 것은? (3점)

<문제점>
Wasting Food

① We should use our own cup.

② We should reuse paper all the time.

③ We should use a cup when we brush our teeth.

④ We should not put too much food on our plates.

⑤ We should turn off the light when we are not using lights.

20. 다음 중 글의 흐름과 어울리지 <u>않는</u> 것은? (3점)

ⓐ<u>Lots of electric energy is wasted around us.</u> ⓑ<u>To solve this problem, let's do these things.</u> First, ⓒ<u>we should turn off the lights when we leave our classrooms.</u> Next, ⓓ<u>we should turn off the classroom computers when we are not using them.</u> Lastly, ⓔ<u>we should use a cup when we brush our teeth.</u> Doing these things will be helpful to our school and the environment.

① ⓐ   ② ⓑ   ③ ⓒ

④ ⓓ   ⑤ ⓔ

[A]
Jennifer: What are you reading?
Eric: I'm reading an article about aquaponics. 그것은 흙 없이 식물을 기르는 방식이다. We can also grow plants and raise fish in just one system.
Jennifer: Is that possible?
Eric: ㉠_____ I'm going to try it at home for my science project.

[B]
Fish, bacteria, and plants are the main parts of aquaponics. After you feed the fish, they produce waste. The waste is turned into food for the plants by bacteria. The plants clean the water by consuming the food. This process is repeated again and again!

[C]
Home Aquaponics   by Eric Jackson
<Questions>
　㉡_____ at home?
　Why is aquaponics good?
<Period>
From May 15 to August 15

<㉮_____>
a pot & small stones, a fish tank, a plastic tube, a water pump, plants, some fish, a box cutter, clay

<㉯_____>
1. I made holes in the bottom of a pot. Then I put small stones and plants in it.
2. I made a big hole in the lid of the fish tank and put the pot in the hole.
3. I fixed the pot in place with clay.
4. I made another hole in the lid and put a tube through it.
5. I put a water pump in the fish tank. I used the tube to connect the pump to the pot.
6. I filled the fish tank with water and put some fish in it. Then I turned on the pump.

<㉰_____>
From this experiment, I grew my plants and raised fish with aquaponics. I just ㉢_____ the fish, but the plants have ㉣_____ 17 centimeters in three months. The fish ㉤_____ healthy and the water is clean all the time.

<㉱_____>
Some important things about aquaponics ⓐwere learned from this experiment. First, water ⓑis saved because the plants don't need watering. Second, it is good for the environment because no chemicals ⓒare used. Finally, you can do aquaponics anywhere because it doesn't need much space.

I found out...
Some farmers ⓓare used aquaponics to produce vegetables and ⓔare raised fish. They ⓕare chosen aquaponics because ㉥그것은 전통적인 식물 가꾸기보다 훨씬 더 쉽다. Also, it is a much more productive way of growing food. The plants grow much faster than plants in soil, and it saves space. I hope more food ⓖis produced in this way in the future because it is healthy for us and the environment.

21. 위 글의 [A]의 밑줄 친 우리말을 〈보기〉의 단어들을 배열하여 영어로 옮겨 쓰시오.　　(4점)

보기

plants / a way / soil / of / it's / without / growing

정답 : _____

22. 위 글의 [A]의 빈칸 ㉠에 알맞지 <u>않은</u> 것은?　(3점)

① Let me know.

② I'll find out.

③ We'll see.

④ I'm not sure.

⑤ I don't know.

23. 위 글의 문단 [B]에서 답을 찾을 수 <u>없는</u> 것은?(3점)

① How does aquaponics work?

② How do you get the fish?

③ What do bacteria do in the process?

④ How do the plants clean the water?

⑤ When does the process end?

24. 위 글의 [C]의 빈칸 ㉡에 알맞은 것은?　　　(3점)

① How can I have food from aquaponics

② How can I make an aquaponics system

③ How can I get materials for aquaponics

④ How can I produce bacteria in aquaponics

⑤ How can I solve aquaponics problems

25. 위 글의 [C]의 ㉮~㉣에 들어갈 말이 순서대로 바르게 짝지어진 것은?　　　(4점)

① Materials – Steps – Results – Conclusion

② Steps – Materials – Conclusion – Results

③ Materials – Results – Conclusion – Steps

④ Steps – Results – Materials – Conclusion

⑤ Results – Conclusion – Steps – Materials

26. 위 글의 내용상 [C]의 ⓒ~ⓜ에 알맞은 것끼리 연결된
    것은?   (4점)

	ⓒ	ㄹ	ㅁ
①	fed	showed	have
②	fed	grown	stay
③	fed	grown	have
④	produced	showed	stay
⑤	produced	grown	have

28. 위 글의 [C]의 우리말 ㅂ를 〈보기〉의 단어들을 사용,
    변형 또는 다른 말을 추가하여 영어로 옮겨 쓰시오.
                                                      (4점)

┌─ 보기 ─────────────────────────────┐
│ tradition / easy / garden / far / it │
└────────────────────────────────────┘

정답 : _____

29. 위 글의 'aquaponics'에 대한 내용 중 [C]의 내용과
    일치하지 <u>않는</u> 것은?   (3점)

① 농업 현장에서 사용되고 있다.

② 더 효과적으로 식품을 생산할 수 있다.

③ 흙에서보다 식물을 더 빨리 성장시킨다.

④ 많은 공간이 확보되어야 한다.

⑤ 사람들과 환경에 도움이 된다.

27. 위 글의 [C]의 ⓐ~ⓖ에서 쓰임이 알맞은 것의 개수
    는?   (4점)

① 2개   ② 3개   ③ 4개

④ 5개   ⑤ 6개

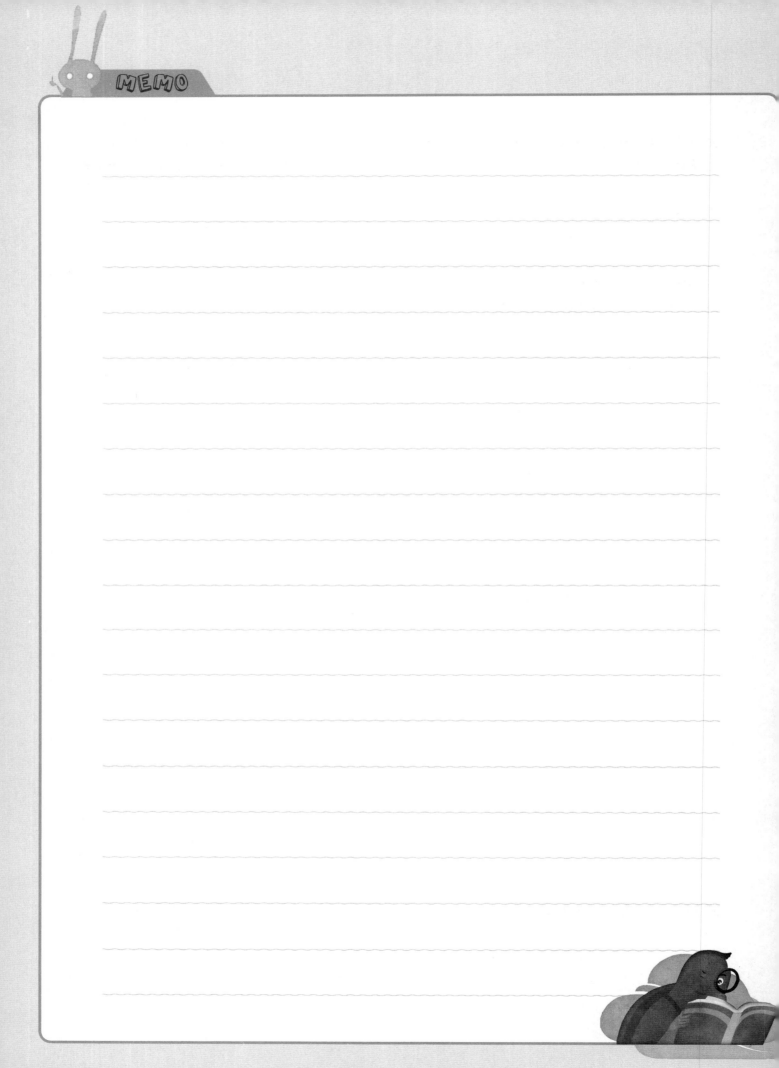

MEMO

정답 및 해설

Lesson 1 (중간)

---

01 ① **02** ④ **03** ① **04** ⑤ **05** ③ **06** ③ **07** ③
08 ⑤
09 (A) Sending messages to him is fun.
(B) Recommending songs to each other makes me happy.
10 ② **11** ⑤
12 (1) Don't forget to pick up the children.
(2) We decided to go to the beach.
(3) Stop making that noise.
13 ④ **14** ② **15** ③, ④ **16** ③
17 (1) It[=Smiling] can help you look more welcoming and cheerful.
(2) they make ordinary pictures look more dramatic
18 ② **19** ① **20** ④ **21** ② **22** ①
23 (1) yourself (2) doesn't it **24** ④ **25** ① **26** ③
27 Robert Cornelius took the world's first selfie in 1839.
28 ① **29** ⑤

---

01 사진을 찍는 사람('a person who takes photographs')이라는 영영풀이가 가리키는 것은 photography(사진)이 아니라 photographer(사진가)이다.

02 suggestion(제안)과 comment(논평, 언급) 두 단어는 비슷한 뜻을 가진 단어들이다. 나머지 단어들은 모두 반의어 관계에 있는 단어들이다.

03 '적절한 사회적 행동을 위한 일련의 규칙들'이라는 영영풀이가 가리키는 것은 ① etiquette(에티켓)이다.

04 ① , and who lives → who lives / ② which → who / ③ who likes it → which she likes / ④ which → whose

05 상대방에게 허락을 요청할 때 쓸 수 있는 표현으로 "Can I ~?", "May I ~?" 등과 같은 표현이 있다.

06 저기 있는 개들에게 먹이를 줘도 되냐고 묻는 A의 물음에 "아니, 난 하면 안 돼."라는 B의 대답은 대화 흐름상 자연스럽지 않다.

07 G가 입장을 해도 되냐고 묻자, M은 입장해도 된다고 대답하고 티켓을 보여 달라고 요청한다. 이에 G는 티켓을 보여

주면서 공연장 안에서 음악을 녹음해도 되냐고 묻는다. M은 안된다고 대답하고 G는 다시 가수의 사진을 찍어도 되냐고 묻는다. 이에 M이 안된다고 말하는 순서로 이어지는 것이 글의 흐름상 가장 자연스럽다.

08 위 대화에서는 음악 공연장에서 사진을 찍어도 되냐고 허락을 요청하고 그에 대답하는 내용을 담고 있다.

09 동명사는 문장에서 주어 역할을 한다. 이때 동명사는 단수 취급하기 때문에 동사는 단수 동사를 쓴다.

10 listen to → listening to / are not → is not / take → taking / who → that[which]

11 ⓐ 동사를 주어에 쓸 경우 동명사 형태로 쓴다. ⓑ 동사 enjoy는 동명사를 목적어로 취한다. ⓒ spend+시간+동명사를 취한다.

12 (1) Don't forget to ~ : ~하는 것을 잊지 마라, pick up ~를 데리고 오다 (2) decide to ~ : ~하기로 결정하다 (3) stop -ing : ~하는 것을 멈추다

13 ④는 현재분사로 쓰여 현재진행형 문장을 만들고 있다. 나머지 ①, ②, ③, ⑤는 모두 동명사로 쓰였다.

14 빈칸 (A) 다음에 오는 대답으로 미루어 볼 때, (A)에 들어갈 말로 가장 적절한 것은 ② what are you interested in?(너의 관심사는 무엇이니?)이다.

15 Amy는 이번 주말 남동생과 야구 경기를 보러 가기로 했으며, Eric은 Jane의 제안에 Hit the Beat를 보기로 결정했다고 위 대화에서 언급되어 있다.

16 빈칸 다음에는 V 사인과 같은 흔한 포즈는 심심하다고 이야기하면서 개성을 드러낼 수 있는 다른 포즈를 이용하라고 말하고 있다. 따라서 빈칸에 들어갈 말로 가장 적절한 것은 ③ create your own poses(자신만의 포즈를 만들어라)이다.

17 (1) 웃는 것은 당신을 더 따뜻하고 발랄하게 보이도록 도와줄 수 있다고 언급되어 있다. (2) 필터들은 평범한 사진을 더 극적으로 보이게 만든다고 언급되어 있다.

18 사진을 위에서 내려다보면서 찍는 것은 소녀들을 더 귀엽게 보이게 도와준다고('For girls, taking pictures from above makes them look cuter.') 언급되어 있다.

19 위 글에서는 셀피에 관한 흥미로운 사실들에 대해서 이야기하고 있다. 따라서 제목으로 가장 적절한 것은 ① Selfie Facts(셀피에 관한 사실들)이다.

20 몇 가지 흥미로운 사실이 여기 있다'라는 문장이 들어가기에 가장 적절한 곳은 흥미로운 사실들이 나오는 바로 앞부분인 (D)이다.

21 셀피를 찍을 적절한 장소를 찾으라고는 이야기했지만 ② Where is the best places to take selfies?(셀피를 찍

을 수 있는 최고의 장소는 어디인가?)라는 질문에 대한 내용은 위 글에서 찾아볼 수 없다.

22 두 번째 문단에서 셀피를 찍을 적절한 장소를 선택하라고 이야기하고 있다. 따라서 빈칸 (A)에 들어갈 말로 가장 적절한 것은 Where am I?(나는 어디 있는가?)이다.

23 ㉠ yourself 너 자신 ㉡ 자신이 한 말에 대해 상대방에게 한 번 더 되물을 때는 앞서 말한 문장을 이용할 수 있다. 이 경우에는 "doesn't it?"이라고 표현한다.

24 ⓐthat은 두 문장을 이어주는 접속사 역할을 한다. ①, ②, ③는 '저', '저것의'를 의미하는 한정사이며 ⑤는 관계대명사 역할을 한다.

25 probably 아마도

26 Buzz Aldrin은 selfie라는 신조어를 만들어낸 사람이 아니라 1966년에 최초로 우주에서 셀피를 찍은 사람이다.

27 흥미로운 사실 첫 번째에 나와 있듯이 최초로 셀피를 찍은 사람은 1839년에 셀피를 찍은 Robert Cornelius이다.

28 동명사가 주어 역할을 하는 경우 단수 취급을 하기 때문에 동사는 단수 동사가 되어야 한다. 따라서 ⓐ는 are가 아니라 is가 되어야 어법상 적절하다.

29 위 글에서는 나이도, 국적도 다른 학생들이 셀피에 관한 자신들의 의견을 드러내고 있다. 따라서 주제로 가장 적절한 것은 ⑤ The students' comments about taking selfies(셀피 찍는 것에 대한 학생들의 발언)이다.

Lesson 1 (중간)

01 ② **02** ⑤ **03** take **04** ④ **05** ③
06 This steak smells delicious. **07** ⑤
08 (A) borrow (B) copy **09** ②
10 (A) The flowers look beautiful.
(B) All the food smells tasty.
11 (1) The singer's voice sounded friendly.
(2) The girl looks happy.
12 ① **13** ④ **14** ⑤ **15** ④ **16** ③ **17** ⑤ **18** ④
19 much time do it → much time doing it
20 (A) girls (B) don't (C) take (D) filters (E) at
(F) school
21 ④ **22** I enjoy taking selfies
23 몇몇 학생들은 셀피를 찍는 데 너무 많은 시간을 보낸다.
24 ② **25** ① **26** ③
27 (A) Where (B) Who (C) What **28** ①
29 ⑤ **30** That sounds easy, doesn't it?

01 '특정한 시간, 상황 혹은 목적에 맞는'이라는 영영풀이가 가리키는 것은 ② appropriate(적절한)이다.

02 위에서부터 순서대로 interest(관심사), balanced(균형 잡힌), advice(조언, 충고), borrowed(빌리다), left(남기다)가 들어가는 것이 문맥상 자연스럽다.

03 take a picture 사진을 찍다 / take a walk 산책을 하다

04 관심사가 무엇이냐는 A의 말에 대해 "응, 난 그래."라는 B의 대답은 흐름상 자연스럽지 않다.

05 a. seeing → to see, d. to clean → cleaning

06 감각동사 smell은 보어로 형용사를 취한다.

07 위 글에서 A가 새 과학책을 빌리려 하자 B는 집으로 빌려 가는 건 안 되지만 몇 장을 복사하는 건 괜찮다고 대답한다. 또한 그것을 온라인에 공유하지 말라고 말하고 있으므로 이에 대한 A의 대답은 "네, 공유하지 않을게요."("Okay, I won't.")가 되어야 한다.

08 위 글에서 Eric이 새 과학책을 빌리려고 했지만 학생들은 집에 새 책을 빌려갈 수 없기 때문에 빌릴 수 없었다. 그러나 Eric이 일부를 복사해도 되냐고 묻자 복사하는 건 괜찮다고 말하면서 온라인에 공유하지 말라는 이야기를 들었다. 따라서 빈칸에 들어갈 말로 적절한 것은 borrow(빌리다), copy(복사하다)이다.

09 keep in mind ~를 명심하다

10 감각동사 look, smell, taste, sound, feel은 목적어로 형용사를 취한다.

11 감각동사 look, smell, taste, sound, feel은 보어로 형용사를 취한다. 따라서 friend는 friendly로, happily는 happy로 바꿔 써야 어법상 자연스럽다.

12 위 글의 흐름으로 볼 때, 셀피를 찍을 때 필터를 사용하면 좋은 사진을 얻을 수 있다는 내용이 되어야 한다. 따라서 빈칸에 들어갈 말로 가장 적절한 것은 ① amazing(놀라운)이다.

13 (A)hard는 '열심히'라는 뜻이다. ① 힘든, ② 딱딱한, ③ 어려운, ⑤ 딱딱한

14 여학생들은 위에서 아래로 향하게 찍는 것이 더 귀여워 보인다('For girls, taking pictures from above makes them look cuter.')고 언급한 바 있다.

15 빈칸 다음 Girl의 말로 미루어 볼 때, 빈칸에 들어갈 말로 가장 적절한 것은 ④ No, you may not.("빌릴 수 없어요.") 이다.

16 밑줄 친 (가)that는 두 문장을 연결해 주는 접속사의 역할을 한다. ③that은 관계대명사의 역할을 하는 that이다.

17 학생들은 학교에서 가장 셀피를 많이 찍는다고 세 번째 문단에 언급되어 있다.

18 (A) 동사가 주어 역할을 하고 있으므로 동명사 형태인

Taking이 되어야 한다. (B) to부정사의 부사적 용법이 사용되고 있으므로 to find out이 되어야 한다. (C) 동사 enjoy는 목적어로 동명사를 취한다. 따라서 taking이 어법상 적절하다.

19 동사 spend는 동명사(동사+~ing)를 취한다. 따라서 (spend) much time doing it이 되어야 어법상 자연스럽다.

20 위 설문조사 내용에 따르면, 90퍼센트 이상의 여학생들이 셀피를 찍으며, 남학생의 85퍼센트는 셀피를 찍지 않는다고 한다. 또한 이 학생들의 93퍼센트는 셀피를 찍을 때 필터를 사용한다고 말했다. 또한 학생들은 셀피를 학교에서 가장 많이 찍는다고 설문조사에 응답했다.

21 look like ~처럼 보이다

22 동사 enjoy는 목적어로 동명사 형태를 취한다. 따라서 'I enjoy taking selfies'가 되어야 한다.

23 spend much time -ing ~하는 데 많은 시간을 보내다

24 위 글에서는 셀피에 관한 흥미로운 사실들에 대해서 이야기하고 있다. 따라서 빈칸에 들어갈 말로 가장 적절한 것은 ② facts(사실들)이다.

25 세계 최초의 셀피는 1839년 Robert Cornelius가 찍은 셀피('Robert Cornelius took the world's first selfie in 1839.')라고 언급되어 있다.

26 두 번째 문단에서는 셀피를 찍기에 적절한 장소를 고르라고 조언하면서 병원이나 공공 화장실 같은 곳은 사람들을 신경 쓰이게 할 수 있기 때문에 피하라고 말한다. 따라서 ⓒ help는 bother라고 고쳐야 문맥상 자연스럽다.

27 위 글에서는 셀피 에티켓에 대해서 살펴보고 있다. 1번에서는 셀피를 찍기에 적절한 장소에 대해, 2번에서는 누구나 셀피를 볼 수 있다는 것에 대해, 3번에서는 다른 사람의 셀피에 어떤 언급을 남겨야 하는지에 대해서 이야기하고 있다. 따라서 빈칸 (A), (B), (C)에 들어갈 말로 적절한 것은 순서대로 where, who, what이다.

28 (가)may는 조동사로 '~일지도 모른다'라는 추측의 의미로 쓰였다. 이와 같은 용법으로 쓰인 문장은 ① Tom bought a new car. He may be rich.(Tom은 새 차를 샀다. 그는 부자일지도 모른다.)이다.

29 네 번째 문단에서는 '다른 사람의 셀피에 좋은 언급을 하라. 무례하게 굴지 말라.'('Write nice comments on other people's selfies. Don't be rude.')고 언급한 바 있다.

30 자신이 한 말에 대해 상대방에게 확인할 때 부가의문문을 쓴다. 이때 부가의문문은 「평서문(긍정문 또는 부정문) + 반대 상황의 의문문」으로 만들어진다. 따라서 'That sounds easy, doesn't it?'이라고 써야 어법상 적절하다.

01 ④ **02** ④ **03** You had better eat fruit. **04** ①
05 (1) A thief is a person who steals things from people. (2) A microwave is a thing which heats up the cold food.
06 ④ **07** ② **08** ③ **09** ② **10** ④ **11** ②
12 I think we should go there. **13** ③ **14** ⑤
15 She often does yoga.
16 (1) 아침식사를 꾸준히 하는 것. (2) 매일 운동하는 것.
17 No, he never eats breakfast.
18 ① **19** ⑤ **20** ① **21** ④ **22** ④
23 a fruit which[that] looks like a banana
24 ② **25** ⑤ **26** ⑤ **27** ③ **28** ① **29** ② **30** ④

01 ④를 제외한 단어들은 동사의 원형과 과거분사형이다. see의 과거분사형은 seen이다.

02 appetizer는 '전채 요리'라는 뜻으로 주요 식사에 앞서 나오는 작은 요리이다.

03 상대방에게 조언을 할 때 "~하는 것이 좋겠다"라는 의미의 "You'd better ~"와 같은 표현을 쓸 수 있다.

04 ② that is → that are ③ were → was ④ which → who[that] ⑤ which is → who is

05 (1) 선행사가 A thief이므로 관계대명사 who 또는 that을 이용해 A thief is a person who steals things from people.라는 문장을 만들 수 있다. (2) 선행사가 A microwave이므로 관계대명사 which 또는 that을 이용해 A microwave is a thing which heats up the cold food.라는 문장을 만들 수 있다.

06 위 대화에서 남자 아이가 "칠면조를 좋아해요. 그걸로 먹을게요."("Oh, I love turkey. I'll have that.")라고 언급했다.

07 위 대화에서 여인이 음료와 샌드위치를 같이 주문하면 500원 할인을 받을 수 있다고 말했고 남자 아이는 오렌지 주스를 주문하겠다고 말했다. 따라서 빈칸에 들어갈 말로 가장 적절한 것은 ② That sounds good.이다.

08 달력에 따르면, Sally는 가끔(sometimes) 방과 후에 도서관에 간다. 따라서 ③ Sally sometimes goes to the library after school.가 가장 적절하다.

09 b. takes usually → usually takes로, d. who → which로 고쳐야 어법상 적절한 문장이 된다.

10 위 대화에서 지우의 대답으로 미루어 볼 때 Mike가 한 질문으로 가장 적절한 것은 ④ When is the party?(파티는 언제니?)이다.

11 Mike가 Chang의 식당을 추천하면서 "음식이랑 가격이 괜찮았어."("The food and prices were good.")라고 언급한 바 있다.

12 Mike가 지우에게 Chang의 식당과 그곳의 메뉴를 추천해 주었으므로 지우가 할 말로 적절한 것은 "I think we should go there."("거기로 가야겠다.")이다.

13 ③ What vegetables does Justin like?(Justin은 무슨 채소를 좋아하는가?)에 대해서는 위 대화에서 언급되지 않았다.

14 A가 이번 주말에 무엇을 할 것이냐고(D) B에게 묻자 B는 남동생과 함께 야구 경기를 보러 갈 것이라고(B) 대답한다. A가 B에게 야구에 관심이 있냐고 묻자(A), B는 관심은 없지만 남동생이 야구를 좋아하기 때문에 보러 가는 것이라고 대답(C)하는 순서대로 이어지는 것이 흐름상 가장 자연스럽다.

15 Dana는 건강을 위해 일주일에 다섯 번 요가 수업에 간다고 언급되어 있다. 따라서 그녀는 자주 요가를 한다(She often does yoga.)는 문장을 만들 수 있다.

16 지우가 요즘 아침에 자주 피곤함을 느낀다고 말하자 인호는 지우에게 "Why don't you eat breakfast?"(아침 식사를 하는 건 어떠니?), "you should also exercise every day."(또 매일 운동을 해야 한다.)라고 조언했다.

17 대화의 I를 지우로 바꿔 대답한다.

18 (A)의 앞부분에서 정크 푸드가 몸에 좋지 않다고 설명했고 뒷부분에서는 몸에 좋은 음식을 소개하고 있으므로 빈칸에 However(그러나)가 들어가는 것이 적절하다. (B) 몸에 좋은 음식을 소개하면서 생선 역시 뇌에 좋다고 설명하고 있다. 따라서 빈칸에 들어갈 말로 가장 적절한 것은 In addition(게다가)이다.

19 첫 번째 문단 후반부에 생선에 들어 있는 무기물인 아연이 사고력과 기억력을 향상시킨다(The mineral zinc in fish can improve your thinking and memory.)라고 언급되어 있다.

20 선행사가 각각 students, people이므로 관계대명사 who 또는 that이 들어가야 어법상 적절하다.

21 주어가 학교 급식이므로 ⓓ sound는 taste로 바꿔 쓰는 것이 적절하다.

22 'A와 B 둘 다' 라는 뜻을 가진 단어 both는 and와 함께 쓰인다.

23 선행사가 사물인 a fruit이므로 관계대명사 which 또는 that을 이용해 A plantain is a fruit which looks like a banana.라는 문장을 만들 수 있다.

24 Belle은 샐러드를 주요 식사 이전에 제공되는 전채 요리로 먹는다(We usually eat a salad as an appetizer)고 언급한 바 있다.

25 Nicole이 싱가폴 급식에서 매일 다른 식단이 제공되는 지에 대해서는 언급하지 않았다.

26 위 글에서는 각각 다른 문화권의 학생들이 학교 점심 급식에 대해서 소개하고 있다. 따라서 제목으로 가장 적절한 것은 ⑤ School Lunches Around the World(세계 곳곳의 학교 급식)이다.

27 다섯 명의 학생들은 각각 자신이 무엇을 얼마나 자주 먹고 마시는지에 대해서 설명하고 있다. 따라서 빈칸에 들어갈 질문으로 가장 적절한 것은 ③ What are your eating habits?(당신의 식습관은 무엇입니까?)이다.

28 (A) B는 식사 시간에 최소 30분 이상 식탁 앞에 앉아 있는 규칙이 흥미롭다고 말하고 있으므로 빈칸에 France가 들어가야 한다. (B) C는 많은 다양한 음식들을 보는 것이 재밌을 것이라고 말하고 있으므로 빈칸에 Singapore가 들어가야 한다 (C) A는 불고기와 함께 밥과 국을 같이 먹는 것을 좋아한다고 말하고 있으므로 빈칸에 Korea가 들어가야 한다.

29 ⓑ의 앞부분에서 정크 푸드가 맛은 좋지만 건강에는 좋지 않다고 설명하고 있다. 따라서 ⓑ는 However(그러나)로 바꾸는 것이 문맥상 적절하다.

30 ④ the right meals that the school cafeteria serves (학교 식당이 제공하는 올바른 급식)에 대해서는 위 글에서 언급되지 않았다.

Lesson 2 (중간) _{2회}

01 ③　**02** He lives next door.
03 they should make healthy food for the contest
04 You'd better make sandwiches that[which] add vegetables.
05 ②　**06** ②　**07** You had better eat breakfast.
08 ②　**09** ②　**10** ③
11 (A) He is a chef who studied cooking in Italy.
　(B) The dictionary which[that] is always on the teacher's table is very old.
12 ④　**13** ④　**14** ③　**15** ②　**16** ②　**17** ①
18 (1) A plantain is a fruit which[that] looks like a banana.
　(2) People who live in Singapore come from many different cultures.

4　정답 및 해설

01 famous는 '유명한'이라는 뜻이며, infamous는 '악명이 높은'이라는 뜻을 갖는다.

02 관계대명사로 연결된 문장을 다시 두 문장으로 나눌 수 있다. 이때 관계대명사가 주격이냐 목적격이냐에 따라 문장이 달라진다. 주어진 문장에서 관계대명사 who는 선행사 the man을 수식하는 주격 관계대명사이므로 The man is an artist.과 He lives next door.라는 두 문장으로 나눌 수 있다.

03 여학생이 남학생에게 샌드위치에 채소를 넣는 것을 추천한 이유는 학교 요리 대회에서는 건강한 음식을 만들어야 하기 때문이다.

04 상대방에게 조언을 할 때 "~하는 것이 좋겠다"라는 의미의 "You'd better ~"와 같은 표현을 쓸 수 있다.

05 ② is made를 are made로 고쳐야 어법상 적절한 문장이 된다.

06 소년은 잠을 잘 못 잤냐는 소녀의 질문에 잠은 잘 잤다고 대답했다.

07 상대방에게 조언을 할 때 "~하는 것이 좋겠다"라는 의미의 "You'd better~"와 같은 표현을 쓸 수 있다.

08 (A) B가 A에게 무슨 메뉴를 원하냐고 물어봤으므로 이에 대한 A의 대답은 ⓑ가 적절하다. (B) A가 무엇을 추천하냐고 물어봤으므로 이에 대한 B의 대답은 ⓒ가 적절하다. (C) B가 배고프지 않다고 하자 A가 건강을 위해 음식을 조금 먹는 것이 낫다고 조언하는 문장인 ⓔ가 들어가야 흐름상 적절하다.

09 학급 파티를 위해 식당을 찾고 있는 G에게 B가 Chang의 식당을 추천해 주었다. 또한 B가 국수를 추천한다고 대답한 것으로 미루어 볼 때, 빈칸에 들어갈 말로 가장 적절한 것은 ② What do you recommend there?(거기서 무슨 메뉴를 추천하니?)이다.

10 남자는 Chang의 식당을 추천하면서 음식과 가격이 괜찮 다고 이야기("The food and prices were good.")한 바 있다.

11 관계대명사는 선행사에 따라 결정된다. 선행사가 사람일 경우에는 who 또는 that을, 선행사가 사물일 경우에는 which 또는 that을 쓴다. 이때 that은 선행사가 사물이나 사람일 경우 모두 쓸 수 있다.

12 빈칸 (가)에서는 뒷부분에 예시를 들고 있으므로 전치사 like(~와 같은)가 들어가는 것이 적절하다.

13 '다른 나라에 사는 학생들은 점심으로 무엇을 먹을까?'라는 질문이 들어가기에 가장 적절한 곳은 음식 리포터들로부터 이야기를 들어보자고 하는 문장 앞인 (D)이다.

14 위 글의 후반부에 다른 나라의 학생들은 점심으로 무엇을 먹는지 음식 리포터들의 이야기를 들어보자고 하였으므로 ③ '다른 나라 학생들의 점심식사'가 위 글 다음으로 이어질 내용으로 가장 적절하다.

15 (가) them은 앞서 언급된 복수 명사를 가리킨다. 따라서 이 경우에는 앞 문장에 언급된 plantains를 가리킨다. (나) yours는 앞서 언급된 명사를 가리키는데, 글의 문맥상 your school lunch(너의 학교 점심 급식)를 가리킨다.

16 첫 문단에서 플랜테인을 주로 튀겨서 먹는다('We usually fry them.')고 언급되어 있다.

17 (A) come with ~에 딸려오다, ~와 같이 나오다 (B) come from ~에서 오다 (C) have in common 공통점이 있다

18 관계대명사가 이끄는 절에서 관계대명사 who, which 또는 that이 주어 역할을 할 때 주격 관계대명사라고 한다. who는 선행사가 사람일 때, which는 선행사가 사물일 때, that은 두 경우 모두 쓸 수 있다.

19 (A) both A and B A와 B 둘 다 (B) 작년의 일이므로 과거형 won이 들어가야 한다. (C) 빈도부사는 be동사 뒤에 쓴다.

20 선행사가 사람인 people이므로 관계대명사 who를 이용해 People who live in Singapore come from different cultures.라는 문장을 만들 수 있다. 이때 관계대명사 뒤에 나오는 동사는 선행사와 수 일치가 되어야 한다.

21 "양파랑 당근은 어떠니?"라는 문장이 들어가기에 가장 적절한 곳은 샌드위치에 채소를 좀 더 넣으라고 조언하는 (D)이다.

22 채소를 좋아하지 않는다는 B에게 G는 요리 대회는 건강한 음식을 만드는 것이 목적이라고 조언했다. 따라서 이에 대한 B의 대답으로 적절한 것은 ④ OK, I'd better put vegetables in my sandwiches.(알겠어, 난 내 샌드위치에 채소를 좀 넣는 것이 좋겠다.)이다.

23 프랑스 출신 Belle이 자신의 학교 급식에 대해서 설명하고 있는 글이다. 우선 전채 요리로는 샐러드를 먹는다고 말하고(B), 다음 주요 식사로는 고기나 생선을 먹는다고 설명한다(C). 마지막으로 학교에 특별한 규칙이 있어 최소한 30분간 식탁에 앉아 있어야 한다고 설명(A)하는 순서로 이어지는 것이 흐름상 가장 자연스럽다.

24 위 글의 목적은 프랑스의 학교 급식을 소개하고 설명하는 것이다.

25 (A)문단에 언급되어 있듯이, 최소 30분 동안 점심 식사 테이블에 머물러야 한다는 것이 Belle의 학교의 특별한 규칙이다.

26 대명사 They가 가리키는 것은 the dolls이므로 선행사를 the dolls로 만들어 The dolls which are on the table are my sister's.라는 문장을 만들 수 있다.

27 ⓓappetizer는 '전채 요리'라는 뜻으로 주요 식사 이전에 제공되는 음식을 의미한다.

28 ⑤ How many side dishes are there in Korean lunch?(한국 점심 급식에는 몇 개의 반찬이 있는가?)에 대해서는 위 글에서 언급되지 않았다.

29 (가)의 앞 부분에서는 특별한 음식을 이야기하면서 뒷부분에서는 그 특별한 음식들의 예시를 들고 있다. 따라서 빈칸에 들어갈 말로 가장 적절한 것은 ④ such as(~와 같은)이다.

30 두 문장을 연결할 때 겹치는 부분을 선행사로 만들고 관계대명사를 이용해 연결할 수 있다. 이때 who는 선행사가 사람일 때, which는 선행사가 사물일 때 쓸 수 있다. 또한 관계대명사 뒤에 나오는 동사는 선행사와 수 일치가 되어야 한다.

Lesson 3 (기말)

01 ③	**02** ①	**03** ④	**04** ③,⑤	**05** ②	**06** ①

07 Have you ever been to a Spanish festival before?

08 ③	**09** ③	**10** ①	**11** ①

12 (1) have been / 나는 전에 영국에 간 적이 있다.
　　(2) has lost / 그녀는 영어책을 잃어버렸다.

13 ①	**14** ⑤	**15** ④	**16** ③	**17** ①	**18** ②	**19** ⑤

20 bats remind people of darkness and scary things

21 ③	**22** ④	**23** ④	**24** ③	**25** ④	**26** ①,③
27 ②	**28** ③,④	**29** ②	**30** ④		

01 '매우 중요하고 유용하며 도움이 되는'이라는 영영풀이가 가리키는 단어는 ③ valuable(소중한, 귀중한)이다.

02 두 대화에서는 돼지 꿈과 우산이 어떤 의미를 갖는지에 대

해서 질문하고 있다. 따라서 빈칸에 들어갈 말로 가장 적절한 것은 ① mean(의미하다)이다.

03 A가 새해에 떡국을 먹는 것은 한국에서 어떤 의미인지 물어 보았다. 따라서 이에 대한 B의 대답으로 가장 적절한 것은 ④ It means becoming a year older.(그건 한 살을 더 먹는 것을 의미해.)이다.

04 ③ 수미가 여전히 피아노를 치는지 물어보는 A의 질문에 대해 수미가 10년 동안 피아노를 쳤다는 B의 대답은 흐름상 자연스럽다. ⑤ gracias가 스페인어로 무슨 뜻이냐는 A의 질문에 대해 그건 고맙습니다를 의미한다는 B의 대답은 흐름상 자연스럽다.

05 A가 브라질에 가보았냐고 묻자(B), B는 가보지 않았다고 대답하면서 A에게 가보았냐고 되묻는다(A). A는 브라질에 작년에 가보았다고 대답하면서, 큰 삼바 축제가 있었다고 말한다(D). 이에 대해 B는 흥미롭게 들린다고 말하면서 언젠가 가보고 싶다(C)고 대답하는 순서로 이어지는 것이 대화 흐름상 가장 자연스럽다.

06 주어진 말은 What brings you here today?(오늘 어떤 일로 여기 왔니?)라는 질문에 대한 대답으로 적절하므로 (A)가 알맞다.

07 Have you ever been to ~?: ~에 가 본 적 있니?

08 B의 대답인 "No, I haven't. Have you?"로 미루어 볼 때, A가 한 질문으로 가장 적절한 것은 ③ Have you been to Brazil?(브라질에 가 본 적 있니?)이다.

09 주어진 글에서 A는 사진을 보면서 그 사진 속의 소년이 무례하다고 이야기한다. 이에 대한 대답으로 B가 어느 소년이냐고 묻고, A는 손바닥을 자신에게 향하게 하면서 브이 표시를 하고 있는 소년이라고 말한다. B가 그게 무엇이 잘못되었냐고 묻고 A는 영국에서 그것은 나쁜 의미이지만 손바닥을 바깥을 향하게 하는 것은 괜찮다고 설명한다. B가 그게 무슨 의미냐고 묻자 A는 그것이 평화 또는 승리를 의미한다고 대답하는 순서로 이어지는 것이 대화의 흐름상 자연스럽다.

10 ⓐfacing에서 face는 '마주하다, 마주보다'라는 의미로 사용되었다. 따라서 이와 같은 의미로 사용된 문장은 ① Most of the rooms face the beach.(대부분의 방들은 해변을 마주하고 있다.)이다. / ②, ④ 직면하다, ③, ⑤ 얼굴

11 '가장 유명한 무용 중의 하나는 사자춤이다.'라는 문장이 들어가기에 가장 적절한 곳은 중국 전통 무용의 종류가 많다고 이야기한 다음 그 예시를 든 (C)이다.

12 (1) have been to~ ~에 가 본 적이 있다 (2) 현재완료 시제의 결과적 용법으로 과거의 일이 원인이 되어 지금 현재까지 영향을 미치는 것을 의미한다.

13 "어느 게임을 먼저 시도해 볼까?"라는 문장이 들어가기에 가장 적절한 곳은 상대방이 러시아 전통 게임인 **gorodki**를 추천해 주고 있는 곳인 (A)이다.

14 ⓐ welcome to ~에 온 것을 환영하다 ⓑ on the ground 땅 위에서

15 대화 후반부에 남학생이 여학생에게 "you should wear white clothes."(흰색 옷을 입어야 해.)라고 언급한 바 있다.

16 '별로 그렇지 않아.'라는 문장이 들어가기에 가장 적절한 곳은 박쥐에 대한 의미가 서양과 한국에서 다르게 받아들인다고 말하는 곳인 (C)이다.

17 위 글의 내용상, 박쥐는 한국에서는 행운과 장수의 상징이라는 내용이 들어가야 자연스럽다. 따라서 빈칸에 들어갈 말로 가장 적절한 것은 ① '상징'이다.

18 위 글에 따르면, 서양과 한국에서 박쥐에 대한 의미가 다르다. 한국에서는 박쥐가 행운과 장수를 의미한다면, 서양 문화권에서 박쥐는 어둠과 무서운 것 등 부정적인 의미를 지닌다.

19 박쥐가 행운을 의미하는 곳은 서양이 아니라 한국이다.

20 remind A of B: A에게 B를 상기시키다

21 ⓒ What does an umbrella mean in China?로 바꿔 써야 어법상 적절하다.

22 여학생의 말에 따르면, "The words for separation and umbrella sound the same in Chinese."라고 언급되어 있다.

23 "나에게 수탉 그림을 그려 줄래?"라는 문장이 들어가기에 가장 적절한 곳은 Peter가 자신은 어둠과 악령을 무서워하기 때문에 그것들을 쫓아준다는 수탉 그림을 부탁하고 있는 (D)이다.

24 대명사 that은 앞서 언급한 단수 명사 혹은 문장 전체를 가리킨다. 따라서 대화 흐름상, 앞서 언급한 수탉이 울면 그것이 악한 기운을 쫓아내 준다는 내용을 가리킨다.

25 Peter에게 수탉 그림을 그려 준다고 약속한 것은 미나의 할아버지가 아니라 미나이다.

26 대화 후반부에 미나는 Peter에게 수탉 그림을 그려 준다고 약속했고("I'll draw a big rooster for you!"), Peter는 그것을 문 위에 붙일 것이라고 ("Yes, I will.")언급했다.

27 상대방에게 어떤 경험에 대해 물어볼 때 "Have you ever ~?"라고 질문할 수 있다. 현재 완료 시제의 경험적 용법으로 쓰인 (A)와 쓰임이 같은 것은 ② I have never been to Paris.(난 파리에 가 본 적이 없다.)이다. / ① 결과적 용법, ③, ⑤ 완료적 용법, ④ 계속적 용법

28 watch over는 '~을 지켜주다, 보호하다'라는 뜻을 갖는다. 따라서 이와 바꿔 쓸 수 있는 단어는 ③ protect(보호하다), ④ guard(지키다)이다.

29 That's why ~ : 그것이 ~한 이유이다

30 물고기가 Peter에게 무엇을 상기시키는지에 대해서는 언급된 바 없다.

Lesson 3 (기말)

01 ①	02 ④	03 ②	04 ④	05 ①	06 ①	07 ④
08 ①	09 ②	10 ②	11 ②	12 ③	13 ②	14 ②
15 ③	16 ⑤	17 ④	18 ⑤	19 ①	20 ③	21 ④
22 ②	23 ⑤	24 ②, ④			25 ③	

26 (a) luck (b) a long life (c) darkness (d) scary things
27 ①, ⑤   **28** ④   **29** ④   **30** ③

01 빈칸에 공통으로 들어갈 말로 가장 적절한 것은 ① represent(대표하다, 상징하다)이다.

02 경험의 유무를 표현할 때 현재완료 시제(have/has p.p.)를 이용할 수 있다. 따라서 베트남 음식을 먹어본 적이 없다는 문장은 'I have not[never] tried Vietnamese food before.'라고 영작할 수 있다.

03 여학생이 남학생에게 한국에서 엿이 무슨 의미냐고 물었고 이에 대한 답변으로 가장 적절한 것은 ② good luck on a test(시험에서의 행운)이다.

04 (A) take off, (B) bow, (C) blow, (E) older people이 들어가야 글의 내용상 적절하다.

05 '지구의 시간'이라는 행사에 어떻게 참여하는지 이야기해 줄 수 있냐고 묻는 A의 질문에 대해 "그건 쉬워. 난 다음 '지구의 시간' 행사에 참여할 거야."라고 말하는 B의 대답은 흐름상 자연스럽지 않다.

06 위 글에 따르면, 홀리 축제는 인도 전통 축제로 색깔 있는 가루와 물을 서로에게 던지는 축제이며, 힌두력의 마지막 만월(보름달)을 축하하는 행사이다. 또한 A는 흰 옷을 입으라고 추천했다. 따라서 (A) Indian, (B) water, (C) full moon, (D) white가 들어가는 것이 적절하다.

07 ④Put five sticks on the ground.(다섯 개의 막대를 땅에 꽂아라.)라는 문장은 대화의 흐름상 자연스럽지 않다.

08 A가 "It's a traditional Indian festival."(그건 인도 전통 축제야.)라고 언급한 바 있다.

09 so+형용사[부사]+that+주어+동사'의 형태로 '매우 ...해서 ~하다'라는 의미이며 원인과 그에 따른 결과를 서술할 때 쓴다. so 뒤의 형용사나 부사는 원인을 나타내며, 접속사 that 뒤에 나오는 내용은 그에 따른 결과를 나타낸다.

10 "어느 게임을 먼저 시도해 볼까?"라는 문장이 들어가기에 가장 적절한 곳은 상대방이 러시아 전통 게임인 gorodki를 추천해 주고 있는 곳인 (B)이다.

11 (가) China는 Chinese로, (마) practicing은 to practice로 고쳐야 어법상 적절하다.

12 보검이는 우산을 구입하는 것을 고민 중("I am thinking about buying an umbrella for her.")이라고 언급했다.

13 (A) for: ~를 위해 (B) for: ~을 나타내는

14 ② When is Ling's birthday party?(Ling의 생일 파티는 언제인가?)에 대해서는 위 대화에서 언급되어 있지 않다.

15 위 대화에서는 rooster(수탉)가 한국 문화에서 갖는 상징성에 대해서 이야기하고 있다. 따라서 빈칸에 공통으로 들어갈 말은 ③ a rooster이다.

16 경험의 유무를 표현할 때 현재완료 시제(have/has p.p.)를 이용할 수 있다. 따라서 (A)에 들어갈 말로 가장 적절한 것은 과거분사인 ⑤ heard이다.

17 미나의 할아버지가 Peter에게 "Put the drawing above your door. Then it will protect you."(그림을 문 위에 걸어 놓거라. 그러면 그것이 너를 보호해 줄 것이다.)라고 말했다.

18 미나의 할아버지가 문 위에 그림을 붙이라고 조언했고 Peter는 그러겠다고 대답했다.

19 "Do you mean ~?"은 "~를 말하는 거니?"라는 뜻으로, 위 대화에서는 Peter가 무엇에 대하여 말하고 있는지 확인하기 위해 사용되었다.

20 Peter가 미나에게 부탁한 것은 수탉 그림을 그려 달라는 것이었다.

21 (A) 접속사 that, (B) 접속사 that이 들어가야 어법상 적절하다.

22 ⓐ shows ⓒ haven't ⓓ have thought ⓔ why로 고쳐야 어법상 적절한 문장이 된다.

23 미나가 "Koreans have thought that fish are good guards."라고 언급한 바 있다.

24 미나는 Peter에게 할아버지의 방에 가서 Peter를 소개시켜 주었다. 또한 한국인들은 물고기가 잘 때에도 눈을 감지 않기 때문에 물고기를 좋은 파수꾼이라고 생각해 왔다. 따라서 ② Where does Peter meet Mina's grandfather?(Peter는 어디서 미나의 할아버지를 만나는가?), ④ Why do Korean people think fish are good guards?(왜 한국인들은 물고기를 좋은 파수꾼이라고 생각하는가?)에 대해서 답할 수 있다.

25 상대방에게 어떤 경험에 대해 물어볼 때 "Have you ever ~?"라고 질문할 수 있다. 따라서 현재완료 시제의 경험적 용법으로 쓰인 ⓑ와 쓰임이 같은 것은 ③ '나는 최근에 그의 소식을 한 번 들은 적 있다.'이다. / ①, ② 완료적 용법, ④ 결과적 용법, ⑤ 계속적 용법

26 위 글에 따르면, 한국 사람들과 서양 문화권의 사람들은 박쥐에 대해 다르게 생각한다. 한국 사람들에게 박쥐는 행운과 장수를 상징하는 반면에, 서양 문화권의 사람들은 박쥐를 어둠과 무서운 것들로 생각한다.

27 위 글에 따르면, 한국에서 박쥐는 행운과 장수의 상징("In Korea, bats are symbols of luck and a long life.")이다.

28 remind A of B A에게 B를 상기시키다, 기억나게 하다

29 박쥐를 무서워하는 건 Peter이다.

30 (A) kinds 종류들 (B) one of+명사의 복수형 ~ 중의 하나 (C) 주어가 복수형이므로 dress and act가 들어가야 어법상 적절하다. (D) 주어가 복수형이므로 are가 들어가야 어법상 적절하다.

Lesson 4 (기말) _{1회}

> **01** ① **02** ③
> **03** She is much more humorous than comedians.
> **04** ② **05** ④ **06** ① **07** ④
> **08** Old jeans will be used to make a bag for her sister (by Sue).
> **09** ⑤ **10** ③ **11** ⑤ **12** ③ **13** ① **14** ① **15** ⑤
> **16** ④ **17** consuming **18** ⑤ **19** ① **20** ④ **21** ③
> **22** ① **23** ④ **24** ③ **25** ② **26** ② **27** ②
> **28** saves space   **29** ④ **30** ②

01 ⓐ reuse 재사용하다, ⓑ consume 섭취하다, 소모하다, ⓒ bacteria 박테리아, ⓓ waste 쓰레기, 폐기물, ⓔ chemical 화학 물질, ⓕ pollution 오염

02 ③ pollution은 '오염'이라는 뜻을 갖는 단어이다.

03 비교급을 강조할 때는 비교급 앞에 much, still, even, far, a lot 등의 부사를 쓰며 '(...보다) 훨씬 더 ~한'이라는 의미를 갖는다. very는 원급의 형용사(또는 부사)를 수식하며, 비교급은 수식하지 않는다.

04 ⓐ waste ⓓ throw away ⓔ are destroyed로 고쳐야 어법상 적절한 문장이 된다.

05 ④ yourself는 '네가 직접, 너 자신이'이라는 뜻을 가진 대명사로, 빈칸에 들어가기에 가장 적절하다.

06 위 대화에 따르면, 오래된 청바지를 찾아서 그것을 작은 조

각으로 자르고 다시 바느질을 해서 가방을 만드는 방법을 설명하고 있다.

07 ⓓIt은 인칭대명사로 가방을 만드는 것을 가리킨다. 나머지는 모두 Ann의 가방을 가리키는 대명사이다.

08 Sue가 여동생에게 가방을 만들어 주기 위해 사용할 것은 오래된 청바지이다. 따라서 이 문장을 수동태로 만들면 Old jeans will be used to make a bag for her sister (by Sue).라는 문장이 된다.

09 지난 주 토요일에 열렸다는 언급은 없으며 다음 주 토요일에 열릴 것이라고 언급되어 있다.

10 ⓒrise는 '오르다, 올라가다'라는 뜻을 가진 단어이다. 문맥상 ⓒraise(기르다)가 들어가는 것이 자연스럽다.

11 물 부족 문제에 대한 기사를 읽은 것은 나리가 아니라 보라이다.

12 위 대화에서는 지구 온난화와 그로 인해 발생한 문제점들, 그리고 그에 대한 해결책에 대해 이야기를 나누고 있다. 따라서 위 대화의 주제로 가장 적절한 것은 ③ how to stop the global warming(지구 온난화를 멈추는 방법)이다.

13 way는 '방법, 방식'이라는 뜻을 가진 단어로 ① solution (해결책)이라는 단어로 바꿔 쓸 수 있다.

14 위 글에서는 아쿠아포닉스가 어떻게 작동하는지에 대해 설명하고 있다. 따라서 제목으로 가장 적절한 것은 ① The Process of Aquaponics(아쿠아포닉스의 과정)이다.

15 물고기가 만든 쓰레기가 박테리아에 의해 식물의 먹이로 변한다는 내용이 들어가야 아쿠아포닉스의 물고기와 식물, 박테리아의 연쇄적 과정으로 설명된다.

16 This process가 주어이므로 동사는 수동태가 되어야 한다. 따라서 ⓓrepeat를 repeated로 바꿔야 어법상 적절하다.

17 전치사 by가 쓰였으므로 동명사형이 되어야 한다. / by ~ing ~함으로써

18 주어가 chemicals이므로 동사는 수동태인 ⓔare used가 되어야 어법상 적절하다.

19 위 글에서는 아쿠아포닉스가 물을 아끼게 해주고 환경에 좋으며 어디서든지 할 수 있다고 설명하고 있다. 따라서 빈칸 (A)에 들어갈 말로 가장 적절한 것은 ① a lot of space is not needed(많은 공간이 필요하지 않다)이다.

20 어떠한 화학물질도 사용되지 않아 환경에 좋다('it is good for the environment because no chemicals used.') 고 언급되어 있다.

21 아쿠아포닉스는 물고기와 식물, 박테리아 간의 연쇄적인 과정을 이용해 동시에 물고기를 기르고 식물을 재배할 수 있는 방법이다.

22 (A) 주어가 Some important things이므로 were

learned가 동사로 적절하다. / (B) watering 물 주기 / (C) chemicals가 주어이므로 are used가 동사로 적절하다.

23 아쿠아포닉스의 과정에 따르면, 우선 화분 바닥에 구멍을 뚫고 화분에 작은 돌들을 넣어 식물을 심은 다음, 어항 덮개에 큰 구멍을 내고 구멍에 그 화분을 넣는다(D). 그 다음 찰흙으로 화분을 제자리에 고정하고(C), 덮개에 또 다른 구멍을 하나 만들어 그 안에 관을 넣는다(A). 그 후, 어항에 수중 펌프를 넣고 관을 이용하여 펌퍼를 화분에 연결(B)하는 순서로 이어지면 마지막으로 물을 어항에 채우고 물고기를 넣어 아쿠아포닉스를 이용할 수 있다.

24 ③ a hole은 '구멍'이라는 뜻으로 재료가 아니다.

25 어항 바닥이 아니라 어항의 뚜껑에 구멍을 뚫는다고 언급되어 있다.

26 ⓑThey는 앞서 언급된 some farmers를 가리킨다. 나머지는 모두 아쿠아포닉스를 가리킨다.

27 비교급을 강조할 때는 비교급 앞에 much, still, even, far, a lot 등의 부사를 쓰며 '(...보다) 훨씬 더 ~한'이라는 의미를 갖는다. very는 원급의 형용사(또는 부사)를 수식하며, 비교급은 수식하지 않는다.

28 save 절약하다, 아끼다 / space 공간

29 위 글에서는 아쿠아포닉스를 사용함으로써 얻을 수 있는 장점들에 대해서 설명하고 있다. 따라서 위 글의 주제로 가장 적절한 것은 ④ '아쿠아포닉스의 다양한 장점들'이다.

30 농부들이 아쿠아포닉스를 사용하는 것은 전통 재배 방식보다 쉽기 때문이라고 언급되어 있다.

Lesson 4 (기말) 2회

| 01 ⑤ | 02 ② | 03 ⑤ | 04 ⑤ | 05 ④ | 06 ⑤ | 07 ② |
| 08 ③ | 09 ⑤ | 10 ② | 11 ② | 12 ④ | 13 ③ | 14 ③ |

15 Can you tell me how to join the event?

| 16 ③ | 17 ④ | 18 ④ | 19 ④ | 20 ⑤ |

21 It's a way of growing plants without soil.

| 22 ① | 23 ② | 24 ② | 25 ① | 26 ② | 27 ③ |

28 it is far easier than traditional gardening   29 ④

01 ⑤ connect는 '연결하다, 이어지다'라는 뜻을 갖는 단어이다.

02 "I'm worried about ~."은 "난 ~이 걱정돼."라는 의미로 어떤 일이나 사람에 대한 걱정을 나타내는 표현이다. 따라서 위 대화의 흐름상 빈칸에는 ② wasting food(음식을 낭비하는 것)이 들어가는 것이 자연스럽다.

03 ⑤ made를 was made로 고쳐야 어법상 적절한 문장이 된다.

04 ① was → is / ② is → was / ③ This problem was discovered solutions → Solutions to this problem was discovered / ④ was invented → was invented by로 고쳐야 어법상 적절한 문장이 된다.

05 위 대화에서는 지구가 더워짐에 따라 발생하는 문제점에 대해서 이야기하고 있다. 따라서 빈칸에 들어갈 말로 가장 적절한 것은 ④ global warming(지구온난화)이다.

06 ⓑthose things는 앞서 언급된 내용들을 가리킨다. 위 대화에서는 'We should use fans instead of air conditioners.'를 가리킨다.

07 위 대화에서 화자들은 지구가 더워짐에 따라 발생하는 문제점에 대해서 이야기하고 있다.

08 ⓒrise는 '오르다, 올라가다'라는 뜻을 가진 단어이다. 문맥상 ⓒraise(기르다)가 들어가는 것이 자연스럽다.

09 ⑤에서 고양이가 실종 되었다고 했고 그 해결책으로 고양이를 찾기 위해선 포스터를 붙이라고 조언했으므로 문제와 해결책이 자연스럽다.

10 빈칸 뒷부분에서 B가 환경 문제에 대해서 이야기하는 대회에 대해서 이야기하고 있으므로 ② I'm worried about the speech contest tomorrow.(난 내일 있을 연설 대회가 걱정이 돼.)가 가장 적절하다.

11 B의 반응 "But isn't there enough water for everyone?"(그렇지만, 모두를 위한 충분한 물이 있지 않니?)으로 미루어 봤을 때, 빈칸에 들어갈 말로 가장 적절한 것은 ② we don't have enough water(우리는 충분한 물이 없다고 말했어.)이다.

12 소년이 읽었던 기사는 물 오염이 아니라 물 부족에 관한 기사였다.

13 (A) very harder → a lot harder / (C) used → are used / (D) was invented → invented / (F) was → were

14 '지구의 시간' 행사는 "on the last Saturday in March"에 참여하는 것이라고 언급되어 있다.

15 상대방에게 무엇인가를 하는 방법을 물을 때, '~하는 방법'이라는 의미의 'how to+동사원형' 구문을 사용하여 'Can you tell me how to+동사원형 ~?' 라고 물어볼 수 있다.

16 '지구의 시간'의 행사 주최자에 대한 내용은 위 대화에서 언급되지 않았다.

17 (a)for는 '~ 동안'이라는 뜻으로 사용되었다. for가 이와 같은 뜻으로 사용된 문장은 (A), (D), (F), (G)이다.

18 문제점이 '음식 낭비'에 관한 것이므로, 이에 대한 해결책으로 가장 적절한 것은 ④ We should not put too much food on our plates.(우리는 접시에 너무 많은 음식을 담아서는 안 된다.)이다.

19 위 대화에서 B는 G가 갖고 있는 가방이 마음에 든다고 하자 B는 직접 만들어 보라고 제안한다. 이에 대한 B의 반응으로 가장 적절한 것은 ④ Can you tell me how to make it?(어떻게 만드는지 설명해 줄래?)이다.

20 위 글에서는 우리 주변에서 많은 에너지가 낭비되고 있다고 말하면서, 에너지를 절약하기 위한 방법들을 제시하고 있다. 따라서 ⓔwe should use a cup when we brush our teeth.(우리는 양치질을 할 때 컵을 이용해야 돼.)라는 문장은 글의 흐름과 어울리지 않는다.

21 a way of+동명사: ~하는 방법 / grow plants 식물을 재배하다

22 ① Let me know.는 '나에게 알려줘.'라는 뜻으로 위 대화의 흐름상 적절하지 않다.

23 ② How do you get the fish?(어떻게 물고기를 얻는가?)에 대해서는 문단 [B]에서 언급되어 있지 않다.

24 위 글의 문단 [C]에서는 집에서 아쿠아포닉스를 만드는 실험에 대해서 설명하고 있다. 따라서 빈칸에 들어갈 말로 가장 적절한 것은 ② How can I make an aquaponics system at home?(어떻게 집에서 아쿠아포닉스 시스템을 만들 수 있는가?)이다.

25 ㉮에서는 필요한 재료를 설명하고 있으므로 materials가, ㉯에서는 과정을 설명하고 있으므로 steps가, ㉰에서는 아쿠아포닉스의 결과를 설명하고 있으므로 results가, ㉱에서는 실험의 결론을 설명하고 있으므로 conclusion가 들어가는 것이 글의 흐름상 가장 적절하다.

26 ⓒ feed 먹이를 주다 / ⓓ grow 자라다 / ⓔ stay healthy 건강을 유지하다

27 ⓓare used → use / ⓔare raised → raise / ⓕare chosen → choose

28 비교급을 강조할 때는 비교급 앞에 much, still, even, far, a lot 등의 부사를 쓰며 '(...보다) 훨씬 더 ~한'이라는 의미를 갖는다.

29 결론(Conclusion)의 내용에 따르면, 아쿠아포닉스는 많은 공간을 필요로 하지 않는다('it doesn't need much space.')라고 한다.

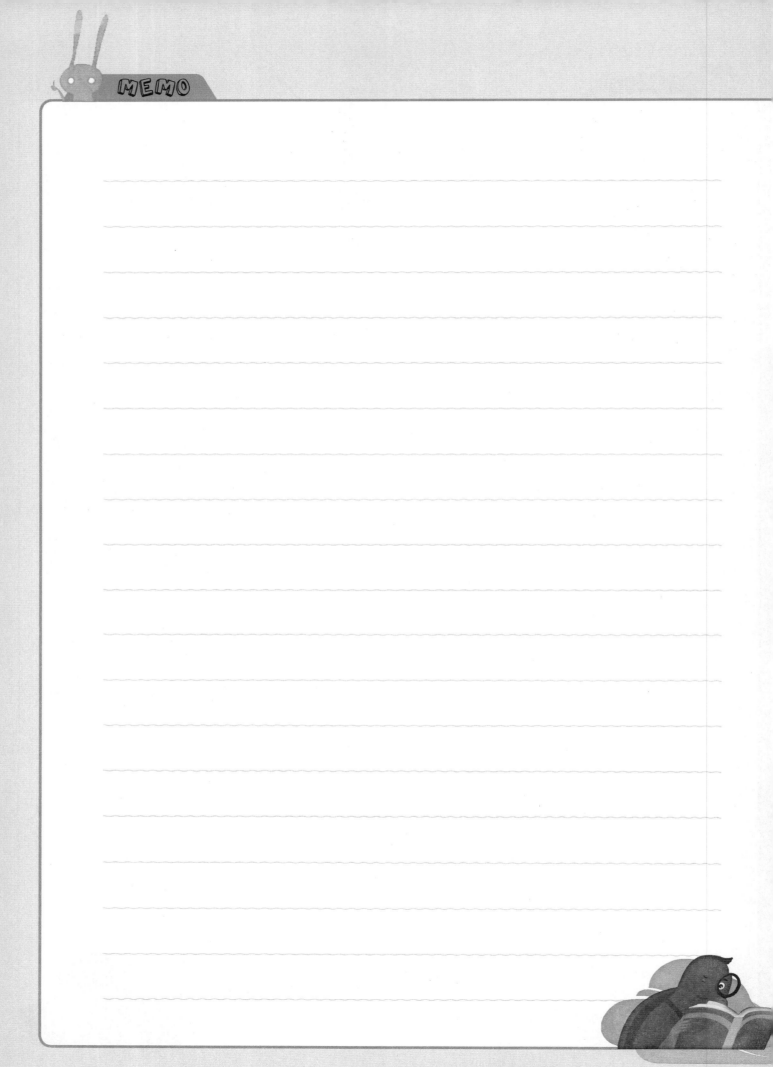

MEMO